ESTIMATING
PAINTING COSTS

by

Dennis D. Gleason, CPE

Craftsman Book Company
6058 Corte Del Cedro, Box 6500
Carlsbad, California 92008

Acknowledgments

The author thanks the following individuals and organizations for furnishing materials and information used in the preparation of various portions of this book.

Howard Shahan, **American Design Painting,** Poway, California
American Society of Professional Estimators (ASPE), Phoenix, Arizona
Jerry Rittgarn, **Arise Scaffolding & Equipment Co.,** San Diego, California
Gordon H. Brevoort, **Brevoort Consulting Associates,** Ridgewood, New Jersey
Randy Martin & Staff, **Dunn Edwards Paint Company,** San Diego, California
Jim Harper & Staff, **Frazee Paint & Wallcovering,** San Diego, California
Bruce McMullen, **McMullen & Son, Painting,** San Diego, California
Joe Garrigan, **Mr. Paints,** San Diego, California
John Meyer, **Navy Public Works,** San Diego, California
Lee Koelfgen, Sr., **Rain Guard Products, Co.,** Inglewood, California
Rediform, division of **Moore Business Forms, Inc.,** Dallas, Texas
Richardson Rapid Engineering Systems, Phoenix, Arizona
Ron Lentz, **Ron Lentz & Associates, Architects,** San Diego, California
Dennis Cripe, **R.W. Little, Inc., Sandblasting,** San Diego, California
Sinclair Paint Company, San Diego, California
Horace Damon, **Southern Painting,** San Diego, California
Steel Structures Painting Council, Pittsburgh, Pennsylvania
Ron Colton, **Wall Dimensions Wallcovering,** San Diego, California

Library of Congress Cataloging-in-Publication Data

Gleason, Dennis D., 1949-
    Estimating painting costs / by Dennis D. Gleason.
        p.   cm.
    Includes index.
    ISBN 0-934041-43-1
    1. Painting, Industrial--Estimates. 2. House painting--Estimates.
  I. Title.
TT305.G64   1989
698′.1′0299--dc20   89-9924
                                   CIP

© 1989 Craftsman Book Company
2nd printing 1991

Cover design & calligraphy -- Sheila M. Scott
Cartoons -- Jim Whiting
Flowcharts -- Artifax Corporation

Contents

Chapter 1

YOU CAN ESTIMATE PAINTING COSTS

This book will help every paint contractor compile accurate labor and material costs for painting. No matter how experienced or inexperienced you may be in the trade, this manual will help make you both a better painter and a better paint estimator.

If you've been in the painting trade for several years, you may have started as an apprentice, working your way up to journeyman. Then, when you felt you could run a paint contracting company better than your boss, you went into business for yourself. You probably have plenty of field know-how already. But most likely it's your business management skills that need a second coat. And your estimating . . . well, that's probably still at the raw wood stage.

Yes, that's right, most painters don't know much about estimating. In fact, many painters think figuring prices comes naturally. "Just stick out your thumb like an artist, tilt your head to the side, squint your eye and the right price will magically pop into your head."

It's not quite that easy, and that's why many new paint contractors don't last very long. They go back to work for wages on another contractor's payroll — most likely making money for a boss who knows that accurate estimating is the key to survival in the painting business.

If you're determined to run a profitable paint contracting company, you're reading the right book. Between the covers of this manual you'll find more valuable information on paint estimating than in any other source.

This book will provide:

1) *Estimating tips, techniques, formulas, tables, methods, systems, and do's and don'ts.* It's all written in painter's language. You'll have no trouble following my suggestions.

2) *A more accurate and predictable system for estimating* — one based on a set of easy-to-use formulas. These formulas will help you predict costs accurately and reduce the number of guesses needed.

3) *A comprehensive reference source* which will help you solve the problems and answer the many questions asked by paint estimators and contractors.

4) *A guide to expanding your business.* Following my recommendations can help you grow into new areas, tackle different kinds of projects, produce more estimates, and get more new work.

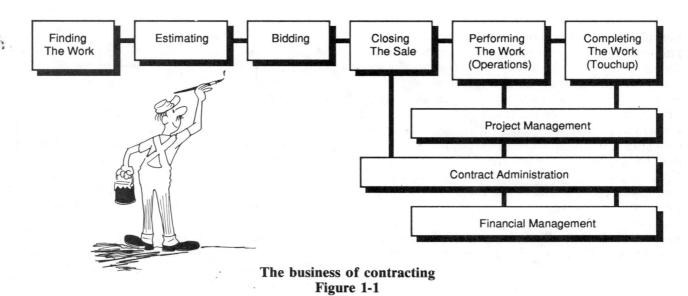

The business of contracting
Figure 1-1

This book is designed to help you be a more successful, professional paint contractor and paint estimator. Your picking up this book tells me that's what you want. Read these pages and follow my suggestions to develop a more successful painting business.

How to Use This Book

First, read the table of contents. Get an idea of the scope of the book. Next, read the entire book, from cover to cover. Skim over any sections that are either too elementary or too sophisticated for your needs. Give special attention to the sections that cover the kinds of projects you handle most often — your "bread and butter." Then *study, practice,* and *use* the information in this manual.

There are hundreds of good ideas here — but reading the words isn't enough. You must make the effort, find the time, and put my recommendations into practice. The only way to profit from my suggestions is to try them.

The sample estimates— This book teaches by example. Included in the text are two complete sample estimates, one on *repaint estimating* and one on *new construction estimating.* There's also an example wallcover estimate. These estimates are explained completely, step by step. The sample repaint estimate is designed for use when there are no construction drawings or plans available. Instead, you use field measurements. The sample new construction estimate will show you how to use building plans and specifications to compile an estimate. The new construction estimate is based on a *sample plan* in Appendix A.

The formulas and tables— There are estimating tables in Chapters 17 through 21 and in Appendix B. They cover just about every operation a paint contractor has to face. Use them to figure the labor required (in manhours) and the material coverage for every operation. The labor figures tell you how much surface area or linear footage can be painted per hour. The material coverage figures tell you how much paint or coating will be needed to cover surface area or linear footage in your job.

The Business of Contracting

"He that is fond of building will soon ruin himself without the help of enemies."

This quotation from the ancient philosopher Plutarch is still accurate today. *Contracting is a risky and complex business.*

It's risky because you have to predict the future — estimating the job cost before work begins. You need a gambler's instincts. With every bid you're gambling that work can be done for no more than the estimated cost.

You *can* reduce the risk by using an estimating system, applying good judgment, and having a sound bidding strategy. You must be ready and able to negotiate prices with customers as well as vendors. It also helps to reduce the risk if you're aware of trends in the painting and construction industry.

There are many cost variables in construction because it's difficult to control some conditions on the job. A manufacturing business, for example, doesn't have to worry about a sudden rainstorm, the neighborhood kids or the client changing his or her mind about the color after the walls have been painted. A painting contractor has to deal with different conditions on every job. Some painters claim accurate estimating is impossible. They say estimating is too complex and involves too many unknowns. I don't agree. It *is* possible to produce consistently accurate labor and material cost estimates. In this book I describe the process in detail and offer many examples. Follow my suggestions and I think you'll agree that good painting estimators can produce good estimates . . . time after time after time.

As an estimator, you may be involved in every part of the contracting process. Here's a general outline of what many paint estimators handle:

- Marketing: Finding enough work to stay busy

- Estimating: Predicting labor and material costs

- Bidding: Making the offer

- Sales and Closing: Negotiating and securing the contract

- Project Management: Starting, managing and completing the work, as well as job costing (comparing actual costs with estimated costs)

- Contract Administration: Handling contract changes and billing

If you think doing all this is easy, it's because you don't understand the problem. There's no quick way to learn everything an estimator has to do. But this manual is a good place to start. And, of course, there's no substitute for experience. Putting my recommendations into practice is always the next step after you've read and understand what this book suggests.

The Big Picture

To give you a clear understanding of the contracting process, you must understand some definitions. So that's where I'm going to start. I'll define the types of estimates, types of work, types of bids and bidding procedure, as well as contracts, and I'll identify the common types of projects.

Types of Estimates

There are many types of estimates. Chapter 4 covers each of them completely. But they all fall into two broad categories, preliminary and detailed.

Preliminary estimates are made before the building plans are complete. With plans that aren't complete, you have to make some assumptions about the work to be done. You're not guessing about costs and prices, but predicting what will be painted and with how many coats. You use your knowledge and experience as a paint estimator to make generalizations about what will probably need to be done.

A *detailed* estimate is prepared from a complete set of working drawings or from measurements taken on site if you're painting an existing structure. The estimator figures manhours and material requirements precisely to arrive at a bid total.

Types of Projects

All painting work can be divided into three categories by the type of owner: *private* work, *semiprivate* work, and *public* (government) work. The distinction is important. For example, bidding for the government requires entirely different procedures.

Private work— The contractor deals with a private individual or company. No government funds are involved.

Semiprivate work— This work might involve a public agency or a government-regulated company such as a public utility.

Public work— This work is done for the government: a city, a county, a state, the federal government, or the military.

Types of Bids (Project Classifications)

A good way to classify project types is by the bidding process. In this manual, four bidding processes will be used to classify projects. They are: individual bids, informal bidding, semiformal bidding, and the formal bidding procedure.

Individual bids— These private bids are usually negotiated with an individual who is the owner. The contract type is typically a combination *proposal and contract,* written by the painting estimator, and accepted by the owner. The project types are always private. This type of work includes:

- Repainting of homes, apartments, and commercial leased space for the owner

- Painting remodels and room additions for a small general contractor

- Painting custom homes for the owner

Informal bids— For the informal bidding process, only selected, prequalified bidders are invited to bid. The announcement isn't published in the local newspaper or construction publications. The individual owner or company will negotiate the contract amount with the painting contractor having the low bid. The contract type is usually a *standard form contract* or a *custom contract* written by an attorney. These contracts are generally issued or offered by the owner, builder or general contractor and accepted by the paint contractor. Project types can be private or semiprivate and include the following:

- New single-family residential: custom homes by a builder, spec homes by a builder (one to four homes), or presold tract homes (five or more homes)

- New multi-family residential, either economy or high quality; condominiums and apartments

- Light commercial: shopping centers, strip centers or office buildings

Semiformal bids— These bid announcements are published requests for *open* competitive bids. The authority is usually either a general contractor or an architect acting as agent for the owner.

The contract type is a *standard form contract.* Bid documents usually include a project manual for specifications and procedures. Project types can be private, semiprivate or public, and include heavy commercial, industrial, institutional, and government projects, both civic and military.

Formal bids— Announcements of formal bids are usually published in the local newspaper or construction publications. These bids are *sealed* competitive bids. They're submitted in sealed envelopes until bid time, when all bids are opened. The authority is either a general contractor or an architect, acting as agent for either a private or public owner. But if a government project is for repainting only, and the painting contractor is the prime (main) contractor, the authority may be the government agency.

The contract type, again, is a *standard form contract.* The bid documents include a complete set of plans along with a project manual for specifications and procedures. The project types are semiprivate or public, and include heavy commercial, industrial, institutional and government, either civic or military.

Production Painting — Volume Work

As you've seen, there are many different project classifications. Usually, the more formal the bidding process, the larger the job. Labor and material costs will vary with the size of the job: the larger the project, the better the discount from your material supplier and the more productive your painters will have to be.

Labor productivity is usually higher on larger production jobs because several units or buildings will be ready for painting at the same time. You can also use specialized, highly productive equipment. The crews learn as they go along, picking up speed as each building or unit repeats itself through the project. With this repetitive process, the painters work much faster than they would if each unit had to be planned and set up individually without the repetition.

On large production projects, you might use the fast manhour production category in the general formulas in Appendix B. The new construction formulas used for the sample estimate in Chapter 19 also use labor rates for production painting. These formulas assume a higher rate of production because each painter or crew can work for more than one day without changing the type of work being done.

Good painters learn to work faster when they do the same type of work over and over. For example, the first door painted on a job might take 30 minutes. If there are 100 doors on the project, the last door painted might take only 12 minutes. If you drew a graph of the time needed to paint each door, from the first to the last, you'd probably be drawing a curved line — from 30 minutes for the first door down to 12 for the last. That's called a *learning curve.* This increase in productivity through repetition is the reason why most manufactured goods are produced on an assembly line.

On smaller projects, without this repetition, each painter and crew must handle many different types of tasks each day. For work like that, use the slow manhour production category in Appendix B. The repaint formulas provided in Chapter 18 use this slower labor rate for nonrepetitive projects.

Your Niche

Painting contractors can be categorized by the type of work their company can handle efficiently and profitably. That's one of the keys to success in the painting business — finding your *niche*. A company that's set up to handle a particular category of work may not be as profitable if they stray too far from that category. Here are several factors that may determine your niche in the painting business.

Manpower Capabilities

The skill and experience of your employees and supervisors can determine the project category or categories your company is best suited for. Skill and knowledge are the foundation for efficient performance in any project category.

You may be able to expand your niche. A good estimator, who may be new to your company but experienced in estimating and managing work outside your niche, *may* be able to help your company expand into other categories. But only if your tradesmen are capable of producing according to the estimator's expectations.

A good foreman with broad experience can also help you expand into another project category, from residential to commercial, for example.

The Dollar Volume That Returns the Most Profit

Your niche can also be defined by project size, in terms of contract amounts. Typically, you'll have a range of contract amounts that are appropriate for your company.

Here's an example. Suppose a production paint contractor is set up to handle a minimum of 20 homes at $1,200 each. The contract size is $24,000. The first 15 homes may actually lose money, with all the profit being made on the last five homes. Why? The painters (and supervisors) are learning while doing the first 15 homes. On the last five homes, they've got it down to a gnat's eyelash, wasting almost no time or effort. The painting goes very quickly. If the job were smaller, the painters

would never develop this momentum. Maybe this contractor would lose money on projects with less than 20 homes.

It can work the other way too. A contractor who has never attempted a project larger than five homes might find that a 20-home project is a money-loser. His crews may not be experienced in setting up for production painting or volume work. He may not have the equipment required for production work or his bank account may not stretch to cover payroll while the work is being done.

Your dollar-volume niche is a function of your manpower, equipment and money supply or capital. Your challenge is to know the contract size that returns the most profit and to get enough of that kind of work to stay busy.

Financial Capabilities

One of the factors that may limit your painting company from expanding into other project categories is the cash and assets you have available. A company's financial condition depends on:

1) Working capital — cash available to pay expenses

2) Cash flow — expenses compared to income

3) Bonding capacity — Project size which an insurance company will guarantee your company will complete

Working capital— Your working capital is your cash on hand available to pay out — in other words, your bank balance. If it's low, expansion may be difficult or impossible. Working capital is needed to pay for labor and materials until your receivable checks arrive. On larger projects you may not be paid until 30 to 90 days after work is completed. That's a long time to wait if you've added painters to your payroll to meet a tight completion schedule. On a big job you're caught from both ends, *paying out* more cash to stay on schedule and *waiting longer* for the money to come in. The combination of these two factors has pushed many painting contractors to the brink of financial embarrassment.

Cash flow— A company must keep cash to pay expenses coming in faster than it goes out. Survival can depend on collecting the money you're owed.

Bonding capacity— The main limit on expansion into the formal contract category will probably be your company's bonding capacity. Larger formal contracts, along with some informal contracts, require a performance bond submitted by a bonding or surety company. This bond guarantees that you will complete the work as promised and according to contract. Your company's bonding capacity depends on the size of your company and the size of the projects your company usually handles. Very few small repaint contractors would qualify for a bond on a large government painting project.

Consider these points when defining your niche or the niche you can expand into. First, find your comfort level, based on your skills and equipment. Second, find the contract size that returns the most profit. Third, don't expand beyond your financial capability. Finally, be sure there's enough of your type of work available. There are more surprises in the painting business than there are packages around the tree on Christmas morning. But most aren't quite as much fun.

Danger Signals: Causes of Failure

Speaking of going in too deep, I know you've heard of construction companies going broke, leaving jobs unfinished with suppliers and other creditors unpaid. This happens. There are danger signals to watch for in your own business. Many times the roots of failure are in poor estimating and bidding: estimates that are not figured accurately resulting in bids which are either too low or too high. Some of the main causes of business failure, in order of frequency, are:

1) Inadequate sales. Sales will be at low levels if your company has poor estimating and bidding habits. What are some of these poor habits? Failing to estimate the job completely, always being the lowest bidder, and using estimating shortcuts to save time, to name a few.

2) Heavy operating expenses. Taking on large, complicated projects too soon in a painting company's growth may result in catastrophe. Many factors can increase operating expenses. Watch out for these: First, having to purchase expensive spray rigs and other equipment. Second, needing highly skilled, highly paid painters to undertake a project. Third, having to wait 60 to 90 days for payment after billing large projects.

3) Overexpansion. When times are good and work is plentiful, it's easy to expand too rapidly, taking on more work than the company can handle. Symptoms of overexpansion include hiring more office help or buying new vehicles and equipment before company income can support this extra overhead.

Overexpansion can lower your profits. Growing too fast means that you have to hire new (and probably inexperienced) painters with marginal ability. Productivity is lower, which raises the cost of the job. It also results in poor workmanship and more touchup work. It's costly, and it may give your company a bad reputation. Overexpansion might cost you more than the additional sales volume is worth.

It's tempting to take on more work than you can handle. But having too much work can hurt as much as not having enough. Taking on too much work will delay building schedules. This will annoy homeowners, cost general contractors money and may cost you penalties for poor performance.

In many painting companies, it's the estimator's responsibility to be aware of the amount of work in progress and control the number of bids submitted and the prices quoted so work in progress isn't excessive. You may decide to pass up a few jobs even though they could be profitable. It's nice to have enough work to be able to be choosy about the jobs you bid.

4) Competitive weakness. Being a weak competitor simply means that your painters aren't fast enough to keep up with the competition or your overhead is too high. As a result, it may be very hard to win a bid. If you lower your profit margin to get the job, you may lose money. Try to hire conscientious painters who work hard and care about being productive.

5) Receivable difficulties. Collecting money owed can be a pain. Many companies fail because they allow their accounts receivable to go past 30 days. You've heard the old saying "The squeaky wheel gets the most grease." When your receivables go past 30 days, *be a squeaky wheel!* It's reasonable to require payment within 30 days of submitting your invoice.

How to Succeed
Now that we know what it takes to fail (and what to avoid), let's look at what it takes to succeed:

A knowledge of how the construction business works— The management of a painting business may be broken down into four broad areas:

1) Marketing — promotion, estimating, bidding, sales

2) Operations — producing a product or service

3) Operations management — managing the paperwork, keeping operations on schedule

4) Finance — cash flow, credit, bookkeeping and accounting

The ability to produce a quality job— Your operations (the actual painting work) must be done with quality to satisfy the customer. Having good *painting skills* and the ability to hire qualified painters are keys to success in the painting business.

Keeping your income greater than your expenses— It's essential that you have *enough working capital* to make the payroll, pay your suppliers and make all payments on time.

A good credit rating and line of credit— If the checks from your customers don't come in as expected, the lack of cash can bring your company to its knees. If you don't have cash resources to fall back on, consider applying for a line of credit at your bank. Make sure that cash will be available in an emergency.

An ability to find the work— Aim for a steady (or preferably a growing) work volume by keeping your company name in front of owners and general contractors who hire painting contractors. Put your company in the market place.

Creativity and inventiveness— Make sure that all painters, foremen, field superintendents and estimators work together as a team to lower project costs. Everyone on your payroll has to be willing to try new ideas, find inventive solutions and identify better ways to perform the work. The estimator has the primary responsibility for cutting costs and making better use of your manpower, materials and equipment.

Well-developed estimating skills— This manual has all the essential information you need to develop good estimating skills.

Every successful paint contracting company has at least one good estimator. Nearly every project requires an estimate or a bid of some type. If you can't estimate well enough to be competitive, you won't get many jobs. Poor estimates waste everyone's time. It's foolish to throw "guesstimates" around in hopes that some of them stick. And if they do, you may be in worse trouble if you get the bid than if you didn't bid at all.

So *decide* right now that you're going to master the art of estimating painting costs. That you're going to abandon the practice of multiplying guesswork by more guesswork to find the bottom line. That you're not going to blame the economy, the competition, the materials, your tradesmen or your clients if you aren't successful in the paint contracting business. *Decide* right now that your future, your professional success, your shot at financial security rests in you own hands and that you're going to do something about it. *Decide* right now that you're going to become the best paint estimator you can possibly be. And then, turn the page. I'm going to explain how you're going to do it.

Chapter 2

THE ESTIMATOR

Before we begin to explain the estimator's craft, let's define what an estimator does. A cost estimator is someone who calculates the quantity and cost of all *labor, material* and *equipment* needed to complete a certain task and then adds *miscellaneous costs, overhead* and *profit* to find the bid price. But that's just the tip of the iceberg. There's more. Lots more. That's why "the estimator" is the subject of this chapter.

In the construction industry, most work begins with an idea and evolves into a set of plans and specifications. Plans can be prepared by designers, architects, owners or sometimes by general contractors. During this planning process, a project budget is established and someone has to produce an estimate for every part of the project, whether it's residential, commercial or industrial. In fact, most jobs have been estimated several times by many estimators before the work actually begins.

As a painting estimator, you may work from a set of plans and specs on new projects. Or you may be required to estimate repaint costs by walking through an existing structure. On these repaint projects, you have the advantage of seeing what has to be painted and the surface conditions before bidding the work. Estimating repaint projects, as you might already know, is much different from new construction estimating.

Depending on the type of painting work your company prefers (your niche), you should feel comfortable basing your estimate on a set of plans, or estimating from the existing building, or both. In this book I'll explain in detail and provide formulas and tables for estimating new work as well as repainting existing structures.

The Estimator's Value

The construction industry is the largest industry in the world. It has the biggest dollar volume, employs the most people, and uses the greatest value of materials. Qualified construction estimators are usually paid well because they provide the seeds (bids) which help a company get new work and grow.

When work is scarce, the survival of a painting contractor may depend on the estimator's ability to produce and submit more bids. More bidding often means more bids accepted. In a healthy economy when work is plentiful, a good estimator helps build company profits by selecting the most profitable jobs.

An estimator's ability usually determines the success or failure of a painting company. *Accurate* estimates can make the company profitable. *Sloppy* estimates can pave the road to bankruptcy.

Every company involved in construction needs at least one good estimator.

The Estimator's Skills

A national survey of construction companies (by Northeast Louisiana University) surveyed construction contractors to find the types of experience and skills most in demand in the construction industry. The results of that survey are listed below in order of decreasing importance. An estimator *must* have the first seven skills. The three other skills may or may not be required, depending on the company.

1) Estimating and quantity surveying
2) Written communication
3) Bidding procedures
4) Oral communication
5) Construction contracts
6) Interpreting specifications
7) Analyzing construction drawings for errors and omissions
8) Project cost accounting systems
9) Cost control methods
10) Construction supervision

Notice that construction supervision is listed last. Some painting companies have their estimators supervise their projects. Others don't involve their estimators in project supervision. In fact, this may seem surprising, but many times the estimator's take-off and ideas about how to best paint a project which were used to win the bid may be completely ignored by the field supervisors and foremen.

The painting estimator should always communicate those ideas and all take-off information to the field supervisor or foreman in a pre-construction meeting. The estimator's detailed knowledge of the methods, systems, and construction techniques used in estimating and bidding helps ensure a good start on the project.

Estimating As a Recognized Profession

The days when contractors could estimate by putting their thumbs at eye level, squinting one eye, and scratching some rough figures on a yellow pad are gone. "Guesstimates" are a thing of the past in today's highly-competitive construction market.

That's why construction estimating is becoming a respected profession with recognized standards.

The British construction industry seems to be far ahead of the United States in recognizing the estimator's importance. In Britain, estimators are called *quantity surveyors*. To become a "chartered" quantity surveyor, a student must complete a rigorous training program and pass qualifying exams. The Royal Institute of Chartered Surveyors acknowledges that a quantity surveyor enjoys the same level of importance and professional recognition as an architect or an engineer.

The title *cost engineer* in the United States comes close to the title Chartered Quantity Surveyor that's used in Britain. The duties of the cost engineer include scheduling and profit planning, as well as estimating.

The Estimator's Education

Whether you're already an estimator or are just entering the field, your goal should be to reach professional competence. Educational programs — whether complete, continuing, or supplementary — are necessary if you're serious about any professional discipline. No estimator can afford to stop learning. Stay informed about changes in paints and coatings and other advances in the painting industry.

Many colleges and universities offer degrees in construction-related fields. These schools award between 3,000 and 3,500 bachelor of science degrees in construction-related fields each year. Many of these programs include specialized training in estimating.

In a survey of 200 general contractors who hold BS degrees in construction, 140 had taken classes in estimating at one time or another.

Every estimator needs both a well-rounded academic education and experience in the field. Technical knowledge is needed to be competent in the estimating of any specialty trade. To be a good estimator, you must master painting application techniques, procedures, methods, and systems. You can't estimate the cost of anything you don't understand.

The best way to get that experience is to do the work. Maybe that's why most estimators were tradesmen at one time. Another way to gain experience is to work as a trainee for an experienced estimator, although many companies can't afford to keep trainees on the payroll while they're learning. Supplement your education in construction by taking classes or reading books like this manual.

An estimator must wear many hats!

The Estimator's Salary

It takes experience and knowledge to estimate every part of a construction project. In estimating, the more you have to know to do the job, the more you can expect to earn. For example, estimators working for general contractors producing costs for entire buildings probably earn more than estimators working for painting contractors. Likewise, estimators working for painting contractors that handle industrial and commercial work usually make more than estimators with paint contracting companies that handle only residential work.

You might also find that the hourly wage of a painting contractor's painters affects the estimator's salary. An estimator working for a contractor who pays top dollar to his painters will probably earn more than an estimator working for a contractor who pays lower wages.

Figure 2-1 lists typical estimator classifications along with a range of hourly compensation which might apply in 1989.

In any case, the more estimating education and experience you have, the higher your salary is likely to be. It's in your best interest to qualify yourself as a knowledgeable professional estimator. Read, study, learn and consider joining one of the professional societies for construction estimators.

Classification	Experience	Hourly salary
Estimator in training	0-2 years	$ 5 to $ 8
Estimator in training	2-5 years	$ 8 to $12
Quantity Surveyor	2 years +	$10 to $12
Estimator	5 years +	$12 to $18
Senior Estimator	10 years +	$20 +
Chief Estimator-Manager	10 years +	$25 +
Consultant Estimator	-independent	$25 to $50

Estimator classifications and typical salaries
Figure 2-1

The Estimator As a Consultant

During exceptionally busy times, you can be so bogged down supervising field work that you don't have enough time to estimate new projects. There are several possible solutions to this dilemma: First, you could hire an independent estimator as a consultant on a part time or per job basis until you get your field supervision under control. Second, you could hire a full time staff estimator. Third, you could hire a supervisor until the backlog of work is eliminated and spend more time estimating.

An independent estimator working as a consultant rather than an employee can fill in as needed to keep the bids going. That may prevent a large gap between project starts — and help keep your company running smoothly.

If you do hire an estimator as a consultant, choose an experienced professional who will estimate "your way," using the estimating systems and formulas that you have tried, tested, and proven to work for your painting company. *It pays to hire experts*. Bad advice can cost you many times more than the expert's fee.

If you're looking for expert estimating assistance, start looking with one of the professional estimating organizations.

Professional Groups for Estimators

In 1956, a group of construction estimators formed the American Society of Professional Estimators (ASPE). Their goal was to increase the level of professionalism within the estimating field by promoting high standards and ethical conduct among construction cost estimators. The education and certification programs of ASPE have now established national standards for professional construction estimators.

ASPE's *education program* has two purposes: to educate young people entering the estimating profession, and to provide continuing education for estimators in new materials, equipment, methods, and technical innovations. The ASPE *certification program* tests the competence of construction estimators. Certification is granted to estimators who have passed standardized tests administered by the ASPE.

The ASPE offers a national education program and encourages estimators to maintain high standards as outlined in the ASPE *Code of Ethics* (Figure 2-2). If you're interested in joining, write:

American Society of Professional Estimators
P.O. Box 5191
San Diego, CA 92105
Attn: Membership

Here are addresses for two more professional organizations for estimators:

National Estimating Society
904 Bob Wallace Avenue, Suite 213
Huntsville, AL 35801

American Association of Cost Engineers, Inc.
308 Monongahela Bldg.
Morgantown, WV 26505

The Estimator's Judgment

Every good paint estimator needs good *judgment*. Your job as an estimator is to find a bid price that's a happy medium between a too-high, noncompetitive figure and a bid that's too low to recover your costs. Every estimate you produce and each bid you submit will require many judgment calls.

Every paint estimate requires that you convert take-off measurements and calculated areas into *manhours, material quantities* and *equipment costs*. Doing the take-off requires skill. But little judgment is needed. Converting surface areas to material and labor costs takes both experience and judgment. If you haven't had enough estimating experience to develop good judgment, this manual can help. The estimating tables in Chapters 17 through 21 and Appendix B can help you develop a system of estimating formulas that will make your estimates more consistent and accurate. They'll also help you verify or adjust your judgment of time and material requirements for each operation. But that's not all. There's more.

The need for good judgment doesn't end when you've figured the *manhours, material, equipment and miscellaneous costs*. The next step is the most subjective and variable of all: applying a reasonable *profit or markup* which results in a comfortable bid price. When you've evaluated the bidding variables that apply to a particular project, you might make adjustments to your standard costs to get the actual bid price. These adjustments may be needed because every project involves a unique set of cost variables. No two jobs are identical.

Some of the bidding variables you'll consider are:

- Comparing your bid figure with published data and your known costs for similar projects.

- Judging whether this job is more or less difficult than most of the other jobs you've handled.

- Considering the possible problems and conflicts that can make any job more expensive than expected.

ATTITUDE

☐ Preserve and protect the integrity and prestige of the estimating profession by praticing, at all times, in a mannner consistent with this code.

☐ Accept responsibility for one's actions and encourage one's professional associates to act in accord with this code.

☐ Treat all professional associates with integrity, fairness, tolerance and respect, regardless of national origin, race, sex, age or persuasion.

☐ Maintain a broad and balanced attitude, recognize merit in the ideas and options of others and acknowledge that merit, provided it meets the standards of this code.

☐ Recognize that membership in and certification by the American Society of Professional Estimators is not the sole claim to professional competence, but support the ideals set forth by this code.

SERVICE

☐ Serve the interests of the client or employer in a manner consistent with the highest standards of professional integrity.

☐ Safeguard and keep in confidence all knowledge of the business affairs and technical procedures of an employer or client.

☐ Serve the client or employer faithfully, in a professional and competent manner; provided that such service meets the standards of this code.

☐ Assist and advise the employer or client in the anticipated consequences of any actions taken in the performance of the estimating process.

☐ Submit professionally accurate results to the client or employer in the preparation of and presentation of all estimates.

☐ Subscribe, at all times, to professional integrity; neither give nor accept, directly or indirectly, any gift, payment or service to or from those having business relationships with the client or employer.

PERFORMANCE

☐ Offer and contribute professional advice, as appropriate, to civic, charitable, professional and other non-profit organizations.

☐ Protect the health, welfare and safety of the public at all times from any and all abuses.

☐ Participate in and support the activities of the American Society of Professional Estimators and report, publish and distribute professional information not subject to legal or proprietary restraints.

☐ Promote the professional standards established by this code and assist in the continuing development of estimating accuracy.

☐ Be prepared at all times to represent the Society in a truly professional manner to the public.

Participate only in honest enterprises worthy of the ideals of this Society and defend the aims and goals established by this code.

EDUCATION

☐ Encourage young people to consider entering the profession through conduct that commands respect.

☐ Endeavor to assist fellow professionals, and all others interested in the profession, in their efforts to acheive personal and professional fulfillment.

☐ Encourage the efforts of those who teach the art of estimating and participate in that teaching process whenever possible.

☐ Encourage those in training in the art of estimating by contributing knowledge, time and financial support whenever possible.

☐ Enlighten those interested in the profession as to its responsibilties as well as its benefits.

☐ Extend personal assistance to those engaged in the education and training of professional estimators.

Courtesy: THE AMERICAN SOCIETY OF PROFESSIONAL ESTIMATORS, 5201 N. 7TH STREET, PHOENIX, ARIZONA 85014 (602) 274-4880

ASPE Code of Ethics
Figure 2-2

- Evaluating how much the company needs the work and how badly you want to win the bid.

Yes, you'll have to use *judgment* when you adjust a bid to meet job conditions or to match or beat the competition. Making these adjustments isn't as difficult if you know the owner, the builder, the competition, and the capabilities of your painters. But these adjustments are always based on your judgment. A later chapter discusses these bidding variables in depth.

The Estimator's Range

Most estimators need skills in three broad areas: The first, of course, is in preparing quantity surveys (take-offs) and estimates. The second is in sales and marketing: finding new customers, presenting bids, and negotiating contracts. Third, the estimator may have a support function in many companies, monitoring project costs during construction. The field supervisor should know whether the job is making or losing money so corrections can be made early enough to preserve a reasonable profit margin.

Here are some of the specific tasks you might handle as an estimator:

Material and labor analyst— Your two most important functions will always be to develop accurate material take-offs and to forecast labor costs. You'll take off the measurements from plans for new construction. If there are no plans, you'll measure the area of an existing building to be painted, noting the type of paint and number of coats. From the area computations you'll estimate the labor, material and equipment required for each coat, convert these quantities into costs, add the miscellaneous costs and overhead, and then add a reasonable profit to arrive at the bid value.

Estimators do a lot of adding, subtracting, multiplying and dividing. An understanding of basic *arithmetic and mathematics* is essential when you're calculating wall and ceiling areas. A little knowledge of basic algebra and geometry will help when calculating unusual surface areas. For example, the gable end of a house is usually in the shape of a triangle. Silos, tanks and smoke stacks are cylinders. A qualified painting estimator must be able to calculate these surface areas and arrive at the accurate square footage to be painted.

You'll also need to *review and double-check* all your figures and calculations to catch any mistakes. Anyone can make a mistake. But only a careless estimator will fail to find those mistakes.

Nobody needs an estimator who's prone to making mistakes and not correcting them. Experienced estimators have learned to double-check their figures by comparing the total painting costs to other similar jobs. A standard method for this double-check system is to divide the total bid amount by the total construction square footage. There are also other methods to identify figures that may be wrong which will be discussed in later chapters.

Before submitting the bid, you'll want to analyze the bidding variables. Bidding variables are those conditions that vary from job to job, such as: What is the reputation of the general contractor or owner who's requesting a bid? Are there unusual conditions that could delay the job or increase costs? Who is your competition? What bid amount will get this job?

Document interpreter— An estimator *must* be able to read and interpret plans and specifications. These are called the *bid documents*. All too often the plans and specs are incomplete, vague or simply wrong. Sometimes the plans show one thing and the specs require another. You'll have to resolve these conflicts, fill in the omissions, and get clarification on the ambiguities (items which are unclear). There's no way to estimate the job if the requirements for painting the job are unclear.

Marketing manager, salesman and buyer— In many companies the estimator is the prime salesman, the person who meets the client, makes up a good, competitive but profitable bid, and gets an agreement to proceed so the company can make that profit and stay in business. Estimators also work with suppliers as a buyer and negotiate good prices on materials so the bids can be more competitive.

You'll probably develop and cultivate leads for future work. That includes both finding new customers and improving customer relations with existing customers. Typically, the estimator will make the first sales contact to introduce your company and follow up with calls as well as pick up the plans and visit the job site. When the estimate is complete, you'll present the proposal, submit the bid, return the plans, do the closing follow-up, negotiate the contract, and finally, close the sale.

As an "ambassador" for your paint company, it's important that you show *fairness, courtesy, cooperation* and *dedication* to the goal of customer satisfaction.

Contract administrator—Someone in every painting company has to understand what the contract requires. While estimating, writing the proposal, submitting the bid and selling the job, the estimator defines what is included and excluded—*the scope of the work.* Often, if your proposals are complete, the exact wording you use in your proposal is used in the contract. That's what you want, the scope of work the way you wrote it.

Being the most familiar with the details of the project when the contract arrives, the estimator is in a perfect position to review the contract and ensure that it's consistent with the work that was included in the estimate.

Once the work begins, the estimator will probably determine the amount to be billed in progress payments, if several payments are due under the agreement. The estimator may have to evaluate the percentage of painting work completed as of a certain date. This percentage is used to calculate the amount that's due under the contract.

Since the estimator is most familiar with the work that was included in the agreement, he or she will probably prepare estimates for additional work if it's requested by an owner, architect or general contractor. The estimator will also be involved in negotiating prices for any extra painting that wasn't included in the original contract. Remember, if it's not clear that a certain item of work was included or excluded, your proposal can be the key document in deciding whether a change order for extra work should be issued. That's why qualified estimators always define completely the work which is included and excluded on every bid proposal.

Arbitrator and negotiator— The estimator is the most familiar with pricing for the job and the wording of the contract. That's why estimators are key mediators if there's a dispute. When change orders and claims for extra work come up, the estimator may be able to suggest a fair and practical solution that will satisfy everyone.

The documents and figures in the estimator's file will back up your company's position and may suggest a reasonable solution, thus avoiding arbitration or a lawsuit.

Scheduler and cost controller— A manhour estimate is part of every cost estimate. Once manhours are estimated, the crew size is determined, and the builder's needs are considered, it's relatively easy to develop a tentative schedule for the project — a beginning date, milestones along the way, and the projected completion date. This schedule can be as sophisticated as a bar chart for a larger project or simply a few notes on a sheet of paper for a small repaint job. As your jobs progress, you'll want to control labor costs by comparing estimated hours with actual hours. Comparing estimated costs with actual costs while the jobs are in progress is also the basis for controlling material costs.

Controlling labor costs is most important because painting is a "labor intensive" business. That is, labor will be the largest cost on every job, far more than your material or equipment costs. But material and equipment costs can also be important. For example, on a large project, suppose your spray painters are not getting the coverage you expected. They may be using 10% to 20% more paint than you estimated. That 10% or 20% is going to come straight out of your profit. The sooner you find out, the more opportunity you'll have to correct the problem, both on the current job and on future estimates.

Every estimator should develop a cost control system for his or her painting company. As mentioned, a cost control system is simply a convenient way of comparing estimated costs with actual costs for labor, material and equipment. The most effective cost control systems are timely, showing cost overruns while the work is still in progress. Once the project is completed, it's too late to start controlling costs. And unfortunately, that's when most companies look at costs, after the job is complete.

With all of those talents and responsibilities, it's easy to see why qualified estimators are a key part of every painting company's management team.

Feeling Tired Already?

You might not have realized that a paint estimator had to do so much. But don't get discouraged. I'm going to explain it all in language you can understand. But before I finish describing the paint estimator's job, let me list a few of the characteristics most successful paint estimators have:

1) The self-discipline to concentrate for long periods, even in a busy office environment.

2) The ability to pay attention to details, be highly organized and keep accurate records.

3) The ability to work under pressure. There are always rush bids. You must be able to work quickly and accurately.

4) The ability to work independently.

5) The ability to communicate effectively, orally and in writing.

6) Imagination. It's your job to find cost-saving solutions and devise new ways to save time and material. That can be the competitive edge necessary to win a bid.

Last, but not least, you need a positive attitude — a "Yes, I can" attitude. You must be ready to estimate any project that comes your way. You have to be willing to handle more and more demanding work. You should be looking for ways to improve your estimating skills and make yourself a better qualified and more competent paint estimator.

Start by *knowing* that your bids will be both successful and profitable. If you lose a job or two, don't be discouraged — you'll make the next bid better. You'll "trim the fat" from the next one. With practice using the formulas and tables in this manual, you should have more than enough bids accepted to keep your painters busy and your company profitable.

Chapter

3

PLANS AND SPECS

There are several types of plans which make up a complete set of drawings for construction work on a building. Some of these plan types include:

1) Architectural drawings— produced by an architect, a building designer or even a homeowner for remodeling his residence.

2) Structural drawings— produced by a structural engineer.

3) Electrical drawings— produced by an electrical engineer.

4) Mechanical drawings— produced by a mechanical engineer.

5) Landscape drawings— produced by a landscape architect.

6) Irrigation drawings— produced by the landscape architect.

7) Grading plans— produced by a civil engineer.

8) Site improvement drawings— produced by a civil engineer.

9) Shop drawings— produced by subcontractors.

The architect is often assigned the responsibility of coordinating the production of drawing types 1 through 6. The grading plans and the site improvement drawings are typically produced independently of the architectural or building plans. The shop drawings are produced without the architect's or engineer's supervision, although an architect will usually want the right to review and approve all shop drawings on a project.

Shop Drawings

Shop drawings are detailed plans actually drawn "in the shop" by subcontractors in a variety of trades. They may include plumbing, fire sprinklers, fire alarms, structural steel (detailed), or heating and air conditioning (HVAC). Estimators use shop drawings only when the other plan sheets don't show enough detail to complete an estimate.

For example, an HVAC estimator may locate the exhaust and intake heat registers on a tracing paper overlay (tracer), then draw in the duct work runs and identify the sizing of each duct. After these drawings are complete, the estimator measures the quantities of the various materials used in the design and produces an estimate. If that company is the successful bidder, these shop drawings may be used for ordering materials and installing the work. Shop drawings are seldom needed for residential projects, but are common on commercial plans.

As a painting estimator, you probably won't have to produce or read shop drawings. But you should at least be familiar with the term as it's used in the construction business.

Architectural Drawings (The "A" Sheets)

The design for construction of new or remodeled buildings is usually shown on the architectural drawings, the "A" sheets. These drawings are the primary source of information for paint estimators. They're usually numbered A-1, A-2, A-3, and so on. Typical architectural drawings are reproduced in Appendix A of this book. We'll use this sample plan to produce several sample estimates.

The Support Drawings

Many residential projects require only architectural drawings. More complex residential projects and most commercial and industrial projects will require drawings done by engineers or landscape architects to supplement and clarify the architectural drawings.

Structural Drawings (The "S" Sheets)

Imagine a multi-story office building with a complicated foundation requiring large concrete footings. The structural engineer designs a foundation and frame strong enough to support the building. The engineer provides a complete set of *structural drawings,* with details. These are usually called "S" sheets and numbered S-1, S-2, S-3, and so on. If there's a conflict between the "S" sheets and the "A" sheets, the "S" sheets have priority.

Electrical Drawings (The "E" Sheets)

In simple residential construction, electrical wiring will be shown on the floor plan. For a more complex building, an electrical engineer will produce a complete set of electrical drawings. These drawings are usually called the "E" sheets. Electrical shop drawings may show wiring runs, wire sizes, switchgear, subpanel locations, sizing and type.

Mechanical Drawings (The "M" and "P" Sheets)

You may also see *mechanical drawings,* the "M" and "P" sheets. A mechanical engineer produces "M" sheets for heating, ventilating, and air conditioning and for other mechanical equipment. The plumbing plans, designed by a mechanical engineer, will be on the "P" sheets. Any mechanical shop drawings will be produced by HVAC, fire system or plumbing subcontractors.

Landscape Drawings (The "L" Sheets)

Landscape drawings show plant, tree and ground cover sizes, types and location both on and off the site. The landscape drawings may also have a *hardscape plan* showing the location, width, and finish of walks, driveways and parking on the site.

The landscape subcontractor will usually produce shop drawings if there is no other landscape plan. These drawings may show landscaping and irrigation plans designed to meet a specified budget. The *irrigation plan* will be part of the landscape drawings. It shows the location, sizes and type of irrigation piping, valves, and heads.

Grading Plans

Grading plans are usually produced separately from the building and related plans. Grading plans use light lines to show the elevation of the existing ground before construction begins, and dark lines to show the finished grade elevations at key locations throughout the project. Grading plans may be shown on the same plan as other on-site improvements.

Site Improvement Drawings

These plans usually have separate sheets for work outside the property line (off site) and work within the property line (on site). The off-site drawings show location and elevations of the "public work" — public streets, sidewalks, curb and gutter, street lights and so on. The on-site drawings can show location and elevations of the "private work" — private sidewalk, curbs or curb and gutter, asphalt areas, carport locations, number of parking stalls, pavement striping, playground equipment (tot lot) locations, and pool and spa locations.

The Sample Plan

The sample plan in Appendix A follows the same format as most architectural plan sets for a small single-family home. Here's what you'll find in the sample plan and most residential plans:

Title sheet— The title sheet shows general information about the project. You'll probably find the architect's name, the owner's name, the project name, the legal description of the property, a vicinity map showing the location of the project (sheet 2 of the sample plan), energy calculations and an index of all sheets included in the plan set.

General notes— The next sheet might include all the "general notes" for the project. These general notes are actually the specifications for smaller projects. They're usually organized into the 16 division system of the Construction Specification Institute (CSI) Masterformat. The general notes describe the construction requirements and specifications for each trade involved with the construction of a building.

Architectural, mechanical and electrical symbols may also appear on the general note sheets. If the plans are complex and include "M" sheets, "P" sheets or "E" sheets, these symbols will appear on a cover sheet for each drawing. General notes are usually found near the front or at the back of the architectural plan set.

On larger, more complex projects, there won't be a sheet with general notes. Instead, there will be a project manual that gives detailed specifications for each trade.

Site plan— The site plan pinpoints locations and elevations of buildings and all off-site and on-site improvements.

Don't confuse the site plan with the plot plan. The plot plan identifies or "plots" the locations of the property boundaries and building locations in a particular area. The plot plan usually doesn't detail any improvements.

Foundation plan— This plan identifies the dimensions of the foundation, footing sizes, size and location of reinforcing steel (rebar), placement of anchor bolts and hardware. The foundation for simple residential buildings with standard loads (weights) and footing sizes may be produced by the architect and appear on the "A" sheets. More complex structures have foundations designed by a structural engineer. Designs for these foundations will be on the "S" sheets.

Floor plan— The floor plan shows the interior layout of a building. See sheet 8 of the sample plan. It provides overall dimensions and room sizes as well as showing the kitchen and bath cabinet and fixture layout. This plan should also identify the location and type of all doors and windows. But details about doors and windows will be on a door schedule and window schedule. You'll work from the floor plan when estimating the cost of painting the interior of a building.

Framing plan— The sample plan is so simple that there's room on the floor plan to show lumber sizes and spacing of the roof members and headers. Wall construction details will probably be in the general notes or project manual. For simple residential buildings, the framing plan will be drawn by the architect and be on the "A" sheets. More complicated buildings will show wall construction details on an "S" sheet drawn by a structural engineer. Painting estimators seldom need to refer to a framing plan.

Roof plan— The roof plan (sheet 9 of the sample) shows roof type and design, direction of drainage, and chimney location.

Section drawings— The section drawings (sheets 11 and 12 of the sample plan) are cross sections through various parts of a building. They show ceiling heights as well as the type of material used for floors, walls, roof and other parts of the building.

The ceiling height and materials used will be important considerations in your painting estimate. For instance, suppose the ceiling is 13 feet high, is constructed with tongue and groove (T&G) material, and has exposed ceiling beams. If you miss that information, chances are you'll lose money on that project. Open beam ceilings 13 feet off the floor aren't easy to paint.

Staircases should be shown in section drawings. Consider the painting required on stair stringers, stair treads, vertical railing, handrail, and any kickboards that run along the treads.

Interior elevations— These drawings show front views of kitchen cabinets and bathroom pullmans (vanities). Be sure to check for light valance trim in bathrooms or kitchens of more expensive homes. Also, check the interior elevations for wine racks and other cabinet work which may require special attention and can be difficult to finish. Check these interior elevation views very carefully when estimating painting costs.

Exterior elevations— The exterior elevations are on sheets 14, 15, and 16 of the sample plan. They show the outside of a building from each side: front, rear, left side, and right side. These drawings identify the exterior finish (whether it's siding or stucco) and the exterior trim, including pot shelves, pass-through shelves, plant-on trim (trim around doors and windows) and gutters and downspouts, among other details.

Always check to see if there's more than one exterior elevation for each floor plan. For example, a housing tract may have several floor plans, each with three different exterior looks. When you work on the sample estimate for new construction, take off the interior painting first, then take off the exterior. That way you can combine the interior subtotal with each exterior subtotal. The result is a different cost for painting each exterior elevation, even though they're all built around the same floor plan.

The elevation views and floor plans are part of the "A" sheets, the architectural drawings. The details are also part of the "A" sheets.

Details— Details are usually enlarged cross sections. They show exactly how the architect or engineer intends to construct the building. Assembly of the various parts is usually well defined. Many detail drawings refer to the structural parts of a building: the foundation and framing. Other detail drawings show how to build any unusual items.

The schedules— Most architectural plan sets include a door schedule and a window schedule. There may also be a finish schedule. All doors and windows are numbered on their respective schedules, showing sizes, types, and specific remarks. These schedules have important information that's needed for final pricing.

The finish schedule lists each room and identifies the finish on each surface (walls, floors and ceilings) of each room. Always review the finish schedule for a project if there's one included in the plan set.

Design Lines, Symbols and Abbreviations

Design lines are used when preparing a set of plans. Each type of line is used for a different purpose. Several of the most common design lines are shown in Figure 3-1.

You'll see many symbols on architectural drawings. They can be grouped into the categories shown in Figure 3-2: architectural, electrical and mechanical (plumbing and HVAC) symbols. Any other symbols used in the plans should be defined on one of the plan sheets.

The drawings will also include many abbreviations. Figure 3-3 lists the most common abbreviations used in the construction industry.

Break Line—Long

Break Line—Short

These lines are used when an area cannot or should not be entirely drawn.

Center Line

A series of short and long dashes used to designate centers and provide a reference point for dimensioning.

Dimension Line

Thin, unbroken lines which designate dimensions.

Extension Line

These lines extend, but do not touch, the object lines; they permit dimension lines to be drawn between them.

Hidden Line

Short dashes used to show lines that are not visible from the view shown.

Leader Line

The lines are used to connect a note or reference or dimension to the part of the building being illustrated.

Object Line

These lines show the main outline of the structure, including exterior walls, interior partitions, porches, patios, driveways, and interior walls. They should be the outstanding lines on the drawing.

Section Line

These are heavy lines consisting of a series of one long and two short dashes with arrows at each end pointing away from the area that is cut away for the purpose of sectioning.

Structural

Stair Indicator

(NOTE: These lines indicate the direction of stairs.)

**Design lines
Figure 3-1**

Measuring Scales

Two types of measuring scales are common on building plan sets: the engineer's scale and the architect's scale.

The *engineer's scale* is used on grading and plot or site improvement plans. It's divided into tenths of an inch. Depending on which scale you're using, each 1/10, 1/20, 1/30, 1/40, 1/50 or 1/60 of an inch on the scale equals one foot on the ground.

The *architect's scale* is the most common. It uses eighths of an inch. For example, 1/8 inch on the scale may equal one foot in reality. Other common architectural scale increments are: 1/4, 3/8, 1/2, 3/4, and 1 inch to the foot.

Identifying the Scale of the Drawing

The sample plans identify the scale for each drawing below the title of the plan. On good architectural drawings, the scale of each drawing will be shown on each sheet of the plan set. If the scale is missing and you don't know what scale to use, there are a couple of ways to identify the scale.

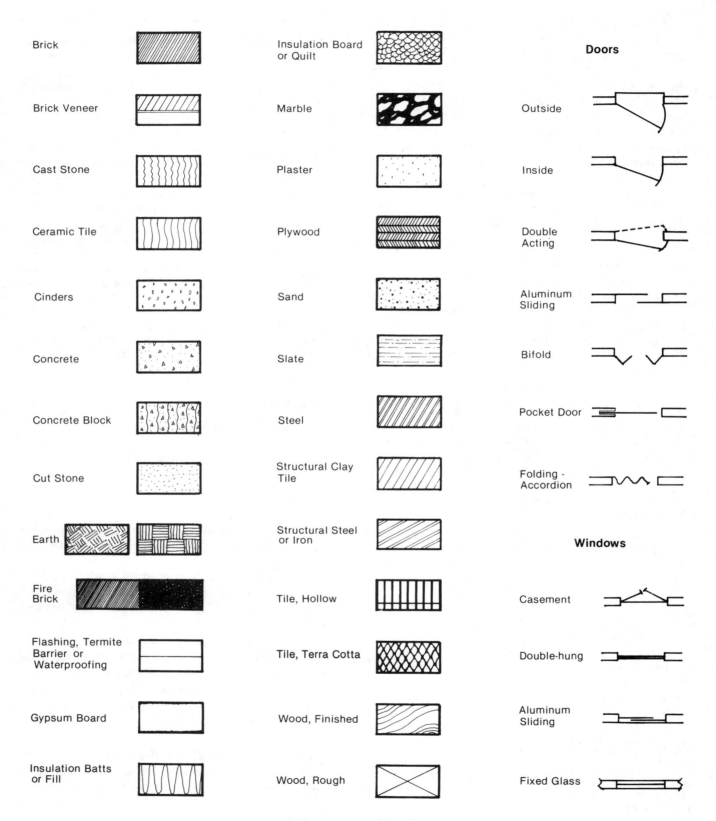

Architectural design symbols
Figure 3-2

Electrical

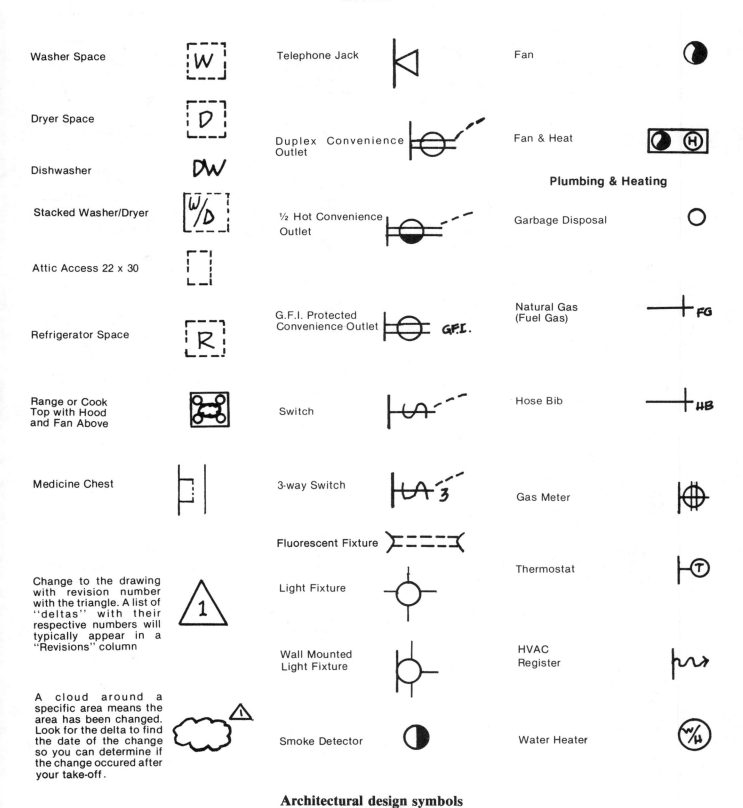

Washer Space

Dryer Space

Dishwasher

Stacked Washer/Dryer

Attic Access 22 x 30

Refrigerator Space

Range or Cook Top with Hood and Fan Above

Medicine Chest

Change to the drawing with revision number with the triangle. A list of "deltas" with their respective numbers will typically appear in a "Revisions" column

A cloud around a specific area means the area has been changed. Look for the delta to find the date of the change so you can determine if the change occured after your take-off.

Telephone Jack

Duplex Convenience Outlet

½ Hot Convenience Outlet

G.F.I. Protected Convenience Outlet

Switch

3-way Switch

Fluorescent Fixture

Light Fixture

Wall Mounted Light Fixture

Smoke Detector

Fan

Fan & Heat

Plumbing & Heating

Garbage Disposal

Natural Gas (Fuel Gas)

Hose Bib

Gas Meter

Thermostat

HVAC Register

Water Heater

Architectural design symbols
Figure 3-2 (continued)

A

ab — anchor bolt
abv — above
ac — acoustical
acpl — acoustical paper
act — acoustical tile
add — addendum
adj — adjacent
agg — aggregate
ac — air conditioning
al — aluminum
apx — approximate
arch — architect(s)
asb — asbestos
asph — asphalt
at — asphalt tile

B

bsmt — basement
ba — bathroom
bm — beam
br — bedroom
bel — below
bet — between
bit — bituminous
blk — block
bd — board
bot — bottom
brk — brick
brz — bronze
bldg — building
bur — built up roof
bbd — bulletin board

C

cab — cabinet
carp — carpentry
cpt — carpet(ed)
cipc — cast-in-place concrete
clg — ceiling
cem — cement
cer — ceramic
ct — ceramic tile
chbd — chalkboard
clo — closet
clr — clear
col — column
compo — composition, composite
conc — concrete
cmu — concrete masonry unit
const — construction
contr — contract(or)
ctr — counter
cft — cubic foot
cyd — cubic yard

D

dem — demolish, demolition
dmt — demountable
det — detail
diag — diagonal
diam — diameter
din — dining room
div — division
dr — door
dbl — double
df/l — douglas fir or larch
d — penny, dryer

E

ea — each
e — east
elec — electric(al)
elev — elevator
enc — enclose(ure)
ent — entry
eqp — equipment
esc — escalator
est — estimate
exca — excavate
ext — exterior

F

fos — face of stud
fn — fence
fin — finish(ed)
ff — finished floor
fa — fire alarm
fe — fire extinguisher
fpl — fireplace
flg — flashing
flr — floor(ing)
flur — fluorescent
fau — forced air unit
fnd — foundation
fr — framed, framing
fg — fuel gas, fixed glass finish grade

G

gal — gallon
galv — galvanized
gc — general contract(or)
gl — glass, glazing
gd — grade(ing)
gvl — gravel
gfi — ground fault intercept
gyp — gypsum
gpdw — gypsum drywall
gpl — gypsum lath
gppl — gypsum plaster
gpt — gypsum tile

H

hdw — hardware
hwd — hardwood
hdr — header
h — heat
htg — heating
hvac — heating/ventilation/air conditioning
ht — height
hm — hollow metal
hb — hose bib
hr — hour

I

incl — include(d), inclusion
ins — insulate(d), insulation
int — interior

J

j — joist

K

kit — kitchen

L

lab — laboratory
lam — laminate(d)
lndscp — landscape
lav — lavatory
lt — light
lw — lightweight
lwc — lightweight concrete
lf — linear feet
lin — linen

M

mfr — manufacture(r)
mrb — marble
mas — masonry
mtl — material(s)
max — maximum
mech — mechanic(al)
mc — medicine cabinet
met — metal
mrd — metal roof decking
mwk — millwork
min — minimum
misc — miscellaneous
mt — mount(ed), (ing)
mov — movable

N

n — north
nic — not in contract
nts — not to scale

O

oc — on center
oh — overhead

P

pnt — paint(ed)
pnl — panel
pk — parking
pbd — particleboard
ptn — partition
p/t — pass-through shelf
pv — pave(d), (ing)
pvmt — pavement
ped — pedestrian
plas — plaster
plam — plastic laminate
pl — plate, property line
pwd — plywood
pt — point
pcc — portland concrete cement
p/s — pot shelf
pfb — prefabricate(d)
ptdf — pressure treated douglas fir
psc — prestressed concrete

Q

qt — quarry tile

R

rl — rail(ing)
rwd — redwood
refr — refrigerator

re — reinforce(d), (ing)
rcp — reinforced concrete pipe
rem — remove
res — resilient, resawn
rfg — roofing
rm — room
ros — roughsawn

S

sl — safety lighting
sch — schedule
snt — sealant
stg — seating
sec — section
shth — sheathing
sht — sheet
sh — shelf, shelving
s&p — shelf and pole
sho — shore(d), (ing)
sim — similar
skl — skylight
s — south
spec — specification(s)
spklr — sprinkler
sq — square
sf — square feet
sst — stainless steel
std — standard
sta — station
st — steel
sd — storm drain
str — structural
sct — structural clay tile
s/s — stucco seal
sub — subcontract(or)
sus — suspended
syn — synthetic
sys — system

T

tkbd — tackboard
tel — telephone
tv — television
tc — terra cotta
tz — terrazzo
t — thermostat
tptn — toilet partition
t&g — tongue & groove
ts — traffic signal

U

unf — unfinished
UBC — Uniform Building Code
util — utility room

V

vin — vinyl
vat — vinyl asbestos tile
vt — vinyl tile

W

wh — wall heater
wp — waterproofing
w — west, washer
win — window
w/ — with
wd — wood
wi — wrought iron

Standard abbreviations
Figure 3-3

First, find a written dimension on the plan sheet and compare the length of that dimension to various scales until you find the right scale.

If that doesn't help identify the scale, measure some dimension that will be the same on most plans. For example, ceiling height in most residential buildings is 8'0'' high. Most second floor ceilings are 17'0'' from the first level finished floor (8'0'' first floor plus 1'0'' floor joist plus 8'0'' second floor). And entry doors in residential units are typically 3'0'' wide.

The following list shows the most common scales for the various drawing types:

- Grading plan, plot plan, site improvement plan: 1/10'' equals 1'0'' or 1/20'' equals 1'0'' are typical.

- Foundation plan, floor plan, framing plan: 1/4'' equals 1'0'' or 1/8'' equals 1'0''.

- Roof plan: 1/8'' equals 1'0'' is typical.

- Sections: 3/8'' equals 1'0'' is typical.

- Exterior elevations: 1/4'' equals 1'0'' or 1/8'' equals 1'0''.

- Interior elevations: 3/8'' equals 1'0'' is typical.

- Details: 1/2'' equals 1'0'' is typical.

- Structural drawings: 1/4'' equals 1'0'' or 1/8'' equals 1'0'' is typical.

- Structural details: 1/2'' equals 1'0'' is typical.

- Electrical drawings, mechanical drawings: 1/4'' equals 1'0'' or 1/8'' equals 1'0'' is typical.

- Landscape drawings, irrigation drawings: 1/10'' equals 1'0'' or 1/20'' equals 1'0'' is typical.

- Hardscape drawings: 1/10'' equals 1'0'' or 1/20'' equals 1'0'' is typical.

Scale reductions for government projects— Here's something important to remember about drawing scales: Many government plan sets are photographically reduced by one-half, to reduce the costs of reproduction and mailing. Look for a note something like this on the cover sheet: *The scale of these drawings has been reduced by 1/2 relevant to the scale indicated on the drawings.*

As a result of this reduction, a plan originally drawn in 1/8 scale will actually be 1/16 scale. To an estimator, this is essential information. Always check the scale of every plan before starting the take-off. A mistake in the scale can lead to the biggest mistake of your estimating career. In fact, it could be your last estimating mistake.

You may also see the abbreviation *N.T.S.* which refers to the scale of a drawing. It means *Not To Scale.*

Use the largest scale possible for the take-off— When you have a choice, take measurements from the drawing with the largest scale. This will improve the accuracy of your take-off. If there's a detail drawing of the item to be measured, use that detail with a larger scale rather than a plan view or elevation. For example, the light valance over the bathroom vanity in the sample plan is on the floor plan at 1/4 inch scale. There's also a detail view at the interior elevations of the sample plan at 3/8 inch scale. The measurements are to be taken from the interior elevation.

Plan Roll-Up Method

This may seem like an insignificant tip, but it annoys most builders to have plans returned with the cover sheet at the center of the roll and the back of the last sheet exposed on the outside. This causes two problems: The plans curl up on the plan table when you lay them out. And when they're rolled up backwards, the title block is on the inside, so you can't tell which set of plans is which. This is very frustrating — and it *can* be avoided. The right way to roll a set of plans is with the cover sheet on the outside. Always leave the title block in plain view so you can see at a glance which plans you have. Rolling the plans this way also prevents the plans from curling up when laid flat on the plan table.

Comparing Plans: The Project Comparison Chart

Every estimator must know how to read and interpret architectural plans and specifications. This section will help you understand what features to expect on the plans for different kinds of projects.

Many types of projects are listed in the construction project category. Room additions, new residential, new commercial, and industrial are just a few. Just as there are different types of projects with various levels or complexity, you'll find levels of sophistication in the plans and specifications for these projects.

Figure 3-4 is a project comparison chart. It separates the various plan types into four categories:

1) Residential additions, remodels and repaints

2) New residential, tract or custom, new light commercial and commercial tenant improvements

3) New heavy commercial

4) Government, industrial and institutional

The chart summarizes some of the typical conditions and requirements for the four categories of building projects, from the quality of the plans you can expect to the amount of markup you'll usually add.

Plan quality— The first column is *Plans/Grade.* In this column you'll find the title of the person who prepared the plans along with a grade for each plan type, A, B, or C. A *C* indicates drawings that only meet minimum requirements. An *A* represents the most sophisticated plans.

An "A" plan is prepared by a registered architect. A "B" quality plan might be prepared by a licensed building designer. And a "C" quality plan is produced by a homeowner or general contractor and may be used for simple projects.

The style and quality of lettering on a set of drawings usually shows the level of skill used in preparing the plans. Sloppy lettering usually means inexperience. The plans may not be complete. Be careful! With incomplete plans, design decisions must be made in the field. That may mean that *you* have to pay for the designer's inexperience.

Of course, some poor plans have excellent lettering. And I've seen drawings that were complete and accurate even though the lettering wasn't first rate. But poor lettering should alert you to a possible problem.

Plan quality can affect your estimate. The quality of the drawings prepared by the owner's designer or architect probably reflects the quality of work expected on the project. For example, if the project plans weren't prepared by an architect, the owner probably decided to save a few dollars. There's a good chance that he'll try to cut costs with every trade on that project. You may want to bid this project only after determining the quality of work expected from subcontractors.

Specifications— The second column in the table refers to the specifications. The specs show sizes, quantities, performance requirements, quality grades, installation procedures, terms, conditions, and so on. The more complex the project, the more detailed the specifications. A small residential addition may have only a few notes. A new residential construction project may have a page of general notes that applies to all trades. These can be very sketchy. Specifications for a complex government or industrial project may be in the form of a project manual, with a section for each trade and sections with general provisions, contract documents, and bidding procedures.

Most specifications make some reference to the Uniform Building Code (UBC). Your building inspector uses the code as his guide when making inspections. No matter what your specs or plans say, you must follow the building code that applies to the project you're estimating.

Don't make the mistake of skipping over the general notes or specifications that apply to the painting trade. A good estimator *always* reads the specifications or general notes to be sure the estimate is based on the architect's requirements.

Bidding process— This column describes the nature of the bidding process, ranging from individual to formal, as discussed in Chapter 1.

Occupancy— Column four indicates the intended occupancy. A residential addition is usually owner-occupied. But a new tract home, or a custom home, may be produced for resale. A new commercial building might be sold after it's completed, or it might be kept as income property with the spaces leased out. An industrial building might be "built to suit" for a future occupant who owns the property and pays for the construction, or who leases the space in the building after construction. A government building is usually owned, financed, and occupied by the government agency that funds the contracts for the construction.

Quality control— Inspection and quality control are covered in column five. The building code sets minimum requirements for all buildings. Other codes and ordinances may also apply. City or county building inspectors check the quality of construction for all types of projects.

Even a residential addition must meet code requirements, as well as satisfy the owner's requirements for quality workmanship.

	Plans/Grade	Specifications	Bidding Process	Occupancy	Inspection/ Quality Control	Bond Requirements	Documentation Requirements	Wages	Overhead and Profit
Residential additions, remodels and repaints	Building designer Grade C	•Specific notes •UBC	•Individual bids	•**Owner occupy** •Rebuild for resale	•Home-owner accepted •City/county inspectors	•Possible completion or performance bond	•Informal verbal request typical	•Non-union scale is typical	•O/H: **15%** •Profit: 15-20%
New residential tract or custom **New light commercial** **Commercial tenant improvement**	•Architect or •Building designer Grade A B or C	•General notes •UBC	•Informal bids	•Resale • Lease	•General contractor quality control •City/county inspection	•Performance per contract if required • Bonding is rare	• Semi-formal requirements •Field authorization typical	•Tract homes: Non-union scale •**Custom homes** Typically non-union	Tract homes •O/H: 10-12% •**Profit: 5%** •**Custom homes** •O/H: 10-12% •Profit: 10%
New heavy commercial	•**Architect** Grade A	•Project manual •General notes •UBC	•Semiformal bids	•Lease •Resell	•Independent inspectors •City/County inspectors	•**Possible payment and/or performance bond**	•Formal documentation is typical	•Union and non-union scale may apply	•O/H: 10-15% •Profit: 10%
Government, industrial and institutional	•**Architect** •Government Engineer Grade B	Project manual with extensive specifications	•Formal bids	•No sales. Government occupied	•Government inspection	•Payment and performance bonds are typically required	•Strictly formal - few exceptions	•Governed by Davis-Bacon Act (Prevailing wage requirements)	•O/H 12-15% •Profit 5-10%

Project comparison chart
Figure 3-4

A new tract or custom home may have to comply with requirements set by the lender, or some other federal, state or local agency or government. In addition, the developer (and the builder's marketing department) must be satisfied with the quality of tract homes. And, of course, tastes and budgets of the prospective occupants must be considered.

A commercial project must meet local codes, of course. Perhaps more important, it has to meet the developer's standards so it can be leased quickly. Commercial projects are often finished only on the exterior, with the painting done on a production basis — as quickly as possible. Interiors are usually finished as the tenants "lease up" the building.

Many government and industrial projects are built to standards more stringent than anything codes require. A government inspector, or an independent inspector, may be on the project full time to oversee each phase of construction.

Bond requirements— The sixth column lists bond types. The owner may request a bond. A bond is a guarantee that the contractor will perform according to the terms and conditions in the contract. Various types of bonds are described in detail in Chapter 16.

Documentation requirements— The next column lists documentation requirements for each project category. These might include written submittals, transmittals, price requests, change orders, extra work requests, inspector's test results, material certification, or traceability documentation. In many companies, processing all this paperwork is the estimator's job. A later chapter discusses documentation in detail.

Documentation requirements are important to the estimator for another reason. There's more paper on complex projects; paperwork that takes more time and increases your overhead. A residential project, for example, may have a 12% overhead. But a government project may require a 15% overhead to cover the extra paperwork processing time.

Wages— Next, column eight shows wage scales likely on the various project types. Small contractors are usually non-union. Workers on smaller projects (room additions, custom homes, and most housing tracts) are paid non-union wages.

Union wages are paid on many commercial and industrial projects, and nearly all government projects. The Davis-Bacon Act establishes prevailing wages (usually union scale) on government projects.

Overhead and profit percentages— Now look at column nine. Overhead and profit percentages vary with the project type.

A residential addition has an average percentage of overhead. But it also has more risk: The risk of non-payment, the chance that you'll be called back again and again to paint and repaint every flyspeck the owners find, and the annoyance of working around people living in the home, plus a few more. Risks like these justify a larger profit percentage. The higher the risk, the greater the profit.

Tract home projects have an average level of overhead and a low-to-conservative profit percentage because bidding is usually extremely competitive. There's another reason for this low profit percentage. Tract homes can be painted quickly because the work is so repetitive.

Custom homes are unique. They take longer to paint and materials usually cost more. Therefore, a high profit percentage is justified. The overhead required is at an above-average level.

As you've seen, commercial or industrial projects usually have higher overhead than residential projects because more documentation is needed. The profit percentage will be similar to other non-repetitive projects.

Bidding for government projects is highly competitive: Many companies specialize in government work. As a result, their overhead percentage is higher, to cover time spent producing the documentation required. Profit percentage will vary with the difficulty of the project. It must be kept as low as possible, or you won't get the bid.

Painting Specifications

In this section, we'll discuss the kinds of painting specifications you're most likely to face. More complex specs are needed for more complex buildings. The simpler the building, the less detailed the specs will be.

Specs for the Individual Bid

For example, the only specification on a residential repaint job is usually what the owner tells you. The owner wants two coats on the exterior and one on the interior, with average-quality paint. It's up to the painter to do a job the customer is happy with. Of course, some details may be assumed. For ex-

Index

Division 0 - Not used
Division 1 - General requirements
Division 2 - Sitework
Division 3 - Concrete
Division 4 - Not used
Division 5 - Metals
Division 6 - Wood
Division 7 - Thermal and moisture protection
Division 8 - Doors and windows
Division 9 - Finishes
Division 10 - Specialties
Division 11 - Not used
Division 12 - Not used
Division 13 - Not used
Division 14 - Not used
Division 15 - Mechanical/plumbing
Division 16 - Electrical

Division 1. General Requirements

Summary of Work

1. Construction of a 148 unit condo complex.

Coordination

1. All work shall comply with applicable State, County and City ordinances, and the 1988 edition of the Uniform Building Code.

2. *Permits* The owner shall secure and pay for the Building Permit; permits shall be taken out and paid for by the subcontractors directly responsible.

3. *Substitution* No substitutions are permitted without the owner's prior written approval. Trade names and/or manufacturer's names referred to are for quality standards. Equal products are permitted if approved by the owner, in writing.

4. *Dimensioning* Written dimensions shall take precedence over dimensions scaled on the drawings.

5. *Changes* The owner may order extra work or make changes by altering, adding to, or deducting from the work, the contract sum being adjusted accordingly.

6. *Intention* The intention of these documents is to include all labor, materials, services, equipment and transportation necessary for complete and proper execution of the work indicated on drawings or reasonably inferred therefrom. The Architect will, in no way, be responsible for how the work is performed, for safety on or about the job site, methods and timeliness of construction.

7. *Scope* Trades shall furnish all labor, equipment, materials and services required to perform all work necessary, indicated, reasonably inferred from, or required by any code with jurisdiction, to complete their scope of work for a complete and properly finished job.

8. *Lines and Levels* Lay out building lines and levels accurately. Compare the lines and levels shown on the drawings with existing site conditions for the location and construction of the work.

9. *Cutting and Patching* The Contractor shall coordinate cutting and patching by all trades to make the several parts come together properly.

10. *Discrepancies in Plans* The Contractor shall immediately call to the architect's attention any discrepancies in the plans or on the site prior to proceeding with the work.

Typical index and general requirements
Figure 3-5

ample, the amount of preparation and under-coating to do on new interior wood is usually left up to the painter. But he must take into consideration the quality of work the owner is expecting.

Specs for the Informal Bid Process

For a residential project with an informal bidding process, the only specifications will usually be the general notes included in the plans. Sheet 4 in Appendix A shows a set of general notes that apply to painting.

Always read the general notes that apply to finishes and related trades. A professional estimator studies these notes. It's the only way to be sure that the architect's requirements are being met.

Specs for the Semi-Formal and Formal Bid Process

More complex projects will have specifications bound into a book called the project manual, which is arranged according to the 16-division system developed by the Construction Specification Institute (CSI). This system of organization makes estimating and bidding easier for all contractors. The CSI system makes it easy to find the specifications that relate to each trade. This system is used on government projects and on nearly all published competitive projects where the architect or builder acts as the owner's agent. Many smaller projects in the informal bid class are also organized using a 16-division system.

Figure 3-5 is an example of the general requirements for a residential project. Figure 3-6 shows the painting specifications for a residential project.

The CSI Masterformat

The first CSI construction specifications format was devised in 1962. Many revisions followed. Since 1983, we use the "Masterformat, MP-2-1 revised." It's by far the most popular method for organizing construction specifications and bid documents and is recognized as the standard for the construction industry. Figure 3-7 is a summary of the CSI Index. This index has superseded the previous Uniform Construction Index (UCI) which also divided the construction trades into 16 divisions.

As a painting estimator, your primary concern is with Division 09000 — Finishes. Within this division, there are three main categories that cover your specialty. They are:

- *09800 Special Coatings*

- *09900 Painting*

- *09950 Wall Covering*

Each of these three categories has subcategories. They're described in more detail in the following sections.

Special coatings— These are high-performance, glazed resinous coatings. They include epoxy polyester, or polyurethane; interior or exterior cementitious coatings; heavy industrial coatings, including chlorinated rubber; heat-resistant elastomeric, and zinc-rich primers; fire-retardant paint. Also included are storage tank coating systems. Here's a listing.

- *09800 Special Coatings*
  09810 Abrasion Resistant Coatings
  09815 High-Build Glazed Coatings
  09820 Cementitious Coatings
  09830 Elastomeric Coatings
  09835 Textured Plastic Coatings
  09840 Fire-Resistant Paints
  09845 Intumescent Paints
  09850 Chemical Resistant Coatings
  09860 Anti-graffiti Coatings
  09870 Coating Systems for Steel
  09871 Protective Linings for Concrete Tanks
  09872 Interior Coating Systems for Steel Storage Tanks
  09873 Exterior Coating Systems for Steel Storage Tanks
  09874 Linseed Oil Protection for Concrete
  09875 Coating System for Steel Piping
  09880 Protective Coatings for Concrete

- Work Related to Special Coatings
  02760 Relining Existing Underground Pipelines
  06300 Fire Retardant Treated Lumber
  07150 Water Repellent Coatings
  07250 Fire Resistant Mastics and Applied Fireproofing
  09230 Aggregate Coatings
  09700 Special Flooring
  13200 Liquid and gas storage tanks

Painting— This is exterior and interior painting with transparent or opaque finishes, including stains, varnishes, lacquers, primers, fillers and waxes, and preparation of surfaces.

Painting and Finishing

1. Scope
Furnish all labor and materials to complete painting and finishing work, including preparation of surfaces other than those that are factory primed.

2. Materials
A. Paint materials shall be as manufactured by *Frazee.*
B. Exterior stains shall be *Frazee Madera semi-transparent.*
C. Interior stains shall be *Frazee Madera semi-transparent.*
D. All materials shall be delivered to the site in sealed original manufacturer's containers.

3. Colors
To be selected.

4. Preparation of Surfaces
A. Surfaces shall be clean and dry, and in suitable condition for finish specified. Remove all oil, grease, bond breaking agents, dust, mill scale and efflorescence.
B. Fill cracks, holes, and knots, sand smooth, and seal. Wood surfaces, except resawn wood, shall be sanded perfectly smooth. Remove sanding dust completely.
C. Remove hardware prior to painting if required.
D. Backpaint trim and other finish work prior to installation.

5. Workmanship
A. Each coat shall be uniformly applied, well brushed out and free of brush marks, runs, sags, or skips.
B. Cut-in paint finishes sharply to line. Protect adjacent surfaces.
C. Mix and apply paint and stain in accordance with the manufacturer's instructions.

6. Exterior Painting
A. All exterior wood, railings, fascia, trim, etc.—two coats stain.
B. Exposed metal, including vent pipes, exhaust vents, grilles, etc., color shall match adjacent surfaces: One coat exterior alkyd semi-gloss enamel over one coat primer.

7. Interior Painting and Finishing
A. Ceilings and walls (except acoustical textured ceilings.)
(1) Kitchen, bathrooms: sealer and one coat semi-gloss enamel.
(2) All other rooms: one coat flat paint to cover.
(3) Exposed post, beams and wood ceilings: one coat of stain to cover.
B. Wardrobes, closets (except shelving): finish as specified for adjoining room.
C. Wood trim, paint grade, doors, frames, wood base, shelf cleats: one coat primer, two coats semi-gloss enamel.

D. Stain grade doors: two coats stain.
E. Hardwood cabinets: two coats spray lacquer sealer-stain.
F. Paint grade cabinets (exterior and interior): one coat undercoat, one coat semi-gloss enamel.
G. Metal surfaces: paint all registers, grills and vents to match adjacent surfaces with two coats of alkyd semi-gloss enamel.

Painting specifications for a residential project
Figure 3-6

- *09900 Painting*
  09910 Exterior Painting
  09920 Interior Painting
  09930 Transparent Finishes

- Work Related to Painting. It's easy to miss painting that isn't in Division 9. Be especially aware of these items:
  02500 Pavement Marking
  09550 Wood Floor Finishes and Waxes
  09800 Special Coatings and Fire Resistant Paints

15050 Mechanical Identification Systems Color-coded Plumbing Lines, Fire Lines or Heating and Air Conditioning Pipes and Ductwork
16050 Electrical Identification Systems Painted mechanical and electrical identification may be specified in this section.

Wall coverings— These include vinyl-coated fabric backed for light, medium, and heavy-duty usage; unsupported vinyl, cork, wallpaper and wall

Bidding requirements, contract forms, and conditions of the contract

00010 Pre-bid information
00100 Instructions to bidders
00200 Information available to bidders
00300 Bid forms
00400 Supplements to bids forms
00500 Agreement forms
00600 Bonds and certificates
00700 General conditions
00800 Supplementary conditions
00850 Drawings and schedules
00900 Addenda and modifications

Note: Since the items listed above are not specification sections, they are referred to as "Documents" in lieu of "Section" in the Master List of Section Titles, Numbers, and Broadscope Explanations.

Specifications

Division 1 - General Requirements

01010 Summary of work
01020 Allowances
01025 Measurement and payment
01030 Alternates/alternatives
01040 Coordination
01050 Field engineering
01060 Regulatory requirements
01070 Abbreviations and symbols
01080 Identification systems
01090 Reference standards
01100 Special project procedures
01200 Project meetings
01300 Submittals
01400 Quality control
01500 Constuction facilities and temporary
          controls
01600 Material and equipment
01650 Starting of systems/commissioning
01700 Contract closeout
01800 Maintenance

Division 2 - Sitework

02010 Subsurface investigation
02050 Demolition
02100 Site preparation
02140 Dewatering
02150 Shoring and underpinning
02160 Excavation support systems
02170 Cofferdams
02200 Earthwork
02300 Tunneling
02350 Piles and caissons
02450 Railroad work
02480 Marine work
02500 Paving and surfacing
02600 Water distribution
02680 Fuel distribution
02700 Sewerage and drainage
02760 Restoration of underground pipelines
02770 Ponds and reservoirs

02780 Power and communications
02800 Site improvements
02900 Landscaping

Division 3 - Concrete

03100 Concrete formwork
03200 Concrete reinforcement
03250 Concrete accessories
03300 Cast-in-place concrete
03370 Concrete curing
03400 Precast concrete
03500 Cementitious decks
03600 Grout
03700 Concrete restoration and cleaning
03800 Mass concrete

Division 4 - Masonry

04100 Mortar
04150 Masonry accessories
04150 Unit masonry
04400 Stone
04500 Masonry restoration and cleaning
04550 Refractories
04600 Corrosion resistant masonry

Division 5 - Metals

05010 Metal materials
05030 Metal finishes
05050 Metal fastening
05100 Structural metal framing
05200 Metal joists
05300 Metal decking
05400 Cold-formed metal framing
05500 Metal fabrications
05580 Sheet metal fabrications
05700 Ornamental metal
05800 Expansion control
05900 Hydraulic structures

Division 6 - Wood and Plastic

06050 Fasteners and adhesives
06100 Rough carpentry
06130 Heavy timber construction
06150 Wood-metal systems
06170 Prefabricated structural wood
06200 Finish carpentry
06300 Wood treatment
06400 Architectural woodwork
06500 Prefabricated structural plastics
06600 Plastic fabrications

Division 7 - Thermal and Moisture Protection

07100 Waterproofing
07150 Dampproofing
07190 Vapor and air retarders
07200 Insulation
07250 Fireproofing

CSI Masterformat
Figure 3-7

07300   Shingles and roofing tiles
07400   Preformed roofing and cladding/siding
07500   Membrane roofing
07570   Traffic topping
07600   Flashing and sheet metal
07700   Roof specialties and accessories
07800   Skylights
07900   Joint sealers

Division 8 · Doors and Windows

08100   Metal doors and frames
08200   Wood and plastic doors
08250   Door opening assemblies
08300   Special doors
08400   Entrances and store fronts
08500   Metal windows
08600   Wood and plastic windows
08650   Special windows
08700   Hardware
08800   Glazing
08900   Glazed curtain walls

Division 9 · Finishes

09100   Metal support systems
09200   Lath and plaster
09230   Aggregate coating
09250   Gypsum board
09300   Tile
09400   Terrazzo
09500   Acoustical treatment
09540   Special surfaces
09550   Wood flooring
09600   Stone flooring
09630   Unit masonry flooring
09650   Resilient flooring
09680   Carpet
09700   Special flooring
09780   Floor treatment
09800   Special coating
09845   Intumescent paints
09860   Anti-graffiti coatings
09900   Painting/paint manufacturers
09910   Exterior painting
09920   Interior painting
09930   Transparent finishes
09950   Wall coverings
09955   Vinyl coated fabric wall covering
09960   Vinyl wall covering
09965   Cork wall covering
09970   Wallpaper
09975   Wall fabrics
09980   Flexible wood sheets and veneers
09985   Prefinished panels

Division 10 · Specialties

10100   Chalkboards and tackboards
10150   Compartments and cubicles
10200   Louvers and vents
10240   Grilles and screens
10250   Service wall systems
10260   Wall and corner guards
10270   Access flooring
10280   Specialty modules

10290   Pest control
10300   Fireplaces and stoves
10340   Prefabricated exterior specialities
10350   Flagpoles
10400   Identifying devices
10450   Pedestrian control devices
10500   Lockers
10520   Fire protection specialties
10530   Protective covers
10550   Postal specialties
10600   Partitions
10650   Operable partitions
10670   Storage shelving
10700   Exterior sun control devices
10750   Telephone specialties
10800   Toilet and bath accessories
10880   Scales
10900   Wardrobe and closet specialties

Division 11 · Equipment

11010   Maintenance equipment
11020   Security and vault equipment
11030   Teller and service equipment
11040   Ecclesiastical equipment
11050   Library equipment
11060   Theater and stage equipment
11070   Instrumental equipment
11080   Registration equipment
11090   Checkroom equipment
11100   Mercantile equipment
11110   Commercial laundry and dry cleaning equipment
11120   Vending equipment
11130   Audio-visual equipment
11140   Service station equipment
11150   Parking control equipment
11160   Loading dock equipment
11170   Solid waste handling equipment
11190   Detention equipment
11200   Water supply and treatment equipment
11280   Hydraulic gates and valves
11300   Fluid waste treatment and disposal equipment
11400   Food service equipment
11450   Residential equipment
11460   Unit kitchens
11470   Darkroom equipment
11480   Athletic, recreational and therapeutic equipment
11500   Industrial and process equipment
11600   Laboratory equipment
11650   Planetarium equipment
11660   Observatory equipment
11700   Medical equipment
11780   Mortuary equipment
11850   Navigation equipment

Division 12 · Furnishings

12050   Fabrics
12100   Artwork
12300   Manufactured casework
12500   Window treatment
12600   Furniture and accessories
12670   Rugs and mats
12700   Multiple seating
12800   Interior plants and planters

CSI Masterformat
Figure 3-7 (continued)

Division 13 · Special Construction

13010 Air supported structures
13020 Integrated assemblies
13030 Special purpose rooms
13080 Sound, vibration, and seismic control
13090 Radiation protection
13100 Nuclear reactors
13120 Pre-engineered structures
13150 Pools
13160 Ice rinks
13170 Kennels and animal shelters
13180 Site constructed incinerators
13200 Liquid and gas storage tanks
13220 Filter underdrains and media
13230 Digestion tank covers and appurtenances
13240 Oxygenation systems
13260 Sludge conditioning systems
13300 Utility control systems
13400 Industrial and process control systems
13500 Recording instrumentation
13550 Transportation control instrumentation
13600 Solar energy systems
13700 Wind energy systems
13800 Building automation systems
13900 Fire suppression and supervisory systems

Division 14 · Conveying Systems

14100 Dumbwaiters
14200 Elevators
14300 Moving stairs and walks
14400 Lifts

14500 Material handling systems
14600 Hoists and cranes
14700 Turntables
14800 Scaffolding
14900 Transportation systems

Division 15 · Mechanical

15050 Basic mechanical materials and methods
15250 Mechanical insulation
15300 Fire protection
15400 Plumbing
15500 Heating, ventilating, and air conditioning (HVAC)
15550 Heat generation
15650 Refrigeration
15750 Heat transfer
15850 Air handling
15880 Air distribution
15950 Controls
15990 Testing, adjusting, and balancing

Division 16 · Electrical

16050 Basic electrical materials and methods
16200 Power generation
16300 High voltage distribution (above 600-volt)
16400 Service and distribution (600-volt and below)
16500 Lighting
16600 Special systems
16700 Communications
16850 Electric resistance heating
16900 Controls
16950 Testing

CSI Masterformat
Figure 3-7 (continued)

fabrics; flexible wood sheets; and prefinished panels applied over solid substrates.

- *09950 Wall Coverings*
  09955 Vinyl-Coated Fabric Wall Covering
  09960 Vinyl Wall Covering
  09965 Cork Wall Covering
  09970 Wallpaper
  09975 Wall Fabrics
  09980 Flexible Wood Sheets and Veneers
  09985 Prefinished Panels

Any of these categories may be included in the "scope of work" for the painting contractor as itemized in the bid documents. As the estimator, you have to review the bid documents thoroughly. It's your responsibility to make sure all painting and coating are included in your bid.

Math Review

As I mentioned in the last chapter, estimators spend hours adding, subtracting, multiplying and dividing. An aptitude for math will help in your work. You should be comfortable working both with fractions and decimal equivalents. If there's any doubt in your mind about your ability to handle the math, concentrate on the remainder of this chapter. This section will review basic conversions, rounding off, lineal measurements, and area measurements. It also includes some useful conversion tables. If you're at home with math like this, skip to Chapter 4.

Identify Your Units of Measure
When recording the measurements from your quantity survey, be sure to identify the units of measure you use. Otherwise, someone reviewing your estimate later may not understand your work. The most common units are dollars ($), hours (Hr), gallons (gal), lineal feet (LF), and square feet (SF).

Converting Fractions to Decimal Equivalents
Why do you need to convert fractions to decimals? Assume you measure 22 feet, 3½ inches of fascia

An aptitude for math will help in your work

board. You want to add it to other lengths of fascia board on the same building. Addition is easier if all measurements are converted to feet with fractions of a foot expressed in decimals. Thus, 22 feet, 3½ inches becomes 22.29 feet. Here's how to make the conversion:

First, convert 3½ inches to 3.5 inches.

Then divide 3.5 by 12 (inches in a linear foot). The answer is 0.29 feet.

Then add 0.29 to 22, for an answer of 22.29 linear feet.

Follow these steps whenever you want to convert a feet-and-inches measurement to the decimal equivalent. Just divide the inches by 12 inches per foot to arrive at a fraction of a foot expressed as a decimal.

Decimal equivalent conversion table— Figure 3-8 is a chart for converting inches to feet and decimals of a foot. It comes in handy when you're taking off measurements using the dimensions written on the plans.

Decimal equivalent	Measurements (in feet)				
	0'	1'	2'	3'	4'
.042	½"	--	--	--	--
.082	1"	13"	25"	37"	49"
.167	2"	14"	26"	38"	50"
.25	3"	15"	27"	39"	51"
.333	4"	16"	28"	40"	52"
.417	5"	17"	29"	41"	53"
.5	6"	18"	30"	42"	54"
.583	7"	19"	31"	43"	55"
.667	8"	20"	32"	44"	56"
.75	9"	21"	33"	45"	57"
.833	10"	22"	34"	46"	58"
.917	11"	23"	35"	47"	59"
1.0	12"	24"	36"	48"	60"

Decimal equivalent conversion table
Figure 3-8

Here's how to use it. To convert a measurement of 15 inches, first find 15" on the chart. Look at the top of the column. It's in the 1-foot column. Look across the row, to find it in the 0.25 row. So 15 inches equals 1.25 feet.

Here's another example. Say you measure 45 inches. Look on the chart. It's in the 3-foot column, and the 0.75 row, so it must equal 3.75 feet. Practice with other dimensions until using this table is second nature.

Rounding off measurements— Round off measurements involving either linear feet or square feet to the nearest foot. Round up measurements of 0.5 foot or more to the next greater foot. Round down measurements of 0.49 foot or less.

Scale Conversions
Do you remember the different scales used for different types of drawings? Sometimes you'll want to convert scales to actual measurements. If you're measuring a drawing in engineer's scale with your tape, which is in architect's scale, you can convert. Let's use the following examples to develop formulas for finding the actual length of a measurement.

Suppose you have to measure the wood fascia on all the carports in an apartment project. The size of the carports only appears on the site improvement drawings where the scale is 1/20'' equals 1'0''. You should make the measurements with an engineer's scale, of course. But if you only have an architect's scale, accumulate the total length of the fascia by measuring the perimeter of each carport in the 1/8'' equals 1'0'' scale. But how do you convert to the actual length in 1/20 scale?

We know that the 1/8 scale is 2.5 times larger than the 1/20 scale. (20 divided by 8 equals 2.5.) So a 750 LF measurement on the 1/8 scale on a 1/20 scale drawing would actually be 1875 LF. (750 times 2.5 equals 1875.)

- Drawing in 1/10'' scale, measurement in 1/8'' scale: Multiply measurement by 1.25. (10 divided by 8 equals 1.25.)

- Drawing in 1/20'' scale, measurement in 1/4'' scale: Multiply measurement by 5. (20 divided by 4 equals 5.)

- Drawing in 1/10'' scale, measurement in 1/4'' scale: Multiply measurement by 2.5. (10 divided by 4 equals 2.5.)

Here's another example: You're taking a measurement from a site plan, drawn in 1/20 scale, using your 1/4 scale tape. You need to convert to the actual length. Let's say your tape shows the distance as 210 lineal feet. Use the following formula:

Actual length equals measured length times the conversion factor.

Actual length equals 210 LF times 5 = 1050 LF

Manhour Conversions
With labor costs so high, every labor hour is important. Round hours to the nearest tenth (0.1) of an hour. As in rounding dollar amounts, round up hourly figures of 0.05 or more to the nearest tenth (.1). And round down figures of 0.049 or less. Here's what I mean:

- 5 minutes equals 0.083 hour: Round it to 0.1 hour

- 10 minutes equals 0.16 hour: Round it to 0.2 hour

- 20 minutes equals 0.33 hour: Round it to 0.3 hour

Figure 3-9 shows some minutes to hours and manhours to minutes conversions. Remember, round off to the nearest tenth of an hour.

Minutes to manhours		Manhours to minutes	
5 minutes =	.08 hour	.1 manhour =	6 minutes
10 minutes =	.17 hour	.2 manhour =	12 minutes
15 minutes =	.25 hour	.3 manhour =	18 minutes
20 minutes =	.33 hour	.4 manhour =	24 minutes
25 minutes =	.42 hour	.5 manhour =	30 minutes
30 minutes =	.50 hour	.6 manhour =	36 minutes
35 minutes =	.58 hour	.7 manhour =	42 minutes
40 minutes =	.67 hour	.8 manhour =	48 minutes
45 minutes =	.75 hour	.9 manhour =	54 minutes
50 minutes =	.83 hour	1.0 manhour =	60 minutes

Manhour conversions
Figure 3-9

Percentage Conversions
The rule of thumb for percentage conversions is: *Move the decimal point two places.* To convert

decimals to percentages, move the decimal point two places to the right, then add the percent sign. For example:

- .37 is 37%

- .505 is 50.5%

- .07 is 7%

To convert percentages to decimals, do the opposite. That is, remove the percent sign and move the decimal point two places to the left. Like this:

- 89% is .89

- 60.5% is .605

- 4% is .04

Rounding Dollar Amounts
Round off dollar amounts, too. It simplifies your work.

Material dollars— When figuring material dollars from gallons, round to the nearest $.10. When transferring dollar amounts from the take-off sheet to the proposal, round off to the nearest dollar for the total material value for each painting operation. Round up any amount of 50 cents or more to the next higher dollar. Round down, to zero cents, any amounts of 49 cents or less.

The IRS accepts this rounding system on income tax returns. If it's good enough for the government, it should be good enough for estimators.

Proposal values— You can round off the total cost of painting a commercial building, or a tract of homes, to the nearest $5.00. Round amounts of $2.50 and more up to the next higher $5.00; round amounts of $2.49 and less down to the lower $5.00. For example: $4,393.00 becomes $4,395.00, and $7,052.25 becomes $7,050.00 on the proposal.

You can also use this method on amounts submitted in progress billings. It simplifies the billing system.

Measuring Lengths, Areas, and Volumes
Measuring lengths, areas and volumes requires some knowledge of a few formulas. This section explains what you need to know.

Linear Measurements
You'll make many linear measurements for painting estimates. For example, you must find the lengths of the fascia board on the exterior elevations of the sample plan in Appendix A. Do this with a continuous measurement, directly from the architectural drawings.

Making a continuous measurement with a tape— Let's measure the linear feet of fascia board. Use a 1/8'' or 1/4'' scale tape. Measure the first segment of fascia board. Hold that length on the tape with your thumb marking the end of the measurement. Now, move the tape and measure the next segment, from where you're holding the tape. Measure the entire length of fascia board to be painted.

Be sure your measurement is accurate: Find a written dimension on the plans and check it with an architectural scale. You're checking the accuracy of the person who drew the plans. On most drawings, the scaled length of any line should be the same as the dimension listed.

A better method of continuous measurement— There's another way to find a continuous measurement. Find the dimensions written on the plans for each segment. On a separate paper, list each length. Add them all up to find the total length. This method is more time consuming, but much more accurate.

In paint estimating, it's O.K. to scale directly from the architectural drawings. That wouldn't be accurate enough for a carpenter, of course. Scaling dimensions directly off the plans is less accurate, but it's close enough when estimating painting costs. Remember this, however: Dimensions written on a plan *always* prevail if there's a conflict between written and scaled dimensions. When in doubt, use written dimensions for continuous measurements.

Angular Measurements
Most angles you'll see when estimating painting are 90 degree *right angles*. Angles less than 90 degrees are called *acute* angles; angles greater than 90 degrees are called *obtuse*. Some custom homes with uncommon designs might have corners that aren't right angles.

Stair railings run at an angle to the floor. Watch out when measuring them on plans. Use the elevation view or a section of the staircase for an accurate measurement. Using the plan view (floor plan) would give you a distorted measurement. To see why, look at the stairs shown in Figure 3-10.

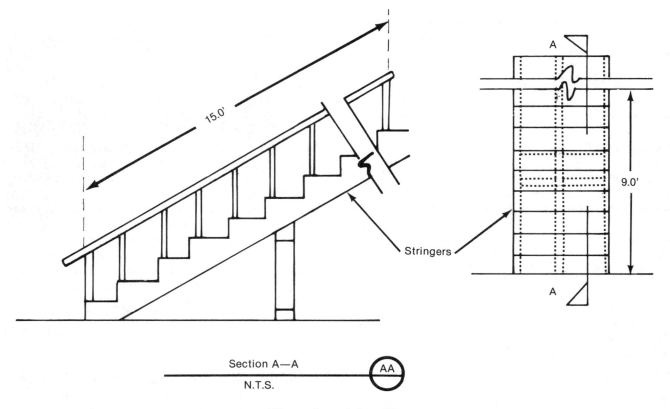

Section A—A
N.T.S.   AA

Measuring stair railings
Figure 3-10

The same thing goes for measuring overhang. Because the roof pitch is at an angle, take the actual width of the overhang from an exterior elevation or a section instead of a plan view, unless there's a written dimension on the roof plan.

Area Measurements

Measuring surface areas is a big part of your job as a painting estimator. Figure 3-11 is a quick reference you can use. It has formulas for finding the area of each of the following shapes.

Squares— Roofing estimates are based on a unit of 100 square feet (10 feet by 10 feet). Each 100 square feet is called a *square.*

Don't confuse the roofing square with measuring the wood floor of a "square" room. The formula for finding the area of that kind of a square is *length times width, or one side squared.*

Rectangles— This is the most common shape. Walls, floors and ceilings are usually rectangles. *Length times width equals area.*

Triangles— A triangle is simply half a rectangle. Look at Figure 3-11. What's the area of a triangle with a base of 6 feet and a height of 3 feet? Three times 6 equals 18. Divide 18 by 2. The area is 9 square feet. *One-half base times height equals area.*

Triangular measurements occur above the 8-foot ceiling line at the interior walls of a vaulted ceiling. On the exterior of the same building, the exterior siding above the 8-foot line at the end of a gable roof under the eave will be a triangle. The sample plan includes both of these examples.

Parallelograms— In Figure 3-11, what's the area of a parallelogram with a base of 6 feet and a height of 3 feet? Multiply the base by the height. The area is 18 square feet. Notice this: each end of a parallelogram is a triangle. These triangles are equal in area. By moving one triangle to the other end, you create a rectangle.

You might use parallelogram measurements on exterior walls for a siding take-off.

Circles— Occasionally you'll have to find the area of a circle. Look at Figure 3-12. Say you're doing

Square
Multiply the base measurement in feet times the height in feet.

Rectangle
Multiply the base measurement in feet times the height in feet.

Triangle
To find the number of square feet in any shape triangle or 3 sided surface, multiply the height by the width and divide the total by 2.

Parallelogram
Multiply the base measurement in feet times the height in feet.

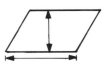

Circle
To find the number of square feet in a circle, multiply the diameter (distance across) by itself and then multiply this total by .7854.

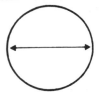

Cylinder
When circumference (distance around cylinder) is known, multiply height by circumference.

When diameter (distance across) is known, multiply diameter by 3.1416. This gives circumference. Then multiply by height.

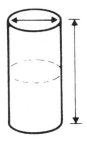

How to figure surface areas
Figure 3-11

an estimate on painting the trim, including the vents, on this home. You have to find the area of the circular vent over the garage.

Let's say the diameter of the vent is 4 feet. Multiply this by itself, for an answer of 16 feet.

Circular vent area must be calculated
Figure 3-12

Then multiply 16 feet by 0.7854. The answer is 12.57 square feet.

Cylinders— You'll have to compute the surface area of a cylinder eventually if you do much industrial painting. Smoke stacks, for instance, are cylinders. So are storage tanks.

Assume the cylinder in Figure 3-11 has a diameter of 3 feet and a height of 6 feet. Find the circumference by multiplying 3 feet (diameter) by 3.1416 (pi). The circumference is 9.42 feet. Then, multiply 9.42 by the 6 feet (height) for an answer of 56.52 square feet.

Measuring Floor Areas
When estimating new construction residential painting (apartments, condos and single-family homes), one of the fastest ways to calculate the manhours and the material quantities for painting the *interior* walls is to use a formula based on the floor area or square footage of the unit.

This area can be called the "construction" square footage or floor area. The architect will often indicate the floor area on the floor plan for each unit. But here's a tip: Don't rely on that figure. Measure it yourself. You want a calculation that's consistent with the way *you* always estimate. This "construction" floor area is measured from outside wall to outside wall on the floor plan. It includes all the area for each floor within the perimeter of the building and the area of the storage rooms for a condo or apartment complex. The measurements are made by dividing the entire floor area into rectangles. To define the boundaries, use the outside of each perimeter wall and the step down at the garage. Calculate the area of each rectangle and add them together carefully. Remember, a mistake in this calculation can be expensive.

This "construction" square footage is not to be confused with the "marketing" square footage used by real estate agents to sell the unit. Their measurement is usually based on the area *within the perimeter walls* which is actually used for living. This area doesn't include the area under the perimeter walls, so it will be less than the construction square footage.

As you know, the floor area measurement helps sell a home. The buyer wants to know how much space the family has for living. The floor area listed in advertisements for homes is the living area.

That's about all the math you'll need to master. If you can handle what I've explained, you're ready to go on to the next chapter.

Chapter 4

THE BASICS OF ESTIMATING

*E*stimating is both a science and an art. As you've seen, it involves two distinct tasks. Taking off the measurements is a *science*. It's objective — there's just one correct answer. A square foot is a square foot and every other answer is wrong. On the other hand, figuring labor, materials, and equipment costs is an *art*. There's no single figure or calculation that applies to all bidders. It's subjective, a judgment call. No two estimators will come up with the same costs. Every contractor can submit a different bid amount, and all can be right — for the way that contractor operates, at least.

Even though there are no right answers, there are good painting estimates and bad painting estimates. All of yours should fall into the first category. To make that happen, you need to follow a consistent, well-defined estimating process like the one in Figure 4-1. You must also use an accurate and reliable estimating system for taking off measurements and pricing each part of your estimate.

That's exactly what this book will provide: an *estimating system* that produces good paint estimates for nearly any type of project. I'm going to begin describing that system in this chapter, including types of estimates, estimating tools, and some of the common problems and estimating traps you're going to face.

This chapter doesn't explain how to compile estimates. That comes in later chapters. This chapter is an overview of estimating. Let's start with a look at the common types of preliminary estimates.

Preliminary Estimates

Preliminary estimates can be made at various stages of a project and include several levels of detail. But all preliminary estimates have something in common: none are based on final construction plans. For that reason, they're all opinion based on limited information. Until final plans are drawn, it's impossible to predict costs accurately.

Here are the types of preliminary estimates: *"guesstimates," feasibility estimates, conceptual estimates, systems estimates,* and *budget estimates.* You'll seldom be asked to make preliminary estimates, but you should still know about them.

Let's deal first with the term "guesstimate." You've heard the term used — as a joke, I hope. A guesstimate is simply a guess about what something

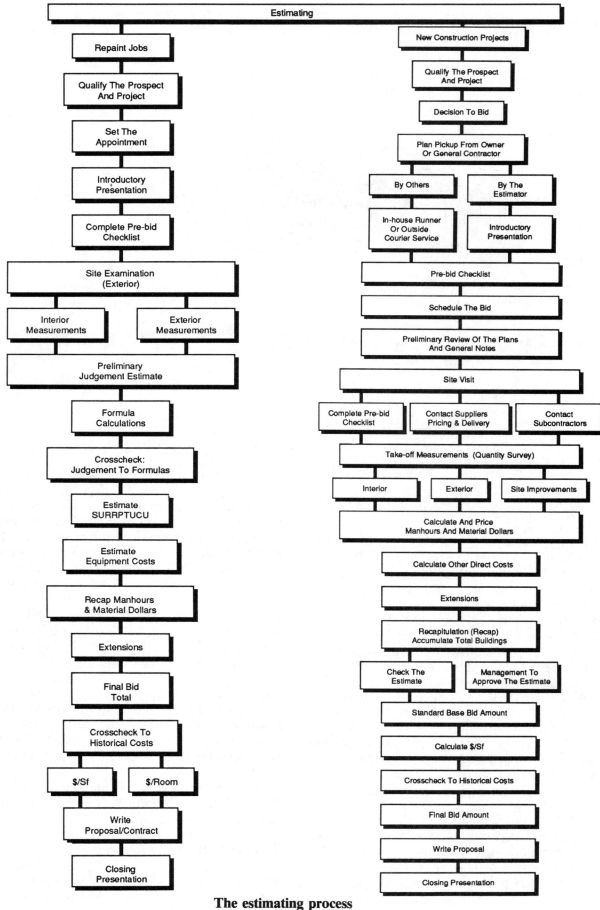

The estimating process
Figure 4-1

You must use an accurate and reliable estimating system for taking off measurements and pricing each part of your estimate

will cost. It's not really an estimate at all. No one followed a systematic procedure to come up with the cost. There's no way to check it. It's just a figure out of someone's head. Professional estimators avoid making guesstimates.

Feasibility Estimate

A feasibility estimate helps the developer decide whether a piece of property is worth buying or a project is worth building. It yields an approximate price per square foot, or price per living unit, for the entire project. But this estimate isn't based on guesswork. It's based on the cost of building similar projects in other areas and at other times.

At this early stage, the developer rarely asks any subcontractors for cost estimates. There aren't any plans yet. You probably won't be involved with feasibility estimates, either.

Conceptual Estimate

A conceptual estimate is based on the preliminary design sketches of the building (or buildings). The design is being worked out, but details aren't complete. This estimate helps the developer make a final decision on whether the project is financially practical.

A general contractor may ask only a few subcontractors in the major trades (structural, mechanical, electrical) for estimates. These figures will be in unit prices, generally a price per square foot, a price per linear unit or a price per fixture (for plumbing or electrical work). The contractor plugs in numbers for the other trades, including painting. Painting contractors are seldom asked for conceptual estimates. But if you're asked, at least you know what a conceptual estimate is and why the information is needed.

Systems Estimate

A systems estimate is figured using a cost for each building system — the foundation, roof system, wall system, and so on. This method may be used to compile the conceptual estimate. Appraisers often make systems estimates to figure the value of a building or the costs of rebuilding a structure. Again, paint contractors are rarely involved in this type of estimate.

Budget Estimate

A budget estimate is based on unit costs. Owners and builders need a budget estimate when they ask for a construction loan. The estimated cost is usually the basis for the loan request. That's why budget estimates must be reasonably accurate. It's better to overestimate than underestimate costs when preparing a budget estimate. The accepted accuracy standard for a budget estimate is within 10% of the final "as-built" (actual) cost.

A good client may ask you for a budget figure for a project, especially if the project has decorator touches, such as a variety of colors, unusual painting specifications, graphics, or wallcovering.

As you see from the descriptions of all of these preliminary estimates, the budget estimate is the only one the painting estimator is likely to be involved with. Let's take a closer look at budget estimates.

What you need to know for a budget estimate— You need to come up with a cost that's reasonably close to the final bid amount. Of course, your estimate can't be any more accurate than the information you have available. Start by asking questions about the proposed plans and specifications. An excellent tool for qualifying the project specs is the pre-bid checklist (in Chapter 6). Some additional questions you might ask are:

• During what time of year will construction take place?

• What's the condition of the site?

• Are any graphics involved?

• Will any special coatings be used?

• Will any wallcoverings or other decorator items be used?

If there are no plans, ask about the design features. Your questions might include:

• How many floor plans and buildings are there?

• How many square feet per plan or building?

• What are the room sizes?

• How many stories are the buildings?

• How high are the ceilings?

• How are the ceilings finished (acoustic, textured, stain grade)?

• What's the percentage of wet area to be enameled?

• Where are cabinets located: kitchen, bath, linen, utility?

• Are cabinets stain grade, paint grade or prefinished?

• What types of doors are there?

• Are doors stain grade, paint grade or prefinished?

• Are windows aluminum or wood?

• If there are wood windows, are they stain grade or paint grade?

• How are exteriors finished?

• What exterior surfaces will be painted?

Figuring the budget estimate— Once you have the answers to these questions, you have a good idea of how much work you'll do on the project. Now you can go on to develop your budget estimate.

As with other preliminary estimates, budget estimates are usually based on some unit of measure such as:

1) Price per square foot of *construction* floor space.

2) Price per living unit.

3) Price per fixture. This method of unit cost estimating is most common in the plumbing trade.

4) Price per cubic foot of interior space—*cubage space*. This method of unit price estimating is most common in the heating and air conditioning (HVAC) trade.

Price per square foot— The most convenient, and most common, unit price for preliminary painting estimates is the price per square foot of *construction* floor space. This estimate is prepared from the floor plan dimensions. Use the construction floor space, measured *from outside wall to outside wall* of a building, including storage rooms with painted walls but excluding garages, patios, entries, stoops and balconies. As of the publication date of this book, the price for most residential painting ranges

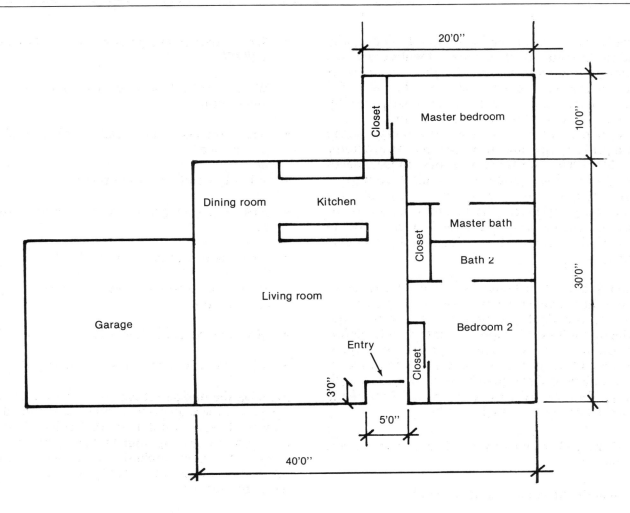

40'0" x 30'0" = 1200 sf

20'0" x 10'0" = 200 sf

(5'0" x 3'0") = (15) sf   Entry deduct

       1385 sf   Living area floor space (excluding garage)

     x $.65/sf   Unit cost: price per square foot

     $900.25   Lump sum per building

"Construction" square footage
Figure 4-2

from $.50 to $1.50 per square foot. Of course, prices will be higher or lower in some areas, on some projects, and for some contractors. Figure 4-2 shows how to find the construction floor space.

Historical cost tables— The historical cost (past performance) tables in Chapter 12 provide an excellent guide for developing preliminary estimates. These tables reflect unit costs of work done by other companies. A much more reliable source of information is cost records on work your company has completed. Most experienced estimators have learned to preserve their cost records and many arrange the information as shown in Chapter 12, so it's easy to use when needed. But note that costs based on a square foot of floor area or per living unit will apply only on similar jobs. Remember, to compare the costs of one project to another, the two projects must be very similar. Don't base a budget estimate for a shopping center on cost records for an apartment job.

Once you've developed a cost per unit, either from my figures or from your own records, add a cushion of about 10%. This allows for changes, variations, and items left out of the original project description. Of course, you must emphasize to your client that your budget estimate isn't an offer to do the job at that price. It's just an estimate based on sketchy information.

A verbal quote will probably be all that's needed. If a written quote is requested, be sure to include a statement that you're not offering to do the work at that price. You'll submit a bid price on request, of course, but only after studying the final plans.

The developer or builder usually wants the budget figure in a hurry, so you'll often take shortcuts when compiling a preliminary estimate. That's O.K. for budget estimating. Actually bidding the job is a different story. Entirely different procedures apply. *There's no substitute for a properly-prepared, detailed estimate.* This book has all the information you need to produce detailed estimates for most projects. There's no excuse for using budget estimating methods to prepare firm bid estimates.

The Detailed Estimate

The term *detailed estimate* describes the most accurate estimate that can be made and will always include a detailed list of labor and material quantities and costs.

When producing a detailed estimate, the first thing to understand is the quality of workmanship required. There's a big difference between standard grade painting (as in most apartment buildings) and custom grade work (such as in an executive office). Know the grade of work required before you begin the estimate. You won't win many jobs estimated as custom quality work if the owner, contractor or architect expected only standard quality.

Begin your detailed estimates by measuring all surfaces to be painted and listing those areas on your take-off sheet. Most experienced paint estimators make their take-off in the same order that the work will be done. This makes it less likely that you'll skip a step or omit an important cost. Once areas are computed, you can begin figuring

costs: *labor, material, equipment, miscellaneous, overhead,* and *profit.*

A detailed estimate takes longer to prepare but it is much more precise and accurate than any of the preliminary estimates. It stands to reason, if you break the project down into small parts (each painting operation) and price each part separately, there is less chance of making a big error. Your estimate is more accurate. A detailed estimate also becomes the standard against which you compare actual costs while the job is in progress.

The more competition there is, the more detailed the estimate must be. If a dozen qualified painters are bidding the project, the only way to get the job and still make money is to develop the most accurate estimate possible.

A good detailed estimate requires:

1)   Use of an estimating system — a step-by-step procedure for estimating painting costs.

2)   Knowledge of manhour production rates (footage painted per hour) and material coverage rates (footage painted per gallon), either from published data or your previous job costs.

3)   Current costs for labor, material and equipment.

4)   Knowledge of your company's overhead expenses, and what percentage to apply to each job.

5)   Knowledge of your company's capabilities and goals so you know what percentage to add for profit.

6)   Experience, so you can foresee problems and evaluate costs accurately.

There are two ways to quote prices on detailed estimates. They're the *unit cost method* and the *lump sum method.* Let's look at both methods.

Unit Cost Method

Costs and prices can be estimated in convenient units like the square foot, linear foot, cubic foot, or cubic yard. Budget estimates are based on unit costs.

Price per face foot— Use this method to estimate the cost of painting cabinets or walls in commercial buildings (the face of a surface). To estimate the area of cabinets, look at the interior elevations in

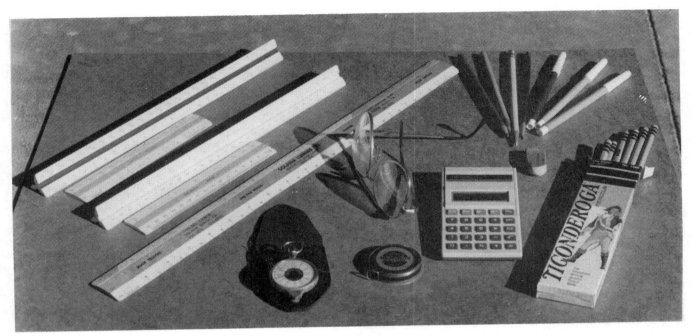

Tools of the estimating trade
Figure 4-3

the plans. To calculate wall surface area, simply find the ceiling height and length of walls on the plans.

Price per linear foot— Use this method when estimating fascia board or plant-on trim, for example. Plant-on trim is trim around doors and windows. It is said to be "planted on" the exterior of the building. Simply measure the length of each piece of trim, determine its size, then use the appropriate manhour production rate and material coverage rate in the estimating tables to arrive at a price.

Lump Sum Method

A lump sum price shows the total price for painting a part of the project, a living unit, or an entire project. *Do not* submit lump sum bids for an entire project unless it's required by the bid documents. If the number of buildings is changed after you submit your bid, there's no way to show if the change is included in your lump sum bid — and there's no guarantee you'll get paid for this change.

Submitting a price per building offers some protection. For example, if an additional building is added after you submit the bid, you should collect for that extra building at the per building price.

Lump sum prices for the entire project may, however, be required in some commercial, industrial, institutional and government jobs.

The Tools of the Trade

Every estimator needs some tools. This section explains what you'll need. Figure 4-3 shows most of the common tools estimators use.

Measuring Tools

To produce accurate estimates quickly, you need a variety of measuring tools. At a minimum, you'll need a tape measure, a scale (or two), and a measuring wheel.

The tape measure— The tool you will use most is a 1/8-inch or 1/4-inch scale tape measure. See Figure 4-4. Get one at a drafting or blueprint supply store. I like the Lufkin Model #W 605A because it retracts automatically.

The 1/8" - 1/4" tape
Figure 4-4

Architectural scales
Figure 4-5

The scale— Also important is an *architect's scale.* See Figure 4-5. It has many scales including 1/8, 1/4, 3/8, 1/2, and 1 inch to the foot, which are the most commonly used by the painting estimator. You need it for taking measurements from architectural plans. It comes in both triangular and flat versions. The triangular scale is the most common, but a flat scale is easier to carry around with you.

You'll also need an *engineer's scale* with each inch divided into 10, 20, 30, 40, or 60 equal parts. It will have scales with 1 inch equal to 10 feet, 20 feet, 40 feet, and so on. The engineer's scale is used to take measurements from a site improvement plan. You'll use it when estimating the painting of carports, trash enclosures, pool railing, fencing and other site amenities. Figure 4-6 shows a typical engineer's scale.

The measuring wheel— Figure 4-7 shows a measuring wheel, sometimes called a plan measure or map measure. To use it, just roll the wheel along the plan and then read the distance measured on the dial. Though you may not use it every day, there are some jobs that are much easier if you have one of these handy devices. For example, you might use it to measure the length of baseboard at the walls of a unit or the fencing around all the patios of a condominium complex. It's the best tool for measuring distances along a curve or circle, like a fence that winds and curves around a large apartment project.

Other Tools
The tools mentioned so far are measuring instruments. You need some other tools that aren't used for measuring.

Pencils— Of course you'll need pencils to record your measurements and calculations. I always make changes when calculating an estimate. A number 2 soft pencil is easy to write with and easy to erase. I try to use all the pencil lead *before* I use up the eraser. If the eraser goes first, I'm making too many wrong entries.

Besides the standard lead pencil, have a set of erasable color pencils. I put a colored check mark on the plans over each item as it's listed on my take-off sheet. When everything has been checked, my take-off is complete. That's also a good way to double check to see if you missed anything during your take-off.

The calculator— Every estimator needs a good calculator. In addition to the standard arithmetic functions, you need a memory with recall and clear functions. Spend a few dollars extra to get a good desk calculator with paper tape for printing figures

Engineering scales
Figure 4-6

The measuring wheel
Figure 4-7

and a full-size keyboard. You'll probably want a second calculator for use on the job. It should be small enough to hold in your hand and have a display that you can read even in direct sunlight. A print function for double checking your entries would also be helpful.

Reference materials— *This book* will be your most useful guide for estimating painting costs. Keep it handy when you're doing a take-off. The only information more valuable will be the estimates of jobs you've already completed. Use cost records from old jobs to project costs for the current job. If you don't have cost records on completed jobs, use the historical costs in Chapter 12 until you develop your own cost information.

The Computer As an Estimating Tool

The computer is a tool. Like any highly productive tool, it's useful only in the hands of a skilled operator. Used correctly, it can help build profits in your company.

Computers can help you produce neat, precise, more professional estimates, reduce the time spent on clerical work, and give you more accurate information for better decision-making. Notice I said *can*, not will. Like all tools, computers have both advantages and disadvantages. Let's look at what you can expect.

Speed— Have you ever said, "I want to put out more bids, but there just isn't enough time in the day"? A computer can help you compile more bids — and more accurate bids. And when you produce more bids, you can expect more jobs, and maybe more profits.

Computers are great calculators and even better at storing and remembering things. For example, a computer can retrieve manhour production rates and material coverage from a file, apply them to the job you're figuring, multiply labor and material quantities times current prices, and total those costs in the blink of an eye. In addition, computers can sort information, do calculations, count, process words, and format reports with amazing speed.

Accuracy— A computer helps make your estimates more accurate. Did you ever forget an item or a step? Better estimating programs have checklists, so it's harder to forget an important cost item. Did you ever make a math error? A computer does this

work faster and more accurately than you could ever do by hand.

Consistency— This is especially important if your paint company has more than one estimator. No two people estimate exactly the same way. With a computerized system, all estimators can figure the final bid value using the same costs and formulas. Consistency is the foundation of a good estimating system, and a computer can help.

Organization— A good computer system makes it easy to organize your company's estimating or accounting work into a format that suits your needs.

Using the Computer for Paint Estimating

Let's look at how a computer can help you estimate costs. First, all of the information you need — costs for labor, material, equipment, and miscellaneous items, as well as overhead calculations and profit data — has to be stored on disk in some organized form. This file of information is usually called a *database*. This database has to be kept current as material and labor costs change. The estimating program should let you update this information easily.

When you make an estimate, enter the area or footage measurements for each operation. The computer can use your current database to:

- Do the area calculations, once you've entered the measurements.

- Process the labor and material pricing, based on the area calculations.

- Add all miscellaneous operations.

- Calculate overhead and profit.

- Arrive at the bid price.

A good estimating program will let you play "What if?" with the estimate. What if productivity is 10% higher or a 5% discount is offered on paint? What if equipment rental rates increase? How would these changes affect your bid?

Since private companies and government agencies each have a different bid format, your estimating program should be able to change the report format to meet job requirements. Your base bid, adjustments to the bid, and alternative bids may have to be submitted in different report formats. Be sure the estimating program you buy or design for your specific needs is flexible enough to meet a variety of job requirements.

What Else Can It Do?

Computers make it easier to analyze your bidding history and historical cost data. You can look at actual bidding volume and bid type, and compare them to your goals. You can analyze your ratio of bids made to contracts won. You can budget proposal preparation costs, record actual costs and print reports showing the results.

You can also use a computer to:

• Create material lists

• Track material purchasing

• Control inventory and equipment

• Plan and schedule jobs

• Keep track of price requests, change orders, and extra work requests

• Keep cost control and job progress records

• Analyze completed project costs

What Are the Disadvantages?

As you've seen, a computer has many advantages. But there are several disadvantages. To round out the picture, let's take a look at some of the common problems.

The cost of hardware— Computer hardware is less expensive than it used to be. In fact, it's relatively inexpensive, compared to costs a few years ago. But you'll still have to pay about $3,000 for a basic system: computer, printer, monitor and software (programs).

Buying your first computer? Support, service and maintenance will be important. *Always* talk to someone — not necessarily a salesman — who knows computers before you buy. My suggestion is to find another paint estimator who's using a computer to compile estimates. Find out what's good and bad about the computer and programs he or she is using. If you're satisfied that the computer and programs would work in your office, invest in the same or similar equipment. Don't be a pioneer, trying to be the first paint estimator in your community to estimate with a computer.

What if you already know something about computers? If you don't need support services, con-

sider buying used equipment. Many are advertised in the classified section of newspapers and in computer magazines and newspapers. Discounted equipment can be purchased as low as 50% of its retail cost and programs may cost little or nothing.

The cost of software— The programs you use can cost as much as the computer if purchased at retail prices. When buying software, make sure the program suits your needs. Don't waste good money on programs that won't be used.

The costs of programming— You can write your own paint estimating program, of course. But it might take months to perfect it — time you could have spent getting out more bids. The time and cost depend on how much of the programming you want to do. I wouldn't advise any painter to learn programming in BASIC or Fortran or Cobol just to write a paint estimating program. But if you enjoy working with computers and know a programming language, putting that knowledge to use may be an irresistable temptation.

If you're not willing to write an estimating program, you could hire a consultant to write one for you. That's going to be expensive, usually several times the cost of the computer.

Many accounting and work processing programs are available from computer stores and directly from software developers. And some are offered at modest cost. Unfortunately, the only programs I've seen for estimating painting costs have been custom designed by painting contractors. I've never seen one that's so good and so easy to learn, that I could recommend it to every reader of this book. Most of the estimating programs available through retail stores don't include painting. But don't give up. New programs are being written all the time. Eventually someone will come up with a good, inexpensive program to estimate painting costs. You'll know it's happened when several other painters in your community are using the program and love it.

For most small volume painters, buying and using a computer for estimating isn't practical right now. You'd spend your time better in the field selling new work or in the office sharpening your estimating skills. You'd spend your money better on a new spray rig or some extra space in the Yellow Pages. A computer won't solve all your estimating problems.

If you decide to invest in a computer system, be sure to check around and look at all the possibilities before you buy. After you find the right system and have learned how to use it, word processing (letter writing) will be so easy you'll wonder why you didn't get the computer sooner. If you want to learn more about computers in the construction industry, and certainly before you lay out hard-earned dollars for one, order a copy of *Computers: The Builder's New Tool* from Craftsman Book Company. There's an order form at the back of this book.

Estimating Variables

No two painting jobs are alike. Every project will have factors that make the job unique. As an estimator, your task is to anticipate those problems and differences before work begins. This section is intended to help you consider the important *cost variables* in every estimate you make.

I'm going to divide cost variables into several categories and consider each separately. As we look at each of these, consider how you would reduce the number and size of each unknown cost so the final bid is as accurate as possible. This is problem solving at its best.

"Remember, there is no such thing as a problem, only a challenge and an opportunity to create a solution."

Errors in Your Estimate

Errors aren't cost factors, of course. But they can make your estimate inaccurate nonetheless. Let's look at the common estimating errors and how to prevent them.

The mistakes you make in your estimate are problems you can control immediately. They're one of the few estimating variables you can control completely. In fact, only you, the estimator, can control them. Here are the kinds of things to watch out for:

Math errors— There's no excuse for an error in math. Double-check every calculation. Be especially alert for misplaced decimal points. *Never omit a decimal point.* Put them where they belong and write them dark enough so you can't miss them later.

Transposing numbers— Transposing means switching the order of the figures. Writing 36 instead of 63 is transposing. It's easy to do. Look for this kind of error as you double-check, cross-check, and proofread your figures and calculations.

Errors in copying— It's easy to make errors when you're copying numbers from one sheet of paper to another. Work carefully. Don't work where there are distractions. Follow these steps to reduce copying errors:

1) Each time you transfer a number from one sheet to another, say the number out loud or at least recite each number to yourself as you make the transfer.

2) Pay attention and concentrate when transferring figures. Don't be interrupted or distracted. Don't copy figures while you're daydreaming.

3) When you've finished the transfer, check that the number was transferred correctly.

Missing or duplicating items— *Don't rush.* It's true, haste makes waste. Rushing wastes time, energy and money. If you rush and make an error by overlooking an item, the estimated value of the item you miss is zero. That's a 100% miss. It only takes a few of these missed items to wipe out the profit for a job. If you rush, and duplicate, or add an item twice, you'll probably lose the job because your bid was too high.

Why sacrifice accuracy for speed when you'll have to live with that error if you get the job? It's not worth it. No matter how much of a hurry a customer is in, don't rush. Every customer deserves an accurate estimate — your best price — and not a guesstimate pulled out of your hat. *Don't throw out bids in hopes that some will stick and your customers will be satisfied.*

What if your customer is desperate and insists on a "quick bid"? Then bid high enough to protect yourself. Bid high enough so you won't be sorry if you get the job. Later, if you have the opportunity to submit a more accurate estimate, this new bid is likely to be lower than the earlier "quick bid." This lower, more accurate bid, will make the customer happy and you'll have a better chance of getting the job.

Here's the best way to avoid missing or duplicating any portion of an estimate:

1) Use a systematic approach.

2) Follow a checking procedure.

3) *Don't rush.*

Difficult Owners

Sometimes repaint jobs can be more trouble than they're worth. It depends on the homeowner's attitude and how much they expect you to do. Owners of new construction projects can be difficult, too. You can avoid many conflicts by being aware of what to look for, and preparing your estimate accordingly. Here are some examples:

The "supervisor"— Occasionally an owner wants to "run the job" and play supervisor. This interrupts your momentum. To avoid this, add a clause something like this to your proposal/contract:

The extent of the owner's involvement with the supervision process is to select paint colors. Any other supervision by the owner will incur an extra charge.

You can change the wording to fit the situation. Add it to the estimate if you think the owner might try to be a supervisor.

How much removing and replacing is expected— Find out whether the owner wants you to remove and replace dishes in cabinets, toys, furniture, books, finish hardware, or doors. If so, increase the estimate to cover the extra time it will take. Be sure the owner understands exactly how much will be done. *Never* offer to move or handle costly antiques or anything of sentimental value. Also, who will cut or tie back trees, bushes, and shrubs? Adjust the bid for any time and material costs involved with moving or trimming the landscaping.

"Difficult" neighbors— The owners of adjacent property can also be difficult. Always consider the costs of protecting the neighbor's house, cars and other property from overspray or other damage. Don't create a difficult situation.

The quality the owner expects— Get an idea of the quality of work the owner expects. Look at other houses in the neighborhood. Look at the present condition of the owner's house. Ask the owner plenty of questions about the specification requirements. Describe how many hours you'll devote to surface preparation, but *don't* ask him what kind of painting job he wants. Of course he'll always want more than he can afford. Try to avoid any surprises. Make it clear in your proposal what you are including and excluding before the work begins. Don't give the owner any reason to say "I thought you said . . ." or "you never told me that

. . ." Put the cards on the table by defining the scope of work at the beginning of the job.

No one wants to pay more than they can afford. On the other hand, you have no obligation to provide more than you're paid to do. If the owner wants custom quality work, fine, provide it — at a custom quality price.

Poor Architectural or Engineering Plans

Most of the problems an architect or engineer can cause involve the plans. Sometimes the plans are incomplete, inaccurate or include mistakes. This may be the result of many factors: outdated data, lack of construction knowledge, or not enough time, to name a few. Here's what to watch for, and how to avoid conflicts.

Errors and omissions and ambiguities— As you review the plans, make a note of anything that's unclear or any errors which directly affect the painting work. List each one on the take-off sheet. Note the page number by each item. Then make *one* call to the architect or engineer and get an answer for all of your questions.

An important point is to avoid making assumptions about anything that isn't clear or about items that are obviously wrong. If you have a question — *ask* — don't be shy or hesitant to pick up the phone. Most questions can be answered over the phone. In some cases, the answer to your question is somewhere on the plan set. If it isn't, and if your question points out a valid error, ask the architect to issue an addendum to the plans to all bidders. Get it in writing. That's the only way to be sure that all bidders are bidding the same job — "apples and apples."

Architects and engineers sometimes make mistakes. Estimators tend to find them. This doesn't mean that designers are incompetent. Designing a building is a complex task. If an architect or engineer misses a couple of points, it just proves they're human. Be considerate. Without them you wouldn't have a job.

Incomplete plans— The construction drawings should show everything the contractors are required to do and should leave no question about how they should do it. In short, the plans have to be complete.

In my mind, there's no excuse for incomplete plans. I've known design professionals to insist that "they didn't have enough time or money to adequately complete the plans." That's a poor excuse. A doctor would never take out half of an appendix and say he ran out of time or money to complete the job. As the saying goes: "There is never enough time to do the job right the first time, but there always seems to be enough time to do it over." A design professional should never take on a project if there's not enough time or money to complete it.

Plans are referred to as "substantially complete" when they are not quite finished yet. Sometimes you'll be asked to submit a preliminary estimate based on plans which are substantially complete. This means you'll have to make some assumptions.

A *bid set* of plans is supposed to be 100% complete and ready to be used for bidding the job. But most plans sent out for bid need at least a few corrections. Construction is too expensive and too permanent to build a defect into a structure just because there's a mistake in the plans. Changes are inevitable.

The *construction set* of working drawings is used to build the project. It includes all the changes, recommendations, and corrections found by every trade during the bidding process. Many times the bid set of plans you work from will be stamped "Not for Construction."

It's the paint estimator's responsibility to be sure the bid submitted is based on work that meets all building code requirements, the owner's or architect's plans and specifications, and government regulations. The Federal Housing Authority (FHA), the Veterans Administration (VA), Housing and Urban Development (HUD), and other government agencies have regulations that must be met. Fortunately, painting isn't as heavily regulated as many other trades.

Drawings which are not legible— Most draftsman have had hours and hours of formal training in lettering and line drawing. Their lettering and line work should be sharp, clear and legible. An original set of construction plans will seldom be illegible. But some plans have been corrected many times with erasures, redrawn and then reprinted before being sent out for bids. The corrections and erasures will be *so* obvious on the blueprints (bluelines) that the plans can be difficult to read.

Sloppy plans— As mentioned in Chapter 3, if you get sloppy plans, *be careful.* Sloppy plans mark an untrained or inexperienced draftsman or designer. They may have been drawn by a homeowner or builder who can't afford professional design work — or who imagines himself a draftsman. Sloppy plans might also come from a drafting student or trainee whose work slipped past a supervisor without being corrected. In any case, if the drafting shows inexperience, there's a good chance that the drawings have errors and omissions. Again, be careful. Qualify your bid, if you decide to bid at all.

Unclear plans— Sometimes you can read the plans but can't figure out what they mean. They can be interpreted more than one way. Again, this shows inexperience. It's hard to bid from unclear plans. It's even harder to figure out how to paint the project — if they aren't corrected by the time construction begins. If so, expect that construction will be run in the same way the plans were drawn. If your company does the painting, be prepared to work on a poorly organized project that's running well behind schedule. I recommend that you avoid bidding on projects that use unclear plans for construction and are managed by amateurs.

Addenda— Addenda are notifications to contractors and subcontractors of revisions to the plans or specs. These can include additions, deletions or corrections to the drawings and often are offered to make the plans more clear and understandable. Most addenda are the result of questions asked by bidders during preparation of their bids. Addenda should be issued *before* bids are submitted and become a part of the contract documents once issued.

Each addendum should be covered in your bid. When you submit a proposal or a bid form, always note which addenda you included in the bid. Do this with a statement such as *"Bid price(s) per plans and specifications with all addenda #1 through #4 recognized."*

Plan revisions— Plans can be revised *after* all the bids are in or *after* construction has started. Sometimes the plans are revised after the bid set is produced and before the construction set is produced. On a good set of drawings, these revisions will have a cloud shape drawn around them. The revision number enclosed within a *delta* (small triangle) will usually appear near the revision cloud. The date of the revision will appear in the title block.

On other plan sets the latest date of any revisions will usually appear in the title block even if the cloud and delta method of identifying revisions is not used. Be sure your bid identifies the revision date of the plans you estimated from. All it takes is a line like this: "Bid based on plans dated 12/10/88, revision #3."

Stubborn Developers, Builders, or General Contractors

All of these people are in business to make a profit. It won't be as easy to close a sale for painting work with them as it is with a homeowner. When they award a contract, the price on your bid proposal is their main concern.

Anyone who always takes the low bid should understand that "the bitterness of poor quality remains long after the sweetness of a low price is forgotten." Although price is important, cooperation and completion on time can make or save money for a general contractor.

Price requests— Price requests are common on projects where design decisions are still being made after subcontracts have been awarded. For example, the owner might want to cut costs or improve quality by substituting materials or using methods different from those originally specified. Although price requests originate with the owner, they will usually be managed by the architect.

The term *submittal* describes the process of submitting information back and forth. The painting contractor (or any subcontractor) submits prices for proposed changes to the architect. This process can take a lot of time. There's often no reward, since many price request submittals are rejected.

Change orders— Change orders are easier to handle than price requests. They're issued for several reasons:

- When a price request is accepted and the plans are altered to reflect the change.

- To make a change that will speed up construction.

- To make a change needed to improve the quality of construction.

Always answer written change orders. If a request for change is made verbally, always require that it be in writing before beginning the work. This is acceptable practice and should be understood by experienced contractors. Keeping a written record or log of all change orders is a must, especially on large projects where there may be many change orders.

Government "Red Tape"

The bidding process on government jobs is the most complex in the construction industry. The government uses a very formal bidding process. They also try to cover all loopholes with one document or another. Expect to do a lot of paperwork when bidding government work. This added paperwork can increase your overhead expense. That won't reduce your profit if you remember to add this expense to your bid. Unfortunately, most painting contractors can't increase their bid price on government jobs enough to cover the extra overhead without losing the jobs to others. Bidding for government projects is very competitive.

Time extensions— Government projects often go out for bid several times. Each time, addenda and revisions are added to change the project. This means that bidders have to prepare new bids, forcing an extension of the time allowed for bidding.

Price fluctuations— During times of high inflation, prices for raw material and manufacturing can increase quickly. This can cause problems with many large projects that take months or years to complete. There's no way to anticipate price changes accurately. It's usually safe, however, to assume that material prices will go up rather than down over the term of the project. Protect yourself and your bid by "locking in" material prices with your suppliers as soon as you receive a fully executed (signed by both parties) contract.

Short Supply Items

Whether it's a public or private project, order early if you need lead time for large quantities of custom colors or specific mixes which are not stock items at most paint dealers. And note that special order materials will nearly always cost more than stock items. Allow enough lead time and include in your bid the extra cost for short supply material. Always get firm quotes from your suppliers on short-supply items, special materials and custom colors.

Problems in the Field

One of your most difficult jobs as a painting estimator is getting the field supervisors — mainly the job foreman — to keep accurate records. For accurate estimating, you need good labor and material use records for each operation on every project. This information is essential if you want to improve your estimating accuracy.

Chapter 5

TIPS ON ORGANIZATION

This chapter explains how to get organized so you have the time and ability to compile good estimates. I've included hundreds of important tips and pointers that will make you both a better and *better organized* estimator. Read through the entire chapter now just to discover what's here. Later, when you're actually preparing an estimate, you'll want to review key paragraphs here to refresh your memory. Eventually, what I've described in this chapter will become second nature to you.

The rules of thumb are especially important. You should be using them regularly. I recommend that you highlight or underline them in the text so they're easy to find.

Organization

Good organization is the key to success in any business. It's hard to keep a painting business growing and profitable if your payroll records are missing, your accounting records are months behind or your cost estimating file doesn't exist. In this chapter I'll explain several ways you can become better organized, more efficient and more productive. Getting organized doesn't take more time. It saves time. Read and follow the recommendations in this chapter and you'll have lots more time to prepare complete, reliable estimates.

Manage Your Time

An organized person knows how to manage time. If you're busy, going as fast as you can to expand your painting business, it may seem like you never have enough time. There are only 24 hours in a day, so you have to use those hours well. To make the best use of your time, be aware of where time is usually wasted. According to a study of 40,000 business people, the ten most time-consuming business activities are:

1) The telephone
2) Crisis management — putting out fires
3) Lack of planning and priorities
4) Drop-in visitors
5) Ineffective delegation
6) Trying to do too much
7) Meetings
8) Personal disorganization
9) Inability to say no
10) Lack of self-discipline

Good organization is the key to success in any painting business

How Time Works

To gain a better understanding of how time works, let's look at a few rules of thumb about time:

Rule 1— *We tend to put things off until the last minute.* Do not procrastinate. Deal with all of your daily activities right away. Don't put them off.

Rule 2— *We tend to do the easy things first.* Establish your priorities and work on the most important item first. Stay with it until it's completed. Working on the easy tasks first is like eating the frosting on the cake first. Then you may not want to eat the cake. When setting your priorities, sometimes it's best to decide what *not* to do. The important items will rise to the surface automatically.

Rule 3— *We tend to give our best customers the least time.* Give your best customers the *most* time. There's a saying that goes like this: "Eighty percent of your time will be spent on only 20 percent of your customers." Think twice about continuing to do business with that 20 percent who use 80 percent of your time: Are they worth it?

Spend your time — or better yet, *invest* your time — with your most important customers. Just think, if 80 percent of your time could be spent with the type of customer who only *takes* 20 per-

cent of your time, you could handle four times as much business with the same amount of effort!

Rule 4— *The first part of a task tends to take more time than the last part of that task.* There's another saying that applies: "Ten percent of the task is completed in the first 90 percent of the time." Now these percentages might be a little exaggerated, but there is some truth to the saying. For example, it takes the most time to think about and organize what you want to say in a letter. But once you start writing, the words probably seem to fall into place almost automatically. The letter is written before you know it.

You've heard of the *learning curve.* It applies to the painting business. When production painters are painting tract houses, the first five houses probably take longer to paint than the last 15 homes.

Rule 5— *Work seems to expand to fill the time available.* Take control and manage your time. If you don't manage your time, it will manage you. Have you ever wondered, at the end of the day, where the time went? Time probably controlled you! It's likely that you were in a "crisis management" mode, trying to put out fires as they ignited all day long. More than an hour of additional work came your way during each hour of the day. After working eight hours you hadn't had a chance to even begin the tasks you had planned to finish that day. If you slowed down long enough to say "Now, where was I?" — another crisis landed in your lap. That's poor time management.

Of course, crisis management and "putting out fires" are sometimes unavoidable. In the construction business, there are always unexpected problems that require you to drop everything and devote immediate attention to a solution. But if you have a plan or schedule for each day, you won't waste time wondering what to do next when the crisis is over.

Time Management Tips

Establish a daily schedule— All successful people have a "to do" list. Or, better yet, use a daily planning calendar that lists the hours from 7 a.m. to 6 p.m., with blank lines waiting to be filled in. This saying applies: "Plan your work and work your plan." Be organized. And don't take long lunches.

Allow for a quiet time each day— Set aside certain hours as your quiet time for doing take-offs and other paperwork. I like to set aside 9:30 to 11 a.m. But it can vary. Sometimes I have to meet customers during those hours, for example. The point is to schedule an hour or two of quiet time each day. During this time, have your answering machine or receptionist take phone messages. Don't take any calls. Have drop-in visitors schedule an appointment and come back later.

Arrange all appointments outside your quiet time, if possible. And set hours when you'll see salesmen. I like seeing them on Tuesday and Thursday, between 1 and 4 p.m.

Keep your desk top clean— Having a clean desk top also helps your daily work. I know, it's hard to keep all those plan sets, project manuals, bids, and proposals organized. But there is a way. Invest in a plan rack and some shelving or file cabinets. And use an organized filing system with everything in its place. Being able to find documents when you need them saves time.

Work on one thing at a time— Want to be a successful estimator? Have only one thing on your desk at a time. Work on that one thing until it's done. Then move on to the next item, in order of priority. This might sound impossible in a busy office, but try for this kind of organization. You'll be much better organized than if you hadn't tried at all.

Handle paperwork only once— Have you ever picked up a piece of paperwork on your desk — and then put it back — several times, without doing anything with it? Avoid handling paperwork more than once. Realize that you have only three choices:

1) Do it yourself
2) Delegate it to someone else
3) Destroy it

But don't delay it. Work on each piece of paperwork and *follow through* until it's complete. Then get it off of your desk.

Make it a practice to follow through on all of those items you've put off. Wrap up all of your "loose ends." Act on those decisions you haven't done anything about. And make those decisions you've been putting off. If you don't take care of them, your loose ends come back to haunt you.

Remember, ten minutes better managed each day gives you an extra work week each year. Fifteen minutes better managed each day gives you eleven extra days each year. Your "reward" is what you choose to do with the time you save.

Set Production Goals for Estimating

Most companies have production goals for the painting crews so projects are completed on time. You should also establish production goals for your estimating time.

Know how many estimates you must produce each month to win enough jobs to keep the bills paid. But that isn't enough. Your goal is to produce as many competitive bids as you can each month, each one as accurate as possible. But remember that there's always a trade-off between speed and accuracy. Anyone can produce an accurate estimate if they work on it long enough. You don't have that luxury. You have to produce accurate estimates in a reasonable time period. Learn to take well-considered short cuts. Balance the risk of a slight inaccuracy against the time lost in getting every last calculation correct to the penny.

The number of painting bids you can complete each month depends on the size and complexity of the projects and on your experience. Here's a rule of thumb: A production paint estimator should produce complete estimates, and submit accurate bids, for 12 to 15 tract home projects a month.

Take Breaks

Taking breaks is another important part of time management. A break lets you clear your head for

Estimating and Operations	Accounting

Labor
  Skill records
  Labor cost control records
	Payroll records

Material and sundries
(Paint) (Tools and supplies)
  Purchase orders
  Inventory control
  Material cost control records
Equipment
  Maintenance records
  Service records
  Scheduling records
  Job cost allocation record
	Accounts payable records

Miscellaneous cost records	
Subcontractor invoices Commissions payable Overhead calculations	Billings
Profit (Job cost analysis) Escalation (Record of cost increase projections) Bids produced (Estimating goals) Contract documents	Cash flow analysis Financial status Accounts receivable (billings)

Records required in estimating and accounting
Figure 5-1

a few minutes. Then, when you go back to the plan table, you'll be able to concentrate better. How many breaks do you need? Well, a good rule of thumb is one five-minute break each hour. But let your experience guide you in this. Most estimators make more mistakes when they try to concentrate on detailed work for more than an hour at a time.

Keep Good Records

There should be two profits in every job. The first is money that goes in your pocket. The second is what you learn from doing the job. If you don't keep a file of completed estimates and compare estimated and actual costs when the job is done, you're missing out on the second profit possible in every job.

File every estimate you compile. Keep track of actual costs and manhours. Compare them to estimated costs. Use what you've learned to make more accurate estimates on the next job.

To stay in business, you must keep records. The I.R.S. requires it. If you don't have adequate business records, the I.R.S. is authorized by law to estimate your taxable income and assess tax accordingly. Few businesses can afford that luxury.

Aside from the fact that you must satisfy the I.R.S., it's good business practice to keep accurate records. Remember, poor record keeping contributes to many business failures.

Keep accurate records of all your costs, both job costs and overhead costs. And keep your records up to date. Figure 5-1 shows how the estimating and accounting functions relate to each other.

Use Printed Forms
A good set of forms will help you remember important items and simplify the record-keeping process. Either make up your own forms or use the forms I've included in this book.

A good labor and material take-off form is important. It will prevent mistakes by making omissions less likely. You'll find my take-off forms for repaint jobs and new construction in later chapters. Both are well designed and time-tested.

Your take-off form should include space to fill in most or all of the following: project name, estimate page number and total number of pages, site location, owner's or agent's address and phone number, who prepared the estimate, date the estimate was prepared, who checked the estimate, who approved the estimate, building type, building square footage, date due (bid date), plan date, architect's name, contractor's name, special conditions, notes and comments.

Forms List

Once you decide which forms you need, make up a numbering system so each form has a unique identification number. For instance, use the initials of your company and a number. Then file the blank forms by I.D. number so you can locate them quickly. Next, make up an index of blank forms. List each form by filing number and add a short description or title of the form. The number and description help you reorder the right forms each time. Figure 5-2 is a sample forms list. It includes the forms you'll need. The identification system here uses the paint company initials (QPD) and a number.

Blank copies of all the forms I use are at the end of the book. To make copies for your use, take these pages to your quick printer and follow the suggestions on the forms list for size, quantity and other specifics. The two door hangers, *Customer Solicit* (yellow) and *Customer Service* (blue), should be printed and "die cut" by your printer. Other standard forms are available at better stationery stores or through printing companies by mail order.

Office Policies and Procedures

No business can operate efficiently and productively without an organized, well-defined set of office policies and procedures. My office policies are shown in Figures 5-3 and 5-4. Use them as a guideline for your own office organization. Review them periodically and update them to keep up with changes in your business.

Use an Estimating System

If your company is well organized, it should be easy to set up and follow a good, consistent estimating system. Consistency is important in estimating. Some of the best estimators are the most consistent estimators. And that means following the same steps in the same order on every estimate.

The CSI Masterformat will help you organize your paint estimates. We looked at the 16 divisions of the Masterformat in Chapter 3. It's important that you understand this system of organizing all construction trades.

Establish a Routine

Paint estimating takes organization and care. Every good estimator follows an established routine when compiling an estimate — just like a machine. Why? Simple. Following a set procedure every time reduces errors. It makes omissions less likely. It reduces the chances of skipping or overlooking an item or some step in the painting process.

Estimate in the Same Order As You Paint

Picture the work being done as you estimate the job. On a residential repaint, work from ceiling to floor, starting in the living room and moving to other rooms in a counter-clockwise direction. When the first floor is finished, go to the second floor, and so on. In commercial buildings, work from the main section of a building to the wings.

Look for design repetitions— Several rooms, floors, or wings in a project are often the same. This means you can estimate one room, verify that they are identical, and just multiply by the number of identical rooms.

Use visualization— Picture the work as it's actually done in the field. Separate the entire project into each operation. Then, picture each operation step-by-step. Visualize the time, the material usage, the equipment needs, and other miscellaneous requirements for each operation. Record them, then move on to the next. This process will help you avoid omitting an important part of the job.

Be a Professional

To be successful, you must *look and act like a professional.* Be prompt for all appointments. Deliver your bids on time. If you can't avoid being late, call and tell the customer. Be informative and informed. Know your paint and coating products and wall coverings as well as you know the ability and skill levels of all of your craftsmen.

Estimating Forms

QPD - 1	Repaint Take-Off Form	Black on white - 20# 8½ x 11 50/pad
QPD - 2	Repaint Recap Sheet	Black on white - 20# 8½ x 11 50/pad
QPD - 3	New Construction Take-Off Sheet	Black on white - 20# 8½ x 11 50/pad
QPD - 4	New Construction Extension Sheet	Black on white - 20# 8½ x 11 50/pad
QPD - 5	Take-Off Summary (format)	Black on white - 20# 8½ x 11 50/pad
QPD - 6	Plan Log (format) (only photocopies necessary)	

Bidding and Sales Forms

QPD - 7	Promotional Door Hanger	Black on yellow - 67# vellum - die cut 5½ x 8½
QPD - 8	Promotional Message	Black on yellow - 20# 8½ x 11
QPD - 9	Take-Off Information Sheet	Black on white - 20# 8½ x 11 50/pad
QPD - 10	Telephone Bid Sheet (only photocopies necessary)	
QPD - 11	Competitor Evaluation (format) (only photocopies necessary)	8½ x 11
QPD - 12	Letter of Introduction	Red and regal blue on white 20# 8½ x 11
QPD - 13	List of References	Red and regal blue on white 20# 8½ x 11
QPD - 14	Proposal/Contract (repaint format)	Red and regal blue on white 8½ x 14 NCR triplicate (white/yellow/pink)
QPD - 15	Proposal Letterhead (new construction format)	Red and regal blue on white 20# 8½ x 11
QPD - 16	Notice to Customer	Black on white - 20# 8½ x 11 50/pad

Project Management Forms

QPD - 17	Contract Information Sheet (only photocopies necessary).	4½ x 11 - 2 up
QPD - 18	Contract Follow-up Log (format) (only photocopies necessary)	8½ x 11
QPD - 19	Time Card	Black and white - 20# 5½ x 8½ 50/pad
QPD - 20	Progress Report	Black on white - 20# 4¼ x 11 50/pad
QPD - 21	Material Purchase Record	Black on white - 20# 8½ x 11 50/pad
QPD - 22	Cumulative Job Cost Record	Black on white - 20# 8½ x 11 50/pad
QPD - 23	Job Cost Envelope	Manila envelope 9 x 12 w/ black print
QPD - 24	Sundry Inventory Checklist (only photocopies necessary)	8½ x 11
QPD - 25	Material Transfer	Black on white - 20# 5½ x 8½ 50/pad
QPD - 26	Material Requisition	Black on white - 20# 5½ x 8½ 50/pad
QPD - 27	Reimbursement Ticket	Black on white - 20# 4¼ x 5½ 50/pad
QPD - 28	Work Authorization	Regal blue on white 5½ x 8½ NCR triplicate (white/yellow/pink)
QPD - 29	Letter of Transmittal	Red and regal blue on white 20# 8½ x 11
QPD - 30	Customer Service Follow-Up	Black on white - 20# 4¼ x 5½ 50/pad
QPD - 31	Customer Service Door Hanger	Regal blue on blue 67# vellum - die cut 5½ x 8½
QPD - 32	Staff Meeting Minutes and Notes	Black on white - 20# 8½ x 11 50/pad
QPD - 33	Certificate of Completion	Black on white - 20# 8½ x 11 50/pad

Administrative Forms

QPD - 34	Activity Log (only photocopies necessary)	8½ x 11
QPD - 35	Telephone Log	Black and white - 20# 8½ x 11 50/pad
QPD - 36	Letterhead	Red and regal blue on white 20# 8½ x 11
QPD - 37	Invoice	Red and regal blue on white 8½ x 11 NCR triplicate (white/yellow/pink)

Sample forms list
Figure 5-2

Employment Policies

1) It is our objective to run a profitable organization, using fair and honest practices, and that our moral conduct reflects our sense of fair play and human values.

2) It is our intent to provide stable, meaningful employment with fair wages for all our employees.

3) It is our policy to encourage open communication, career advancement and to consider the best interest of our employees.

4) It is our intent to pursue creative employee benefits for all our employees.

5) We are sympathetic to personal problems, and will provide the option for leave of absence without pay for any employee needing time to solve personal difficulties.

6) We pledge to our employees our best efforts in providing these benefits and expect the entire organization to abide by the policies set forth.

It is our expectation that all employees will abide by the following rules:

A) For office staff, the normal work day is from 8:00 a.m. to 5:00 p.m. Exceptions can be made only with prior management approval. One hour lunch is mandatory, with one morning and one afternoon break of 10 minutes each.

B) We do not allow any employee to come to work under the influence of alcoholic beverages or drugs. Immediate dismissal is guaranteed if this rule is violated.

C) All corporate assets must be used for corporate activity rather than personal use. Facilities or equipment can be used for personal gain or convenience only with prior management approval.

D) Due to the competitiveness of our industry, all files, blueprints, customer lists, accounting records and contracts are considered **trade secrets** and cannot be divulged without prior management approval. Violation of this rule will result in termination.

E) A time clock is in the coffee area for hourly employees. If you are hourly, you must clock in and out at the beginning and ending of each day. You must also clock out for lunch.

F) Appropriate dress must be worn to project a professional image.

Employment policies
Figure 5-3

Office Procedures

---

1) **Corporation minutes** to attorney by the 5th of each month.

2) **Close books** and submit to accountant by the 15th of each month.

3) **Complete job cost analysis** each day by 3 p.m. for review.

4) **Nothing is to be purchased** without prior approval. Use purchase order for all materials or subcontracted work, no matter how small. *No exceptions.*

5) **All staff to report** destination and time of return to receptionist before leaving the office.

6) **Staff meetings:** first Monday of each month at 3 p.m. sharp.

7) **Safety meetings:** first Monday of each month at 4 p.m. sharp.

8) **Mail** placed in "in" basket(s) as soon as delivered. "Out" basket(s) to be checked several times each day.

9) **Preliminary notices** to be in the mail 5 days prior to start date.

10) **Accounts receivable** list to comptroller on the first each month.

11) **Accounts payable** list to president by the 7th of each month.

12) **All paperwork** must be kept current, delivered on time and dated.

13) **Shipping invoices** must be checked against P.O. for proper quantity delivered.

14) **Billing invoices** to be matched against P.O. to check for proper job number and pricing before submitted for approval.

15) **Leave desks** orderly each day with machines off and covered.

16) **Relay messages** to president immediately. Do not wait for return to the office.

17) **Inform** the president of everything that happens in the company that pertains to company business.

18) **Lock up.** The last person to leave the office must turn off the copy machine and the heat/air conditioning and check everything.

19) **Two-way radio** manners must be observed. Make all messages brief.

20) **All personal phone calls** are to be limited. This is a business.

Office procedures
Figure 5-4

Understand Your Client

You must understand your client's needs, whether that client is an architect, owner or general contractor. *Do not assume anything.* Visit the site, ask questions, listen, and take notes. Research the needs of your client.

Establish good working relationships with your clients. Show them you're serious about bidding their work. Tell them flatly, "We want to be your painting contractor." This approach, which shows your sincerity, can open many doors.

Take-Off Tips

What if you're interrupted by a phone call or visitor in the middle of a take-off? Always mark your place. Write down the quantities up to that point so you can pick up where you left off. To be sure your take-off is accurate, remeasure the quantity you were on when you stopped.

Here are some other ways to make sure your take-offs are complete and accurate:

1) Sometimes the plans aren't clear. For example, you may not understand an abbreviation on the plans. Figure 3-3 in Chapter 3 is a list of common abbreviations. If that list doesn't help, you may have to call the designer. But don't do that until you've finished as much of the estimate as you can. If something else isn't clear, make a note on the take-off sheet and list the number of the plan sheet next to the note. When your take-off is complete, you may have several questions which are not resolved. Review your questions to make sure they're not answered on the plan sheets. Then ask the designer to answer all of your questions at once.

2) Check plan scales. Look for plan-size reduction notices. You'll often find them on the cover sheet of government drawings. Check for notes indicating that dimensions are "not to scale" (NTS). Pay attention to scale changes throughout the drawings. And watch for differences between the specifications and the drawings.

3) Know the document priority: Written plan dimensions have priority over measurements made on the plans. Use the written dimensions on the plans whenever possible and check all measurements against written dimensions. Also, specifications have priority over plans. If the plans

show one thing and the specs say another, believe the specs.

4) When using a tape measure for continuous measurements, mark each stopping point with your thumb *before* moving to the next starting point. When you mark it, say the measurement out loud or silently to yourself. This may sound silly. But if the tape slips or the phone rings, you'll have a better chance of remembering where you stopped.

5) Once you finish each measurement, write it down. Do it before you make the next measurement. Don't try to keep measurements or quantities in your head, hoping to recall them later. You probably won't.

6) As you count items during the take-off, mark each item on the plans with a colored pencil. This trick is useful when counting doors and windows, for example.

7) When adding a series of areas, write out every length and width multiplication on a sheet of paper. For example:

11 x 8	=	88
15 x 8	=	120
10 x 8	=	80
12 x 8	=	96
		374

8) Round off totals on the take-off sheets, recap sheets, and extension sheets. Round labor hours to the nearest tenth of an hour, and material costs to the nearest dollar. But don't round off prices when bidding by unit costs — painting 100 apartments for 67 cents a square foot, for example.

9) Use only standard abbreviations. Abbreviations invented on the spot cause trouble. Many times the abbreviations will be on the plan set. If not, use the standard abbreviations provided in Chapter 3.

10) Memorize and use decimal equivalents. Converting manhours and dimensions into decimal equivalents makes your work much easier.

11) Identify units. Always specify and label each unit you use in an estimate. (*Lineal feet* is *LF,* for example). This helps you tell which items are which, so you don't mix them up. Letter abbreviations are fine. But avoid using tick marks (' and '') to identify feet and inches on a take-off. They're too easy to misread.

12) Substitute ''or equal'' (equal or better) materials whenever possible. But only after gaining approval from the architect.

13) Don't rush. If you *must* hurry, bid high or not at all.

14) Be neat. Your take-off must be neat and easy to read for several reasons. In a neat estimate, errors and inconsistencies tend to jump out at you when checking the figures. A neat, well-organized estimate makes it easy to compare your preliminary figures with cost data from other projects you've done. An organized estimate also makes it easy for someone else to check your work. Remember, you might refer to an estimate many times after the contract is awarded — for price requests, change orders, and extra work requests. You'll compare it to actual job costs during the course of work. Keep it neat so anyone can check it, use it, and modify it as needed.

15) Use plenty of paper. Paper is cheap compared to the cost of leaving something out of an estimate. Don't crowd figures and calculations onto one sheet. Leave lots of room for additions and comments. If it helps you, use printed columnar estimating or accounting forms for clarity. And use only the front side of any form or sheet of paper. It's too easy to overlook something on the back.

Use a Checking System
Follow a checking procedure. Never trust your results until you've checked them — and checked them again. Here's what to do:

Double-check— Review all your math. Be sure all plans, specs, measurements, and counts are accurate and complete. Review all addenda and amendments thoroughly. When estimating from plans, always recount all door and window openings.

Crosscheck— Compare the total price per square foot on the current estimate with the total price per square foot on similar jobs you've done. If your current estimate seems too high or too low, there may be a reason. Find it. If the reason is that you've made an error, correct it. There's a sample crosscheck in the chapter on repaint estimating.

Check for related work items— Some items are easy to miss. Look for painting items which are *not* in the ''Finish'' schedule. Don't consider your estimate complete until you've scanned all the plan sheets and all related specification sections as itemized in Chapter 3. Look for anything that might require painting, as some items of work may not be well defined.

See checklists— Checklists will help you avoid overlooking or omitting items of work. Figures 5-5 and 5-6 are checklists for all preparation and painting operations. You can also use the take-off sheets for repaints and new construction in Chapters 18 and 19 as checklists. Refer to these checklists while estimating each project. Review them frequently until you become familiar with all the items of work listed.

Check your calculator— Know roughly what the answer should be before the calculator tells you. If you have a ballpark figure in mind before you enter the numbers, any answer that's obviously wrong will stick out like a sore thumb. Always be alert for big errors, the kind that can really hurt. Punching the wrong numbers on your calculator or putting a decimal point in the wrong place can throw your estimate way off.

Second-party check— Once you've finished the estimate, have someone else check your work. Getting this second opinion is good professional practice. You can go over the calculations again and again, yet miss an error. You may have become blind to it. It's easier for another person to spot mistakes or overlooked items, or to find an unchanged price extension after a cost or quantity has changed. Always have the checker initial the take-off sheets.

Check for transposition errors— That's an error made when transferring a figure or word from one place to another. Be very careful when transferring your bid amounts from the estimating sheets to the extension sheets, and then again to the rough draft of the proposal. Always *proofread* every figure and all the wording on the final draft of the proposal. Don't let an error by your typist slip by and ruin your bid.

Preparation Operations
- [ ] Bleach
- [ ] Burn
- [ ] Caulk
- [ ] Chip
- [ ] Clean
- [ ] Degloss
- [ ] Fill
- [ ] Patch
- [ ] Putty
- [ ] Repair damage
- [ ] Repair defects
- [ ] Replace hardwood
- [ ] Replace trim
- [ ] Sand
  - [ ] light
  - [ ] medium
  - [ ] heavy
- [ ] Sand & putty
- [ ] Sandblast
- [ ] Scrape
- [ ] Set nails
- [ ] Spackle
- [ ] Steel wool
- [ ] Strip
- [ ] Unstick
- [ ] Wash
- [ ] Waterblast
- [ ] Wipe
- [ ] Wire brush

Preparation Paint
- [ ] Primer
- [ ] Undercoater
- [ ] Wall sealer

Preparation Materials
- [ ] Crawfords putty
- [ ] Caulking gun
- [ ] Dap caulk
- [ ] Glazing compound
- [ ] Protective coating
- [ ] Spackle

Stripping Materials
- [ ] Acetone
- [ ] Bleach
- [ ] M.E.K.
- [ ] T.S.P.

Setup Operations
- [ ] Equipment setup
- [ ] Mix paint
- [ ] Tool setup
- [ ] Spread protection
- [ ] Unload

Protection Operations
- [ ] Coatings
- [ ] Cover
  - [ ] counters
  - [ ] floors
  - [ ] furniture
  - [ ] landscape
  - [ ] windows
- [ ] Drop cloth
- [ ] Masking
  - [ ] tape
  - [ ] paper
- [ ] Rags
- [ ] Trim guard (blade)
- [ ] Tarpaulin
- [ ] Visqueen
- [ ] Wallcover

Remove and Replace Operations
- [ ] Bath accessories
- [ ] Cabinet contents
- [ ] Doors
- [ ] Furniture
- [ ] Hardware
  - [ ] cabinet
  - [ ] door
  - [ ] window
- [ ] Light fixtures
- [ ] Outlet plates
- [ ] Phone jack plates
- [ ] Screens
- [ ] Shutters
- [ ] Switch plates
- [ ] TV jack plates

Cleanup Operations
- [ ] Equipment cleanup
- [ ] Load up
- [ ] Remove protection
- [ ] Overspray cleanup
- [ ] Tool cleanup

Master preparation checklist
Figure 5-5

Exterior Painting
Door Operations
- ☐ Paint grade
  - ☐ undercoat
  - ☐ split coat
  - ☐ exterior enamel
- ☐ Stain grade
  - ☐ stain
  - ☐ sanding sealer
  - ☐ polyurethane
  - ☐ shellac
  - ☐ varnish
- ☐ Metal
  - ☐ primer
  - ☐ exterior finish

Door Types
- ☐ Flush (exterior)
- ☐ French
- ☐ Garage
- ☐ Hollow metal
- ☐ Louvered
- ☐ Paneled (entry)

Floor Surfaces
- ☐ Concrete
- ☐ Decks
- ☐ Patios
- ☐ Stair treads

Masonry Operations
- ☐ Filler
- ☐ Fireplaces
- ☐ Planters
- ☐ Veneer
- ☐ Walls

Masonry Types
- ☐ Block (CMU)
- ☐ Brick
- ☐ Stone (slump)

Roofing
- ☐ Asbestos shingle
- ☐ Wood shakes
- ☐ Wood shingles

Trim, Metal
- ☐ Chimney caps
- ☐ Diverters
- ☐ Downspouts
- ☐ Flashing
- ☐ Gutters
- ☐ Railing
  - ☐ handrail
  - ☐ pipe railing
  - ☐ wrought iron
- ☐ Roof jacks
- ☐ Sheet metal
- ☐ Vents

Trim, Wood
- ☐ Corbels
- ☐ Fascia
- ☐ Lattice
- ☐ Overhang
- ☐ Pass-through shelf
- ☐ Plant-on trim
- ☐ Railing
  - ☐ decorative
  - ☐ handrail
  - ☐ rough sawn
- ☐ Stringers
- ☐ Trellis

Wall Surfaces
- ☐ Cement plaster (stucco)
- ☐ Concrete
- ☐ Masonry
- ☐ Plaster
- ☐ Siding
  - ☐ aluminum
  - ☐ asbestos shingle
  - ☐ plywood
  - ☐ rough sawn wood
  - ☐ smooth wood
  - ☐ wood shake
  - ☐ wood shingle

Window Operations
- ☐ Protective coating
- ☐ Sash and trim

Window Types
- ☐ Aluminum
- ☐ Awning
- ☐ Bay
- ☐ Casement
- ☐ Double hung
- ☐ Fixed
- ☐ Frames
- ☐ French
- ☐ Screens
- ☐ Shutters
- ☐ Single hung
- ☐ Steel
- ☐ Wood (muntins/frame)

Interior Painting
Cabinetry
- ☐ Bars
- ☐ Bookcases
- ☐ Kitchens
- ☐ Pullmans
- ☐ Shelves
- ☐ Vanities
- ☐ Wine racks

Ceilings
- ☐ Acoustic
- ☐ Gypboard (drywall)
- ☐ Plaster
- ☐ Tongue and groove

Door Operations
- ☐ Paint grade
  - ☐ undercoat
  - ☐ split coat
  - ☐ enamel (trim coat)
- ☐ Stain grade
  - ☐ stain
  - ☐ sanding sealer
  - ☐ lacquer
- ☐ Metal
  - ☐ primer
  - ☐ exterior finish

Door Types
- ☐ Aluminum sliding
- ☐ Bifold
- ☐ Bipass (closet)

Painting and wallcovering checklist
Figure 5-6

☐ Flush
    ☐ hollow core
    ☐ solid core
☐ Frames
☐ French
☐ Hollow metal
☐ Louvered
☐ Paneled
    ☐ hollow core
    ☐ solid core
☐ Pocket

Trim, Metal
☐ Heat registers
☐ Railing
    ☐ handrail
    ☐ wrought iron

Trim, Wood
☐ Baseboard
☐ Beams
☐ Firewood box
☐ Kickboard (stairs)
☐ Mantel
☐ Molding
☐ Railing
    ☐ decorative
    ☐ handrail
    ☐ rough sawn
☐ Stringers
☐ Valance

Wall Operations
☐ Sealer
☐ Flat wall
☐ Enamel

Wall Surfaces
☐ Gypboard (drywall)
☐ Paneling
☐ Plaster
☐ Wainscot
☐ Wood siding

Window Operations
☐ (Same as doors)

Window Types
☐ (See exterior)

Subcontract Checklist
☐ Rentals
☐ Sandblast
☐ Scaffold
☐ Striping
☐ Stripping
☐ Wallcover
☐ Waterblast

Site Improvement Painting
☐ Benches
☐ Carports
☐ Entry sign
☐ Fencing
☐ Laundry buildings
☐ Light posts
☐ Mailbox structures
☐ Masonry
☐ Meter enclosures
☐ Pavement marking
☐ Recreation buildings
☐ Tot lots
☐ Trash enclosures
☐ Trellis
☐ Utility enclosures

Industrial Painting
☐ Conduit
☐ Decking and siding
    ☐ metal (corrugated)
    ☐ metal (flat pan)
☐ Doors, hollow metal
☐ Field painting
☐ Field welds
☐ Mechanical equipment
☐ Piping
    ☐ bare
    ☐ color-coded solid
    ☐ color-coded bands
    ☐ insulated
    ☐ vertical
☐ Sandblasting
☐ Shop painting
☐ Steel
    ☐ hoppers
    ☐ silos
    ☐ tanks
    ☐ vessels
☐ Structural steel
☐ Windows, steel

Wallcover Checklist
☐ Sizing
☐ Wallcovering
    ☐ cork
    ☐ flexible wood
    ☐ prefinished panels
    ☐ wall fabrics
    ☐ wallpaper
    ☐ vinyl coated

Equipment Checklist
☐ Air compressors
☐ Air hose
☐ Boomlifts
☐ Ladder jacks
☐ Ladder racks (truck)
☐ Ladders, extension
☐ Ladders, rolling
☐ Masking paper dispenser
☐ Picks
☐ Planks
☐ Platforms, rolling
☐ Safety gear, swing stage
☐ Safety nets
☐ Sandblast accessories
☐ Sandblast hoods
☐ Sandblast hoses, 10' long
☐ Sandblast hoses, 50' long
☐ Sandblast machines
☐ Sandblast nozzles
☐ Sandblast units, complete
☐ Sanders
☐ Scaffolding, rolling
☐ Scaffolding, stationary
☐ Spray guns
☐ Spray line
☐ Spray rigs
    ☐ airless pump
    ☐ conventional pump
    ☐ emulsion pump
☐ Storage containers
☐ Striper (parking lot)
☐ Swing stage equipment
☐ Swing stage safety gear
☐ Towers, rolling
☐ Trailers, office
☐ Vehicles
☐ Wallcover steamer
☐ Waterblaster

Painting and wallcovering checklist
Figure 5-6 (continued)

Chapter 6

MARKETING AND PROMOTION

Most paint estimators probably don't think of themselves as salesmen. But most are — or should be. Nearly everything a paint estimator does affects sales in some way. Maybe that's why the most effective paint estimators I know are also very good at developing new business. They don't simply wait for their estimates to win bids. They're active in soliciting new work, finding what it will take to win each job, and then ensuring that their offer is accepted on the jobs they want most.

Good estimators understand that getting good, profitable work (and plenty of it) isn't simply a matter of submitting the lowest price. Most painting jobs aren't necessarily awarded to the lowest bidder. They're given to the painting firm that can best meet the owner's or general contractor's needs. Price is important, of course. But it isn't the whole picture. To be effective as a paint estimator, you have to see the whole picture — and be prepared to respond to what you see.

This chapter is intended to broaden your horizon as a professional paint estimator. I'll describe a good marketing plan for a painting company and suggest how you, the paint estimator, can help that plan succeed. I'll also suggest how you should approach general contractors who need your service and sell repaint jobs to homeowners.

Let's start by defining *marketing* as it should be understood in a painting company. I think of marketing as the *four P's:*

- Product (or service) development
- Promotion
- Pricing
- Packaging, distribution and delivery

I'll agree that paint estimators are concerned primarily with pricing. But aren't paint estimators also involved in product development, promotion and packaging? Let's see if we can identify a role for the painting estimator in each of these important marketing functions.

Product (or service) development— Companies grow by developing their product, improving it so more can be sold, and to a wider customer base. In the painting business, your product is a service — new paint applied to a home exterior, for example. As a paint contractor, there are two ways to develop or expand your service so it can be sold to more customers. The first is by taking on new types of painting work (finding another niche), such as bidding industrial or commercial projects in addition to your current residential business. This kind

Every painting company needs a good marketing plan

of expansion requires developing new skills, improving supervision, and adding manpower and the equipment needed to handle this type of work at a profit. The estimator's knowledge of what it takes to make a profit is valuable to any company deciding to expand into another niche.

Another way to develop your market is to learn new and better ways to serve the customers you're selling to already. If you're going to grow by doing the same type of work you've always done, you've got to find better or cheaper ways to do that work. Searching for ways to improve productivity or reduce costs is a challenge for the company estimator.

Promotion— The painting estimator is the link between the customer and the company on many jobs. As the estimator, you'll meet the person who chooses the painter (and signs the checks) for most residential repaint jobs and many new construction projects. You'll find out exactly what the customer wants and needs — and is willing to pay for. In the customer's eyes, you *are* the painting company. If you're sincerely interested in the job, responsive to the owner's requests, and promote the company effectively, your bid is likely to be accepted.

It's also part of your job to maintain contact with old customers and supplement the pool of existing customers with new prospects that may become customers. You do this through public relations, customer service, sales promotion, and advertising.

Pricing— The estimator's number one responsibility is to establish prices for the painting service. The chapters in this book on bidding and estimating cover this subject in detail.

Packaging, distribution, and delivery— The painting service is delivered at the customer's choice of site, of course. And it must be delivered *on time*. But the way this service is "packaged" is also important. Think of an item sitting on a supermarket shelf. What makes you pick it up? The package is well designed so it attracts your attention. It's neatly arranged. Your bid proposals and painting service should both be packaged and delivered with the same qualities. Every paint estimator should have customer satisfaction (both during the job and after completion) as a primary goal. That's part of being a professional.

In this chapter, I'll concentrate on the estimator's role in finding the work by using advertising, promotion and bidding published jobs. The flow chart in Figure 6-1 shows the process. We'll talk about business development for your painting service throughout the book as we discuss the specific project categories.

Your Advertising and Promotion Plan

To make your advertising and promotion most effective, you have to work from a plan. Here are

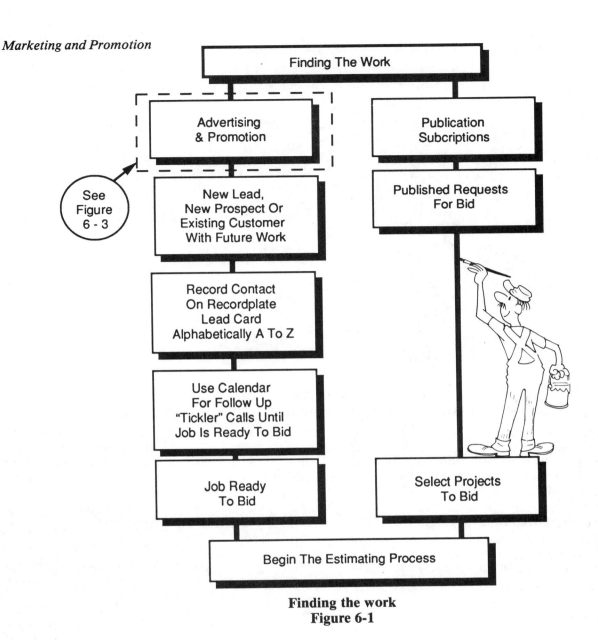

Finding the work
Figure 6-1

the three most important parts of an advertising plan:

1) *Define your target market.* First, establish the geographical area where you want to do business. A good rule of thumb is to look for jobs within 30 minutes of your office or shop. Next, if you're looking for repaint work, pinpoint areas within those boundaries where the buildings are old enough to need repainting. If you're painting new construction, identify the general contractors and developers who build projects that fit your niche.

2) *Establish an advertising budget.* For many companies, the advertising budget will be about 2% of gross sales. It may be more for a new business and less for an established business. But

promotion must *never* stop. Keep your company name in front of your target audience in one form or another.

3) *Track the results.* Using a discount coupon is a good way to track results when advertising for repaint work. And ask everyone who calls for a bid how they heard about your company. Keep a log of the responses. This log and the coupons you get back should suggest what advertising works best.

The Basics of Promotion

For new painting companies, the first and most basic promotion decision is naming the company. The second is designing a distinctive company

Prospecting is an essential part of every growing paint contracting business

logo. The name and logo will both be important elements in all of the promotion you do. Give them the time and attention they deserve.

Business Name and Company Logo

You want your company name to identify what the company stands for, to establish credibility by reflecting an *image* to the customer. That image might project:

- Quality craftsmanship
- Honesty and integrity
- Service
- Competitive prices

Thinking up a good company name and designing an effective logo can be hard work. Fortunately, it's easy to get some help. To get some ideas, go to a local library that has telephone books for cities outside your area. Pick up the Yellow Pages for any major city and go through the display ads in the painting contractor section. Jot down some names and logos that appeal to you. Then move on to other cities until you've accumulated enough ideas to start the wheels turning.

Over the next day or so, think about the name and logo. Be sure to select a name that's easy to remember, easy to say, and easy to understand. You don't want a name you have to spell every time you're on the phone introducing your com-

pany to a prospective customer. Once you've decided on a name, go through your *local* telephone directory to be sure no one is already using it. You don't want to use a name that's even similar to a name another painter's using. You want to be unique, not confused with another company.

Select a type style for the logo that's neat, clear, bold and easy to read, with a high contrast to the background. Don't choose a fancy Olde English type style. It may be impressive, but it's not instantly legible — and that's important. The image reflected by your name and logo will appear over and over again — on your business card, letterhead, forms, signs and any advertising you do. Notice the logo on the flyer in Figure 6-2. It meets all these criteria, while projecting an image of quality.

One important note here: Some states require that your contractor's license number appear on all printed matter. Even if it's not required, listing your license number helps to establish your credibility as a licensed professional.

Prospecting

This *prospecting* isn't looking for gold, unless you consider potential customers to be as good as gold. Prospecting means looking for prospective customers — finding the work. That's an essential part of every growing paint contracting business.

QUALITY PAINTING & DECORATING
Contractor's License Number: 717273

INTERIOR & EXTERIOR
PAINTING SPECIALISTS

- **RESIDENTIAL**
- **COMMERCIAL**

- **CONDOMINIUMS**
- **RENTAL PROPERTY**

─── SPRAY-ON ACOUSTIC CEILINGS ───

- Texture Coating
- Airless Spraying
- Graphic Arts Lettering

- Roll or Brush Wall Covering
- Waterblasting & Sandblasting
- Expert Color Matching

- Bonded
- Insured
- Financing available
- *Competitive pricing*
- *Friendly*

- *Reliable*
- *Professional*
- *Efficient Service*
- *References*
- *SATISFACTION GUARANTEED*

FREE ESTIMATES
in writing

graffiti removal
FROM CONCRETE AND MASONRY

CALL TODAY
555-1512
777 Main Street, Yourtown, USA 77777

Flyer featuring company logo
Figure 6-2

The value of a lead— It's been said that there's nothing sweeter than hearing that phone ring — when there's a new customer on the other end. Always consider new business a top priority. There's nothing more valuable to the success of your organization.

Not everyone understands the value of a good lead. You know how important every lead is if you've beat the pavement, wearing out shoe leather, looking for new business. All experienced salespeople know that leads are their bread and butter. If you haven't had sales experience, take my word for it.

Never waste a lead— All leads are valuable. If one of your promotions turns up a prospect who needs specialized painting work you can't provide at reasonable cost, service that lead by referring the prospect to another qualified painter. Someday that painter will return the favor. This isn't just good customer service, it's also valuable public relations. The prospect will remember your company as helpful and professional. Who knows, that prospect may refer others to you — people who need painting work within your niche.

The Basics of Advertising

Advertising is simply using publicity to find prospects. Everyone who owns or is building a structure needs a painter at one time or another, unless they're willing to do the painting themselves.

The whole point of advertising is to get your name and phone number before people so they'll call you when they need an estimate. Let's look at some of the ways painters can promote their service.

The Promotional Message

Here's one rule for successful advertising: Leave your prospects with something they won't throw away. They're less likely to toss out a flyer or newspaper ad with a money-saving coupon or a guarantee, than one that doesn't offer any incentive to keep it around.

When getting the word out about your painting services to potential customers, whether on a flyer, circular or in a newspaper display ad, you want your promotional message to answer these key questions:

- Who
- What
- When
- Where
- Why
- How

For maximum impact, the promotional message should include a discount coupon with an expiration date. The coupon will help you keep track of the effectiveness of the promotion. The expiration date will *imply urgency* so prospects are more likely to act now instead of procrastinating. Use yellow paper with black or dark blue print. Yellow paper is the most visible. Dark print makes a good contrast for easy reading.

Copy Writing

The copy is the actual text of your message. In writing copy for your promotional messages, keep it simple, uncluttered and to the point. Here are some of the words experienced copywriters use to get results:

Advantage . . . benefits . . . discovery . . . easy . . . guarantee . . . health . . . money . . . new . . . now . . . positive . . . proven . . . results . . . save . . . security . . . you

Some popular "buzz words" and phrases more directly related to the construction trades are:

Bonded . . . competitive prices . . . conscientious . . . dependable . . . effective . . . efficient . . . fair . . . guaranteed . . . insured . . . quality workmanship . . . references . . . reliable . . . satisfaction . . . service

When writing copy for your ads, use enough of these "glitter" words and phrases to attract attention. But don't use them all. Credibility is important too. Look again at Figure 6-2. You'll find several of these key words on the flyer.

Layout and Design

While you're at the library going through phone books to get ideas for the company name, notice the design of the ads in the Yellow Pages. You can get a lot of layout and design ideas from the ads there. But don't copy directly from these ads. Improve on them. Create your own distinct layout and design based on the designs and layouts of others.

Choosing the Medium

You have a memorable company name, attention-getting logo, and crisp, persuasive copy. Where do you go with it? The advertising medium is the method you choose to reach your future customers. The flow chart in Figure 6-3 shows some of the possibilities.

The Yellow Pages— If your company niche is based on repainting existing homes, you *must* have a display ad in the Yellow Pages. When designing your ad, make the phone number large enough so it can't be missed by anyone who's scanning the phone numbers of local painting contractors. The content of the ad (the copy) and the graphic design should set your ad apart from those of your competitors. Figure 6-4 shows a good Yellow Pages ad for a paint contracting business.

An effective display ad in the Yellow Pages is designed to attract attention. The size of your ad will depend upon your budget, of course. If possible, make it large enough so it stands out among all the other contractor's ads. A good ad will pay for itself many times over.

A well-designed Yellow Pages ad will bring in many inquiries. You should be able to convert at least 10% to 20% of all phone inquiries into jobs. The disadvantage of a Yellow Pages ad is that you're likely to get calls from people who just want to know how a professional painter would do the job.

Signage— A sign at the job site is an example of *image advertising* — designed to project a good company image. Design signs with the company name and phone number standing out in bold letters. Silkscreened signs on adhesive-backed vinyl attached to the doors of a clean, shiny truck are an effective form of advertising. And the same silkscreen can be used to print project signs on Masonite to place in front of homes you're working on. This is a good way to make passers-by aware of your presence in the area.

Advertising specialties— Give-away items such as pens, pencils, calendars, match books, rulers, and the like are usually a luxury for a new business. If you're just beginning your business, your limited start-up dollars are probably needed elsewhere. But when you're established, these items can help you get your company name in front of prospective customers in a convenient form.

You want to have your company name right there when your future customer decides he needs painting work. You want your number to be on the pen in his hand or on the calendar next to the phone. Some advertising specialties can be enclosed with direct mailings to prospective customers.

Newspaper ads— If you're looking for repaint work, classified or display ads in local newspapers can reach prospects in your targeted areas at reasonable cost. The paper's sales staff can help you design the ad or you can use your Yellow Pages ad.

Newspaper press releases and interviews— Send out press releases to the newspaper about anything that's newsworthy about your company. They won't use them all, of course, but you may eventually get a mention that can create name recognition and good will. As an example, if you're elected to an office in a charitable organization or builder's association, make sure that information is sent to the local paper. You should get your name, along with the name of your business, in the paper as often as you can.

Direct mail— For *repaint* business, select a target geographical area where there are houses or apartment buildings old enough for repainting. For *new construction business,* target your mailing to general contractors. Send out a promotional flyer or letter of introduction at bulk mail postal rates. But remember, there's a minimum number of pieces you must send for bulk mail. Your post office can supply information on rates and mailing requirements. The cost of postage on bulk mail is usually about half the cost of first class postage.

You can buy address labels preprinted from direct mail houses. Look into this possibility before using your staff's time to compile names and type labels.

Co-op mailings— Many residential communities have shopper newspapers or co-op mailing services that combine the announcements from several stores and businesses in a single mailing piece. The mailing cost is lower because it's shared by all companies using the service. If you receive co-op mailings, save the next one you get. Call the office that's running the co-op and get information on insertion rates and deadlines.

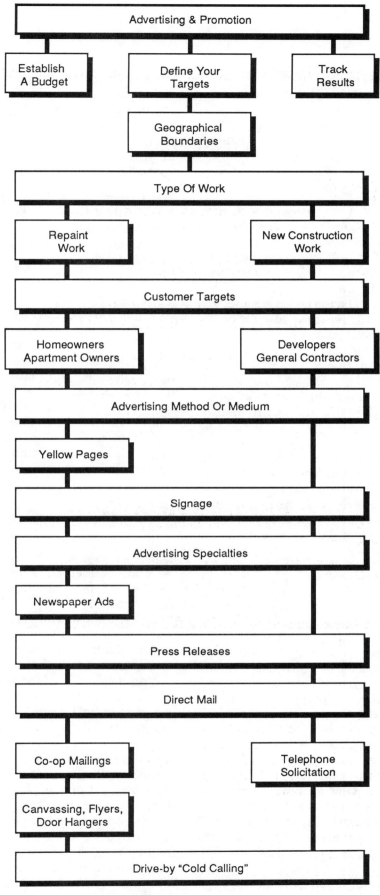

Advertising and promotion
Figure 6-3

Yellow Pages display ad
Figure 6-4

Canvassing— Distributing your flyers by hand using a delivery company can be effective, but it's probably more expensive than mass mailing. But there's another form of canvassing that doesn't cost anything but a little time and the printing costs. Every time you repaint a home, send your helper around the neighborhood to drop off flyers or put door hangers on door knobs. Figure 6-5 shows a door hanger that fills the bill.

Notice the paragraph that says "We are currently painting the _____ home at . . . ." Have the name and address of your customer typed in at the office. Make enough copies to distribute to all the neighbors within a block or two of your customer's home. *Be sure to get permission and approval from the homeowner before directing anyone's attention to that home.*

Here's one more form of canvassing: drive-by cold calling. When you're driving around on your daily business trips and you see a home that needs painting — stop and knock on the door. Introduce yourself and drop off a flyer or leave a door hanger. You should always have a supply with you, along with your business cards. And I mean stop *right now.* Don't believe it when you say to yourself "I'll do that later." You probably won't.

Door hanger
Figure 6-5

Do it now unless you're late for an appointment.

Once you've decided to stop for a sales call, make the most efficient use of your time. Use the *five-point system*. That means you drop off another flyer at each of your prospect's next-door neighbors and at the three homes directly across the street. That makes the stop worthwhile.

If you're looking for new construction work, every time you see a site under construction, stop. You may get an opportunity to bid that project. If nothing else, you'll develop a lead for bidding future work.

Telephone— The telephone is a powerful sales tool. Use it for follow-up calls and to stay in touch with anyone who's considering an estimate you've submitted. But you'll probably find that it doesn't pay to make ''cold calls'' to homeowners by phone. You may have to make a hundred unsolicited calls to find anyone who would even consider repainting — and only a small fraction of those leads become customers.

Make Your Advertising Effective

Here are some of the important principles of effective advertising:

• *Repeat contact:* Most people don't respond to the first advertising message. It might take three or four contacts before they'll act. Don't give up if you get a disappointing response from your mailings. Keep mailing to the best prospects.

• *Consistency:* All of your advertising messages should feature the company name and logo. The prospect should associate your name and logo with quality painting. Each repetition reinforces the image. At some point, even the thought of painting brings your company to mind.

• *Response tracking:* Use coded discount coupons in all of your printed advertising so you can measure the response to each ad. That's important. You want to eliminate the ineffective ads and spend more advertising money where it does the most good.

Finding New Construction Projects

Of course, repainting isn't the only game in town. Painting new construction can be good business too. To get this work, you have to sell to general contractors and developers. Here are some effective ways to find the names of builders in your area:

• Look for articles and ads in the real estate section of your local paper.

• Subscribe to construction or legal newspapers.

• Subscribe to service publications (Dodge Reports, for example).

• Read trade publications.

• Get the rosters of builder associations in your area.

• Drive by sites where construction is in progress.

• Takes notes on radio, television and newspaper advertisements.

• Look in the Yellow Pages under Real Estate Developers, Construction — General Contractors.

After finding the names of builders who may need your service, telephone to introduce yourself and confirm that the prospect builds the kind of projects you want to paint.

Consider joining a builder's association and mailing a letter of introduction to all builders on the association roster.

Establish Contact with Builders

Salesmanship begins on the first call, when you establish a rapport with the builder or the builder's purchasing agent. Your goal is to introduce your painting company so you can be placed on their *selected bidders list.* You want builders to call you when they have a project ready for painting bids.

If you've established contact with the general contractor and found that there aren't any projects currently out for bid, ask to be placed on the bid list. Then send a letter of introduction and a list of references along with two business cards arranged so they fall out when the letter is removed from the envelope. That's a subtle way to draw attention to your letter.

Letter of Introduction

A letter of introduction will be the first promotional piece you write. Make it short, sweet and to the point. This letter can be aimed at homeowners or general contractors, but the object is the same: to persuade these new prospects to call your painting company every time they need an estimate.

The letter should define these points about your company:

1) Strength (including manpower quality, office efficiency, supervision capabilities, and equipment available)

2) Reputation (customers satisfied with your work and suppliers satisfied with your payment history)

3) Goals (especially customer satisfaction and company growth)

4) Objectives (to deliver quality and service at competitive prices)

Figure 6-6 shows a typical letter of introduction. Use it as a guide. Revise this letter so it sells *your* company.

List of References

Send a list of references along with all of your letters of introduction. You'll only include good references on your list, of course — contractors who will verify your on-time performance and quality workmanship. And give the name, address and phone number of the builder along with the name of the individual within the company who will give you a favorable recommendation. This is an important point. Every construction office is a hotbed of rumors and gossip. If your prospect talks to someone who doesn't personally know how your company performs, he may get a third-hand opinion — and it may be damaging. Also, list the projects your company has painted along with the number of units or square footage for commercial projects. Figure 6-7 shows the format for a typical reference list.

Initial Presentation to General Contractors

Your initial presentation to a general contractor or developer should *break the ice*. When plans for a new project are available for pick up, make an appointment for a brief meeting. Here's a four-step plan you can use to organize the meeting so your time is as productive as possible:

Introduction— Start off by introducing yourself and your company. To make the best impression, remember to smile and make continuous eye contact while talking. Shake hands firmly with a man, and with a woman if she offers her hand first. Ask an involvement question: When will your project start? When is completion scheduled? How many units are you building?

Body— Discuss any problems or difficulties the builder is having or has had with other painting contractors. This is the time to demonstrate your product knowledge and experience in the painting business. Make it clear that you're a knowledgeable, experienced professional painter who knows paints and coatings. That's the first step in convincing your prospect that you should be bidding his work.

Specifications— Go over the items on the pre-bid checklist in Figure 6-8. Discuss all the items listed as well as any unusual painting requirements. Be sure to ask the builder if there's anything not shown on the plans.

Using the pre-bid checklist in your presentation shows that you're organized and efficient. Fill out this form for all projects. It's a handy format for itemizing specification requirements when the general notes aren't accurate. There's a completed sample in Chapter 19, Estimating New Construction.

Summary— Close the meeting by asking for the opportunity to bid the next job. If plans are now available, ask to take a set of prints with you. There may be a plan deposit of $10.00 to $50.00. Offer to write a check for this deposit. It will be returned when you return the plans.

Meet a Few Key People

If you're bidding a larger job, it's good practice to meet the general contractor's job superintendent before submitting the bid. At the very least, find some reason to call the superintendent. If you get the bid, you'll have to work closely with the job super. Understanding his personality and having his trust will be important once your portion of the work begins. Call him and introduce yourself.

QUALITY PAINTING & DECORATING
777 Main Street, Yourtown, USA 77777 (515) 555-1512

Gentlemen:

To introduce Quality Painting & Decorating to your organization, we would like to explain some of our qualifications and goals.

Quality Painting has a labor force ranging from 30 to 60 painters in the field, and a five-person management team working to run our projects efficiently. We're a member of the Painting & Decorating Contractors Association and the Chamber of Commerce.

We have two main production goals: First, to stay in close touch with your superintendents in order to complete jobs on schedule. Second, to always provide the highest quality work possible. We work diligently to meet the requirements of our clients, and frequently advise them on alternatives which can save time and money.

We invite you to contact any of the general contractors for whom we have worked. (A reference list is enclosed.) Our suppliers include Old Quaker Paint Co., Frazee Industries, Dunn Edwards Paint Co., and Kelly Moore Paint Co.

Quality Painting & Decorating is currently undertaking work in the entire Yourtown area, with as many as fifteen projects being conducted simultaneously. All of this work is on schedule. We would like to place bids on any projects where you have need for a conscientious and efficient painting contractor.

We look forward to hearing from you soon.

Sincerely,

John Jones
President

Enc.

Letter of introduction
Figure 6-6

QUALITY PAINTING & DECORATING
777 Main Street, Yourtown, USA 77777 (515) 555-1512

Reference List

Company	Contact & Phone	Project Names	Number and Type of Units
Bigtime Developers 1234 Main Street Yourtown, USA 77777	Jim Big 722-2222	Beautiful Acres Happy Village	42 houses 74 houses
Building Development Co. 5678 Elm Street Yourtown, USA 77777	Joe Brown 666-6666	Mile High	125 condos
John Doe Construction 555 Broadway Yourtown, USA 77777	John Doe 222-1515	Viewridge	65 apts.
Atlantic Builders 3333 Broadway Yourtown, USA 77777	George Johns 626-7373	Yourtown Center Business Park	21,000 SF retail 22,000 SF office

List of references
Figure 6-7

PROJECT NAME: _____   **DATE:** _____

PROJECT LOCATION: _____   **BUILDER:** _____

| Interior | Exterior |

Interior

Paint brand:
_____
_____
_____

	Pre-finished	Paint grade	Stain seal lacquer
Kitchen cabinets	_____	_____	_____
Pullmans	_____	_____	_____
Linen closet	_____	_____	_____
Forced air unit	_____	_____	_____
Passage doors	_____	_____	_____
Wardrobe doors	_____	_____	_____
Other _____			

Wet area walls and ceilings:
 Undercoat + 1 coat _____
 Undercoat + 2 coats _____

Pullmans, linens, doors and casings:
 Undercoat + 1 coat _____
 Undercoat + 2 coats _____
 Split coat _____
 Brush coat _____
 Other _____

Walls:
 1 coat flat _____
 2 coats flat _____
 1 coat sealer _____

Interior wood (mantel, siding, etc.)
 1 coat _____
 2 coats _____
 Other _____

Tongue & groove (T&G) ceiling:
 Finish _____

Fireplace masonry _____

Base:
 Stain _____
 Paint _____

Exterior

Paint brand:
_____
_____
_____

Exterior wood (plant ons, overhang, fascia):
 1 coat _____
 2 coats _____
 Clear seal per FHA _____

Siding:
 Heavy body stain _____
 Semi-transparent stain _____

Shingles:
 Clear sealer _____
 No finish _____

Stucco:
 Paint _____
 Sealer _____

Fireplace masonry: _____

Fencing: _____

Other: _____

* *

Total number of units _____

Number of phases _____

Painting start date _____

Completion date _____

Price expiration date _____

Present painter _____

Customer's phone _____

Purchasing agent _____

Pre-bid checklist
Figure 6-8

Recordplate lead slip
Figure 6-9

There's more to paint estimating than just figuring areas, quantities, manhours and costs. The best estimators are good salesmen too, selling both themselves and their companies. They don't rely on accurate bids and low prices alone to bring in all the work they can handle. They've learned that every customer has a unique attitude and personality. They've learned to identify what motivates buyers and found ways to provide what's needed to close the sale. Don't just sit back and wait for the jobs to roll in. Find better, more effective ways to convince your prospects that you can meet their needs.

If the general contractor is a large company, you may want to meet the company vice president. Introduce yourself, but don't be a nuisance. All you want to do is make sure your name and the name of your company are known by key personnel in the general contractor's company.

Keeping Track of Prospect Leads

If your promotional activities are successful, you'll have plenty of leads. But you'll never keep track of 100 to 150 builder leads, 25 homeowner leads and 35 "active" proposals without a system. I use the *Recordplate* system for alphabetical listings, along with a calendar system to remind me when to call the prospect back.

The Recordplate System*
The Recordplate system includes a 6½" x 8½" multi-ring binder which holds lead slips for each prospect and customer (Figure 6-9). These leads

can be organized with alphabetical tabs. There's also a refillable calendar for recording your daily activities and follow-up calls. The binder's compact size makes it easy to carry with you when you're in the field and have to look up an appointment, a phone number, or address information. If used properly, this binder will be your sales bible.

Each lead slip should be filled out completely, showing your prospect's name, address, zip code, phone number and contact name along with the date (including the year) of the initial contact and each call-back date. These slips will become your master lead cards, arranged in alphabetical order within the binder. Supplies for the Recordplate system are sold at many stationery stores.

Prospecting Abbreviations
Any time you call a prospect, make abbreviated notes on the Recordplate slip. This abbreviation system saves time and space but will remind you of the important facts about every customer in a glance. Here are some of the abbreviations I use:

1) B	=	Busy signal
2) CB	=	Call (the prospect) back
3) LMAS	=	Left message with answering service
4) LMAM	=	Left message on answering machine
5) LMWC	=	Left message, will call
6) NA	=	No answer
7) WCB	=	(Prospect) will call back

* *Recordplate is a registered trademark of the Rediform Division of Moore Business Forms, Inc.*

8) WC IF = (Prospect) will call if (a project comes up for bid)

9) WC WHEN = (Prospect) will call when (a project is ready for bid)

10) WI = Wasn't in (call back)

Use *WC if* when the owner or builder doesn't anticipate another project in the near future. Be sure to get a date to call back. Use *WC when* if the owner or builder anticipates a project will be ready for bid soon. Again, get a call-back date.

"Tickle" Your Prospects

Use your Recordplate calendar for listing follow-up "tickler" call dates for each of your prospects.

After making the initial contact with new prospects, record the date of that contact on the lead card, as well as the date to call your prospect back. Then write your prospect's name on the call-back date on your calendar, as shown in Figure 6-10. As you refer to your calendar each day, you'll be reminded which of your prospects are ready to be tickled. Just look up the phone number in your binder and make the call. Always keep your binder with you, so you can make your call backs whenever you find the time.

Using the System for Prospecting

Once you have a list of builders in your Recordplate file, flip through the cards periodically and contact those prospects you haven't called in a while. If you review your prospects about once a month, there's a good chance you'll find new opportunities to bid.

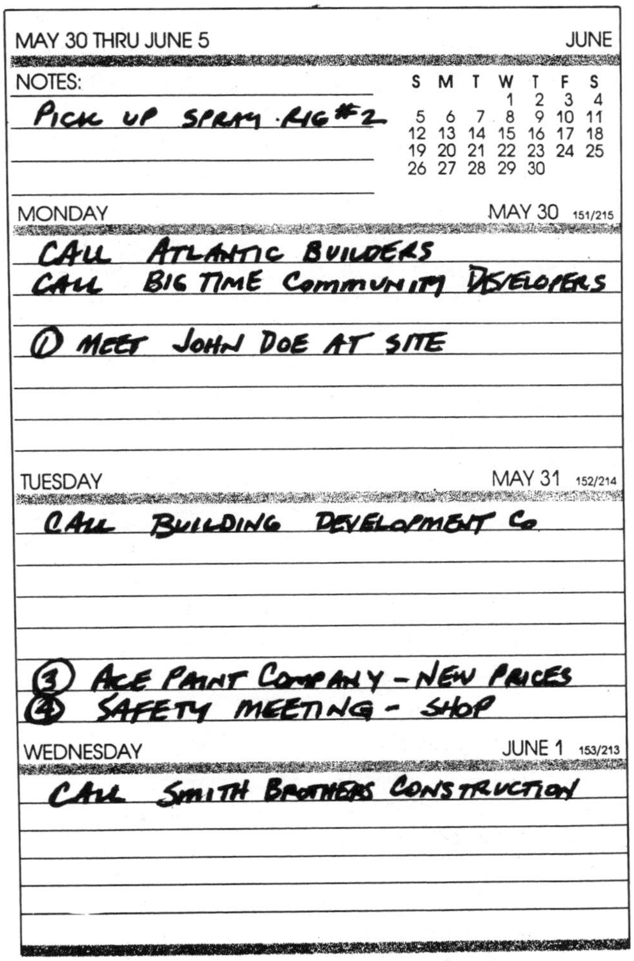

MAY 30 THRU JUNE 5 JUNE

NOTES:

PICK UP SPRAY RIG #2

S	M	T	W	T	F	S
			1	2	3	4
5	6	7	8	9	10	11
12	13	14	15	16	17	18
19	20	21	22	23	24	25
26	27	28	29	30		

MONDAY MAY 30 151/215

CALL ATLANTIC BUILDERS

CALL BIG TIME COMMUNITY DEVELOPERS

① MEET JOHN DOE AT SITE

TUESDAY MAY 31 152/214

CALL BUILDING DEVELOPMENT Co

③ ACE PAINT COMPANY – NEW PRICES

④ SAFETY MEETING – SHOP

WEDNESDAY JUNE 1 153/213

CALL SMITH BROTHERS CONSTRUCTION

Calendar tickler file
Figure 6-10

Don't assume that your company is on the bid list and will be called automatically. Most general contractors have a couple of favorite painters they always call, plus many other painters on a bid list. Persistence with call backs will pay off. Without them, you're likely to be lost in the shuffle. But don't call back too often and become a pest.

Taking the Next Step

Most of what I suggest in this chapter will apply whether you're targeting homeowners for repaint jobs or general contractors for new construction work. With either target, you have to identify pro-spects and put them on your prospect list.

But your prospect list is just the pond in which you go fishing. The bait you use for homeowners is very different from the bait you use when fishing for business from general contractors. When your prospect is a homeowner looking for an interior re-paint, you have to *sell* the job. When it's a general contractor's purchasing agent sitting across the desk, he's looking for a *bid,* and his decision will be made largely on price.

But whether it's a homeowner or builder, you'll need to present a bid before asking for the job. And that's the subject of the next chapter: the bid-ding process. Later we'll look at sales techniques and closing strategy.

Chapter 7

WINNING BIDS

Submitting a bid for construction work is like submitting an offer on a piece of real estate. Your bid is an *offer* to do the work at a specific price. If your bid is *accepted,* you have a contract to do the job at an agreed upon price.

It's the estimator's task to submit as many bids as possible. But don't be surprised when you lose a few. Remember, *you're not going to win them all.* If you win every bid, you're bidding too low and will probably be out of business in six weeks! No matter how precise and accurate you are, there's always a competitor who can underbid you. Perhaps the competitor has better and faster crews, uses short cuts to get the job finished in less time, or has an estimator who left something out of the bid. You can't win them all. But don't be discouraged. Just sharpen your pencil and resolve to make the next bid a winner.

Bidding Output and Tracking Are Important

The rule is simple: The more bids you submit, the more jobs you'll win. But no matter how many jobs you bid, keep track of the number of jobs bid and the number of bids that are accepted. That's your win ratio. This ratio is a percentage of jobs won, and you can calculate it by dividing the number of jobs won by the total number of jobs bid. For example, if you bid 40 jobs and win 10 of them, you're winning 25% of your bids. Review your win ratio regularly. Draw a chart that shows your win ratio each month and you'll see the bidding trend at a glance.

Note how the win ratio fluctuates from month to month. If it's too high or too low, the prices you're quoting are either too high or too low for the market. If your winning percentage is headed lower, it may be due to more intense competition or fewer projects available for bid. If your percentage of wins is higher than normal, your bid prices may be too low.

In either case, if you're uncomfortable with your win ratio, it's time to make adjustments. Maybe you should make changes in the profit margin. If the profit margin isn't excessive but you're still losing too many jobs, maybe it's because the crews aren't working efficiently. Your company may need a *field tune-up*. I've seen the president of a

Don't throw out bids hoping some will stick. Bid to win!

painting company clean house, laying off most of the painters and hiring new painters. In his opinion, that was the only way to improve field productivity.

When your painting company needs work, the pressure is on the estimator to put out a large number of competitive bids. To keep the field crews busy, you may have to bid lower than normal just to get the work. But under no circumstances would I advise bidding carelessly, throwing out bids, hoping some will stick. That's not professional. Remember, *every bid counts.* Bid every job as if you expected to do the work. Use a consistent estimating system and evaluate every cost in each job.

If you're winning more bids than usual and have enough work, be more selective in choosing the projects to bid. On less desirable projects, submit a *courtesy bid*, a figure slightly higher than your normal competitive bid. But even that courtesy bid should cover all the costs involved. Who knows, you may end up with the job.

But even if you have enough work now, there's always a need for future work. Keep sending out competitive, professional bids. Could it be said that "an estimator's work is never done"?

The Bidding Process

Figure 7-1 shows a flow chart of the bidding process. And it is a *process,* not an event. Your estimate is the result of *reviewing, analyzing, comparing, considering and evaluating* every cost in the job.

The bidding process begins after the estimator has calculated the cost of the job, using a consistent estimating system, and added the usual markup. Then you should compare the total price with previous bids and actual costs on similar jobs you've completed. You'll probably want to re-examine key bidding variables, which are discussed later in the chapter, and make a visit to the site. When this evaluation is finished, you may want to

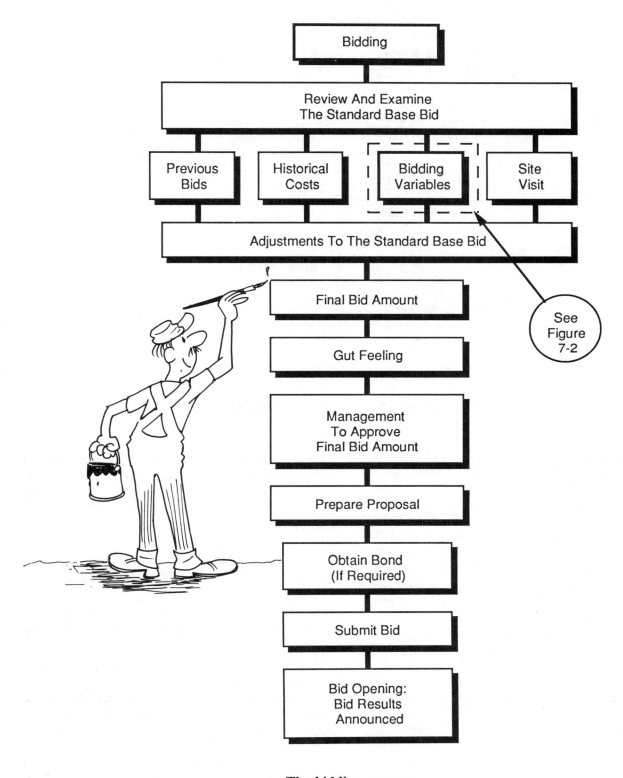

The bidding process
Figure 7-1

make adjustments to the standard bid. Any adjustments should be based on reliable data, instinct, and on company policy, if there is one.

When you've made the final adjustments, present the bid to company management for review. You'll usually have to give reasons why adjustments were made. Management will have to approve any adjustments you've made to the base bid. When preparing for this management meeting on bid strategy, you should be ready to respond to questions about:

1) Bids submitted on similar jobs

2) The actual cost of work done on similar jobs

3) The bidding variables

4) Your "gut feeling"

If you're both the estimator and the owner or manager of a painting company, you'll both set the standard profit margin and make sure that the percentage is included in the bid.

Bid Price Compared to Previous Bids

Compare your bid on the current job to bids submitted on similar jobs. But before comparing prices, make sure that the jobs really are similar. If they are, the price per square foot of floor area on the two jobs should be very nearly the same.

If your bid wasn't accepted, try to find out the amount of the winning bid. Sometimes the general contractor will reveal this information. On larger jobs, especially government jobs, the winning bid will be published in construction newspapers or will be released to anyone who asks for it. Record the percentage difference between your bid and the winning bid. This information will improve your chances of winning future jobs.

Comparing Actual Job Costs

Compare your bid to *actual* costs on similar jobs that you completed profitably. These *historical costs* are your best guide to the cost of future jobs. But don't make comparisons to unprofitable jobs. Are your base bid costs higher or lower than your actual costs? If they're higher, there's room to reduce your bid prices and still earn a profit.

Your analysis isn't complete until it's been compared with actual costs from jobs already completed. That's why it's so important to keep cost

records. The historical cost tables in Chapter 12 suggest a format for accumulating cost records on completed jobs. Search through your cost records until you find a completed job similar to the job being estimated. Compare the price per square foot of floor area for each job. Allow for changes in labor and material costs if the completed job was done more than a few months ago.

Every time you complete a project, list actual costs in the same format. The goal is to have a complete set of cost records for each type of project your painters handle.

For a complete manual on keeping cost records, you may find *Cost Records for Construction Estimating* helpful. It can be ordered with the order form in the back of this book.

Bidding Variables

You'll hear paint estimators insist that no paint estimating system can be accurate. They claim that since no two jobs are the same, every job has to be bid differently. These "old school" paint estimators may have an estimating system in their heads, or they may use guesses, approximations and their instincts to estimate costs. Some are pretty good at it. Some just *think* they are, and can't figure out why they're not making any money. They claim it must be the economy. But you *can* accurately estimate painting costs. That's why I've written this book.

Estimating and bidding by guesses and approximations without measuring and calculating is like baking a cake without following a recipe. Mixing a little bit of this and a pinch of that may turn out O.K. *if* you know exactly what you're doing — and if luck is on your side that day. But for most of us, the results would be pretty unpredictable.

I agree that every job is unique. But that doesn't mean you can't follow a set *routine* designed to help reduce errors and improve accuracy. Using an estimating system and bidding procedure may take a little more time. And it certainly does require that you learn something new. But higher profits and fewer losses will make it worth the effort.

Yes, no two jobs are the same. Every job has a different set of *bidding variables*. It's your job to analyze the variables and bid high enough to make a reasonable profit, but low enough to get the job. Figure 7-2 shows a flow chart of the bidding variables you have to consider. Let's look at some of these variables, one at a time.

Risk vs. profit potential— Every job has the risk of loss and the potential for profit. The risk of a loss is the chance that costs will exceed your final bid amount. All of the following bidding variables address this risk in one way or another.

Reputations and attitudes— Reputations of the parties running the project are important. There are several questions you should ask about the parties you deal with. The answers to these questions help define the risk in a job:

- Do you have experience with them? Have you worked with them successfully on other projects?

- How are they to work with? Are they particular and sticklers for quality?

- Are they competent? Do they know the construction business?

- Do they pay their bills on time? Are they reliable?

- Are they flexible, or strictly "by the book"?

Consider the prospect's attitude and reputation when selecting projects to bid *and* when adjusting the standard base bid. If the owner's attitude and honesty appeal to you and the project is the type you handle well, that's probably a job you want to bid — and win.

I can only remember one time that I didn't bid a project that was our kind of work. While I was picking up a set of plans for a housing tract from a developer, I asked him a few questions intended to determine his attitude toward painters and subcontractors. His responses included this flat statement: "We're in business to make money for ourselves, not the subs." I gave him back the plan set and left his office. I just didn't want to work with someone who had so little respect for subcontractors. I sometimes wonder how the painter who took the job made out. I bet he's got quite a horror story.

Working on a large construction project takes a lot of teamwork. If every subcontractor works together with the owner or general contractor, everyone can make a profit.

Lenders and fund control— A fund control system should increase your chance of getting paid on time. A fund control company gets the loan proceeds from the lender and distributes them to the general and subcontractors as work is completed. Having funds disbursed that way is better for subcontractors than having progress and retention payments issued through the general contractor's office.

The architect and engineer— Are the architect and engineer competent? Do they have a reputation for producing complete sets of plans? A preliminary review of the plans and specs before you begin the take-off will tell you plenty about the design team.

The general contractor— Here are two important things to consider when analyzing the general contractor's reputation: the business size, and the ability to pay on time. Many larger construction companies take 60 to 90 days to pay invoices submitted on progress billings. On the other hand, with a small construction company, you may never be paid at all!

The general superintendent— Can the superintendent run a good job? If you bid several projects for a general contractor, you may work with the same general superintendent more than once. After the first job, you'll recognize a "super" who can help you make a profit by getting you in and out smoothly. If it's a super you don't know, make it a point to meet him during your site visit. After a little conversation, you should be able to evaluate his competence and attitude. If you have any reservations, make sure it's reflected in your final bid.

The inspectors— On many projects there will be an independent or government inspector to inspect your painting work. The inspector's job is to be sure that the project meets the quality standards in the specs and building code. You may want to adjust the markup if the inspector has a reputation for being excessively picky.

Quality control requirements— Inspectors and general contractors must satisfy the owner's quality requirements. That makes many general contractors very quality-conscious.

Consider the quality control requirements of your customer before bidding. Remember, if the quality of your work is below acceptable standard, extra manhours will be needed to make corrections. That means higher costs. Do it right the first

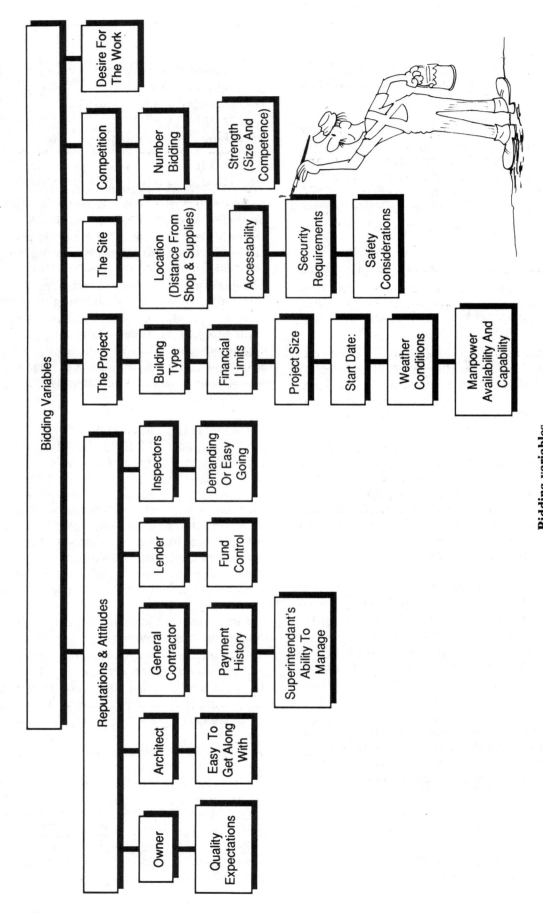

Bidding variables
Figure 7-2

time, or don't do it at all. Save those rework expenses and gain repeat business from your satisfied customers.

Project size and type— Is it the type of project your company can consistently make money on? And is it the size project that lets you use crews and equipment efficiently? Finally, is the project so large that you'll need financing to meet payroll between progress payments? If so, are the interest rates, points and other finance costs included in the bid?

Project length— Are your manpower and financial resources adequate to last through the entire project even if, in the worst case, it lasts twice as long as originally scheduled?

Manpower capability and availability— Does your company have painters with the skills needed to handle the complexity of the project? Do you have enough painters to do this job *and* the other jobs you've got scheduled?

Financial limits— Consider if the project is within your financial means. Does your company have the purchasing power and cash flow to keep up labor and material payments if the billing cycle runs up to 90 days? If the project requires a bond and additional insurance, are the bonding requirements within your company's capacity? Are insurance requirements within your limits?

Project start date and weather conditions— Consider the season when you'll be working. Will the project be completed before bad weather is expected? Bad weather will delay the work and increase costs. The weather can have other effects as well. For example, high humidity can affect coatings, causing lacquer to fog or blush during spraying.

The site location— Make sure the project is located within a reasonable distance from your home or office. A good rule of thumb is to avoid work more than about 45 minutes from your place of business. Also consider these factors:

- Cost of the craftsmen's travel time
- Craftsmen's per diem expense
- Distance to supply sources
- Distance to rental yards

Site conditions— Before bidding on any large project, you'll want to visit the site. *Accessiblity* is an important cost variable to consider. When access to the work area is limited or restricted, the painters are less productive. You'll probably have to spend more time moving materials and you may need additional spray line, scaffolding or specialized equipment to reach parts of the job.

On a well-managed new construction painting project, the units are kept clean and the painters have good access to the work area. That increases productivity, saves manhours, reduces fatigue and ensures that skilled tradesmen can concentrate on doing what they do best — applying paints and coatings. Here are some site conditions to consider:

Soil condition: Work will be much slower if your painters have to walk, drive or work in mud or standing water. Will the streets and driveways be paved and the yards be graded for drainage before you begin work?

Existing structures: Do adjacent structures or automobiles need to be protected from overspray? If so, allow for this cost in your estimate.

Storage availability: For repaint projects which last more than one day, on-site storage of materials can save up to an hour of setup and cleanup time each day. Another consideration is the security of tools and materials stored on site. If you'll be storing materials on site, keep a daily log of what's stored there. That way, if something valuable is stolen, you'll have documentation to show the insurance company.

On new construction projects there's usually a garage where painters can store tools and materials. But don't assume that the garage is a safe storage area. Security can still be a problem even if the builder has a guard on the project every night.

Safety considerations— It's more dangerous to work at heights above 8 feet and on slippery surfaces. Painting contractors who have too many accidents pay higher insurance premiums than the rest of us. Consider the risk of accident when bidding work to be done more than 8 feet off the ground.

Competitor	Builders/Projects	Percentages		Comments
		They won by	We won by	
Able Painting	Giant Construction/Forest Glen		1%	
	Homebuilder's/Seaview Condos	2%		Non-union
Best Painting	Tri-State Construction/The Lakes	6%		Must deduct to win
Calhoun's Painting	Smith Development/North Village		3%	Union shop
	Tri-State/Hillside Villas		2%	
City Decorating	Jones Builders/Jones Lake		8%	Bid higher against them
	Giant Construction/Mountain View		12%	

Competitor analysis
Figure 7-3

The competition— Always consider the strength of your competition. That's one of the most important bidding variables. Are they competent professionals or are they "low ball" bidders? How many competitors are there? If more than five painting bids are requested, you might not want to bid the job at all.

After bidding in the same project category for some time, you'll know what to expect from the competition. Of course, it's unethical to ask about a competitor's prices before the contract is awarded. But most owners, builders and purchasing agents will tell you the bid price of the winning contractor if you ask after the contract is awarded. If bid prices are published, it's easy to figure the spread between your bid and the winning bid.

Use the competitor analysis form in Figure 7-3 to keep track of your competitor's activity. It's a simple alphabetical listing of your competitors, followed by a list of the projects on which each competitor bid against you. The most important column on this form shows the percentage by which you won or lost the job. This percentage is the amount you could have *deducted from* or *added to* your final bid to match a competitor's price.

But remember, you don't want or need every job you bid. There's no advantage in bidding below your bottom line just to beat the competition. If you can't make money on the job, skip it!

Use this competitor analysis system, along with your "gut feeling," to determine where the competition might be on a particular project.

Desire for the work— How hungry are you? Does your company need the work to meet overhead expense?

Adjusting the Standard Base Bid

I'll use the term *standard base bid* to describe a bid that assumes normal labor productivity and material costs and includes your usual markup. Of course, sometimes labor productivity and material costs will be higher or lower than normal. And sometimes the usual markup will be either too much or too little. In that case, the standard base bid has to be adjusted.

All adjustments to your estimate must be made before the bid is submitted, of course. It's not professional to request adjustments after the bid has been analyzed by the owner or general contractor, although it's often done.

When you review the standard base bid to begin adjusting it, consider these items:

1) Review the estimate to identify operations which may appear to be overvalued or under cost.

2) List and analyze all cost-saving alternatives

that may apply. Determine what cost savings you would recommend and list these as alternates on the bid.

3) Identify operations which may be subcontracted to save money — wallcovering, sandblasting or scaffolding, for example.

Additions or deductions— Your analysis of historical costs and the bidding variables may show that it's prudent to add to or deduct from the standard bid price. For example, on a large housing tract built by a general contractor with a good reputation, you may deduct 3% from the bid price because the painters can be expected to have higher than usual productivity. That justifies a lower price. If you deduct 3% from a base bid, you're not cutting your profit margin, only the anticipated labor cost.

Additions or deductions to the standard base bid price can range from a deduction of 5% to 10% on a large project to an addition of 30% for a custom home job by a builder who's not known for paying bills on time.

Understand here that I'm not talking about cutting your overhead allowance or profit margin to get a job. Not at all. I'm simply customizing the bid based on an evaluation of the cost variables.

Check the final bid value— After adjusting your standard base bid, double-check your final bid amount by calculating the price per square foot. Is that price higher or lower than your usual bid for this type of project? If so, why? If it's much higher or much lower, you've probably made a mistake somewhere.

Finally, use your intuition— In the final analysis, your experience with similar jobs has to be considered. Use your intuition to temper all the logic that brought you to this stage. Use this gut feeling to make any final adjustment to the bid price. What are the chances that you can make a good profit on this job? When you've answered that question and adjusted the bid accordingly, it's time to assemble your proposal.

The Proposal

A proposal is a concise offer to perform work on a specific project for a set price. To reinforce the professional image of your company, always have proposals typewritten. You might give an occasional handwritten bid to a homeowner on a rush job. But when you do, use carbon paper and print neatly. And remember, if you're rushed, bid high to protect yourself.

In general, there are three levels of written proposals. If you're bidding to a homeowner for a repaint, use a proposal/contract form. You'll find an example in Chapter 18. For bidding a new construction project, type the proposal on your company letterhead. There's a sample letterhead proposal in Chapter 19. Finally, on semi-formal or formal bids, you might use the form provided by the owner or architect.

Writing a Proposal

Writing a proposal can be difficult and time-consuming without a system. I recommend using a *proposal outline* to save time. The outline lists the proposal phrases which describe the various painting operations along with a letter abbreviation or code number. This format is used on the new construction proposal outline in Figure 7-4 and on the repaint proposal outline in Figure 7-5.

Use these proposal outlines for preparing a dough draft of the proposal, listing the abbreviations for each of the interior and exterior painting operations included in the proposal. Your typist can type the final draft, converting all of the abbreviations to full descriptions. You'll find examples of the rough draft and final proposals for both repaint and new construction estimates in Chapters 18 and 19.

In this chapter, we'll take a look at the components of a good proposal.

The Heading

The heading of your proposal form should show the name and address of the client and the cross streets or address of the job site. It's important to specify the location of the project so there's no misunderstanding about where the work will be done. Bidding the wrong project or sending painters to the wrong job or to an address they can't locate can be expensive mistakes.

Superseding proposals: If you've submitted another bid on a job since the architect revised the original plans, your proposal form should make it clear that the current bid supersedes all previous proposals.

I

   a ***This proposal will supersede all previous for this project.***

   b ***This proposal will supersede the proposal dated _____ and all previous.***

   c We propose to furnish labor, material and equipment to paint the referenced project as follows:

II **Interior:**

A   Enamel areas, doors and casings; prime and one coat enamel.

A-1   Enamel areas; prime and one coat enamel.

A-2   Doors and casings; prime, split coat and one coat enamel.

A-3   Shelves and poles; prime and one coat flatwall.

B   Flatwall areas; one coat flatwall.

B-1   Flatwall areas; seal and one coat flatwall (2 coats).

C   Kitchen cabinets; stain seal and two coats lacquer.

C-1   Kitchen and bar cabinets; stain seal and two coats lacquer.

D   All cabinets to be prefinished by others.

E   Kitchen cabinets to be prefinished by others.

F   Pullmans and linens; prime and one coat enamel.

F-1   Pullmans and linens; prime, split coat and one coat enamel.

F-2   Pullmans and linens; stain and lacquer.

F-3   Pullmans, linens, doors and casings; prime, split coat and one coat enamel with final coat brushed.

G   Rough-sawn wood; one coat heavy-bodied stain.

H   Tongue-and-groove ceiling; one coat semi-transparent stain.

H-1   Tongue-and-groove ceiling; one coat heavy-bodied stain.

J   Metal railings; preprimed by others, one coat paint.

K   Base to stain.

K-1   Base to paint per walls.

K-2   Base to enamel.

L   Handrail caps; one coat stain.

L-1   Handrail caps; two coats of polyurethane.

M   Entry doors; two coats of polyurethane, both sides.

N   Figured for one basic off-white color throughout.

III **Exterior:**

A   Wood; one coat heavy-bodied stain.

A-1   Wood; one coat semi-transparent stain.

New construction proposal outline
Figure 7-4

A-2 Wood; one coat heavy-bodied stain or semi-transparent stain.

A-3 Wood; one coat clear sealer and one coat heavy-bodied stain.

A-4 Wood; two coats heavy-bodied stain.

A-5 Shingle siding; one coat clear sealer only.

A-6 Other wood; one coat heavy-bodied stain.

B Metal; preprimed by others, one coat paint.

B-1 Metal; two coats paint.

C Stucco; one coat masonry paint.

C-1 Stucco; one coat clear hydro sealer to 4'0" and 2'0" around openings.

IV **Exclusions:**
   a Stucco paint

   b Masonry

   c Fencing

   d Perimeter fencing

   e Shingle siding

   f Parking stripes

   g Light posts

   h Mailbox structures

   . . . . . are not included.

   i Split coat on pullmans, linens, doors and casings is listed as an alternate.

V **Addenda**

VI **Notes:**
   a Bid based on plans dated _____. Plan set #_____.

   b Bid based on specifications and plans dated _____. Plan set #_____.

   c Bid based on plans not dated. Plan set #_____.

VII **Prices:**
   Prices:

VIII **Expiration:**
   Prices expire _____.

New construction proposal outline
Figure 7-4 (continued)

I
RP-1   ***Scope of work to include and limited to the following:***

RP-2   Removal and replace or protect by contractor:

RP-3   Removal and replace or protect by owner:
   a   Cabinet hardware

   b   Kitchen dishes

   c   Other cabinet or closet contents

   d   Furniture to be moved at least three feet from wall

   e   Other personal property

RP-4   Preparation work to include:
   a   All preparation work as required

   b   Powerwash exterior surfaces

   c   Trim or tie back landscaping

   d   Scraping

   e   Wire brushing

   f   Patching

   g   Puttying

   h   Caulking

   i   Sanding

   j   Other

RP-5   Additional preparation work to be charged at $25.00 per hour.

II Interior Painting
A   Enamel areas, doors and casings; prime and one coat enamel.

A-1   Enamel areas; prime and one coat enamel.

A-2   Doors and casings; prime, split coat and one coat enamel.

A-3   Shelves and poles; prime and one coat flatwall.

B   Flatwall areas; one coat flatwall.

B-1   Flatwall areas; seal and one coat flatwall (2 coats).

C   Kitchen cabinets; stain seal and two coats lacquer.

C-1   Kitchen and bar cabinets; stain seal and two coats lacquer.

D   All cabinets to be prefinished by others.

E   Kitchen cabinets to be prefinished by others.

Repaint proposal outline
Figure 7-5

F   Pullmans and linens; prime and one coat enamel.

F-1   Pullmans and linens; prime, split coat and one coat enamel.

F-2   Pullmans and linens; stain and lacquer.

F-3   Pullmans, linens, doors and casings; prime, split coat and one coat enamel with final coat brushed.

G   Rough sawn wood; one coat heavy bodied stain.

H   Tongue-and-groove ceiling; one coat semi-transparent stain.

H-1   Tongue-and-groove ceiling; one coat heavy-bodied stain.

J   Metal railings; preprimed by others, one coat paint.

K   Base to stain.

K-1   Base to paint per walls.

K-2   Base to enamel.

L   Handrail caps; one coat stain.

L-1   Handrail caps; two coats of polyurethane.

M   Entry doors; two coats of polyurethane, both sides.

N   Figured for one basic off-white color throughout.

RP-6   Interior color selection(s):

III **Exterior Painting**

A   Wood; one coat heavy-bodied stain.

A-1   Wood; one coat semi-transparent stain.

A-2   Wood; one coat heavy-bodied stain or semi-transparent stain.

A-3   Wood; one coat clear sealer and one coat heavy-bodied stain.

A-4   Wood; two coats heavy-bodied stain.

A-5   Shingle siding; one coat clear sealer only.

A-6   Other wood; one coat heavy-bodied stain.

B   Metal; preprimed by others, one coat paint.

B-1   Metal; two coats paint.

C   Stucco; one coat masonry paint.

C-1   Stucco; one coat clear hydro sealer to 4'0" and 2'0" around openings.

RP-7   Exterior color selection(s):

Repaint proposal outline
Figure 7-5 (continued)

IV **Exclusions:**

- a   Stucco paint

- b   Masonry

- c   Fencing

- d   Perimeter fencing

- e   Shingle siding

- f   Parking stripes

- g   Light posts

- h   Mailbox structures

       . . . . .are not included.

- i   Split coat on pullmans, linens, doors and casings is listed as an alternate.

V **Notes:**

RP-8   Start of work will be within _____ working days from the acceptance and receipt of this agreement by the contractor.

RP-9   For the sum of: $_____

RP-10   Payment to be made as follows:

- a   30% upon arrival to the job for preparation work and material purchases. The balance:

- b   at the completion of the work.

- c   progressively as work is completed:

       _____% upon completion of interior.   _____% upon completion of exterior.

RP-11   Proposal expires within _____ days.

Repaint proposal outline
Figure 7-5 (continued)

Statement of Intent

The statement of intent serves as the introduction of the proposal. It's similar on most proposal formats: "We propose to furnish all labor, material and equipment to paint the referenced project as follows: . . . ."

The Body of the Proposal

The body of the proposal describes the scope of work, qualifications, and prices as follows:

Interior painting: All work included at the interior

Exterior painting: All work included at the exterior

Exclusions: Items of work not included in the bid

Addenda recognized: The numbers of any addenda covered in your bid

Notes: Plan set number and date, cost-saving recommendations, clarifications, corrections, and comments

Prices: Your final bid amounts

Alternate prices: If required

Option prices: If required

Expiration date: Typically 30 to 60 days

The proposal must reflect the actual requirements of the plans and specs, just the way you estimated the project.

Now let's look at each of these sections of the proposal in more detail.

Superseding proposals— After submitting the original proposal, the builder may change the plans or specs enough to require a re-bid. On any second bid, use this statement: *"This proposal will supersede all previous for this project."* Use this if more than one re-bid is required: *"This proposal will supersede the proposal dated 4-2-89 and all previous."* Either of these statements indicates to the builder that the old prices on any previous proposals have expired.

Interior and exterior painting operations— Many of the most common painting operations are listed on the repaint and new construction proposal outlines. Some of these painting operations require an explanation:

A-1:   Enamel paint is usually required on doors and casings as well as on walls and ceilings in rooms where moisture may be present. These rooms usually include kitchens, baths and utility rooms. You may hear them called *wet areas.* Sometimes enamel is also required in other rooms. A primer or sealer and one coat of enamel will be needed.

A-2:   Indicates an alternate coating, something other than a prime coat and enamel on doors and casings. In this case, both *A-1* and *A-2* may be used in place of item A.

Item *J* makes it clear that all metal is to arrive on the job site primed and installed and ready for one finish coat of paint.

Item *N* is one of the most important items on the proposal. If the proposal isn't clear about painting one off-white color throughout, the paint contractor may be forced to paint the interiors with different colors. This is time consuming and expensive if it wasn't included in the estimate.

Exclusions— List items which are not included here. Itemize the exclusions from the outline which apply, as well as other exclusions specific to the project.

Addenda— Addenda are common when bidding semi-formal or formal contract work. An addendum is an addition to the plans and specifications which serves to clarify the work. Read the addenda as soon as you receive them. Include a line in your bid that identifies the number of addenda included in your proposal: for example, "Four addenda, I, II, III and IV, are recognized."

Notes—
Plan dates and plan set number: If the estimate is taken from a set of plans, it is *essential* that the plan date be included in the proposal. This will identify the plan set used for the take-off after you've returned the plans to the builder. A typical entry on your proposal would be "Plans, dated 1-18-89, set #7." If the plans aren't dated, say "Plans not dated, set #9."

Cost-saving recommendations: Include cost-saving recommendations in your painting proposals whenever possible. It's called *value engineering* when you can make changes to achieve the same quality results the owner wants for less money. Owners and builders are always interested in saving money. These recommendations will draw attention to your professionalism and experience. An owner interested in your recommendations will probably call and ask for more information. When properly presented, value engineering recommendations can help you win more jobs.

For example, you could suggest substituting less expensive materials for the materials specified for the project. You might phrase it like this: *"Cost-saving recommendation:* By substituting XXX brand paint for the AAA paint brand specified, a deduction of $55.00 per living unit would apply."

Clarifications: Clarifications could include any exceptions, additions or changes to the plans or specifications. For example, you might include a statement like this: *"Clarification:* The size of the fascia board is not noted on plans. This bid is based on 2 x 10 fascia per phone conversation with architect on 4-18-89."

Corrections: Corrections to the plans and specifications are sometimes a touchy subject. In a competitive bid, use your judgment on whether an item should be corrected prior to the bid. Corrections before the bid may require an addendum which could delay the bid. That may give your competitors an advantage. On the other hand, the general contractor may ask selected bidders to inform the architect of these corrections. Corrections which affect the painting bid should be identified as an addition or a deduction to the base price. A correction on a proposal might read: *"Correction:* The drawings reflect a mixture of 2 x 6 and 2 x 10 fascia with the majority of 2 x 10 material. *Add* $25.00 per living unit for painting 2 x 10 fascia in place of 2 x 6 fascia as indicated on the plans."

Comments: Use this heading to pass on relevant observations and information to the general contractor. Here's a comment you might make to explain why you've extended your expiration date: *"Comment:* Due to the fact that your work has been delayed by wet weather, bid prices are extended to 7-18-89."

All of these qualifying categories won't be required for every project, of course. You'll probably need some notes to qualify the scope of the bid. But keep them concise and to the point.

Prices— Prices are the most important figures in the proposal. Be sure prices are copied correctly from the recap sheet to the rough draft, and from the rough draft to the typed proposal. Both you and your typist should proofread all proposals before they leave your office.

An error in copying or typing can be both embarrassing and expensive if the proposal is accepted.

Alternate and option prices— Submit alternate and option prices if they're requested in the bid instructions or on the plans. These prices are typically lump sum amounts.

An *alternate* might be requested for using various colors on the interior of a home rather than a single off-white throughout. You could also be asked to quote an alternate price for painting a second coat.

An *option* might be for an addition to the plans. For example, the home buyer might want to make two bedrooms out of one large playroom by adding a dividing wall and closets. Architects will often design-in these options. The owners will make their decision sometime before framing is complete. The price for painting this option would apply only if the homebuyer chooses the option.

You may want to include an *allowance* in the proposal. Sometimes the paint required isn't identified when you bid the project. For example, an owner with exotic tastes may not have decided on the paint color or paint brand for the project. In this case, base your estimate on a set limit (preferably high) for the cost of material: "Material allowance for paint not to exceed $15.00 per gallon including tax." If wallcovering is required, a material allowance will almost certainly be specified.

When plans are incomplete or still in the preliminary design stages, add a *contingency allowance* — say 3% to 10% — to cover any uncertainty about the work to be done. When complete plans and specifications are not available, assume that any details missing will increase your cost.

Expiration Date— Your bid is a legal offer, open for acceptance for a *reasonable time* unless you specify an expiration date. If you don't name an expiration date, don't be surprised if your proposal is accepted six months or a year after your bid is submitted (and both material and labor costs have increased). Set an expiration date for your bid. Discuss the price expiration date in your initial conversation with the owner or general contractor. If they've determined a painting start date and completion date, you can calculate an expiration date which will allow the owner or general contractor enough time to award and execute a contract for the painting work. Identify that date on the face of your proposal.

Be aware of projected labor and material increases when setting price expiration dates. Will higher labor rates go into effect before the job is completed?

If labor and material rates are expected to increase around the time when painting will begin, you might submit two sets of bid prices with different expiration dates. See Figure 7-6. Submitting two sets of prices protects you, of course. But it also may be good sales strategy. It gives the owner or general contractor a choice between two prices. Of course, he prefers the lower cost. It can help nudge the builder into awarding the contract before the first expiration date.

The life of the proposal will depend on the size of the project and the stability of your labor and material prices. I suggest expiration periods no longer than 10 days for repaint projects, 30 days for new construction projects up to four units, and 60 days for new construction of five or more units. If you're submitting two sets of prices because of labor or material cost increases, don't go beyond 30 and 90 days for the two sets of prices.

Prices	Expiration dates	
	3-31-89	6-30-89
Plan 1		
A	$700.00	$750.00
B	750.00	775.00
C	800.00	825.00
Plan 2		
A	$770.00	$810.00
B	835.00	860.00
C	910.00	940.00
C option 1 - add	75.00	100.00
Plan 3		
A	$810.00	$850.00
B	790.00	825.00
C	875.00	915.00
Plan 4		
A	$860.00	$895.00
B	895.00	930.00
C	930.00	955.00

Bid prices for two expiration dates
Figure 7-6

Your bid should expire in 90 days, at the longest. Otherwise you're guaranteeing that prices will not increase. That's usually bad business.

The signature lines— Sign on the signature line before submitting the proposal. This verifies and validates your commitment to do the job at the prices quoted. With your signature, you assume full responsibility for the content of the proposal. Make sure it's correct.

For a repaint project, the owner will usually be the person who accepts or rejects your proposal. When accepted, it becomes a binding contract. It's rare for a general contractor to sign your proposal. But your bid price will set the contract amount.

Bidding Tips
1) Base your bids on plans and specifications. Give a firm price for what is clear and certain on the plans.

2) Always *qualify your bid,* especially when you're bidding for a marginal contractor or a semiprofessional owner-builder. Even experienced professional contractors you haven't done business with before might throw you a curve if you don't qualify your bid.

3) Include all items which are called out on the plans and exclude items which are not specified.

4) Always describe which items are *included* and the items which are *excluded* in your bid.

5) List alternate costs for those items which are not on the plans or in the specifications but may be required to complete the job.

6) Know your bottom line. Don't go below the minimum amount you can bid and still make a profit. (Your cost records will tell you what that amount should be.) Don't try to underbid cutthroat competitors who don't do professional work or who don't know how to bid to make a profit. Don't worry about missing out on no-profit jobs. Low-ball painters who do that type of work will go belly-up soon enough. There's lots of work out there — in every neighborhood. You just have to define your niche and go after it.

7) Finally, sleep on it. This applies to every major decision. Whenever you're in doubt about a decision, sleep on it. After a good night's rest, your head will be clear and you will have had time to evaluate the pros and cons.

Bid Bonds

On some jobs you'll have to submit a bid bond with the bid. This bond is a guarantee by an insurance company that you'll enter into a contract at the bid price if your proposal is accepted. Bid bonds may be required on larger jobs.

Selling the Bid

On public projects, the law usually requires that the job be awarded to the lowest qualified bidder. There isn't much you can do to influence the award of the job. But when you're submitting a bid on a private job, there's nothing wrong with delivering a sales presentation along with your bid. I'll discuss that in detail in the next chapter.

Chapter 8

SALES AND CLOSING

Most paint estimators have to do more than just figure labor and material cost. They have to make sure their time isn't wasted — by influencing the buyer to accept each bid that's been prepared. I call that *selling*. You may know it under a different name. But everyone can agree that it's an important part of the job for most paint estimators.

There are many ways to sell a paint job. Submitting the lowest bid is only one of those ways — and probably a poor way to get the most profitable work. The sales technique you use depends on the situation. For example, your sales presentation on a residential repaint to a homeowner will be very different from your approach to a general contractor who's doing a 50-home development. In this chapter, we'll look at both kinds of selling. We'll begin with the presentation to the general contractor. But first, I want to focus on the *words* you use to clinch the job.

Sales Language: The Right Words

It's important to use the right words when making a sales presentation. In normal conversation, we use a familiar vocabulary that's the product of our environment: childhood, family, friends and co-workers. To become more successful in sales, however, you need a specialized vocabulary that identifies you as a professional in the field. Here are some examples of *right* and *wrong* words when you're closing a sale.

Contract. Don't use it. Many people are afraid of the word. Contracts are for lawyers and courts. Your prospect wants nothing to do with either. Instead, use *agreement* or *paperwork*.

Sign. Did your mother ever tell you not to sign anything? A demand for a signature will always meet resistance, blocking the sale. Instead of asking for a signature, ask your prospect to *approve, authorize, endorse* or *O.K.* your agreement.

Extra. No builder likes to hear about extras — it's a dirty word. Use *additional cost* or *added value* instead.

Buy. People would rather *own* than buy.

Deal. Deals are for car salesmen. Professionals offer their customers *opportunities*.

Pitch. Circus barkers give pitches. Professionals give *presentations*.

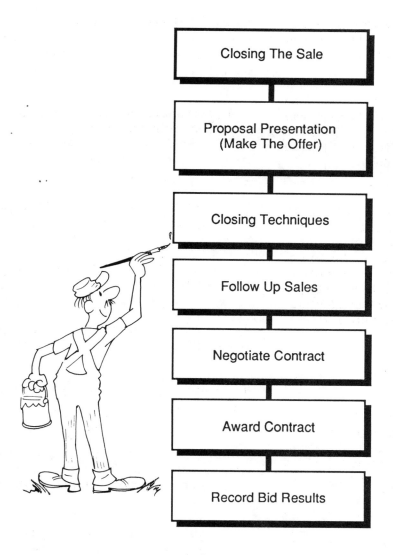

Closing the sale
Figure 8-1

The Sales Presentation

After the project proposal has been typed, proofread and triple checked, it's ready to submit to the general contractor. As indicated in the flow chart (Figure 8-1), closing the sale begins with the proposal presentation. So put on your salesman's hat — it's time to secure the contract.

You can deliver your bid proposal to the owner or general contractor by telephone, by mail, or in person. Many general contractors will want you to telephone in your prices and submit a written proposal by mail. Others will allow you to set an appointment and deliver the proposal in person. That's a sales opportunity.

Setting the Appointment

Set up an appointment with the general contractor. Ask for a few minutes to review the proposal and return the plans.

Setting an appointment may seem like a simple order. When a homeowner is requesting a repaint, it *is* simple. But the buyer for a general contractor may be very busy, having three to four bids for each of forty trades to consider for each project. It may take some planning to get in the door. But don't be pushy. There are few things worse than a pushy salesman. Just ask a busy buyer who avoids them like the plague.

Whether you're seeing a homeowner or a general contractor, there are a couple of techniques you can use for setting the appointment.

1) Make sure your appointment is with the authorized buyer for the project, *the person who writes the check.* An appointment with anyone else is a waste of time unless the buyer is so busy that an assistant is assigned to receive all bids.

2) Use the *alternate of choice* closing technique to set the time for the appointment. Give the customer only two choices. He or she must pick one of the two, or give you an objection. For example, it's hard to refuse an appointment when you're offered this series of choices: Would an appointment on Tuesday or Wednesday be better? Which would you prefer, morning or afternoon? What is best for you, 2 p.m. or 4 p.m.?

Making the Presentation

A good presentation will tell the customer three things: Who you are, what you've done, and what you will do for them. Whether you're making your presentation to a general contractor or a homeowner, your objectives are the same. You want to accomplish these four steps:

1) *Introduction:* Introduce yourself and your company. *Break the ice.*

2) *Benefits:* Demonstrate your product knowledge and experience. Convince the owner or builder that your painting company is capable of doing quality work and on time. Identify the benefits of doing business with your company.

3) *Objections:* Uncover and resolve all of your prospect's objections, including anything that delays awarding the contract to you.

4) *Closing:* The ultimate objective of any sales presentation is to close the sale and secure the agreement.

Using visual aids— You can use visual aids in a presentation to a general contractor, but it'll have a greater impact on the homeowner. General contractors are more concerned with price than visual aids.

A presentation binder (the same one you use to carry your estimating forms) will help you present the visual aids in sequence. Here's the most effective order of presentation:

1) A letter of introduction which describes the company goals and objectives.

2) A list of the benefits of doing business with your company.

3) Photographs of your work enclosed in plastic covers. Before and after shots are best.

4) A photograph of your office staff, your crews, your shop and your equipment.

5) A list of references (general contractors or homeowners, whichever is appropriate), who can verify your quality and on-time performance.

6) Testimonial letters from satisfied customers confirming their satisfaction and pointing out reasons to use your company. Be sure to get permission from your previous customers to use their testimonial letters in your presentation. Some will get calls from prospects who want to verify their satisfaction with your service.

Body language— Here's a point to bear in mind. Human beings are influenced only through one of the senses: sight, hearing, taste, smell or touch. When an impression is made on one of the senses, there's a reaction that may be expressed in the face, hands, eyes, shoulders, or other parts of the body. These reactions, commonly referred to as body language, indicate what's going on in the prospect's mind. They help you pace the presentation for maximum impact.

Get the prospect's senses involved with the presentation and observe their reactions to produce better closing results.

Presentation techniques— Here are some tips for making an effective presentation:

• You must know what is on each page in your visual aid binder.

• Keep your presentation binder in good condition.

• Use a pen, pencil or your finger to direct attention to the binder.

• Maintain eye contact. If you look at them, they'll look at you.

• Place yourself so you can watch the prospect's reactions.

• Speak in terms the prospect can understand. Avoid frequent use of trade phrases which may not be clear to your prospect. Make your presentation at the client's level.

• Use questions to keep the prospect involved and to maintain control of your presentation.

• Your presentation should be well organized, concise, to the point, and tailor-made for the homeowner or general contractor.

Emphasize the Benefits

Here's one of the primary points you must get across to sell your prospect: Why should the customer choose your painting company over the competition? Why is *your* company the best for the job?

Your letter of introduction has already summarized the benefits of doing business with your company. Point them out again and add some more. These benefits, as they apply to your company, can be strong presentation points:

• Large available labor force

• Competent management staff

• Conscientious and efficient crews

• Our prices are competitive

• We suggest ways to save time and money

• Can handle many projects simultaneously

• Radio-equipped supervision vehicles

• Superintendent visits each job daily

• Our craftsmen apply the "extra touch"

• Our in-depth knowledge of the market

• Work cooperatively with other trades

• Commitment to customer satisfaction

Summarizing these benefits will impress most customers, whether they're homeowners or general contractors. Address any problems and difficulties the general contractor is having by providing logical solutions. Finally, review the quality of work produced by your company. Present your references — including suppliers who can verify your on-time payment history and subcontractors of other trades who can vouch for your cooperative attitude on the job — as well as the general contractors or homeowners on your reference list.

Answer the Objections

Your salesmanship begins when the customer objects, or says no. Here's an important point to remember: Objections are just honest doubts about points which are not clear. Objections usually take the form of questions. Questions indicate interest and a need for more complete information. Present this information in the form of facts, figures and truths which neutralize or satisfy the objections so the sale can be closed.

The best way to overcome objections is to anticipate them whenever possible and have a logical response for each. There's a six-step process to answering objections:

1) *Hear them out.* "I'm concerned with quality."

2) *Feed it back.* "So you're concerned with quality."

3) *Question the objection.* "Are you sure that quality is your main concern?"

Objections are just honest doubts about points which are not clear

4) *Answer the objection.* "If we can guarantee your satisfaction with our workmanship, are you ready to accept our proposal? Let me show you some photographs and testimonial letters which will show you the quality of our work."

5) *Confirm the answer.* "Then you'll authorize the proposal today if we can guarantee your satisfaction with the quality of our work? Well, that settles that."

6) *By the way* . . . The final step is to change the subject by saying "By the way." Then continue with your presentation.

During your presentation, completely answer each of the customer's objections so there's no reason not to purchase your painting services. Identify the reasons for any hesitation or doubt which you detect during the presentation. Welcome objections because they mean you're a step closer to answering all their questions and solving their problem.

Realizing a customer may have many objections, you must isolate each one and work on it until it's resolved. Then try to draw out the next objection and work on it until *all* objections are answered.

Typical objections, with responses, might go something like this:

Objection— How do we know you're reliable, will produce quality work and will complete the painting work on time?

Response— Just call any of our references and they'll verify our reliability, quality and scheduling efficiency. If any of them say they weren't satisfied for any reason, let me know and I'll correct the problem immediately. We take pride in customer satisfaction. Our main source of business is from referrals from our satisfied customers.

Objection— I want to think about it.

Response— Just what is it you want to think about? Is it the way I've presented myself? (No.) Is it the reputation of the company? (No.) Is it the quality you feel we can give you? (This answer should be no if you've given a convincing presentation.) Is it the price? (*Yes* — it's always the price, but save this price comment for the last question in the sequence).

Objection— Your price is too high. (In all my experience, only once have I heard "your price is too low, you'd better check your figures and call me back." You're much more likely to hear about high prices than low ones. In fact, it's the most popular objection of all.)

Responses—

- Our price is in line with the quality of work we produce.

- You get what you pay for.

- How high is it?

That last one is the best response because the purchasing agent or owner may tell you where your price must be to get the job.

Objection— I'm satisfied with my present painter. (You may hear this from a general contractor.)

Response— (History readback) Did you have another painter before this one that you're satisfied with? (Yes.) Were you happy when you made the change from the old painter to your present painter? (Yes.) If you received satisfaction from the previous change, why don't you give yourself the chance to find even greater satisfaction by making another change to our painting company?

This is a rather complicated response, so rehearse the history readback before you try it on a customer.

Summary

First, summarize the benefits by reviewing your major presentation points. Second, answer the general contractor or homeowner's questions and final objections. Finally, emphasize the importance of time and the costs of financing. Of course, the builders and owners are well aware of this, but a brief reminder might instill urgency in their decision to award the painting contract, hopefully to your company.

Closing the Sale

Closing is the process of helping people make decisions that are good for them. Homeowners are typically more easily sold (or *closed*) than are general contractors. Homeowners' decisions are more likely to be based on emotions. General contractors tend to make their decisions on a more logical basis, because of their experience and knowledge. Their main concern is your price and a verification of your quality. But closing a sale to homeowners *or* builders depends on solving their problems.

Solve the Customer's Problems

The essence of closing the sale involves solving the customer's problems. If you can provide faster,

more efficient service at less cost than the competition, you have a good chance of winning the contract. Before starting your close, make sure you've answered all of the customer's objections and provided solutions for all of his painting problems. Tie up all loose ends so the customer will have every reason to award the contract to your company.

If you try a closing sequence in your presentation and it doesn't work, don't be disappointed or discouraged. Closing may require many tries before it's successful. Try using a technique called the *test close* to determine if the customer is ready to buy.

Questions are a primary tool for selling. Asking open-ended questions which can be answered with either a *yes* or a *no* will let you know if your customer is close to a buying decision. Find out which questions the customer answers with a *yes* so you can ask the same questions again in the closing sequence when you're "looking for those yesses."

Test closes are questions that, when answered, show the prospect's high interest. When the wants and needs of the customer are defined and the interest is high, you can begin the closing sequence.

The Closing Sequence

There are usually six steps in the closing sequence:

1) Benefit summary

2) Ask questions which you know have a "yes" answer.

3) Close. "Let me write up a proposal for $1,200.00 for the work we've discussed. You can approve it now and I'll schedule the painting of your home for this week. That sounds good, doesn't it?"

4) Resolve objections

5) Question again for a *yes*.

6) Close. Ask the customer again to authorize the agreement. If necessary, repeat steps 4, 5 and 6 until the agreement is approved. You can expect several attempts before the customer gives the final *yes*. If you don't succeed, don't be discouraged. You won't be able to close them all on the spot, so review the proposal and contract with the customer and follow up in a couple of days. Don't leave a copy of the proposal. If you do, the customer may use it to shop for a better price from another painter.

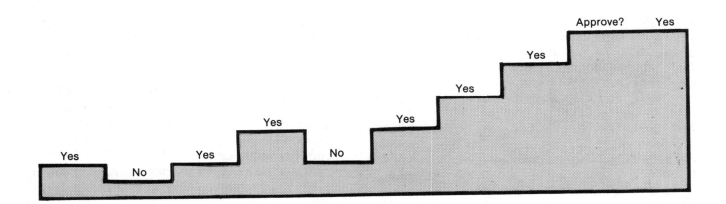

The yes ladder
Figure 8-2

Here's an important tip to remember: After you ask the closing question, *shut up!* Don't say a word after you ask for authorization of the proposal or agreement. Just hand the prospect the pen and the agreement, and sit silently. Put the ball in their court. Make them speak first, no matter how much silent time elapses. There's a theory in sales that goes like this: Whoever speaks first after the closing question is asked, loses.

Closing Techniques

Yesses— Here's another sales theory: The more *yesses* you can get from the prospect, the closer they are to saying *yes* when you close the sale. How do you get them to say yes? Simple! Just ask questions which you know will result in a yes answer. I call this closing sequence the *yes ladder*. Look at Figure 8-2.

Tie-downs— The tie-down is a technique which actually *ties down* the customer, requiring a yes answer to your carefully worded question. Some tie-down phrases are:

Isn't it?	Won't you?
Isn't that right?	Shouldn't it?
Didn't it?	Wouldn't it?
Don't you agree?	Wasn't it?
Doesn't it?	Haven't they?
Don't you?	Can't you?
Aren't they?	Won't they?

Here are some examples: "It would be nice to have a freshly painted house, wouldn't it?" . . . "You know that painting costs have been going up, don't you?" . . . "A good job in preparing the surface is important, isn't it?" . . . "You do want a quality paint job, don't you?" . . . "You'd like to work with a well established, reputable company, wouldn't you?"

Use these tie-down phrases at the end of a sentence, as shown, or at the beginning or in the middle of the sentence. Vary the form of the question so you're not too obvious. And practice the phrases so they come out smoothly during your presentation.

Hot potato— Answer a question with a question. Imagine trying to hold a potato that's much too hot to handle. You and another person toss it back and forth, since neither of you can hold it for long. In the same way, when your prospect asks a question, answer by tossing a question back in response. For example:

Question: "Can I have the bedroom painted blue?"

Response: "Is blue the color you want in the bedroom?"

The obvious answer here is a yes, and with that yes, you're a step closer to closing the sale. These question responses will allow you to maintain control of the presentation and lead the prospect to your next closing question.

Alternate of choice— If you give your prospects two choices, there are only three ways they can respond: They can pick one of the two, tell you what they want instead, or give you an objection. In any case, their response to the *alternate of choice* question leads you a step closer to closing the sale.

Involvement questions— Those are questions your prospects might ask themselves after their home is painted. To get the customer involved, you might combine a tie-down and an involvement question. For example: ''Won't it be nice to have your home freshly painted and spotless again?'' This will make your prospect visualize their pleasure after you've painted their house.

If the prospect asks the question before you do, they're indicating that they're serious about going ahead with the decision to paint their house. For example, the homeowner might say, ''It sure will be nice living in a freshly painted, spotless house again.'' In either case, make sure your prospect is involved with the image of how nice his house will look after you paint it.

Urgency— An expiration date on a proposal can serve as a sales tool. It implies urgency, perhaps spurring the general contractor to make a decision soon. To create urgency with a homeowner, you can suggest that prices will be going up soon. This method is sometimes overused, so take it easy. But it can be effective when it's used in appropriate situations.

Higher authority— If you're faced with a question you can't answer (typically about lowering the price), tell the prospect you'll have to get approval from the boss or supervisor, so you'll get back to them with an answer. This lets you off the hook and still allows you to be the good guy.

The ''if — then'' close— If we can give you the quality you want, then will you authorize the agreement?

Similar situation— When a prospect brings up an objection or problem which is similar to one you have previously overcome, tell them about that similar situation. For example: ''Last week we painted a house for a customer who had a question about quality. When we finished the job, they were completely satisfied. You'd like to be satisfied, too, wouldn't you?''

Testimonials— Reference lists and testimonial letters are closes in themselves. All owners and general contractors understand their value. They verify your claims of expertise.

Follow-Up Sales

If you don't make the sale on the spot, you'll have to follow up and try again later. After the bid has been presented to the homeowner or general contractor, file a copy of the bid package in an *active file*. The bid package includes all the bid documents and estimating paperwork, stapled together with the typed proposal on top. Use the active file for reference when you're making your follow-up calls.

Once a week, or as requested by your prospect, call all the names in your active file to see if they're closer to making a decision. I tell every prospect that I'll call them periodically to check the status of the contract award. With each call I probe for information on where we stand and how we can get the job.

Your follow-up calls might begin by asking if the prospect has any questions about your bid. Hopefully, this will make him pull your bid out and take a look at it. Remember, the more your prospect hears and sees your company name, the more familiar he'll become with you, and the better chance you have of winning the job. After you've found out the status of the bid evaluation process, ask when to check back again.

Keep notes on these follow-up calls, both on the cover sheet of the proposal and on the master Recordplate slip.

Contract Negotiations

It's common practice for a general contractor to seek competitive bids from several subcontractors in each trade. Ideally, several subcontractors will submit bids for painting a project, and your company, as low qualified bidder, will be awarded the contract. But it's usually not that simple. After selecting the low qualified bidder, the general contractor may try to bargain to reach an agreement on a reduced price. He'll call it *negotiating the contract* to match the amount he has budgeted.

This practice may sometimes be justified, if the general contractor has bid too low in a competitive bidding situation. He might ask the subcontractors to help him make the job break even. Of course, this doesn't mean you *have* to negotiate and lower your price — but you may not be awarded the contract if you don't.

Occasionally, a general contractor might try to make all trades lower their price just to make more profit for himself. He may be looking for subcontractors who are so hungry for work that they'll take a job at no profit just to stay in business. Stay away from operators like this. This practice is unethical and can only lead to trouble. The subcontractor who takes a contract which was negotiated to a lower price will usually do lower quality workmanship, such as crooked studs by the framer or poor taping by the drywall subcontractor. This can make your painting work appear shoddy, when it's not. It doesn't take many of these to ruin your reputation. Usually, one is enough.

Contract Award

If the contract is awarded to a competitor, file the bid package away in a *dead bid* file which is alphabetically organized by prospect name. Be sure to keep these dead bids for future reference. They'll come in handy when you're producing future estimates for the same prospect, especially if they're using the same tract home or apartment building floor plans.

On the other hand, if you win the contract award, the typical reaction is to immediately review the bid to make sure you didn't leave anything out. But if you've followed a systematic estimating process, you should never find yourself in a panic situation. In any case, you'll want to get a set of plans and specs to review your bid before the work is scheduled.

Record the Bid Results

When you lose out on a bid, try to find out the name of the successful bidder and the percentage difference between your bid and the bid that won the job. Use this information to fill out a competitor analysis chart like the one in Chapter 7.

If you're the successful bidder, record the difference between your bid and the second and third bids. That difference is called the *spread* or *money left on the table*. The objective of the painting estimator is to reduce the spread to as little as possible. This isn't an easy task, unless you know the bid amounts of the competition.

You don't want to leave a lot of money on the table, but it's more important to submit a bid you can live with and get a profitable job. Know your bottom line and submit your best bid the first time.

Chapter 9

CONTRACT ADMINISTRATION

In a larger painting company, the estimator is usually a specialist, spending most of the time compiling estimates. In a small painting company, the person doing the estimating will have many other responsibilities: administering contracts, running jobs as a project manager, and, in the smallest companies, even running the entire company.

Figure 9-1 shows the functions that fit under the broad heading *Contracting Administration*. Notice that Figure 9-1 is divided into two parts. The top half is contract administration. That's the work you're probably most familiar with. The second part is financial management. Notice the subheadings listed under each of these major divisions.

In this chapter, I'll cover contract administration in depth and offer only a brief look at financial management. In most companies, financial management is done in the bookkeeping or accounting department. Usually, the estimator's only responsibility in the area of financial management is to make sure that the information needed is available when required.

The Contract

Your contract or agreement with an owner or general contractor will usually be written. I strongly recommend having a written contract for all of the work you do, even though verbal contracts are usually enforceable.

In construction contracting, the contract usually consists of a written offer or proposal to perform the work described for a set sum. When the offer is accepted, a contract is formed.

Contract Categories

The prime contract— A prime or primary contract is the main contract written for a project or a portion of a project. Your company would be the prime contractor on a repaint project where there's no general contractor.

The subcontract— A subcontract is an agreement written by a general or prime contractor and issued to a trade contractor to do part of the work required under a prime contract. On many jobs you're the subcontractor to a general contractor. A wallcovering contractor might be your subcontractor on a job where you're a subcontractor to the general contractor.

Types of Contract Forms

Here's an important fact to keep in mind about contract documents: Generally speaking, the party

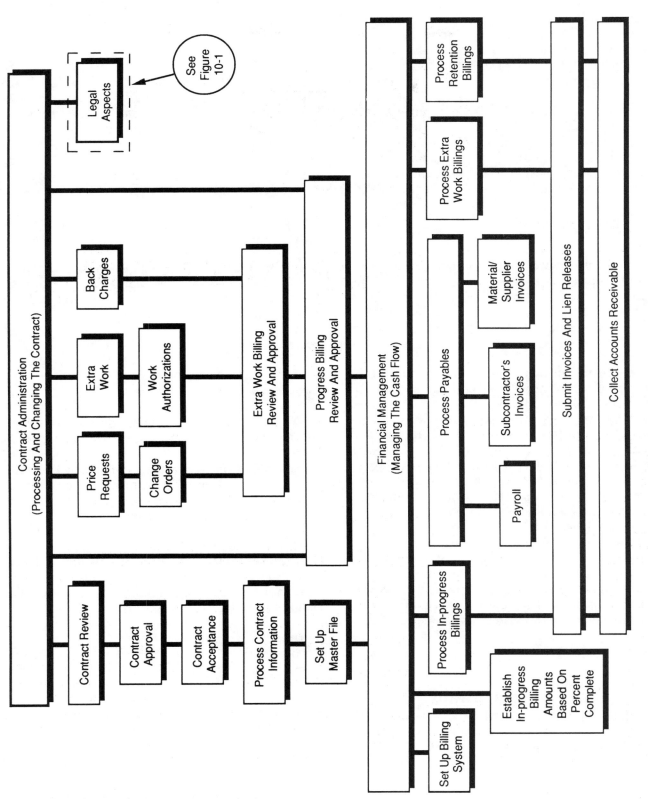

Contract administration and financial management
Figure 9-1

that writes the contract has the advantage. The wording in the document will favor the writer, and include all the terms and conditions the writer wants. That's why builders almost always write their own contracts. They'll rarely accept the subcontractor's proposal.

The proposal/contract— When a painting contractor is doing repaints for homeowners, the *proposal* will usually serve as a contract. The painting contractor writes a proposal that describes the scope of the work, including all inclusions, exclusions, and qualifications. When the proposal is accepted and signed by the homeowner, it becomes the contract. I've included a sample proposal/contract form for repaint work in Chapter 18.

Basic purchase orders— Some government contracts require periodic work on a project where the quantity and the timing of the work isn't established. Instead of issuing a contract, the agency may issue a basic purchase order (BPO) to a low bidder on a time and material or a cost plus basis.

Standard form contracts— Most construction contracts you'll receive from a general contractor will be a standard form contract. Three of the more popular construction contracts are published by the Building Industry Association (BIA), the Associated General Contractors (AGC), and the American Institute of Architects (AIA). All three are generally accepted within the industry. If you're interested in reviewing any of these contract forms, contact the local association in your area.

Non-standard contracts— Many construction contracts are drawn up by an attorney for an owner or general contractor. Examine these contracts very carefully. They may or may not be fair. Non-standard contracts are usually drafted to give a special advantage to the writer. These contracts can be much more one-sided than the standard contract.

The Contract Award

Contracts may be awarded by negotiation, by competitive bid, or by a combination of the two. Let's look briefly at various methods of awarding contracts:

Negotiated contracts— In this case, a proposal is submitted and evaluated by an individual owner. The scope of work is agreed on and a final price,

equitable to both parties, is negotiated between the owner and the contractor. This type of contract award is common in the repaint business where the owner is getting only one or two bids.

Negotiated with low competitive bidder— An owner or general contractor will select the most competitive bid, then negotiate the final scope of work and the contract amount with this low qualified bidder. This is common in residential construction purchasing. It's an *informal bidding process*, and may involve favoritism toward the current painting contractor.

Published competitive bids— This is a competitive bid submitted to an owner or general contractor, who has the option of qualifying the bidders before selecting the winning bid. This method is common in the commercial, industrial, and institutional contracting business. It's a *semi-formal bidding process,* and there's usually no favoritism shown.

Sealed competitive bid— This is a competitive bid which is usually submitted on standardized bid forms in sealed envelopes to an architect or government agency. The bid envelopes are all opened at the same time and the apparent low bidder is announced at the time of the opening. This bid is then checked to be sure that all contract requirements are met. This *formal bidding process* is common on government contracts.

Notification of Contract Award

When you win a competitive bid, you'd better review the estimate right away to be sure nothing was left out. But after the excitement is over, it's time to review the contract documents completely and thoroughly and compare them with your estimate.

Verbal Notification

An owner or general contractor will generally call to relay the news that you've won the bid. They may want you on the job as soon as possible. But be careful. No contractor should go to work on a job without a signed agreement. Although a verbal agreement may be legally binding, it can boil down to your word against theirs in a court of law.

Many painting contractors won't move on a job until the written contract has been signed by both parties. I think that's a good idea. If the owner or general contractor insists that you begin work before the contract is issued, have them sign your proposal or issue a *letter of intent*. That covers you with a written authorization until the contract is written and executed by both parties.

Letter of Intent

The letter of intent is a pledge to enter a contract at some future date. The letter of intent should include:

- A description of the project

- The contract amount

- A description of the work or a reference to the work as defined in your proposal

- A reference to the payment method, usually "to be paid progressively upon completion of the work"

- A time limit for the contract to be delivered

Contract Pricing Methods

There are several ways to price work done under a contract:

Lump sum method— This method is used when all work is well defined. Payments under lump sum agreements are usually progressive, based on a percentage of the work completed within a given time period. Agreements based on lump sum pricing may be negotiated or competitively bid. This is the most common pricing method in building construction.

Unit price method— Unit pricing is common when the quantity or amount of work is hard to determine in advance. Payments for unit price agreements are based on a set price for each unit of work completed. For example, if a painting contractor finished 1,000 square feet of fencing before the billing deadline at a unit of $.35 per square foot, the bill would be for $350.00.

Agreements based on unit pricing can be competitively bid or negotiated. Unit prices are often used with a variety of contract payment methods, including cost plus, time and material, and time and equipment.

Cost plus: Unit prices for labor, material, and equipment are the basis for cost plus agreements. A cost plus contract is used when it's hard to define the scope of work in advance. The plans may be in-

complete, for example, or if there's been a fire, the amount of damage may not be apparent until the work begins. The *plus* is an allowance for overhead and profit, which may be a percentage of costs or a fixed sum. These contracts are typically negotiated.

A guaranteed maximum price can be set when the cost plus contract is used. If the painting contractor has done similar projects and knows the costs involved, he can guarantee the owner that the cost won't exceed a predetermined maximum amount. As an incentive to complete the work on time, the painting contractor will usually share in any cost savings if the actual costs come in under the ceiling set in the contract.

Time and material: Unit prices are used to establish time and material contracts. When a fixed fee isn't possible because you can't provide a detailed estimate, the customer may agree to pay for all labor at a predetermined hourly rate and for all materials at cost. Then a percentage of markup is added to cover overhead and profit.

The painting contractor will usually specify one hourly rate which includes time and material with markup. That rate is calculated using the average journeyman's wage including the employer's burden. Material cost is calculated based on the quantity of material used for the particular application method. To find the time and material rate, sometimes called the *shop rate*, just calculate the labor and material costs, then add the overhead and profit percentage.

A painting contractor might use a time and material cost for the model homes in a residential development. Since it's impossible to predict ahead of time what the decorators will do, the T&M contract offers a perfect solution. A T&M contract might also be used where a general contractor issues a change order for a small amount of work which needs to be completed quickly. The time required to do the work would be recorded on a work authorization (Figure 9-2) or a time card, and approved by the general contractor's superintendent on a daily basis until the work is completed.

In the repaint business, the T&M payment method might be used if a homeowner wants to direct, supervise, or inspect the job. With this homeowner involvement, it's hard to estimate the labor hours that will be required. But my advice is to avoid time and material price quotes for repaint work. Few homeowners understand the painting business. Contracts for residential painting based on time and material costs can end in a dispute.

WORK AUTHORIZATION

To: _JOHN DOE CONSTRUCTION_ From _QUALITY PAINTING & DECORATING_

Address _797 FIFTH AVENUE_

YOURTOWN, USA 77777

Job Number _87-29A_   Date _5/28/89_

Job Location _PRAIRIE MOUND WAY_

Nature of Work _REPAINT SIDING AT LOTS 37,_

38 + 39 BECAUSE OF PLASTER STAINS.

TIME & MATERIAL BASIS @ 26ºº/HR + 12ºº/GAL.

APPROXIMATE COST 95ºº × 3 EA. = $285.ºº

Written by _Russ Johnson_ _____ for

Supervisor or Foreman

John Doe _____   _5/28/89_

Authorized Signature for General Contractor   Date

Work authorization
Figure 9-2

Time and equipment: This pricing method is very similar to the time and material method. Charge for time and equipment when an owner has the material and wants the painting contractor to provide only labor and equipment. In this case, the estimator would set an hourly rate for labor with the spray rig — along with markup for overhead and profit, of course.

The Contract Review

General contractors sometimes accuse subcontractors of not reading the contract carefully. It's important to review the details in every contract to be sure you understand and approve of what you're asked to sign. Once you've read through several contracts, it's easier to understand the language used. Even though the vocabulary and terminology are unfamiliar, keep reading until you understand every clause. Understanding what your contracts require can save you a bundle of cash over the years.

The estimator is the likely candidate to review the contract, since he's most familiar with the scope of work and pricing in the proposal. The most important sections of a contract are the scope of work, the contract sum, and the payment schedule. With the proposal and the quantity survey in hand and the plans and specifications available for ready reference, begin your contract review. Concentrate on these most important sections first.

Scope of Work
The contract scope of work should be consistent with the work items included in your bid proposal. Be sure the general contractor didn't slip anything into the job without your knowledge.

Figure 9-3 shows a typical sample scope of work section for an apartment project. It will give you an idea of what the general contractor might require.

Contract Sum
Always confirm the accuracy of the contract sum. The prices on the contract must add up to the total you had on your bid proposal or the negotiated amount. If there's a discrepancy between the proposal amount and the contract amount, make sure it's corrected before you start work. But before calling the general contractor, be sure to double-check your figures. What seems to be a discrepancy may just be another way of expressing the correct contract amount.

Payment Schedule
Contract payments are usually made as the work progresses, based on the percentage of work completed within a given pay period.

Progressive payments on a lump sum contract— Payments are usually scheduled when key milestones are completed. You can request adjustments if the percentages seem unreasonable. Columns A, B, and C below show three of the most common payment schedules for housing tracts.

Case	A	B	C
Billing Payments			
Progressive	90%	90%	90%
Retension	10%	10%	10%
Payment Schedule			
Exterior prime	20%	15%	20%
Exterior finish	20%	15%	25%
Interior prime	25%	30%	25%
Interior finish	25%	30%	20%
Touchup	10%	10%	10%

Be sure to check the billing cycle to make sure it's not longer than one month. If you can get away with it, *front-load* the payment schedule so the larger payments are made at the beginning of the job. Front-loading gives a boost to your cash flow.

Progressive payments on a unit price contract— Payments are made as the work is completed, based on your unit prices. For example, a painting contractor might enter into an agreement with a state highway department to paint all railings on freeway overpass bridges for one year for $1.50 per lineal foot, with a minimum production of 200 lineal feet per day. The painting contractor receives work orders as the work is authorized, and bills as each work authorization is completed or on a monthly basis, according to the terms of the contract.

Progressive payments on a cost plus contract— Payment on a cost plus contract would be based on:

Labor:	Certified payroll
Material:	Receipted bills
Equipment:	Prearranged schedule of equipment costs
Overhead and profit:	A prearranged percentage

Scope of work to include but not necessarily limited to the following:

I. Interior Operations

A) Wet area walls and ceiling at all units, public restrooms and laundry room
   1. One coat sealer - spray application is acceptable
   2. One coat enamel - rolled
B) Enamel at all interior window sills
C) Roll one coat flat latex to cover at:
   Unit living area and rental office walls
   (ceilings at these areas to receive acoustic texture by others)
   Unit storage rooms, pool equipment and maintenance room walls and ceilings
D) No finish at walls or ceilings in electric meter room or water heater closets
E) Shelves, poles and linen at plan "B" to paint. Shelves in linen at plan "C" to be prefinished.
F) All entry, storage and passage doors, casings and trim:
   1. Sand, caulk and putty
   2. One coat undercoat - spray application acceptable
   3. One coat enamel - rolled with stipple finish
   4. All doors painted six sides with additional coverage at areas exposed to weather
G) Cabinets at kitchen, pullmans and linen at plan "C" to be prefinished, linen at plan "B" to paint
H) Baseboard to stain
I) One off-white color throughout

II. Exterior Operations

A) Wood trim at all buildings, one coat stain to cover. It is acceptable to pre-prime wood trim (i.e. plant-ons, stair stringers etc.) prior to installation with finish coat applied after installation. It is the subcontractor's responsibility to coordinate all pre-prime painting with the project super.
B) Carport fascia and column trim painted by others
C) Exposed metal vents, flashing, roof jacks and other miscellaneous metals: Prime as required and one finish coat to cover. Roof jacks at tile roof are to be painted by roofing subcontractor with this subcontractor to furnish all materials.
D) Wrought iron pool fencing to be prefinished by others with this subcontractor to touch up as required.
E) Color schedule to be determined by Contractor prior to painting.

III. Subcontractor to apply full coverage and touch up to the satisfaction of the owner.

IV. Pricing for all painting work is firm for all labor, material and equipment through the completion of the project.

V. The intent of this agreement is to include all work and related work normally conducted by painting subcontractors.

Typical scope of work section
Figure 9-3

On a cost plus contract, the overhead and profit percentage is usually in addition to the actual costs. Each billing period, the painting contractor *must* submit the labor, material and equipment costs, verified by backup documentation, along with the overhead and profit amount.

Contract Clauses

I'll list what I consider some of the more important contract clauses. But please don't misunderstand me. I'm not suggesting that any contract clause is unimportant. By all means, read *every word* when you're reviewing the contract. In fact, I recommend reading the whole contract thoroughly several times prior to final approval and acceptance.

Retentions

Retentions are sums *retained* or held back by the general contractor as each progress payment is made. If 100% of the job is complete, the progress payments will usually total 90% of the contract price, with 10% retained to ensure that all the work is completed according to plans and specifications. The amount retained is usually only a small part of the entire contract price. But that small percentage may be your total profit on the job.

The retention amount is usually billed after the last progress billing and is usually payable thirty days after the owner or general contractor accepts and approves the paint job. Read the retention clause closely to be sure that the final retention payment is paid thirty days after the painting work is complete, not thirty days "after the completion of the project" or "after occupancy." Acceptance of the "after occupancy" terms means that retention payments could be held up until several months after the painting is completed.

Retentions can range from 5% to 15%, but 10% of the total contract amount is common. The retention amount is deducted from each of the progress billings submitted.

Liquidated Damages

The liquidated damages clause is designed to penalize a subcontractor if the project isn't completed by the scheduled completion date. Liquidated damages are usually part of the contract between the owner and the prime contractor, but they may be part of the subcontract agreements as well.

Liquidated damages are like a penalty and are assessed at a specific dollar value — say $350 each day the project is delayed because painting work isn't complete.

If a general contractor tries to make you pay liquidated damages, consult your attorney. The courts in most states are reluctant to enforce liquidated damages clauses, especially if the amount claimed is out of proportion to the loss or if the delay was unavoidable.

Insurance Requirements and Certification

Your insurance carrier will probably have to provide a certificate of insurance to the general contractor. This certificate describes the coverage you're paying for. Figure 9-4 shows some typical insurance coverage limits.

Most general contractors will require only one certificate of insurance for "all operations" from each subcontractor, no matter how many jobs each subcontractor is handling for that general contractor. But some general contractors require a separate certificate of insurance for each project. Check with your insurance agent for a quote on the cost of each certificate. Be sure to add this amount to your bid.

Additional Insured

Many times a developer, property owner or general contractor will insist on being named as *additional insured*. This protects the individual from any legal action against personal assets — possibly at the cost of an added premium for the subcontractor. This added premium would apply only for that particular contract. If this additional coverage is needed, get a quote from your insurance carrier and add the extra cost to your bid.

Contract Acceptance

The contract is considered a fully binding agreement only when signed by both parties. Without that written agreement, there's no deal — so be very cautious about proceeding with any work. The painting work should begin only when you have a properly executed contract.

Master File

When a contract is awarded and accepted, set up a job folder to organize all project documents. I prefer the 2" thick, heavy stock, legal size folder with six tabs for each job. Each of the six sections has clips which receive documents with two holes punched in the top. These folders come in brown or light green, and are available in most stationery stores. Set up the tabs like this:

Type of insurance		Limits of liability in thousands (000)	
		Each occurrence	Aggregate
General Liability ☒ Comprehensive form ☒ Premises-operations ☐ Explosion and collapse hazard ☒ Products/completed operations hazard ☒ Contractual insurance ☒ Broad form property damage ☒ Independent contractors ☒ Personal injury	Bodily injury	$	$
	Property damage	$	$
	Bodily injury and property damage Combined	$500	$ 500
	Personal injury		$ 500
Automobile Liability ☒ Comprehensive form ☒ Owned ☒ Hired ☒ Non-owned	Bodily injury (each person)	$	
	Bodily injury (each accident)	$	
	Property damage	$	
	Bodily injury and property damage Combined	$500	
Excess Liability ☒ Umbrella form ☐ Other than umbrella form	Bodily injury and property damage Combined	$1,000	$1,000
Workers' Compensation and Employers' Liability	Statutory		
		$ 100	(each accident)
Other			

Description of operations/location/vehicles

All operations of the named insured covered under the terms, conditions and exclusions of the policy

Typical insurance coverage limits
Figure 9-4

1) *Estimate and proposal:* Include all of your documents through the contract award.

2) *Contract documents:* The contract plus all the addenda and amendments.

3) *Change orders, price requests, extra work orders, and work authorizations:* Keep an activity log on top.

4) *Correspondence:* All of your transmittals, submittals, or letters, with a covering activity log.

5) *Job cost record:* Use this tab section for filing field progress reports, time cards, and purchase orders for material and equipment. After the labor hours on the time cards are converted to dollar amounts for payroll, record these labor costs along with material, equipment, and other costs on the job cost record sheet. Keep the job cost record sheet up to date, and file it on top of all the other records in this section.

6) *Progress billing invoices:* File copies of all invoices sent to date, by invoice number, with a covering activity log. Include a record of retentions held, and the balance due.

Contract Information Log

Use the contract information log in Figure 9-5 as a checklist when processing a new contract. This form helps keep all the contract information for a project on hand for easy reference. This form will save many hours of searching for important information. File it under the contract tab in the master file.

A few of the items on the form require some explanation:

Project number: Include a job number as well as a separate number for the model homes on a project. Treat the model homes in a new home development as if they were a separate project. The model homes are usually painted under a separate agreement, typically on a time and material basis.

Owner, builder and lender: Gather address information so that the preliminary notice (if required in your state) can be sent to each party. It's always a good idea to have these addresses at your fingertips.

Contract amount: Verify the total contract amount and write it in this space.

Authorized signature: Be sure the contract is signed by someone who has authority to sign contracts.

Manhours: The manhours used in the original estimate may be adjusted several times during contract negotiations. To find the actual manhours budgeted in the final contract amount, you have to work backwards. Starting with the contract amount, deduct the original profit, then the overhead amount. Next, deduct the material value, the employer's burden, and the amount budgeted for supervision. Divide the remaining amount by the labor rate. The result is the total manhours available to complete the job. Then divide this total by the number of buildings to find the manhours available for painting each building or unit. Figure 9-6 shows a sample calculation for a $50,000 contract.

After you've calculated the total hours per unit, deduct 10%. These "saved" hours are held in reserve. They're your cushion to use in case the field needs more hours to complete the work. In our example, you would save 2.16 manhours per home, and they'd be used only if the field needed the extra time. The next step is to distribute the remaining 20 manhours per home to the field for the various painting operations.

The combination of this system for allocating manhours and the progress reporting system I'll describe in Chapter 11 is an excellent tool for controlling the manhours for each unit on a new construction project. Use this manhour system on every project to create a time "budget" before painting begins. That's essential for making your jobs profitable.

Plans in house: A reference set of construction plans and specifications should be in your possession at all times during the job. You should confirm that these plans and specs are available.

Sequence list: The sequence list defines the order in which the units are painted. The estimator usually gets the sequence list from the owner or general contractor. Copies are distributed to the estimating department (for changes and cost control), operations personnel (the field superintendent), the accounting department (for billing), and to the master file.

Plot plan (site location): Provide the project foreman with a plot plan or a map that shows the project site location. He'll distribute copies to the

Contract Information

Project name: __VISTA PARK__

Address: __177 MAIN ST., YOURTOWN, USA__

Cross streets: __MAIN AT BROADWAY__

Project number: __87-29__

Model number: __87-29 M__

Owner: __DYNAMIC PROPERTIES__
__789 SECOND ST., YOURTOWN, USA 77777__

Builder: __JOHN DOE CONSTRUCTION__
__555 BROADWAY, YOURTOWN, USA 77777__

Lender: __FIRST NATIONAL BANK__
__123 MAIN ST., YOURTOWN, USA 77777__

Contract amount: __50,000.—__

Authorized signature: __JOHN SMITH__

Start date: __6/1/88__

Projected completion date: __10/15/88__

Building type: __SFD__

# of buildings: __50__

# of models: __3__

# of actual manhours: __1108__

✓ Contract signed — President	✓ Field manhours 1052 — Estimator
DDG Plans in house — Estimator	DDG Contract prices correct — Estimator
DDG Specifications — Estimator	JOAN Billing setup — Accounting
DDG Sequence list — Estimator	JOAN Release forms — Accounting
DDG Plot plan (site location) — Estimator	JOAN Preliminary notices sent (all three)
DDG Color schedule — Estimator (with cabinets and beams)	JOAN Union registration sent — Accounting
	JOAN Master file setup (six tab) — Accounting
DDG Certificate of insurance — Estimator	DDG Office map labeled — Estimator

Contract information log
Figure 9-5

Contract amount	$50,000.00
Deduct profit @ 5%	(2,500.00)
Subtotal	47,500.00
Deduct overhead @ 12%	(5,700.00)
Direct cost subtotal	41,800.00
Subtract material value	(15,000.00)
Subtotal (labor cost)	26,800.00
Deduct employers burden @ 35%	(9,380.00)
Subtotal	17,420.00
Deduct supervision @ 1 hour/home	
$16.00/hour x 50 homes	800.00
Subtotal	$16,620.00

Divide by hourly rate @ $15.00 = 1,108.00 hours

Divide by number of houses @ 50 = 22.16 actual manhours per home
Deduct hours saved @ 10% © 2.16 hours saved
Distribute field hours = 20.0 field manhours per home

Manhour calculations
Figure 9-6

painters. You don't want painters driving around lost when they should be painting.

Color schedule: Be sure you have a color schedule (Figure 9-7) or a written summary of colors for every job. You don't want to have to repaint a project because the colors are wrong. Copies should go to estimating and operations departments and to the master file.

Certificate of Insurance: Make sure that you meet the minimum coverage requirements set by the owner or general contractor. Identify any *additional* insurance requirements. Only one person in your office should have authority to order this certificate.

Field manhours: As indicated in Figure 9-6, the manhour budget for field work should be about 10% less than the manhours calculated in your estimate. Try to save from one to three hours per unit. If these extra hours aren't used, it's extra profit from the job.

Contract prices correct: Verify that all contract prices and totals are correct.

Billing setup: The accounting department will set up the job file to record progress billings and any other procedures or paperwork required by the general contractor. Billing cycles and progress billings are discussed later in this chapter.

Release forms: Labor and material release forms may be provided by the general contractor, or you can use standard forms. Initial this item on the contract information log when the proper release forms are provided to accounting.

Preliminary notice sent: In California, the law requires each subcontractor to give advance notice to the owner, builder, and lender that the job will be liened if that subcontractor isn't paid. This is called the preliminary lien notice. To be able to enforce a lien on a job, a California subcontractor must send this notice to all three parties within a specific time period after receiving a contract. If he doesn't do this, he's waived all rights to lien the job even if he's not paid for the work. This item must be initialed when the forms have been sent to all three parties.

If the preliminary lien notice applies in your state, you can probably get standard forms in your local stationery store.

	Scheme A	Scheme B
Stucco	Expo stucco 2	Expo stucco B180
Siding	Frazee exterior color-Cape Cod Gray 115	Frazee exterior color-Newport Blue 351
Trim	Frazee exterior color-White 001	Frazee exterior color-White 001
Front door	Frazee exterior color-Newport Blue 351	Frazee exterior color-Cape Cod Gray 115
Roof (All vents painted to match roofing)	Manville "Woodlands Roof"-Black Moss or Prestique "Elk 30" 300#-Sablewood	Manville "Woodlands Roof"-Black Moss or Prestique "Elk 30" 300#-Sablewood
Wood decking	Frazee solid color stain-115 Cape Cod Gray in a semi-transparent stain	Frazee solid color stain-115 Cape Cod Gray in a semi-transparent stain
Gutters/ Downspouts	Frazee exterior color-White 001	Frazee exterior color-White 001
Windows	Baked on white enamel	Baked on white enamel

Note: Pavilion, laundry building, and rental office to be Scheme B. Maintenance building to be Scheme A.

Trash enclosures	Scheme B
Mailboxes (wood trim)	Frazee solid color stain-115 Cape Cod Gray in a semi transparent stain
Pre-cut wood fencing	Frazee solid color stain-Pepperwood 204
Stucco walls	Expo stucco 2
Concrete block walls (no stucco)	Split face gray block
Stamped concrete	Dark gray
Signage	Frazee Aroplate semi-gloss enamel-Newport Blue 351 (letters to be primed with Frazee Acrylic Metal Primer)
Light standards (and decorative iron where applicable)	Frazee Aroplate semi-gloss enamel-Cape Cod Gray 115 (to be primed with Frazee Acrylic Metal Primer)
Carports/carbarns	Scheme A

Note: Paint all registers, grills, and vents to match adjacent surface.

Color schedule
Figure 9-7

Union registration: If your company is a union shop, each new job must be registered with the local union. When this registration is complete, the item must be initialed.

Master file (six tab): We discussed the master file setup earlier in this chapter. An initial here means the master file has been opened.

Office map labeled: When you have 10 to 15 projects going on at the same time, keeping track of the location of each job can become a problem. One easy solution is to have a large map in the office with all of the project locations pinpointed for easy reference. When processing each new job, initial the contract information log when you have identified and marked its location on the office map.

Contract Follow-Up Log

When you're processing several contracts at the same time, it's sometimes hard to remember all the details. Use the contract follow-up log (Figure 9-8) to record the completion of each phase of contract processing for each project. If you keep the log current, you can see the contract processing status for each job at a glance. This follow-up log should be the top sheet under the second tab in the master file (contract documents). The contract information log goes directly under it.

Price Request Control Log

Many architects and general contractors will request price quotes when an owner is looking for ways to cut costs. They're usually called RFPs (requests for price). The owner and architect will evaluate the prices you submit on the RFP and decide whether or not to issue a change order.

When pricing change orders, add the typical overhead (15%) and profit (10%), instead of the percentages you applied to your competitive bid. Also be sure to include supervision costs in the price.

If a price request involves a deduction which will reduce the contract amount, *don't give back your overhead and profit* unless it's a requirement of the contract. When you originally bid the project, you included a certain value for overhead and a minimum profit margin. A slight reduction in the contract price isn't going to reduce the overhead expense or your need for that minimum profit.

Use a price request control log like Figure 9-9 to record and track all price requests on large projects. If the owner is undecided about paint type or color or the number of coats, you'll get a lot of requests for price quotes. Use the price request control log to keep the price requests straight.

Change Orders

Many change orders are the result of a previous price request. Some change order prices can be calculated quickly just before the change order is issued.

Change orders usually originate in the office of a general contractor or architect after the owner has agreed to the prices submitted on the RFP. Make sure every change order is signed by someone with the authority to authorize changes.

Even the most complete, professionally-drawn plans and specifications can omit some important point or be inconsistent in some way. But don't be too impatient. Put yourself in the architect's shoes. There are so many details to cover, it's only human to miss a couple.

But even though you're tolerant of errors, make it known that all change orders, no matter what their size, will cost money.

The Effect of Change Orders

Too many change orders can disrupt the production momentum, causing the work to slow down. Craftsman don't like to repaint or rework surfaces they've already done. Consequently, changes usually take longer than the original work. If there are too many major changes, you're sure to see some of the following:

- Reduction in crew morale
- Crew size inefficiency
- Learning and productivity curve losses
- Job delays
- Wage escalation due to overtime work
- Problems in the scheduling of trades

Extra Work

Field requests for extra work can be considered emergency change orders. These requests usually originate in the field with verbal approval from the general contractor's office. This verbal approval makes it especially important for the painting foreman to get a written approval on a work authorization form (Figure 9-2) signed by a person who has the authority to approve the extra work.

This emergency work is usually charged on a time and material basis because there's no time for a price request and an accurate cost estimate. Make sure that your T&M rate has been approved. Have

Job & builder	Job name & address	Contract price	Prelim. notice sent	Cert. ins.	Contract Rec'd	Contract Sent	Spec	Plan	Seq. list	Color sched.	Proj. map to field	Map site loc. in-house	Field manhours	union reg.	Billing info releases
87-29/29M INTERSTATE	SATTLERIDGE 1776 MAIN YOURTOWN	50,000	6/7	6/7	6/7	6/9	6/8	6/8	6/16	6/16	6/18	6/9	1330	N/A	RECEIVED

Contract follow-up log
Figure 9-8

Project_____

Date received	Request number	Description of work	Date returned	Amount	Remarks	Change order number
7-15-88	001	2 COATS FASCIA	7-22-88	754 00	—	012
7-30-88	002	2 COATS WALLS	8-5-88	1421 00	ROLL	NONE

**Price request control log
Figure 9-9**

the superintendent verify the hours worked and material used by signing a daily time sheet or the work authorization.

Here's a good rule of thumb: Never begin to act on a change order or request for extra work until the change order has been signed or the time and material rate for extra work has been approved in writing.

Back Charges

Back charges are assessments by a general contractor (or claims of damage from a subcontractor) against another subcontractor. Back charges are common when one trade doesn't complete their work, doesn't clean up after their work, or damages the work of another trade. In each case the costs of completing the work, cleaning up, or repairing damage must be *charged back* to the responsible (or irresponsible) subcontractor.

You don't want back charges. Try to work out all disputes with the general contractor or your fellow subcontractors without having to go through the back charge process. You might offer to swap some painting work as a possible solution to any discrepancies. Be flexible. Give a little and take a little.

Financial Management

Financial management is managing the company's receipts and expenditures, paying for labor and materials and collecting the money that's due. Neglecting finances can cause your company to fail very quickly.

Part of your job, if you're the contract administrator, is to make sure the financial management team has all the information they need to pay the bills and collect accounts receivable on time. You can help by using a purchase order system and supplying the completed labor and material release forms which must accompany the billings to the general contractor.

Billing Cycles

On large projects, billings are typically sent out monthly. Most contracts specify a payment schedule, which usually includes deadlines for submitting monthly billings and a date on which the subcontractors will be paid. For example, billings submitted by the 25th of each month will be paid by the 10th of the following month. Most builders will require all subcontractors on a project to follow the same schedule — and they're probably too busy to make an exception just because you didn't get your bill in by the deadline. Generally, if you're late, you lose. Make it a point to get those bills in on time. After all, the sooner you get your money, the better.

Progress Billings

Contracts with progress payment schedules based on the percentage of work complete usually require the general contractor's superintendent to verify and approve the percentage completed. The amount to be billed in each cycle is calculated by multiplying the completion percentage by the contract amount and subtracting that total from the amount which has been previously billed. The retention amount is then deducted (if required) to arrive at the total due. For example:

Contract amount	$50,000.00
Verified percent complete	50%
Total amount of contract complete	25,000.00
Previously billed	15,000.00
Total this billing	10,000.00
Less retentions at 10%	**1,000.00**
Total due this billing cycle	**$9,000.00**

Lien Releases

Labor and material lien releases are usually submitted with each billing. These releases may be provided by the general contractor. Each subcontractor will complete the proper labor and material lien releases for submittal with each monthly billing. The labor release will include the signatures of all craftsmen who worked on the job during that month, attesting that they have been paid through the date on the release. The material suppliers must also sign a release verifying that the painting contractor's payments are up to date for that project. This process essentially releases the owner or general contractor from claims to pay any of the craftsmen or any of the material suppliers for that month.

In the next chapter, we'll look at another important part of the paint contracting business — what every paint contractor should know about ethics and the law.

Chapter 10

LEGAL ASPECTS OF CONTRACTING

*B*efore we begin this chapter, understand this: I'm not a lawyer and I'm not offering legal advice. You'll have to hire counsel when the time comes. But I've been an estimator for many years and have learned to avoid most of the legal snarls that paint estimators fall into. In this chapter I'll explain what I know about estimating, bidding, and the law.

Unfortunately, paint estimating and bidding bring on legal headaches far too often. And I've never seen a painting contractor *really* win in a legal battle. Maybe that's because there's seldom a winner in any legal contest. More often, one party is the loser and the other party is a bigger loser — with the lawyers being the only winners.

Nothing you can do will guarantee that you won't be sued. But there are many ways to prevent disputes and protect yourself as well as your company from construction claims. That's the focus of this chapter — how to stay out of court.

First, you should understand what a contract is. You should follow some simple rules for preventing most disputes. You should be familiar with arbitration remedies. And you should know how to prepare and how to rebut claims. Armed with this information, you should be able to avoid most disputes and have a better chance of coming out ahead in those that are unavoidable.

Figure 10-1 shows the major topics we'll cover in this chapter.

Contractor Ethics: The Unwritten Laws

There's one easy way to avoid most conflicts, disagreements, disputes and claims: Be ethical and honest in your business practices. Integrity is the golden rule of business conduct. People threaten suit and sue when they're mad, when they're surprised, and especially when they think they're being cheated. Don't put people in that position and you'll avoid most disputes.

In the end, being ethical is good business. The American Society of Professional Estimators has a code of ethics that can serve as a moral foundation for all estimators. It's quoted in Chapter 2.

Here are some of the important ethical principles in the contracting business:

1) No contractor should take advantage of an obvious error in plans and specifications, or other documents, that are to his advantage and to the disadvantage of another contractor. Disclose errors, omissions and ambiguities on your proposal.

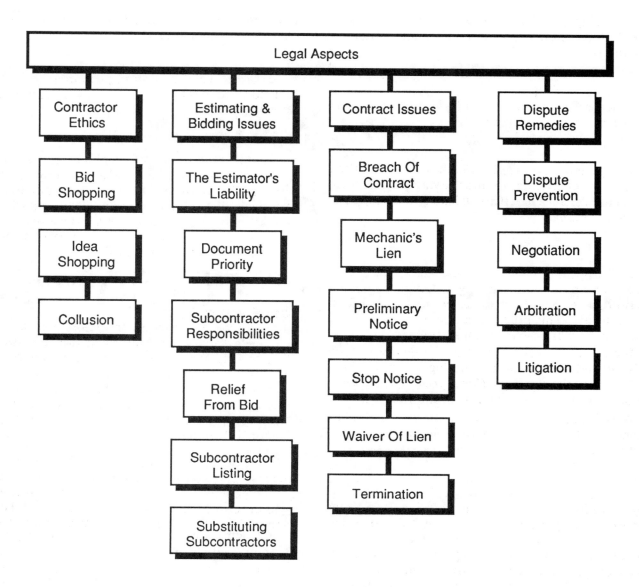

The legal aspects of contracting
Figure 10-1

2) A subcontractor shouldn't lower his bid after it's been submitted if the owner or general contractor has received other bids for the same work. Submit your best price the first time.

3) Subcontractor bidders shouldn't accept or seek information about competitor bids. Base your bids solely on your own estimates.

4) A contractor shouldn't downgrade or belittle his competitors. Urge your prospective client to make a fair comparison of the quality of your workmanship and your ability to complete work on time, based on a thorough investigation of all the competitors.

5) Base each business transaction on that which is morally right rather than that which may be legally enforceable.

6) Bidding jobs without including overhead and profit gives this industry a bad name. It's poor professional practice.

7) Bidding for work below cost in hopes that you'll make money on extras or change orders is unethical.

8) General contractors should always keep subcontractor bids confidential.

9) A general contractor shouldn't solicit further bids from subcontractors after having received and opened bids. This practice can lead to *bid shopping* or *bid peddling.*

Bid Shopping

Bid shopping or bid peddling is letting one competitor know the others' prices before the award of the contract. This practice can be used to secure a lower bid from a favorite competitor.

If an owner or general contractor tries to squeeze a lower bid out of you by quoting a competitor's bid, don't take the bait. *Know your bottom line.* Submit your best and final price the first time.

Avoid bid shopping. Bid only for reputable owners and general contractors. Follow these simple *rules:*

• Before your bid amount is called in, submit a *flyer* or *abstract* which defines your included scope of work and the items you exclude. This protects your bid amount until the last minute. It works well on larger public and private jobs where sealed bids are opened at a specified time. Have the abstract (without your bid amount) in the hands of the owner or general contractor at least 48 hours before bid opening. That gives them time to compare your scope of work with the flyers from other painting contractors before the deadline.

If there are questions about your bid, they can be asked and answered before bid day. The abstract will be repeated on your proposal, but this time the price will be quoted, of course. At bid opening, there shouldn't be any surprises and no room for quibbling or negotiating about what's included and excluded.

• Make your painting abstracts and proposals as clear as possible, with a minimum number of exclu-

sions. Make your bid quotation consistent with the plans and specifications.

• Organize your quotation according to the instructions to bidders, with the specification sections identified.

• Submit your best and final bid at least four hours before the deadline. Many painting contractors will wait until the last possible minute to submit their bids. That's supposed to reduce the possibility of bid shopping. But it also makes the analysis of your scope of work compared to your competitors' nearly impossible.

Idea Shopping

Many owners or general contractors will *shop* the subcontractors· — asking them for cost-saving ideas to help them meet or beat their construction budget. They may use your ideas, but not use you as a subcontractor. Remember, your ideas are valuable. They might help you win a contract. Don't let the owner or general contractor take them for nothing.

While doing your take-off, you'll probably find areas where costs can be cut. If you do, itemize these ideas on your take-off form. Let the owner or general contractor know that you have several cost-saving ideas. Give them the dollar amount of savings without disclosing the specific ideas. This will make them curious. Curiosity about cost-saving ideas may lead to a negotiated contract or an award of the contract at your price.

Price Fixing

Don't discuss your prices or the scope of work you're bidding on with competing contractors. Even if your intentions are innocent, discussing the bid before the bids are submitted could be considered *collusion.* To be safe, don't talk about your bid and estimate with any competitor. I know some very good paint contractors who were embarrassed when they got caught with their hands in the cookie jar — and paid large penalties for fixing prices among themselves.

Estimating and Bidding Issues

The Estimator's Liability
Estimators working for wages have no legal liability to their employers or to anyone else for mistakes or bad judgment. But an independent estimator working for a fee may be liable for negligence (mistakes) in compiling estimates. If you hold yourself out as an experienced estimator and make a foolish mistake, you may be liable. Like all professionals, independent estimators are held to a reasonable standard of performance.

Document Priority
When there's a conflict between the contract, the plans and the specifications, which should you trust? Here are the usual rules:

1) The contract *scope of work* has priority over plans or specifications.

2) Written dimensions prevail over measurements taken from the plans.

3) Information in specifications prevails over information on the plans.

4) Specific, hand-written notes have priority over standard or "boilerplate" general notes.

Subcontractor Responsibilities
Every subcontractor has legal responsibilities:

• You must know and comply with the law, as well as all federal, state and local codes which apply to the painting business.

• It's your duty to seek clarification of ambiguities in the plans and specifications. If something isn't clear, you have to get clarification. Otherwise you have to perform according to the intent of the architect. Ask questions if something is unclear on the plans or specs.

Relief from Bid
There are three cases where a subcontractor can get relief from a bid or contract that's been accepted:

1) When it is proven that the plans or specifications are poor and ambiguous.

2) When the general contractor makes a counter offer. A counter offer is asking the winning bidder to change the terms and conditions of the original proposal in any way. Being asked to change your scope of work, to modify the payment terms, or to reduce your price can be considered a counter offer. If any of these occur, you can withdraw the original bid and have no further obligation to the general contractor.

3) Clerical or math errors by the subcontractor *may* be considered an excuse for withdrawing a bid. (This isn't an excuse to skip double-checking your work and proofreading the bid before submitting it.)

Subcontractor Listing
Many bid documents require the general contractor to supply subcontractor names, addresses, and license numbers on the bid form. The general contractor must use the subs listed unless a subcontractor can't be bonded or is financially unstable and may not be able to finish the job. If a subcontractor is hired even though he's not bondable or financially stable, the general contractor is responsible for the work of that subcontractor.

Some bid documents require that a list of subcontractors be submitted only when the contract is awarded. This is usually a disadvantage to the subcontractors because the owner or general contractor can look for more competitive bids between the bid time and the contract award date. That could be weeks. Even though your bid may have been the best bid at the time, you could lose the job.

Fortunately, few general contractors shop bids. Most of them know they'll need your help to win more bids in the future.

Substituting Subcontractors
On a semi-formal or formal bid project, subcontracts must be awarded to the apparent low bidder — unless the apparent low bid subcontractor:

1) Refuses to perform the work according to the contract.

2) Refuses to sign the contract.

3) Is unable to meet bonding requirements.

4) Produces unsatisfactory and unacceptable work.

5) Is unlicensed (in a state where a contractor's license is required).

6) Is determined to be financially unstable.

Contract Issues

Breach of Contract

Under contract law, if one of two parties to a contract fails to perform an important part of the contract, that party has *breached* the contract. If a breach occurs, the other party is excused from further performance and is entitled to recover all losses. Occasionally you may have to decide if an owner or general contractor has breached the contract. If he has, you may be allowed to pull your crew off the job and sue to collect your loss. If you keep working, you may, by doing so, waive the right to claim a breach of contract later. But if you stop work and a court decides there was no breach of contract, *you* may have breached the contract by stopping work.

In almost every case, failure to make a progress payment is a material breach of contract. This can relieve you of the obligation to continue.

Being behind schedule isn't a breach of contract unless the contract states that "time is of the essence." Even then it may not be considered a breach unless the delay is serious.

A statement by either party that he has no intention of completing the contract is usually considered an *anticipatory breach* which relieves the other party of the obligation to continue work.

Always seek professional advice before taking action when you suspect a breach of contract.

The Mechanic's Lien

A mechanic's lien is like a mortgage. It's supposed to secure payment for the value of work done, materials supplied, or equipment used on a building. The concept is a good one. It should guarantee that you always get paid. Unfortunately, the law doesn't always work that way.

To have any rights under the mechanic's lien law, you have to comply with the letter of the law in your state. This may include getting the architect's verification that the work was completed as evidence of payments earned.

Many states give subcontractors a priority lien on the amount of money due from the general contractor at the time the lien is issued. Other states give those who have performed labor or furnished materials priority over general creditors of an insolvent owner or general contractor. These states give priority to day laborers over contractors and subcontractors, regardless of when their liens are filed. Material suppliers may have priority over contractors or subcontractors. Check with your attorney for details about mechanic's lien laws in your state.

Mechanic's Lien Procedure

The information provided here is only a guide for filing and serving private claims on mechanic's liens. It's based on California law. Procedures in other states may be different. I'd recommend that you always get legal advice before filing any claim.

There are two phases for processing a mechanic's lien in the private sector:

1) The preliminary notice
2) Recording the claim of lien

The Preliminary Notice

The preliminary notice must be given within 20 days after the claimant first furnishes labor, materials, equipment or services to the job site. If the claimant gives notice later than that, he's only entitled to file a lien for labor, materials, equipment or services furnished 20 days before the notice and at any time after the notice.

All persons claiming a lien or stop notice must file a preliminary notice except the prime contractor, workers performing labor for wages, and express trust funds who aren't required to give the preliminary notice.

In general, the owner, original contractor, and construction lender must be notified. But a subcontractor dealing with an owner when there's no general contractor must give the notice to the construction lender. The notice may be served at the residence, place of business, the address shown on the building permit, or the address shown on the construction trust deed.

There are three ways to serve notice: personal service, registered mail with return receipt requested, or certified mail with return receipt requested. When the notice is served by mail, service is complete when the registered or certified mail is deposited. This is the recommended method of service.

The notice must include a description and estimated price for the labor, materials, equipment or services furnished, the names and addresses of the person giving the notice and the person who contracted for the purchase, a description of the job site, and a required notice to the property owner.

Only one notice need be given for each job on which you have furnished labor, materials, equipment, or services, unless you've contracted with one or more subcontractors. For example, if your painting company hires a wallcovering or scaffolding contractor, that subcontractor must give notice independently. They're not covered by your notice.

A subcontractor can't record a lien until he has stopped furnishing labor, materials, equipment or services. Then he can record within 30 days from the valid notice of completion or notice of cessation of labor, or 90 days from actual completion if there's no notice of completion.

The lawsuit must be filed within 90 days after the lien is recorded and it must be filed in the county where the real estate is located. You can extend your time limit for filing the suit for up to one year by filing an extension of time to foreclose within 90 days.

Stop Notice

A stop notice informs the person holding the construction funds to withhold money to pay the claimant for work performed, materials supplied, equipment used, or other services furnished. This notice, subject to certain qualifications, obligates the person holding the funds to retain an amount sufficient to pay the claimant.

Waiver of Lien

A waiver of lien for material and labor is an authorization to release a lien placed on real property. A subcontractor will issue a waiver of lien to the general contractor after the subcontractor has been paid in full. Figure 10-2 shows a typical waiver of lien. Many stationery stores carry forms like this.

Termination

Many contracts include a *termination clause*. This clause may require that the subcontractor perform according to the construction schedule and provide enough manpower and supervision to meet the requirements of the general contractor, or be terminated within 48 hours.

Upon termination, the subcontractor is replaced with another subcontractor to complete the work. This new subcontractor would then be paid with the money retained by the owner or general contractor.

It's very bad business to be terminated on any job. Faithfully fulfill all requirements of the contract even if you lose money. Remember, when you signed that contract, you gave your word. Stick to your promise and live up to your commitment. The reputation of your company is at stake.

How to Prevent and Resolve Disputes

Although there's no sure way to stay out of court, there's plenty you can do to minimize the legal risk. Here's a preventative law checklist.

1) Check your subcontract for blank spaces. Make sure they're all filled in before you sign it. Review the work schedule and get a copy if it's mentioned in your subcontract.

2) Be sure the plans and specifications are well identified on the subcontract. Compare the date on the plans you used for your estimate to the plan date identified in the contract. Be sure the plans referred to in the subcontract show the proper information: architect's name, sheet numbers, dates, and revision date.

3) Watch out for plans that are revised after you've compiled an estimate. If you find changes, note those changes along with the date. Also keep track of your extra costs for this work.

4) Be sure the scope of work in the contract is consistent with the painting work on the finish schedule and in the specifications.

5) Be sure that the general contractor has the authority to subcontract the work. If possible, review a copy of the master contract before signing the subcontract.

6) Get *signed copies* of all change orders and work authorizations.

7) Save all paperwork related to the project, including telephone messages, handwritten notes, and activity logs.

8) Keep a daily log detailing:

   a) Who worked on what days, and their assignments.

   b) All significant conversations with owners, architects, and contractors.

   c) Dates of all inspections, name of inspector, type of inspection, and company or governmental agency conducting the inspection.

   d) Trouble with any trade that relates to your work.

STATE OF _____ ⎫ SS
COUNTY OF _____ ⎭

𝔚𝔞𝔦𝔳𝔢𝔯 𝔬𝔣 𝔏𝔦𝔢𝔫

𝕶𝖓𝖔𝖜 𝕬𝖑𝖑 𝕸𝖊𝖓 𝕭𝖞 𝕿𝖍𝖊𝖘𝖊 𝕻𝖗𝖊𝖘𝖊𝖓𝖙𝖘: *that* _____

Date _____

WHEREAS, the undersigned, _____ ha _____
                                             (Name of Contractor)

been employed by _____
                                    (Name of party by whom employed)

to furnish _____
                            (Type of work or material)

for the building located at _____ in _____
                                        (Street address or location)   (City)

NOW, THEREFORE, KNOW YE, that the undersigned, for and in consideration of
$ _____ and other good and valuable considerations, the receipt whereof is hereby acknowledg-
ed, do _____ hereby waive and release any and all lien, or claim or right of lien as to the above
described building and premises, and also with respect to, or upon, monies which may be due from the
Owner, under the Statutes of the State of _____ relating to Mechanics' Liens, on account of labor,
services, fixtures and materials, or either, furnished _____ by the undersigned to or an account of the said _____ for said building or premises.
                                                   (Name of party by whom employed)

Dated this _____ *day of* _____ *19* _____

at _____

_____ (SEAL)

_____ (SEAL)

signed, sealed and delivered in the presence of:

_____

_____

ALWAYS MAKE AND RETAIN A COPY FOR YOUR FILES

Waiver of lien
Figure 10-2

e) Problems with ability to perform your work. For example, if the plaster contractor leaves surfaces splattered or the drywall contractor does poor taping and texturing, document this in your daily log. There's a rule that goes like this: You paint it, you buy it. That means that if you paint over a surface which isn't complete or is damaged, you're responsible for bringing that surface up to acceptable quality standards.

9) Keep work authorizations (and carbons) on the construction site at all times. When a superintendent gives oral instructions or requests extra work, fill out the work authorization and have him sign it before picking up a brush.

10) Have your job foreman make notes on anticipated problems. Give written notice to the owner or general contractor about the problem and what's going to happen if it's not resolved. Let them know of the risk

11) Check plans, specifications and contract to see if they include reference to the Uniform Building Code, Federal Housing Administration or Veterans Administration requirements. If the contract or specifications refer to some publication, get a copy. Have it ready for review when needed.

12) Read every contract you're asked to sign. If you don't understand something, find someone who does. Be particularly careful of indemnity or "hold harmless" clauses. They can turn you into an insurance company, making you liable for anything that goes wrong.

13) On the subject of insurance, be sure of your own coverage. Most policies exclude some types of risk. Understand what *materials* and *painting operations* may be excluded from your policy.

Negotiation

The best way to resolve a dispute is for everyone to act like adults, taking responsibility for their actions. Of course, that's easier said than done. In many cases, you'll need either arbitration or the threat of litigation to settle a dispute.

Arbitration

Arbitration is sometimes a good alternative to costly legal action. There's no sense making the lawyers rich if you don't have to. Many contract documents require the parties to use arbitration before filing suit. Look for an arbitration clause in your contracts. The American Arbitration Association has published *Construction Industry Arbitration Rules* for your use. For more information, contact the American Arbitration Association at their regional office in your area or at their main office:

American Arbitration Association
140 West 51st Street
New York, NY 10020

Litigation

The last and worst choice for settling a dispute is to sue. Many lawsuits are bleeding contests, each party trying to run up the legal fees of the other until, after several years, one side is no longer able or willing to pay. Disputes like that are usually settled for the cost of the legal fees alone, with no other money changing hands. Only the lawyers benefit from that kind of justice.

Your job is painting. Stick to it, and stay away from the courts.

Chapter 11

PROJECT MANAGEMENT

*B*y *project management* I mean managing the painting work so it's completed in the least amount of time with the highest possible quality of workmanship. It includes planning, scheduling, controlling costs, and recording the progress of the job.

The flow chart in Figure 11-1 shows the project management tasks we'll discuss in this chapter. They may not all apply to your company, of course. And most of these functions are directed at new construction. But you can use them for repaint jobs, as well.

But wait a minute. How does project management relate to painting estimating? They go hand in hand. On the one hand, the job must be well-managed to meet the production goals the estimator used to price it. On the other hand, the estimator bid the job using actual manhour and material figures from previous jobs.

Information must flow both ways for the company to be as competitive and profitable as possible. The relationship between the estimator and the project manager is the basis for developing the historical costs that make your estimates accurate.

In fact, in many small painting companies, the estimator is also the project manager. In a larger painting company the estimator and project manager will probably be different people. But the two must work together closely.

Many paint estimators have worked as job foremen or project supervisors at one time or another. This field experience is invaluable for an estimator. Most supervisors become good judges of what the job requires and how long it will take.

Planning

As soon as the contract's accepted and a foreman assigned to the job, schedule a meeting to begin the planning. You'll hold this first meeting in your office or shop. Include the field superintendent, the job foreman, the project manager, the contract administrator and the purchasing agent (if different people are handling these tasks).

The purpose of this meeting is to *hand off* estimating information to the job supervisors. After all, the estimator has spent hours evaluating the job and planning the most cost-effective way to approach it. It makes sense to have this knowledge passed on to the people who'll actually supervise the work. They shouldn't have to duplicate the estimator's effort.

During the meeting, the field supervisors are given the plans, specs, estimated manhours and material quantities, and ordering deadlines. Other topics for discussion might include contract inclusions and exclusions, any unusual requirements in

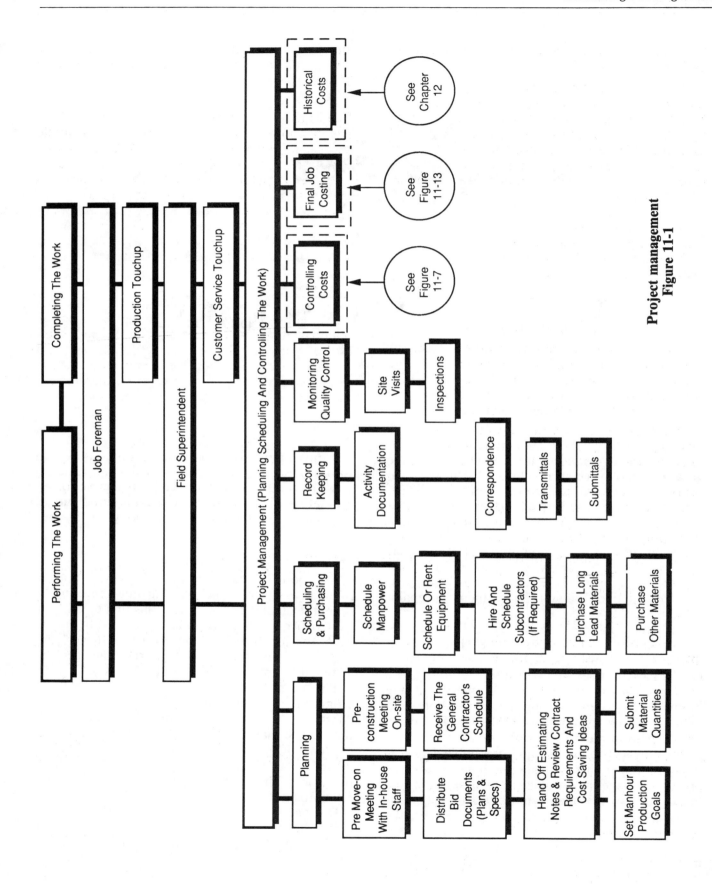

Project management
Figure 11-1

the specifications, and any complications that are likely to crop up.

The second meeting is the on-site *preconstruction meeting.* It's typically held on the construction site. The painting contractor is usually represented by the field superintendent, foreman, and estimator. The general contractor probably sends his project manager or purchasing agent. The job superintendent typically conducts the meeting. They'll discuss:

1) Work schedules
2) Manpower requirements
3) Interaction with other trades
4) Special circumstances of the job

Scheduling

During the on-site preconstruction meeting, the general contractor and the painting contractor work out the painting schedule. Once that's done, you can organize your manpower, order the materials, and schedule the equipment.

When the general contractor calls to schedule the painting work, your field superintendent must inspect the job to make sure it's ready before sending in any painters. Here's what he'll look for. Is the work accessible and are the surfaces to be painted complete and clean? If you're painting stucco exteriors, are there plaster spills, splatters, and overspray on adjacent wood trim?

Schedule the painting of the fascia before roofing is installed — especially if the building has concrete or clay tile. Otherwise the painters have to mask off the edge course of tile before spraying or rolling the fascia. Avoid this extra expense.

The drywall and acoustic ceilings must be complete before you can begin painting the interior, including wall texturing and having the acoustic ceilings scribed at the edges. If you're painting cabinets and pullmans, finish them before the counter tops are installed. The flooring is installed when all interior painting is done.

To an experienced painter, this scheduling is second nature. But don't take anything for granted. Make sure everyone involved knows the schedule. The manhour tables in this book don't allow for time lost due to inefficient scheduling. Yours shouldn't either.

On repaint projects, scheduling is easier because the painting contractor is the prime contractor. But

the work must still be accessible and ready for preparation and painting with *no* interruptions. That's always your goal.

The Manpower Schedule

The manpower schedule in Figure 11-2 is a simple but reliable bar chart scheduling system. The upper bar chart lists the number of painters and the days required for each job. The bottom part of the chart summarizes the number of painters needed to complete the scheduled work each day. The arrows at the end of the month show that work on that job continues into the next month. A chart like this makes it easy to schedule your painters.

Purchasing

As soon as the contract is accepted, order all materials that aren't readily available on short notice. For example, place orders right away for custom colors, special mixes, items from out-of-state suppliers, and other materials which require more than a few days for delivery or preparation.

Record Keeping

This isn't the first time I've emphasized the importance of good record keeping and an organized estimating system — and it won't be the last time. Let's look at some of the records you'll need for managing a project.

Activity Log

The activity log at Figure 11-3 will be your cover document in every master file. Log in all activity and communications in chronological order by date and time. Your project might involve change orders, damaged work, disputes, back charges, misunderstandings, poor communication, or even accidents. Without an accurate log of each activity as it happens, it's just your word against theirs in a dispute.

When unexpected problems occur on a job site, note it in your activity log immediately. It's a good idea to follow up with a letter to the owner or general contractor explaining your position on the problem. That way your side is on record if a dispute ends up in arbitration or in court.

Transmittals

Have a *transmittal* letter accompany all documents submitted to architects, owners, or contractors for review and approval. My letter of transmittal form

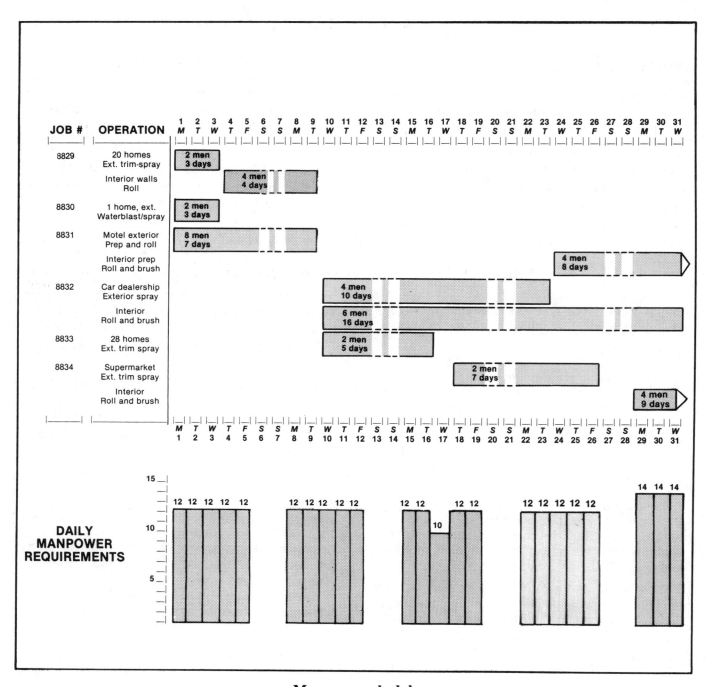

Manpower schedule
Figure 11-2

ACTIVITY LOG

Job no. _8829_   Page no._____

Date	Person/Agent/Contact Company	Activity	Action/ Follow up
5/1/87	JOHN SMITH - PURCHASING AGENT	VERBAL AWARD OF CONTRACT	ACCEPTED
5/7/87	INTERSTATE CONSTRUCTION	RECEIVED CONTRACT FOR REVIEW	— REVIEWED—
5/8/87	JOHN SMITH	QUESTIONED PAYMENT SCHEDULE	CHANGED SCHEDULE IN OUR FAVOR
6/15/88	JOE JOHNSON — FOREMAN TED JONES — SUPER	PRE-MOVE ON MEETING — IN-HOUSE	REVIEWED SCOPE OF WORK
6/16/88	JOHN SMITH TED JONES	PRE-CONSTRUCTION MEETING — FIELD	RECEIVED CONSTRUCTION SCHEDULE
6/20/88	JOHN SMITH	CALLED TO CONFIRM MOVE-ON DATE	— CONFIRMED—
6/22/88	TED JONES	MOVED ON — SPRAY MAN	FASCIA & OVERHANG
7/2/88	JOHN SMITH	CHANGE: ADDED PLANTERS AT PLAN 1A	WORK AUTHORIZATION

Activity log
Figure 11-3

(Figure 11-4) includes a convenient checklist. It's quicker and more efficient than writing a cover letter for each document you send.

Set up a tickler file for time-sensitive documents. When the transmittal letter accompanies correspondence that requires a response, make sure you get the answer in a reasonable time.

Quality Control

Every job must be checked daily. If the field superintendent is strict about quality, the customer should have few requests for touchup at the end of the job. Here are some of the things to look for when you're monitoring quality:

• Sinkers or cat eyes: Indentations in the surface where the paint roller or brush missed.

• Holidays: Spots missed when the painter was "on holiday" and not paying attention — including the backs of closet poles, door jambs, and the top and bottom of all doors. Here's a tip: Use a dentist's mirror for the inspection. Make sure the backs of garage doors are sealed on projects financed by the FHA or VA.

• Test all wet area walls to see if they're sealed. (The test is to wet the surface with saliva. If the moisture runs off, it's been sealed. If the moisture is absorbed, it hasn't been.)

• Look for light coverage due to thin paint, double roll marks and streaks, and rough surfaces caused by dirty paint or a worn-out roller. Watch for poor caulking at windows, door casings, and baseboards.

Site Visits
If you're acting as project manager, plan to visit the job site about once a week. You'll check the quality of the work and confirm that the foreman and the field superintendent have costs under control. Even if you're not in charge of project management, visit the site from time to time. The more you know about field operations, the better estimator you'll be.

Inspections
The general contractor, and perhaps a government inspector, will also conduct inspections to check on the quality of the job. It's a good idea to have some combination of the project manager, estimator,

field superintendent, and foreman attend these inspections. They can answer the inspector's questions and note any deficiencies for immediate correction. That's good customer service.

Here's the key to success in the painting business: Satisfy your customers at all costs. Keep them coming back. Show them you care about quality and getting the work done on time.

Touchup Work
There are two kinds of touchup. First is production touchup, which includes corrections found by the touchup painter. It's supervised by the project foreman. The second type is the customer service touchup, after the owner or general contractor has inspected the job. It's usually supervised by the field superintendent because the job foreman is on another project by then.

Here's a tip that will save time for both you and the general contractor. Buy some orange fluorescent stickers at any stationery store. Have the owner or general contractor stick them on any area that needs touchup. Your touchup painter can quickly find the areas to be corrected, pull off the sticker, and touch up the area. It's a lot faster than writing out detailed touchup lists.

When you're painting a home or condo project where the owners will be moving in at different times, you'll have to schedule appointments for the final touchup. The customer service follow-up form (Figure 11-5) is a good way to keep track of these appointments. But homeowners are more likely to miss appointments than your business associates. Use the "Sorry we missed you" door hanger in Figure 11-6 when the homeowner's not home or when the touchup painter wants to cover a block of homes or condos in one sweep.

Controlling Costs

Painting is a labor intensive business. That's why it's so important that the painters be supervised very carefully. You also need good controls on material and equipment costs, of course.

Too many contractors don't have an effective cost control system. That means they don't realize they're in trouble until the job is done. By then, it's too late to save their profit. Job costing while the work's in progress lets you identify cost overruns while there's still time to make corrections.

Don't let the name *job cost control* scare you.

QUALITY Painting & Decorating
777 Main Street
Yourtown, USA 77777
555-1512
Contractor's License Number: *717273*

LETTER OF TRANSMITTAL

Date:_____

To: _____   Quality Job No. _____

Address: _____   Project _____

City: _____

Attn: _____

Gentlemen:

We transmit:
_____ A request for
_____ Herewith
_____ Under separate cover
_____ Parcel post
_____ Personal delivery
_____ Messenger
_____
_____

The following:
_____ Plans (____ sets)
_____ Specs (____ sets)
_____ Sequence list
_____ Color schedule
_____ Release forms
_____ Subcontract
_____ Brochure
_____ Color samples
_____ Price request info
_____ Work authorization
_____ Invoice
_____ Proposal
_____ Change order
_____ Copy of letter
_____

For:
_____ Approval as noted
_____ Owner approval
_____ Architect approval
_____ As you requested
_____ Correction and resub
_____ Field information
_____ Review and comment
_____ Your use/files
_____ Your action
_____ Immediate action
_____ **BID DUE**_____
_____
_____
_____

Remarks: _____

_____

_____

Please return: _____ **Urgent:** Immediate response requested.
_____ signed copies to this office
_____ approved copies to this office

Very truly yours,
Quality Painting and Decorating

cc: _____

_____

_____   By:_____

Letter of transmittal
Figure 11-4

CUSTOMER SERVICE FOLLOW UP

Date _____

Name _____

Address _____

Lot # _____

Builder _____

Job name _____

Phone # H _____

W _____

Time Preference: Morning/Afternoon

Specific appointment time _____

☐ Work completed: Date _____

☐ Reschedule appointment _____

COMMENTS: _____

_____

_____

**Customer follow-up form
Figure 11-5**

Yes, it does sound like a complex and time-consuming task. But it doesn't have to be. You just need accurate, complete, and up-to-date records of all expenses on each job. To get these records, you'll need the cooperation of your field superintendent and job foremen.

Figure 11-7 shows the process of controlling labor and material costs.

The Progress Report

The *progress report* is the key to monitoring and controlling field manhours. While the work's in progress, you use it to compare actual labor hours

SORRY WE MISSED YOU

Date: _____

We were here today regarding your corrective request.
Please phone us to arrange for another date.
TELEPHONE 555-1512

Thank you.
Customer Service

By: _____

QUALITY PAINTING & DECORATING
777 Main Street
Yourtown, USA 77777
555-1512

Contractor's License Number: 717273

**Touchup door hanger
Figure 11-6**

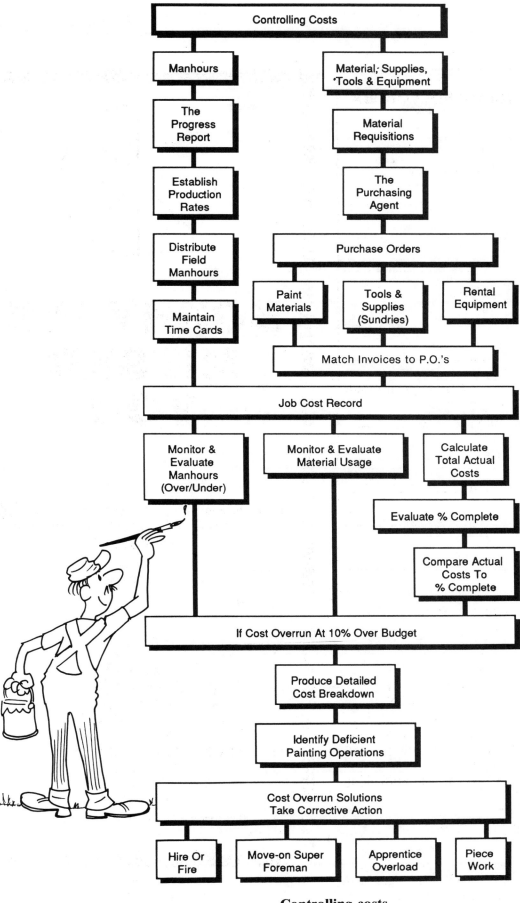

Controlling Costs

- Manhours
  - The Progress Report
  - Establish Production Rates
  - Distribute Field Manhours
  - Maintain Time Cards

- Material, Supplies, Tools & Equipment
  - Material Requisitions
  - The Purchasing Agent
  - Purchase Orders
    - Paint Materials
    - Tools & Supplies (Sundries)
    - Rental Equipment
  - Match Invoices to P.O.'s

Job Cost Record

- Monitor & Evaluate Manhours (Over/Under)
- Monitor & Evaluate Material Usage
- Calculate Total Actual Costs
  - Evaluate % Complete
  - Compare Actual Costs To % Complete

If Cost Overrun At 10% Over Budget

- Produce Detailed Cost Breakdown
- Identify Deficient Painting Operations

Cost Overrun Solutions Take Corrective Action

- Hire Or Fire
- Move-on Super Foreman
- Apprentice Overload
- Piece Work

Controlling costs
Figure 11-7

PROGRESS REPORT

Job foreman SUPER FOREMAN
Job name VISTA PARK
Week ending 6-30-88
WEEK 2

		Estimated hours per operation	Units completed	Total hours this week
EXTERIOR PRIME	Fascia			
	Overhang			
	Siding & Garage door			
	Plant-ons			
	Exterior doors SEE INTERIOR			
	Entry doors SEE INTERIOR			
	Clear seal			
EXTERIOR FINISH	Fascia 8/DAY =	1.0	12	12
	Overhang 8/DAY =	1.0	12	12
	Siding & Garage door			
	Plant-ons 4/DAY =	2.0	10	20
	Exterior doors	.3		
	Entry doors	.4		
	Vents & flashing	.3		
	Roof jacks	.1		
	Garage door, inside			
	Stucco			
	Seal K & B 16/DAY =	.5	24	12
	Undercoat 4/DAY =	2.0	10	20
	Split coat			
	Caulking			
	Woodwork			
	Blot out			
INTERIOR FINISH	Stain cabinets 6/DAY =	1.3	10	13
	Walls 2/DAY =	4.0	5	20
	K & B enamel 4/DAY =	2.0		
	Enamel trim 4/DAY =	2.0		
	Beams			
	Railing			
	Interior wood			
	Base STAIN	.2		
	Touchup	2.0		
	Customer service T/U	.4		
	Extras			
	Supervision	.5	16	8
	Total hours	20.0		117.0

	This week	To date
Estimated hours	117	256.1
Actual hours (from time cards)	115	256.0
Over or under	(2)	+ .1

Progress report
Figure 11-8

Exterior Production Rates

Fascia only	8 units per day — roll
Overhang only	5-7 units per day — spray
Fascia & overhang	6 units per day — spray
Siding & garage door	3 units per day — roll
Plant-ons & other trim	4 units per day — roll
Metal (vents, flashing & roof jacks)	8 units per day — brush

Interior Production Rates

Seal kitchen and bath walls	16 units per day — spray
Undercoat (doors, casings, pullmans and linens)	Average 15 openings/unit, 4 units per day — spray
Cabinets, stain, seal and lacquer	16 units per day — spray (2 men)
Walls	2 units per day — roll
Enamel kitchen and bath walls	4 units per day — roll
Enamel trim (doors, casings, pullmans, linens)	Average 15 openings/unit, 2 units per day — roll
Touchup (production)	2 units per day — brush
Touchup (customer service)	4-5 units per day — brush

Typical production rates
Figure 11-9

with your estimated hours weekly. Jobs will be more profitable if actual hours match estimated hours.

I designed the progress report in Figure 11-8 for use on large new-construction projects. But you can adapt it to jobs of any size. Just make sure your progress report includes the same categories, in the same order, as your take-off. This consistency is important in all of your reports. It reduces errors and makes record keeping easier. For maximum efficiency, organize all of your accounting and bookkeeping systems with a chart of accounts that matches the progress report and estimating forms.

Using the progress report is a five-step process:

1) Calculate the field hours per unit for each job. I explained how to do this in Chapter 9.

2) Establish production rates and goals.

3) Distribute the hours per unit based on the production rates.

4) Use time cards to fill in the actual hours.

5) Compare the estimated hours to the actual

hours on the "over or under" line each week.

Base your production rates on the number of units which must be completed each day for each painting operation. Record the projections on the progress report. For example, look at Figure 11-9. It shows a typical per-day production rates for a tract of 1,600 to 1,800 square foot single-family homes.

The first column of the progress report shows the estimated hours per unit for each operation. The second column shows the number of units actually completed for the week. For the third column, multiply the estimated hours by the number of units actually completed. That shows the number of hours scheduled for each operation. At the bottom of column 3, total the estimated hours for that week.

In the section at the bottom of the progress report, compare the estimated hours to the actual hours from the time cards. This tells you how many hours you're *over* or *under* the estimate.

The time card in Figure 11-10 is designed to record the actual hours each painter spends on each operation. The job foreman is responsible for keeping track of the painters' hours. Then he compares painter productivity with production goals in the progress report.

TIME CARD

| Employee's name | JOHN JONES | | | | | | | | | Week ending | 6-12-88 |

Project	Operation	M	T	W	T	F	S	S	Total hours	Total earnings	Office use
#8752	WALLS	8	8	8					24		VAC
	UNDERCOAT				8				8		F.I.C.A.
	TRIM					8			8		Fed. tax
											S.D.I.
											State tax
											Sick
											Dues
Rate $ 15.—	TOTAL								40	600.—	Net

Time card
Figure 11-10

Controlling Material Costs

Whether the job foreman does the purchasing from the field or a purchasing agent does it from the office, every painting contractor needs a good system for controlling material costs. And that process begins with accurate and detailed records of all purchases. Use material requisitions and purchase orders channeled through a purchasing agent to compile an accurate job cost record. That makes it easy to post all purchases to the appropriate operation on each project.

Material requisitions— The material requisition is a request from the field for the purchase of materials. Field supervisors or job foremen should submit a material requisition for *all* materials they need. Figure 11-11 shows the material requisition I use. It includes the material quantity, description, and the operation for which the material will be used.

Material requisitions are sent to the purchasing agent, who verifies the request, fills out a purchase order, and orders the material. This allows one person — who's familiar with purchasing procedure — to control all purchases.

Purchase orders— A purchase order system is the best way to keep a record of the quantity and cost of all materials, supplies, tools, and equipment rentals for each project. A good purchase order includes complete information for all materials purchased and identifies the painting operation where they'll be used.

You can buy purchase order forms at a stationery store, or create your own. In either case, make sure the purchase orders are numbered consecutively. Then require all vendors to include the purchase order number on every invoice. Notify them in writing that you won't pay any invoices that don't include a purchase order number.

The purchasing agent— The purchasing agent must be familiar with the materials, supplies, tools, and equipment used by the company. He should also

MATERIAL REQUISITION		No. _____1_____

Date: _6-2-88_   Job no. _8829_____

Quantity	Description	Operation
20 GAL	ENAMEL UNDERCOATER	UNDERCOAT
30 GAL	ENAMEL	ENAMEL TRIM
20 GAL	PVA SEALER	SEAL WALLS
30 GAL	ENAMEL	ENAMEL WALLS
100 GAL	FLAT WALL - NAVAJO WHITE	WALLS

_____
FOREMAN

Material requisition
Figure 11-11

know the pricing system used by each supplier. In many painting companies, the estimator is also the purchasing agent.

The purchasing agent is responsible for making sure the purchase orders are detailed enough to reconstruct a complete material purchase record if necessary. He must also review all purchase orders for accuracy. Remember, suppliers aren't liable for incorrect purchase order information. He'll also check to see that the requested material is included in the estimates for that job.

Verifying purchases begins with the material deliveries. Match the packing slip to the purchase order to make sure the purchase was authorized and the quantity is correct.

Finally, when supplier invoices arrive, match the purchase order to the invoice. If the invoice is accurate, enter the material quantities and costs on the job cost record for that project.

Job Costing

Job costing is simply recording all the labor costs (including the employer's burden), material costs, and other direct costs for a job. The job cost record in Figure 11-12 is the format I use for recording job costs and expenses for each project.

Use your job cost records to:

1) Calculate the profit (or loss) at the completion of a job by comparing the total costs with the contract amount.

2) Evaluate labor productivity both during and after the job. With good job cost records you can pinpoint wasted manhours caused by inefficient crews, overmanned jobs, or time lost waiting for materials to arrive or the weather to clear.

3) Identify poor supervision and wasted or stolen materials.

TOTAL CONTRACT AMOUNT $ 50,000.—

Date	Description	Quantity or hours	@		Materials		Labor		Other direct expenses		Cumulative total cost	
3/12	WEEK OF 3/12/88 – LABOR	80 HRS	10	00			800	—			800	—
3/13	SPRAY RIG RENTAL – P.O. 4110								100	—	900	—
3/17	MATERIALS – P.O. 4120	100 GAL	LUMP SUM		1000	—					1900	—
3/19	WEEK OF 3/19/88 – LABOR	90 HR	10	00			900	—			2800	—
3/19	EXTENSION LADDER – P.O. 4121								50	—	2850	—
3/26	WEEK OF 3/26/88 – LABOR	75 HR	10	00			750	—			3600	—
3/27	MATERIALS – P.O. 4127	80 GAL			950	—					4550	—

REMARKS				TOTAL MATERIAL		TOTAL LABOR		TOTAL OTHER		TOTAL COST	
								TOTAL CONTRACT		50,000	—
								Less TOTAL COST			
								GROSS PROFIT			
								LESS OVERHEAD COSTS 15 % of Contract			
								NET PROFIT			

Job cost record
Figure 11-12

4) Calculate the percentage of completion for billing progressive payments.

5) Produce final job costs which you'll use to establish historical costs.

6) Adjust estimating formulas or create new formulas. The estimating tables in this manual were created from detailed job cost information.

For smaller companies handling mostly smaller jobs, a record of job costs, manhours, and materials used can be recorded on the outside of a 9" x 12" manila envelope. You can have your job cost record printed on the envelope, or attach a copy to the front. In the envelope, file receipts, invoices, and time cards. For larger companies, I recommend a standard bookkeeping and job cost accounting system.

Monitor and Evaluate Manhours

At the beginning of each week, the project foreman should get a new progress report that shows manhour totals to date. At the end of the week, the project foreman should update the progress report and calculate the labor hours over or under the estimate. Then the completed progress report and the weekly time cards go to the field superintendent for evaluation. The field superintendent checks the math to make sure that line totals are correct.

A quick look at the week's "over or under" line tells the story for each job. You can see at a glance which projects need help. If a job's heading for trouble, you have time to take action to get it back on track. Since you check the condition of each project each week, you should never have an unexpected loss on a job.

On some projects, you may have to evaluate and redistribute the field manhours about two or three weeks into production. That way you can compensate for operations which are behind or ahead of schedule.

You could just use the time cards to keep track of the hours spent, but the progress reporting system is more complete. Whether you use the time cards or the progress report, compare the actual manhours to the hours you estimated for the percentage of work that's complete. For example, assume that you've estimated a total of 230 manhours for a project. It's 50% complete, so you would expect to have spent 115 manhours. The progress reports show a total of 110 manhours

spent. You're five hours (or 4%) ahead of the game — and the profit picture looks good.

If the actual hours spent are more than 10% (or your profit percentage) over the estimate, evaluate each painting operation to find which ones are over budget. Make manpower adjustments and then monitor those operations for the rest of the project. Keep the final job cost as close as possible to the original bid, to salvage what profit you can.

Compare Actual Costs to Percent Complete

Begin by entering direct expenses on the job cost record. Include the labor costs from the time cards (including employer's burden), material costs, equipment, tools and other miscellaneous costs. Total all the direct expenses to find the job cost to date. But don't include overhead. That's an indirect cost.

Next, have your field supervisor or job foreman give you a report of the percentage of the project completed on the date of your evaluation. Verify this with the percent complete used by the accounting department for progressive billings.

Finally, multiply the percent complete by the direct cost subtotal in your estimate. If the work is 50% complete and your estimated direct costs were $41,800, you would expect to have spent $20,900 so far. If actual costs from job cost records are only $20,000, you're on the way to a healthy profit.

But these figures are reliable only if the variables you're using are accurate. If all of the materials and supplies were purchased at the beginning of the job, the actual costs would be skewed. You'd have to multiply the material costs by the percent complete to get an accurate picture.

Cost Overruns

If your cost comparison is less than 10% over the estimate, your costs are in line for that job. If you're more than 10% over the estimate, take the time to do a detailed cost breakdown to find the reason for the cost overrun.

Begin by reviewing the manhours spent. That's the most likely culprit. If that doesn't pinpoint the problem, look for discrepancies in the material costs. Your job cost record of material quantities and costs may contain all the information you need. If it doesn't, reconstruct a detailed material purchase record from the requisitions and purchase orders. Check that the amount of material you estimated for each operation was accurate.

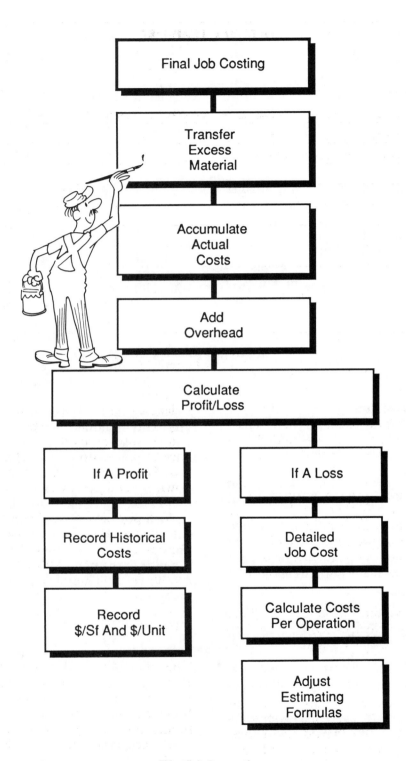

Final job costing
Figure 11-13

MATERIAL TRANSFER

Date: *9-28-88*

From: *8829*   To: *8836*

Items: *10 GALLONS — FLAT WALL — NAVAJO WHITE*
         5 GALLONS — THINNER
         5 GALLONS — LACQUER

By: *Russ*

Form #:_____

Material transfer
Figure 11-14

Solutions to Cost Overruns

If your job cost analysis indicates that you're behind on the job or that the job was underbid in the first place, there are several solutions you can try:

1) The obvious solution to cost overruns is to fire unproductive painters and hire young, honest, aggressive painters who are experienced and productive. But who can find painters like that when you need them? If you could, you wouldn't be in trouble in the first place! So let's look at some other solutions.

2) Assign your best and most productive foreman to make up the cost deficiencies. Use his field expertise to organize the job better and to motivate the painters for greater productivity.

3) Consider pulling all of your apprentice painters from other projects to work on the job with the cost overrun. I call this *apprentice overload*. By substituting lower paid apprentices for journeyman painters, you'll reduce your hourly labor costs. Although each painter will be less productive, with good supervision you should be able to lower your labor costs over all.

4) Here's another suggestion. Try paying your painters on a *piecework* basis. That means paying for the number of "pieces" of work produced at a set price for each piece. That can increase productivity and reduce the cost overrun. It's also a good way to break in an inexperienced painter or for a painter who needs a few days to catch up to the pace of production work. But there's a down side, too. The quality of workmanship will probably go down — and piecework is frowned on by labor unions.

With payment on a piecework basis, the painter functions almost like a subcontractor. He can work at his own pace. But unless the painter is a licensed painting contractor with insurance, he's still your employee. You must carry insurance and deduct taxes from his wages, just like any other employee. If you're considering using independent contractors, check the requirements with your accountant.

The Final Job Cost Analysis

Here's a safe assumption: The actual costs for a job won't ever be exactly what you estimated. When a project is finished, analyze all the job costs to measure the success or failure of the job. Figure 11-13 shows the process for final job costing. Let's go through the steps one at a time.

Material transfer— The first step is to transfer all excess inventory from the completed job and deduct the costs from the job cost record. The material transfer slip (Figure 11-14) will keep track of the inventory transferred from the shop to a job or from one project to another. This form insures that all materials, supplies, tools, and equipment are charged to the project where they're actually used.

Accumulate actual costs— Calculate the actual job costs from the job cost record. Then add the overhead percentage back into the costs. Remember, you deducted the overhead when calculating the field manhours.

Calculate profit or loss— Compare the actual costs and overhead to the estimates to find the profit or loss on the job. If you made a profit, record the unit costs in your historical cost record. If you took a loss, take a detailed look at those job costs. Find out which operations ran over estimates — and why.

Adjust estimating formulas— If there were cost overruns, were they the result of a one-time problem, or do you need to adjust your estimating formulas? Make sure you know the answer to that question before you estimate the next job. When you use actual field performance to adjust your manhour and material estimating formulas, you're making future estimates more accurate.

Chapter

12

HISTORICAL COSTS

*E*very job should have two profits. The first is the cash that goes in your pocket. That's important, of course. But the second profit could be even more important. It's what you learn from the job — both bidding the work and getting it done.

Sometimes what you learn on a job is more valuable than the profit earned. But on every job, profitable or otherwise, make the most of the lessons available. Prepare an estimate that shows item by item your anticipated costs for both labor and materials. File that estimate for future reference. If your bid is accepted, keep accurate records on material costs, quantities used, and the manhours needed. Compare actual costs with estimated costs. If they don't match, find out why.

Anyone can make an estimating mistake. No estimator is perfect. But keeping good cost records and using them regularly should keep you from making the same mistake twice. That's going to save you many thousands of dollars over a career in the painting business.

The previous chapter explained how to gather job cost information. This chapter explains how to make that information more useful. Sometimes you'll hear this cost information called *historical costs* or *past performance costs*. No matter what the name, your cost records are unique. No cost figures from any other source are more useful than costs of work done by your crews. My costs are my costs — for my crews, in my area, for the type of work we handle, with our equipment, and our supervisors. I'll show you some of my costs later in this chapter. But these are *my* costs, not yours. You can use my costs until you develop your own. But accumulate your own cost records as quickly as possible. There's no better way to improve the accuracy of your estimates.

The record of costs on completed jobs can make future estimates more accurate, of course. But that's not all. As you get better at estimating, you'll probably want to develop estimating formulas and standards from your cost records. A few simple formulas can cut the time needed to prepare routine estimates, make estimating errors less likely, and help identify your company's productive capacity.

When you consider all the ways they can save money, it's amazing that so few painting contractors keep cost records on completed jobs. But some paint contractors have an excuse. No one has ex-

Specifications

Interior: 1 COAT WALLS
            1 COAT UNDERCOAT
            1 COAT ENAMEL

Exterior: 1 COAT

Date	Contractor	Plan #	Square footage	Hours per unit	# of stories	# of openings	High ceilings	Hours for siding	Excessive Exterior painting	$ unit	$ /SF	Profit (loss)
7-88	JOHN DOE	1A	1000	20	1	15	LIV TO 13'	1	NONE	1200	1.20	
		1B	1100	21	1	16	LIV TO 13'	1	WHITE FASCIA	1250	1.14	
		2A	1200	22	2	17	NONE	1	NONE	1300	1.08	4%
		2B	1200	25	2	17	NONE	2	SIDING	1400	1.17	
8-88	ACE BUILDERS	1	1500	34	2	18	LIV TO 15'	1	2 COATS	1700	1.13	
		2	1600	35	2	19	LIV TO 15'	2	"	1750	1.09	7%
		3	1100	22	1	NONE	NONE	1	"	1300	1.18	

Historical costs for single family homes
Figure 12-1

plained how important cost records can be. Having read this chapter, you don't have an excuse.

A new painting contractor is at a real disadvantage without good cost records. He can't check his bids. And without manhour records and material cost information, he's bidding blind, *guesstimating*, not estimating. Could that be the reason why so many contractors go broke in their first year or two?

Recording Accurate Cost Records

When each job is complete, record the final job costs. The key is to express unit costs in a unit that makes comparisons easy and convenient. Here are the best units to use:

1) Cost per square foot of floor space for all projects

2) Cost per building for single family detached homes

3) Cost per living unit for apartments or condominiums

4) Cost per room for repaint projects

Also record the percentage of profit or loss on each job. You don't want to base future estimates on jobs that lost money.

There are other ways to organize job cost information. I won't insist that my way is the only way. Invent your own format if that suits you better. What's important is that you be able to use historical costs to forecast the cost of future jobs. My system is to organize all costs into groups of projects with similar specifications and work descriptions. Be sure you're comparing apples to apples.

I organize job costs by the project category: single family detached homes, condominiums, apartments, office buildings, shopping centers, and repaint projects. Except for single family homes, most of these project types will be quite similar. Since homes vary more widely, you'll need more detailed records to make valid comparisons.

Costs for Single Family Homes

Many residential developers use similar floor plans for detached homes and condos. But homes and condos are likely to have more special features than apartments or commercial buildings. I developed the historical cost format in Figure 12-1 for single family homes.

Costs for Apartments and Commercial Projects

Because most apartment and commercial projects are similar, you can group cost estimates by category. Keep a separate cost table for each category of work performed by your company. You might have separate records for apartments, office buildings, restaurants and shopping centers, for example.

Figure 12-2 is my format for recording costs for apartments and commercial projects. You can also use it for other building types and for repaints. Be sure to include the cost per square foot for all buildings and the cost per room for repaints.

The most important information is in the columns headed *cost per square foot ($/SF)*, *cost per unit*, and *percent profit (loss)*. The other columns, along with the specifications, help you identify the complexity of each project. That makes comparisons easier and helps you spot unusual conditions that will increase or decrease costs.

Cost per square foot— For commercial buildings, the price per square foot is the most important information.

Cost per unit— In multi-family buildings like apartments, hotels and condominiums, this is the price per dwelling unit. For single family detached homes, it's the price per building.

Cost per room— The cost per room is the key unit for repaint projects. If you're using Figure 12-2 for repaint costs, use the cost per unit column to record the cost per room.

Historical Cost Table

The costs suggested in Figure 12-3 are based on my cost for work done in 1987. When you review the tables, remember pricing varies in different areas and for different types of projects. Not all contractors had these costs, of course. But the tables provide an example of how you can organize your historical cost records. Tables like these, based on your own cost information, can improve your estimating accuracy and should save you estimating time and money on nearly every job.

Specifications:

Interior: Ceilings (height and finish) _ACOUSTIC – NO PAINT_

Flat walls (number of coats) _1 COAT FLAT LATEX TO COVER_

Wet area walls (number of coats) _1 COAT SEALER & 1 COAT ENAMEL_

Trim (number of coats) _1 COAT UNDERCOAT & 1 COAT ENAMEL_

Windows (aluminum or wood) _SLIDING ALUMINUM. NO PAINT_

Cabinets (prefinished, enamel or stain & laquer) _STAIN, SEAL + 2 COATS LACQUER_

Base (painted or stained) _PAINT GRADE, PAINTED PER WALLS_

Wallcover _MATERIAL ALLOWANCE @ $15.⁰⁰/ROLL FURNISHED BY OWNER_

Exterior: Wood trim (number of coats) _2 COATS STAIN_

Stucco (paint, seal or no finish) _NO FINISH_

Metal trim (number of coats) _1 COAT PRIME + 1 COAT METAL PAINT_

Location	Project type	Contract date	Number of floors	Total units	Gross SF	Avg unit SF	$ unit	$ SF	% profit (loss)
San Diego	Apartment	1/88	2	96	70,812	738	436.—	.63	(1%)
Poway	Apartment	6/88	2	107	74,927	700	528.—	.75	7%
Livermore	Fast Food	9/88	1	1	1,000	—	—	1.25	2%
Redding	Restaurant	10/88	1	1	3,000	—	—	1.75	4%
Red Bluff	School	10/88	1	77	40,000	—	—	.89	5%
San Diego	Office	10/88	2	—	15,000	—	—	.60	8%
Carlsbad	Hospital	11/88	4	150	75,000	500	475.—	.95	3%
Palm Springs	Hotel	11/88	2	120	34,800	290	290.—	1.—	8%
Redding	Hotel – Paint	12/88	3	110	45,209	411	205.—	.50	4%
	Wallcover						137.—	.33	(1%)

Historical costs for apartments and commercial projects
Figure 12-2

Single Family Homes
Interior Repaint Guide

Specifications: Quality painting with adequate preparation. Costs given are per room.

Included: All walls and trim
Paint grade kitchen cabinets

Excluded: Stain grade kitchen cabinet refinishing

Room size SF	1 coat flat finish	1 coat enamel finish	2 coats flat finish	2 coats enamel finish	Wallcover or 3 coats finish
50	$85.00	$131.00	$110.00	$159.00	$181.00
75	111.00	176.00	141.00	203.00	231.00
100	131.00	198.00	168.00	242.00	276.00
125	160.00	237.00	194.00	277.00	317.00
150	175.00	265.00	215.00	310.00	355.00
175	194.00	292.00	236.00	341.00	390.00
200	212.00	318.00	257.00	371.00	424.00
225	228.00	342.00	276.00	399.00	456.00
250	243.00	365.00	295.00	426.00	487.00
275	258.00	387.00	313.00	452.00	517.00
300	271.00	408.00	330.00	477.00	546.00
325	285.00	428.00	347.00	501.00	574.00
350	298.00	449.00	363.00	525.00	601.00
375	311.00	468.00	379.00	548.00	628.00
400	324.00	488.00	395.00	571.00	654.00

Exterior Repaint Guide

(Average 1,000 to 1,200 SF home)

Example 1.

Specifications: Quality, long-lasting job with well-prepared surfaces

Preparation: Complete power wash, putty, patch

Prime: 1 coat complete, spray or roll

Paint: 1 coat with 2 colors - 1 color siding or stucco and 1 color trim

Historical cost guide
Figure 12-3

Pricing: $1,000 to $1,200

Example 2.

Specifications: Inexpensive "advertised special" repaint

Preparation: Minimum preparation, scrape and light sand

Prime: 1 coat spot prime, brush coat

Paint: 1 coat with 1 color

Pricing: $700.00 to $850.00

Add-on extras: 2 colors. Trimming or tying back bushes. Painting doors.

New Construction Guide

Specifications

Included: Cabinets. Deduct 15% to 20% if prefinished

Excluded: Ceilings. Add 10% to 15% if painted
Exterior siding and stucco paint. Add 15% to 20%

Economy homes (1 coat flat, 2 enamel. Minimum amenities)

   Tract production (5 or more units): $.60 to $1.00/SF

Average homes (1 coat flat, 2 enamel. Few amenities)

   Spec production (1 to 4 units): $.85 to $1.10/SF

Quality homes (2 coats flat, 3 enamel. Many amenities)

   Tract production (5 or more units): $.90 to $1.40/SF

   Spec homes (1 to 4 units): $1.25 to $1.75/SF

Custom homes (2 coats flat, 3 enamel. Custom amenities and colors)
   Wide price variation. May exceed $1.50 to $2.50/SF

Apartments

Interior Repaint Guide

Specifications: Inexpensive production job, more than 5 vacant units. Minimum preparation. 1 coat to cover on all surfaces, 1 off-white color throughout.

Studios:	$140.00 to $150.00 each
1 BR/1 BA:	$160.00 to $180.00 each
2 BR/1 BA:	$175.00 to $195.00 each
2 BR/2 BA:	$190.00 to $225.00 each

Historical cost guide
Figure 12-3 (continued)

# Chapter 13

PARTS OF AN ESTIMATE: LABOR

The next few chapters cover the five cost categories in your estimates: labor, material, equipment, overhead and profit. You'll also find some valuable information on price escalation, contingency allowances, commissions and subcontracting.

This chapter covers labor cost, your largest single cost category. Not only is labor the biggest cost on most jobs, it's also the hardest to predict. To be a good painting estimator, you need experience with paints and coatings, of course. But, most important, you need good judgment. How long will it take your crews to finish the job? Answering that question is always easier if you can refer to cost records from similar jobs already completed.

Estimating Labor Costs

Your labor cost depends on the hourly labor rate, the employer's labor burden (taxes and insurance), and the productivity of your crews. All of these will vary, of course. But the procedure remains the same. Base your estimates on the hourly labor cost and the expected productivity for each painting operation. Some painters are slower.

Others are faster. Adjustments must be made for slower crews and more difficult work. That's where your judgment is essential.

Labor rates vary from year to year. In the eight years from 1979 to 1986, average union wages for painters in large cities, including fringe benefits, rose from $12.37 to $19.50 per hour. I can't foresee the future. But it's a safe bet that wages will continue to rise as the value of the dollar falls. Always base your estimates on the current journeyman rate for your painters.

Wage rates also vary from area to area. Recently I saw a survey of hourly union rates for painters in most large U.S. cities. The lowest rate shown was $8.40 an hour for painters in El Paso, Texas. The highest rate was $27.75 for painters in Anchorage, Alaska. You might ask, "Why haven't all the painters in El Paso moved to Anchorage?" I don't know the answer, except to suggest that painters aren't starving in El Paso. Nor are they getting rich in Anchorage. Working conditions and living costs are very different in those two cities.

Foremen are usually paid $.50 to $1.00 per hour more than journeymen, and field superintendents usually make $3.00 to $3.50 per hour more than journeymen. Painters with special skills are paid at a higher rate than ordinary painters. On average, you'll add $.25 to the journeyman base rate for swing stage brush painters, spray painters or paperhangers, $.50 for iron, steel and bridge painters (ground work), $1.00 for sandblasters and iron, steel and bridge painters (swing stage), and $1.50 for steeplejacks.

Most painting on government and defense projects is done at the "prevailing wage." Under the Davis Bacon Act, contractors on government jobs must pay at least the prevailing wage in that area.

On private jobs, non-union or *open shop* wage rates will usually apply. Non-union rates don't vary as much from city to city. What contractors are paying depends on supply and demand and will be influenced by the skill and dependability of each individual painter.

Employer's Burden

Every paint contractor must include payroll taxes and the cost of employee insurance in the hourly labor cost. These expenses are called the *fixed employer's burden*. There's no legal way to avoid paying these taxes and insurance costs:

1) Social Security tax is required by the Federal Insurance Contributions Act (FICA). All employers must pay FICA tax on each dollar of payroll. Employees also pay FICA tax. You deduct it from employee payroll and pay your share and the employee share monthly or quarterly. Most banks will accept your FICA payments.

2) Federal Unemployment Insurance tax is required by the Federal Unemployment Tax Act (FUTA). It's paid by the employer and none is deducted from employee wages.

3) State Unemployment Insurance varies from state to state.

4) Workers' Compensation Insurance provides employee benefits in case of injury or death caused during employment. Every employer is required to provide this coverage for employees.

Tax rates vary from year to year and from state to state. Your accountant will know the rates that apply to your employees. Figure 13-1 shows some typical fixed burden rates for painters and office staff.

In addition to the fixed burden, you'll probably also provide fringe benefits such as vacations and

	Craftsmen ($15.00 base pay)	Office staff ($10.00 base pay)
FICA - Social Security	7.15% ($1.07)	7.15% ($ .72)
Unemployment Insurance	5.6 % ($ .84)	5.6 % ($ .56)
(FUTA - Federal Unemployment Tax Act)		
(SUI - State Unemployment Insurance)		
Worker's Compensation	10.6 % ($1.59)	3.0 % ($ .30)
Subtotal	23.35% ($3.50)	15.75% ($1.57)

Fixed labor burden
Figure 13-1

sick pay. These may be voluntary contributions or they may be required by a collective bargaining agreement. The cost of fringe benefits can range from 10% to 20% for open shops and 30% to 40% for union shops. These costs are called the *variable labor burden*. Figure 13-2 shows some representative benefits and their costs for craftsmen and office staff, and the total employer's burden for the two groups.

	Craftsmen ($15.00)	Office staff ($10.00)
Vacation (2 weeks)	.05	.03
Sick leave	.0	.05
Medical insurance	.75	.50
Life insurance	.24	.24
Retirement/pension	.64	1.00
Profit sharing	.0	.50
Education (apprentice training)	.07	.0
Subtotal	$1.75 (11.65%)	$2.32 (21.68%)
Total employer's burden:		
Fixed	$3.50 (23.35%)	$1.57 (15.75%)
Variable	1.75 (11.65%)	2.32 (21.68%)
	$5.25 (35.00%)	$3.74 (37.43%)
Total cost per hour:	$20.25	$13.74

Variable labor burden
Figure 13-2

Labor Productivity

As a painting estimator, you must work closely with your field superintendent to monitor the progress of every job. The more you know about the ability of your painters, the more accurate your estimates will be. But don't expect your estimates to be exact. Painters are human beings, not robots or computers that can be programmed to run at exactly the same speed every time. That's why estimating is an art, not an exact science. Here are some of the things you should think about when compiling every estimate:

Overtime— Excessive overtime puts a strain on your craftsmen, draining their energy. It only takes a few days of overtime to reduce the productivity of most painters. Try not to work anyone more than two consecutive overtime days.

Working environment— Work efficiency is lower when men, materials and equipment are confined in a small area. Painters need elbow room to work efficiently and get maximum productivity. They're also more productive in a clean environment. It's easier — and safer — to work in an area free of debris.

Supervision— Your project foreman and field superintendent can make or break a job. The better they are, the more work will be done. You want a foreman who can put the right painter on the right job, using the most experienced tradesmen to work on tasks that require more skill, and using other painters where less skill is needed. The project foreman is also responsible for job safety and quality control.

The field superintendent is the foreman's supervisor. His primary responsibility is to be sure that each foreman has the manpower, materials and equipment needed to get the job done.

Your estimates will be more competitive if you can assume high labor productivity. That's only possible when you have good supervision, from both foremen and superintendent. Here's what it takes to make a good supervisor:

1) Be respected rather than liked. Many good supervisors limit their socializing with employees. Don't go out of your way to make friends with your employees. It's hard to criticize a friend — and even harder to fire one.

2) Ask your field and office staff for their suggestions and assistance. Encourage individual thinking. Invite employees to find better ways to get their work done. Be open to suggestions.

3) Pay attention to employee complaints and ideas. Have an open door policy. Be willing to discuss problems with anyone on your staff. Make it easy for employees to express opinions, air complaints and communicate ideas.

4) Develop responsibility in your staff. Delegate authority. Hold employees accountable for results and give them freedom of expression.

5) Emphasize skills rather than rules. Give your employees a task to complete and then give them the freedom to do it.

6) Be tactful with criticism. Make sure it's constructive. Praise before you criticize. Don't be too quick to blame or assume fault — wait for the facts. Never lose your temper. Mistakes happen. Focus on how you'll keep the mistake from happening again, not on blaming someone. Keep your sense of humor. It's the best way to relieve tension.

7) Keep your staff informed. Everyone likes to be in on what's happening. Let people know where you stand. Be sure everyone knows how changes will affect them. Avoid last minute changes. Plan ahead to avoid emergencies.

Add for Supervision

The Foreman — Your Job Site Supervisor
The project foreman is usually one of your most responsible painters. The foreman is in charge of:

1) Organizing and scheduling painters on his projects according to their skills and abilities

2) Meeting the production schedule and goals

3) Completing time cards. Every foreman should be accountable for the accuracy of time cards.

4) Preparing labor progress reports based on employee time cards

5) Getting approval for extra work on work authorization forms before the work is started

6) Keeping cost records for "time and material" billing

7) Completing material requisitions or purchase orders for purchasing agent

8)   Ordering material for timely delivery

9)   Checking deliveries for proper quantities of material

10)   Transferring material from one job to another and completing the material transfer paperwork

11)   Maintaining an adequate inventory of tools and supplies for use on the job site

12)   Preparing the daily log of activities

13)   Overseeing job site safety

14)   Maintaining quality control

The cost of keeping a working foreman on the job must be included in all of your estimates. In fact, most general contractors have a clause in their contracts requiring all subcontractors to staff their project with adequate supervision to complete the project in a timely manner. A good foreman is the key to profitable production.

Field Superintendent — Supervises All Field Activities

The field superintendent oversees the work of all foremen. A company with only one or two projects at a time may not need a superintendent. But when six or eight crews are working six or eight jobs at a time, your field superintendent will be very busy keeping track of those jobs. The salary of the field superintendent is usually an overhead cost, since he covers many projects.

The primary job of the field superintendent is to be sure that the right manpower, materials and equipment are available on each job. Your field superintendent should:

1)   Work closely with each project foreman.

2)   Distribute job progress hours to each operation and set production goals for the foremen to meet. Review progress reports weekly to be sure production goals are being met.

3)   Assign manpower to each job according to the manpower available or at the request of the foreman.

4)   Schedule roving spray crews and the touchup painters when needed.

5)   Make sure each foreman has enough paint, equipment and supplies to keep the craftsmen busy so production goals can be met. There's no excuse for failing to complete a job on schedule.

6)   Establish an open line of communication with the owner or general contractor to minimize or avoid problems and misunderstandings.

7)   Keep field personnel informed of decisions made in the company office.

8)   Assist foremen in solving problems that they can't handle by themselves.

9)   Keep an activity log of the work completed and record all charges for extra work performed. Notes kept by the superintendent and foremen are essential if you want to collect for extra work.

Field Discipline

Good supervisors are known for being fair and honest, but also inflexible in demanding the best from their crews. The result of this attitude will be:

1)   More respect from the craftsmen
2)   A better working relationship
3)   Greater productivity
4)   Better quality workmanship

Don't be afraid to criticize someone who is loafing or hurting crew performance. Everyone feels better when a "goof-off" gets what's coming to him, especially the most conscientious, ambitious, competent painters. Put marginal painters on piece work until they can pull their own weight. *Your company is only as strong as your weakest link.*

Don't allow any drinking or drugs on your jobs. Give letters to all newly-hired employees stating the terms and conditions of their employment. There are copies of the three letters I use for employee policies and procedures, safety, and theft and vandalism in Chapters 5 and 16. You may be held liable if employees are involved in an accident after drinking on the job — even if the beer cans weren't opened until after quitting time. Terminate any employee who is caught drinking or using drugs on the job.

***What contractors are paying depends on the skill and dependability
of each individual painter***

The learning curve— Productivity increases when painters repeat a task many times. When there are many similar units to paint, you should see productivity increasing. Monitor the work being done. If a crew starts falling behind, spot the problems before it's too late.

Manhour Production Tables

The manhour tables in Appendix B and Chapters 17 through 21 are the figures I use for most preparation and painting operations. They're labor rates expressed in square feet of surface area or linear feet painted per hour. These are *my* production rates for *my* crews and the type of work *my* company handles. They work very well for me. They may or may not work as well for you. If you have them, use figures based on your own crews' productivity. Otherwise, use my figures until you've accumulated historical costs for your painters' capabilities.

Add in Supervision Costs

Not all labor cost is productive labor. A foreman can't get as much work done when he's scheduling, instructing and organizing a job. There's a cost to all supervision. Of course, that cost varies with the type of project. Here are my rule of thumb allowances for non-productive labor by type of job.

On a custom home, non-productive labor will vary with the square foot area. I allow 2.5 hours on a home up to 1,500 square feet, 3 hours on a home over 1,500 SF to 2,000 SF, 4 hours on a home over 2,000 square feet to 2,500 SF, and 5 hours on any larger home.

The model homes in a housing tract will require more supervision. Figure 1 hour of non-productive supervision for each day your crew will be on the job. But the production houses in a tract require less non-productive labor. I estimate 1 hour of non-productive labor per house on the lowest cost tract homes and 2 hours per house for larger homes in better quality tracts.

In apartments and condos, allow 1 hour of non-productive time per unit if there are 10 units or less. For 11 to 30 units, allow 0.75 hours of non-productive time per unit. If there are more than 30 units, allow one-half hour of non-productive time per unit.

Commercial, industrial, institutional and government projects vary considerably in size and complexity, so you'll have to use your judgment. Estimate non-productive time by the square foot of project size, using your experience on previous projects as a guide.

The Shop Rate

When you're bidding for a semi-formal or formal contract, you may be asked to quote a lump sum price for a job, as well as your *shop rate*. The shop rate is your hourly charge for a painter working in the field. That's the figure you'll charge for touchup work, for example, if you send a painter out for an hour or two at the owner's request.

To calculate your shop labor rate when only small amounts of materials will be used, simply add an allowance for material plus overhead and profit to the total labor cost. Adding one dollar per hour of labor is typical.

Here's an example. Assume your hourly labor cost, including employer's burden, is $20.25 and the cost of paint applied by brush will be $1.00 per hour. The total is $21.25. Assume your overhead adds 15% to the $21.25 cost. Fifteen percent of $21.25 is $3.19. Adding the two figures, we get $24.44. But don't use that figure. It doesn't include your profit. Remember profit? That's what you're in business for. Adding 10% for profit, we get the total hourly shop rate, $26.88. If those were my figures, I'd round the number to $27 and quote that amount any time I was asked to supply a painter on an hourly basis for a job that uses little material, like a touchup job.

When the quantity of material is significant, such as when rolling or spraying, be sure to use the shop rate for labor and add the material cost (based on supplier's invoices), plus tax, overhead and profit. For example, suppose the materials cost $80 with a 6% tax, overhead is 15% and profit is 10%. Here's how to figure your material price:

Material cost		$80.00
Tax @ 6%		4.80

	Subtotal	$84.80
Overhead @10%		12.72

	Subtotal	$97.52
Profit @10%		9.75

Total material billing amount		$107.27

If you have a customer who wants to be billed by the gallon for the paint used, use the shop rate for labor and itemize your costs from supplier invoices. Here's how to calculate the material costs. Suppose the material costs $10 a gallon, with tax. For tools and supplies, add 10% or $1 per gallon. Then add overhead and profit:

Material cost (including tax)		$10.00
Sundries @10%		1.00

	Subtotal	$11.00
Overhead @15%		1.65

	Subtotal	$12.65
Profit @10%		1.27

Total charge per gallon		$13.92

That doesn't include labor, of course.

In the next chapter we'll go on to the second largest cost in most jobs, materials.

Chapter

14

PARTS OF AN ESTIMATE: MATERIAL AND SUNDRIES

This chapter will suggest a simple way to estimate painting materials, including paint, tools and supplies. I'll follow the painting industry custom of using the term *materials* when referring to paints and coatings, and the term *sundries* when talking about painting supplies and expendable painting tools. I'll get sundries out of the way first and then devote the rest of the chapter to the more difficult task of estimating paint materials.

Estimating Sundries

Figure 14-1 is a sundry inventory. It lists all the expendable tools and supplies you're likely to need on most jobs. Use this list to keep track of your sundry inventory. Use the column "Inventory Quantity" to list the quantity on hand and the "Cost" column to show the price you paid on the last order.

How do you figure the cost of sundries on each job? It isn't practical to figure the cost of each sheet of sandpaper or each pound of rags. There's no way to predict accurately how many jobs you'll get out of each brush or roller, or out of each roller handle, ladder, or drop cloth. But don't let that keep you from including these important costs in your estimate. Leaving any item out of an estimate

is the same as estimating the cost for that item at zero. That's a 100% miss. Too many of those, and you're out of the painting business. Better to make a reasonably good estimate than to omit some costs entirely.

Here's an easy, quick and fairly accurate way to include the cost of these sundry items in your bids. I've found that sundries cost about 10% to 20% of the cost of the paint for most projects. If you spent $3,000 on paint, you'll probably use up around $300 worth of sundries. And the more paint you use, the more sundries you'll need. That's reasonable. And it's also fairly accurate. This method eliminates detailed, time-consuming calculations on the quantity of supplies needed and the life expectancy of expendable tools.

There's one major exception to this 10% rule. On repaint jobs, where extensive prep work is required, the cost of sundries may be much more than 10% of the paint cost. For this type of work I recommend adding 10% to the paint cost for the usual sundries and then adding the actual cost of the preparation materials which are in excess of the normal 10%. You might even double up on some of the normal preparation charges. When it comes to prep work, it's important to have enough money in your estimate to cover all the costs of the job.

Sundry Inventory Checklist

Suppliers: *D - DUMPHY PAINTS*
F - FISHER PAINTS
S - SUPERIOR PAINTS
P - PIONEER PAINTS

Supplier	Product number	Product	Inventory quantity	Unit	Cost			
D	#	Bender paint pads		Each	$			
D	# 792	Brush - 3" nylon PEACOCK	2	Each	$ 12.00	1		
D	# 783	Brush - 4" nylon SCOOTER	2	Each	$ 16.00		1	
D	# 115	Brush - 5" nylon PACER	2	Each	$ 16.20		1	
D	# 784	Brush - 3" bristle	2	Each	$ 11.10		1	
D	# 2170	Caulking bags	2	Each	$ 2.25			
D	# LATEX	Caulking -DAP ACRYLIC LATEX	12	Each	$ 2.00	12		
D	# 2172	Caulking gun (Newborn)	2	Each	$ 1.50	1		
P	# —	Hydraulic fluid	2	Qt	$ 3.60			
P	# —	Lemon oil	2	Pint	$ 2.80	1		
F	# —	Masking paper 18" wide	3	Roll	$ 14.00			
F	# ANCHOR	Masking tape 1½"	24	Roll	$ 1.40	12		12
P	# 2176	Lacquer	2	5's	$ 26.00		1	
P	# 2173	Sanding sealer	2	5's	$ 25.00	1		
P	# 9850	Resin sealer	2	5's	$ 22.00			
P	# 131	PVA sealer (CLEAR)	2	5's	$ 23.00	1		
F	# 8500	Particle masks 100/BOX	1	Box	$ 11.25		1	
P	# —	Putty (Crawfords)	3	Qt	$ 3.75	2		
F	# R-10	Respirators	1	Each	$ 47.05			1
F	# R-49	Respirator cartridges 20/BOX	2	Box	$ 11.40			
F	# R-51	Respirator filters 20/BOX	2	Box	$ 22.90		1	
P	# —	Rags	10	Lb	$ 12.00			
F	# AR691	Roller covers 9" x ¾"	6	Each	$ 2.50	2		
F	# AR692	Roller covers 9" x ⅜"	6	Each	$ 1.75	3		2
F	# AR671	Roller covers 7" x ¾"	3	Each	$ 2.20		1	
F	# AR672	Roller covers 7" x ⅜"	3	Each	$ 1.50	1		
F	# AR611	Roller covers mini	3	Each	$ 1.75		1	
F	# 95	Roller frames 9"	6	Each	$ 2.30	1	2	
F	# 75	Roller frames 7"	5	Each	$ 2.10	3	3	
F	# TSR	Roller frames mini	2	Each	$ 3.25			
D	# 40	Roller poles 4' wood tip	3	Each	$ 1.00		1	

Sundry inventory checklist
Figure 14-1

Supplier	Product number	Product	Inventory quantity	Unit	Cost				
D	# *10*	Roller poles 6' wood tip	*10*	Each	$ .75				
P	# *1—*	Roller pole tips metal	*2*	Each	$ 23.00			*2*	
P	# ___	Sandpaper (120C production)	*2*	Slve	$ 23.00			*2*	
P	# ___	Sandpaper (220A trimite)	*2*	Slve	$ 21.00				*1*
P	# ___	Sandpaper (220A garnet)	*1*	Slve	$ 20.00		*1*		
D	# ___	Spackle (Synkloid)	*3*	Qt	$ 2.90	*1*		*1*	
D	# *42/61*	Spray bombs (black/white)	*12*	Each	$ 1.60	*12*			*12*
F	# ___	Spray gun tips #3 or #4	*10*	Each	$ 6.25			*3*	
F	# *2762*	Spray gun couplers	*10*	Each	$ 1.00			*5*	
F	# *S-27*	Spray socks *48/BOX*	*1*	Box	$ 65.00				
D	# *5271*	Stip fill	*1*	Gal	$ 5.30			*1*	
D	# *5927*	Strainer bags	*2*	Each	$ 1.25	*1*			
D	# *JT-21*	Staples - 5/16"	*2*	Box	$ 2.00				
P	# *50 GAL*	Thinner, lacquer	*1*	Drum	$ 160.00				
P	# *50 GAL*	Thinner, paint	*1*	Drum	$ 120.00				*1*
P	# ___	Thinner, shellac (alcohol)	*1*	Gal	$ 6.90				
D	# *5775*	Work pots (2 gal, plastic)	*3*	Each	$ 1.75		*1*		*2*
	#				$				
	#				$				
	#				$				
	#				$				
	#				$				
		Order date				*7/21*	*7/27*	*8/3*	*9/10*
		Ordered by: (initials)				*JH*	*JH*	*JH*	*JH*
		Purchase order no.				*03 52*	*03 56*	*03 61*	*03 71*

Sundry inventory checklist
Figure 14-1 (continued)

Estimating Paint Quantities

Estimating paint is much harder. I'll use the rest of this chapter to show you how to make accurate estimates of the materials you'll need for each job. Let's begin with the spread rate.

Spread Rate

The quantity of paint needed depends on the *spread rate* for the paint you're using, the surface you're painting and the mil thickness required in the specifications. The manufacturer's recommended coverage rate will usually be on the label of the paint container. Use this figure (or the material coverage rates in this book) as a *starting point* for spread rates. Once you have experience with a coating and a type of surface, you'll probably have your own opinion on material coverage.

You'll find the material coverage tables I use in the chapters on preparation, repaint and new construction estimating. But neither the label nor my tables will be completely accurate for your jobs. And remember that my material coverage rates are only for jobs where the mil thickness of the coating isn't specified.

At the end of every job, make it a habit to calculate the material quantities used and the actual material coverage rate for that job. This requires the cooperation of your job foremen and field crews. They must record how much paint was used for each operation — walls, fascia, siding, and so on. Use the forms in Chapter 12 to accumulate this important historical cost information.

Waste and Spillage

There will be some waste and spillage on every job. Be sure to consider this when figuring spread rates. Professional painters don't waste materials. They don't kick over five-gallon buckets of paint. But there's always some waste. My material coverage tables include the appropriate waste factor for each application method, whether it's brush, roll or spray. Of course, the actual amount of waste will depend on the skill of the painters and the method of application. But here are the waste factors *I* use for different application methods:

Brush	3% to 5%
Roll	5% to 10%
Airless spray	20% to 25%
Conventional spray	25% to 35%

Mil Thickness

The material specifications in government and other formal bid commercial or industrial projects may specify the thickness of the material you have to apply to each surface. The thickness is given in *mils,* or thousandths of an inch. One mil is 0.001 inch.

The thickness of the dry paint film will depend on the percentage of solids the paint contains. If you apply a gallon of paint containing 100% solids over 1,600 square feet, the dry film will be 1 mil thick — if 100% of the paint adheres to the wall, that is. But you have to consider waste. For in-

stance, with a 10% waste factor, 90% of the material will be applied. You would multiply by 0.90 to find the actual thickness of the paint film.

Here's a formula that makes it easy to calculate mil thickness, including the waste factor:

$$\frac{S\% \times 1600}{MT} \times (1.00 - WF) = CR$$

Here's what the abbreviations mean:

S% = percentage of solids by volume
MT = mil thickness
WF = waste factor
CR = coverage rate

Let's do a couple of examples. Assume you're applying paint with 40% solids (by volume), using a roller. The waste factor is 10%. You need a thickness of 5 mils. Here's the calculation:

$$\frac{.40 \times 1600}{5} = (1.00 - .10) = 115.2 \text{ SF per gallon}$$

You may have to apply several coats to get a thickness of 5 mils. Now let's see how to find how much paint we'll need for the job if there's 125,000 square feet of surface area.

$$\frac{125,000 \text{ SF}}{115.2} = 1085.07 \text{ gallons}$$

The percentage of solids in any paint will be listed either on the paint labels, in supplier's literature, or in government specifications.

Material Pricing

Always keep our supplier's current price list handy. And make sure it reflects your current wholesale discount for all products. Post a list of all suppliers, their phone numbers, and the salesperson's name beside your phone.

Discounts

Prices from your supplier may change often. Paint quality, your supplier's discount programs, their marketing strategy, and the intensity of the competition will all influence the price you'll pay.

Never take anything for granted when it comes to pricing paints — especially out-of-the-ordinary coatings. Don't assume that a product you haven't used before costs about the same as similar products. It might not. A heavy-duty urethane finish, for example, will cost about twice as much as a heavy-duty vinyl coating. If you don't know that, your profit for the job can go down the drain.

Most paint dealers offer quantity discounts to their best customers. These discounts are usually based on the average quantity of paint purchased each month. The more paint you buy, the better discount you get. A high-volume painting contractor might get a discount of 40% off the retail price. Generally, discounts off retail range from 10% to 50%.

Sales Tax

If you'll be paying sales tax on the paint and supplies you buy, don't forget to include this tax in your estimates. In most states sales tax must be paid by the "final consumer" of any product — that's probably you, the paint contractor. If your state considers the building owner the final consumer, you won't pay tax at the paint store but you might have to collect it from the owner and remit it to the taxing authority. Your accountant can answer any questions you have about tax procedures in your state.

Material Handling and Storage

On repaint jobs, if materials can't be safely stored at the job site, add the cost of loading and unloading the materials each day to your estimate. Include it in the cost for *setup* and *cleanup*. If a job lasts more than one day, you'll save setup and cleanup time if the paint materials can be stored on the job. On a residential job, ask if you can set up a shop in the garage or on the back patio. But there's no savings if you lose stored materials. Balance the risk of theft or vandalism against the cost of removing all materials from the job each night.

On new construction projects, your dealer will usually deliver directly to the job site. You won't have to move very much material from the shop to the job. Of course, materials must be moved around the job site. An allowance for this is included in my new construction estimating formulas in Chapter 19. There's no need to add extra time in your new construction estimates.

On new residential projects, the garage doors are usually installed by the time the painting contractor needs to set up a shop. See Figure 14-2. Ask the general superintendent to assign you a garage for storage. Have separate keyed locks installed on all access doors and put a padlock on the garage door itself.

On commercial and industrial projects, you may want to rent a storage container, like the one in Figure 14-3, for storing materials. If so, add the rental cost to the estimate as an equipment cost. This cost will include the delivery and pickup charge for the container and rental on the container for the duration of the job.

Substitution of Materials

Before submitting your bid, ask if you can substitute materials of equal quality (but lower price) for some of the materials specified. Specifications often allow for substitution in what's commonly known as an *"or equal"* note. *But make sure the materials you plan to substitute are approved by the architect as being equal to the specified product.* If your substitute paint is rejected after your bid is accepted, you may have to use the higher cost paint and absorb the additional cost. You assume the risk of substituting *or equal* materials if you don't have written approval for that substitution. In government work, the performance specs typically restrict a contractor to only *one* manufacturer who can meet the specified performance data.

If you *can* substitute materials, it's worth spending some time getting approval for less expensive products. Finding the right substitutes may make you low bidder, or at least keep you competitive. Substitute alternate materials whenever it's to your advantage.

Paint shop in garage
Figure 14-2

Paint shop in storage container
Figure 14-3

Federal Government Specifications

The federal government has a material classification system for all construction materials. Most of the materials related to painting are listed by number in the Federal Specifications and Commercial Item Descriptions list. You can get a copy of this list by calling or writing to:

Naval Publications and Form Center
5801 Tabor Avenue
Philadelphia, PA 19120
(215) 697-2000

It lists the items by their *document number,* which refers to the document which describes the material. These documents include:

1) The Military Specifications Service Numeric Index. It identifies each of the material documents and their revision dates according to their document number.

2) The *abstract* of the detailed document. An abstract is an abbreviated statement which summarizes the important points of a given text. In this case, the abstract offers a summarized description of the qualities, content and uses of the paint product.

3) The document itself. The document gives a *detailed* description of each type of paint product.

Paint Bases

Every good painting estimator I've met has a good working knowledge of paints and coatings. The more you know about estimating, the more you're likely to know about paints. If there are major gaps in your understanding of paint products, use the section that follows as a refresher course. If you want a complete education on paint products, order a copy of *Painter's Handbook*. There's an order form bound into the back of this book.

Most paints are based on a binder which is dissolved in a solvent or emulsified in water. When applied in a thin film, the paint dries and forms a durable, tough coating.

Solutions of binders in a solvent are called clear finishes, varnishes (if they dry by oxidation), or lacquers (if they dry by evaporation). If opaque pigments are dispersed in the binder, the product is called a paint. Paint can be formulated to produce a high gloss, a semigloss or a flat finish. Special pigments such as red lead and zinc chromate can be used to provide corrosion resistance in primers. Metallic pigment (such as aluminum) can be added to varnishes to produce metallic coatings.

The way a paint performs depends on the type of binder used. Figure 14-4 is a chart of the principal properties of paint binders. Let's look at the common binders.

Alkyd

Most alkyd binders are oil-modified phthalate resins. Economical alkyd finishes are available as clear or pigmented coatings, in flat, semigloss and high gloss. They're easy to apply, and can be used on most clean surfaces except fresh concrete, masonry or plaster. Alkyd finishes are very durable except in corrosive environments.

Cement

Portland cement-based paint is useful for rough surfaces like concrete, masonry and stucco. It dries to form a hard, porous film that allows water to pass through without damaging the surface. Since cement paints are powders, you can make a filler material out of them by adding masonry sand and less water than the directions suggest.

You'll use cement paints most often on fresh masonry. The surface must be damp when they are applied, and must be kept damp for a few days to ensure proper curing. When properly cured, good quality cement paints are durable. When improperly cured, they chalk heavily and soon need repainting.

Epoxy

Most epoxy binders are a combination of two components, an epoxy resin and a polyamide hardening agent. When mixed, the two ingredients react to form a hard coating. Apply epoxy paint thick enough on concrete or masonry and you get a tile-like glaze coating. The surface can also be textured if a gloss surface isn't wanted. The cost per gallon is high, but you don't have to apply as many coats to get an adequate thickness. Epoxy paints will chalk on exterior jobs. They lose their gloss and fade. Otherwise, their durability is excellent.

	Alkyd	Cement	Epoxy	Latex	Oil	Phenolic	Rubber	Moisture curing urethane	Vinyl
Ready for use	Yes	No	No[3]	Yes	Yes	Yes	Yes	Yes	Yes
Brushability	A	A	A	+	+	A	A	A	—
Odor	+[1]	+	—	+	A	A	A	—	—
Cure normal temperature	A	A	A	+	—	A	+	+	+
Cure low temperature	A	A	—	—	—	A	+	+	+
Film build/coat	A	+	+	A	+	A	A	+	—
Safety	A	+	—	+	A	A	A	—	—
Use on wood	A	—	A	A	A	A	—	A	—
Use on fresh concrete	—	+	+	+	—	—	+	A	+
Use on metal	+	—	+	—	+	+	A	A	+
Corrosive service	A	—	+	—	—	A	A	A	+
Gloss - choice	+	—	+	—	A	+	+	A	A
Gloss - retention	+	x	—	x	—	+	A	A	+
Color - initial	+	A	A	+	A	—	+	+	+
Color - retention	+	—	A	+	A	—	A	—	+
Hardness	A	+	+	A	—	+	+	+	A
Adhesion	A	—	+	A	+	A	A	+	—
Flexibility	A	—	+	+	+	A	A	+	+
Resistance to:									
abrasion	A	A	+	A	—	+	A	+	+
water	A	A	A	A	A	+	+	+	+
acid	A	—	A	A	—	+	+	+	+
alkali	A	+	+	A	—	A	+	+	+
strong solvent	—	+	+	A	—	A	+	+	A
heat	A	A	A	A	A	A	+[2]	A	—
Moisture permeability	Mod.	V. high	Low	High	Mod.	Low	Low	Low	Low

+ = Among the best for this property   A = Average
− = Among the poorest for this property   x = Not applicable
   [1] Odorless type
   [2] Special types
   [3] Two component type

Properties of binders
Figure 14-4

Latex

Latex paints have little odor, are easy to apply, and dry very rapidly by evaporation. Interior latex paints can be used as a primer or finish coat on plaster or wallboard walls and ceilings. Exterior latex paints are used directly on exterior masonry or primed wood. These paints are nonflammable, economical, and fade very little. Also, blistering caused by moisture vapor is less of a problem than with solvent-thinned paints. But they don't adhere very well to chalked, dirty or glossy surfaces. Careful surface preparation is essential.

Oil

The major binder in oil paint is linseed oil. Oil paints are used primarily on exterior wood and metal. They dry too slowly for most interior uses and can't be used on masonry. They're easy to use and can be applied thick. Oil based paints tend to soak into the surface well enough so that surface preparation is less critical. They aren't particularly hard or resistant to abrasion, chemicals or strong solvents, but are durable in normal environments.

Rubber-Base

Chlorinated rubber, vinyl toluene-butadiene and styrene-butadiene are three types of rubber-base paints. These are lacquer-type products that dry rapidly to form water-resistant finishes. They're also resistant to mild chemicals. Rubber-based paints are available in a wide range of colors and gloss levels. Use them for exterior masonry and for areas which are wet, humid or subject to frequent washing, like swimming pools, kitchens and laundry rooms.

Urethane

There are two types of urethane finishes: oil-modified and oil-free moisture-curing. Both types are available clear, but only the oil-free can be pigmented.

Oil-modified urethanes are more expensive and have better color than varnishes. They also dry quicker, are harder, and resist scuffing better. They can be used on all surfaces, as exterior varnishes, or as tough floor finishes. But like all clear finishes, they're not very durable. They must be repainted as often as clear finishes.

Moisture-curing urethanes cure by reacting with moisture from the air. Store them in full containers to keep moisture out. Otherwise the contents will turn to a gel.

Other Binders

Here are other binders with properties similar to the ones listed in Figure 14-4:

Oil-alkyd: properties similar to oil and alkyd paints.

Cleoresinous: similar to alkyds but with less color retention.

Phenolic-alkyd: similar to phenolic and alkyd paints.

Oil-modified urethane: also similar to phenolic and alkyd paints.

Vinyl-alkyd: similar to vinyl and alkyd paints.

Types of Paints

Up to this point we've been talking about paint bases. But paint can also be described by its type. You're probably more familiar with types of paints than types of bases.

Lacquer

All coatings which dry solely by evaporation of the solvents are lacquers, including rubber-base coatings and vinyl coatings. Lacquers dry rapidly even at low temperatures, making brushing difficult. The solids content is usually low, so several coats may be needed. Recoating, especially by brush, must be done very carefully to avoid lifting the existing coat.

Varnish

Varnishes are alkyds or resins in solvent with driers added so that they dry by oxidation. The film is clear or nearly clear. Many types of varnish are available.

Paint and Enamel

The difference between paint and enamel is mostly in the way it's used. When used on large areas such as walls, it's called paint. If it's fast drying, levels out to a smooth, hard finish, and is used on relatively small areas or smooth materials such as woodwork, it's called enamel. Enamel can be rolled on, but brushing leaves a more even, smooth finish.

The amount of pigment determines the gloss. Generally, gloss is reduced by adding non-opaque, lower cost pigments called extenders. If no extenders are added, the paint is glossy, durable and easily washed.

House paint is a broad term that includes many paint formulations, both oil-based and latex. Some of them have added ingredients that make them chalk or mildew resistant.

Primer for Paint and Enamel

Most paint jobs require two coats. The first coat is called the primer. The top coat produces the finish color and texture.

Primer-sealer is used to seal a porous or alkaline surface. This protects binder in the top coat from damage from below the surface. Some paints, such as interior latex wall paints, are self-priming. They usually don't need a special primer. Enamel undercoater is a coating which dries to a smooth, hard finish that can be sanded. When sanded, the smooth surface is ideal for a top coat of smooth enamel.

Use primers with anticorrosion pigments such as red lead, zinc chromate, lead silicone chromate, or zinc dust when painting iron and steel. They slow corrosion of the metal but must be protected by other types of coatings.

Figure 14-5 is a paint selection chart. You can use it to choose the proper coating for each surface. It also shows when a primer or sealer is needed.

Aluminum Paint

Metallic paints, including aluminum paints, are available in two forms: ready mix and ready-to-mix. Ready mix aluminum paint is ready to use after normal stirring. It's more convenient to use than the ready-to-mix form and eliminates errors in mixing.

	Alumi-num	Cement base paint	Exterior clear finish	House paint	Metal roof paint	Porch-and-deck paint	Primer or under-coater	Rubber base paint	Spar varnish	Trans-parent sealer	Trim-and-trellis paint	Wood stain	Metal primer
Wood													
Natural finish	-	-	P	-	-	-	-	-	P	-	-	P	-
Porch floor	-	-	-	-	-	P	-	-	-	-	-	-	-
Shingle roof	-	-	-	-	-	-	-	-	-	-	-	-	-
Shutters & trim	-	-	-	P+	-	-	P	-	-	-	P+	-	-
Siding	P	-	-	P+	-	-	P	-	-	-	-	-	-
Windows	P	-	-	P+	-	-	P	-	-	-	P+	-	-
Masonry													
Asbestos cement	-	-	-	P+	-	-	P	P	-	-	-	-	-
Brick	P	P	-	P+	-	-	P	P	-	P	-	-	-
Cement & cinder block	P	P	-	P+	-	-	P	P	-	P	-	-	-
Cement porch floor	-	-	-	-	-	P	-	P	-	-	-	-	-
Stucco	P	P	-	P+	-	-	P	P	-	P	-	-	-
Metal													
Copper	-	-	-	-	-	-	-	-	P	-	-	-	-
Galvanized	P+	-	-	P+	-	-	P	-	P	-	P+	-	P
Iron	P+	-	-	P+	-	-	-	-	-	-	P+	-	P
Roofing	-	-	-	-	P+	-	-	-	-	-	-	-	P
Siding	P+	-	-	P+	-	-	-	-	-	-	P+	-	P
Windows, aluminum	P	-	-	P+	-	-	-	-	-	-	P+	-	P
Windows, steel	P+	-	-	P+	-	-	-	-	-	-	P+	-	P

"P" indicates preferred coating for this surface.
"P+" indicates that a primer or sealer may be necessary before the finishing coat or coats (unless the surface has been previously finished.)

Exterior paint selection chart
Figure 14-5

Oil Stain

Oil stains use a drying oil, usually linseed oil, which is thinned enough to penetrate the wood easily. Interior stains should be applied only to a sanded, dust-free surface, and allowed to dry for a short time. Then the excess is wiped off so that only the stain which penetrated the wood remains.

Paint Colors

Cost of paint can vary with color. The soft, light shades of tan, gray and off-white are less expensive than bright colors like orange, green and bright blue. You're likely to find these expensive colors used in custom homes or the model homes in a housing tract. Normally, painting of model homes is done on a time and material basis. So the extra cost for bright colors isn't your problem. But if you're making a lump sum bid for a custom home, watch out for colors that command a premium price.

There's one other color you have to watch out for. If white is specified for exterior trim (such as fascia, overhang or plant-ons), two coats will probably be needed for complete coverage. Include that cost in your bid.

Paint Brands

Most communities have at least several paint dealers who stock a good selection of materials and offer them to painting contractors at wholesale prices. It's your task to find the supplier who can give you the best combination of price and service. Experienced paint buyers know that some materials from some suppliers carry higher markups. If a general contractor or architect specifies one of these expensive "custom" brands, find out if substitutions are allowed before you bid the job.

Application Methods

If you've spent years in the painting trade, you know how to apply paint on nearly any surface. But I suggest that you read through the following section anyway. The estimating tables in this book assume that you follow the application methods outlined here. For complete details on calculating material quantities, refer to the chapters on estimating repaint jobs and estimating new construction.

Brush Application

Brushes are made with both synthetic and natural bristles. To get a good quality paint job in the shortest possible time, it's important to match the brush to the job. Many sizes, shapes and designs are available — each suited to a particular set of tasks. There are special-purpose brushes for walls, sash and trim, enameling and varnish, and stucco and masonry.

Paint Pad Application

Flat, rectangular pad applicators are sometimes used on shake and shingle surfaces when spray application isn't practical. With their rug-like texture, one or two downward strokes will force paint into the surface grooves. Pad applicators don't splatter, and they allow you to paint right up to the edge of trim without getting paint on the trim.

A bender paint pad is an excellent tool for painting over and under doors. It's simply a bendable strip of sheet metal with a sponge-like pad on the end. You can find them in most paint supply stores. Even if the contract doesn't call for painting all six sides of a door, it's good professional practice to do it anyway. Painting the top and bottom edge takes only a minute or two extra and can prevent warping of exterior doors.

Roller Application

Most rollers are made from lamb's wool, angora, or synthetic fibers. The nap ranges in length from 3/16'' to 1¼''. Rollers range from 1½'' to 2¼'' in diameter and from 1½'' to 18'' in length. Rollers, like brushes, are designed to do a particular job. Short, fine naps are used for enamels and varnishes on smooth surfaces. Longer naps are good for porous, rough, or hard-to-reach surfaces, like chain link fences and porous masonry.

Spray Application

A wide variety of spray equipment is available. Conventional spray equipment uses an air compressor that supplies air to a spray gun attached directly to a paint container.

Airless sprayers are popular for smaller projects. They use a compressor to force liquid under high pressure through a specially shaped orifice on the gun. This causes the paint to atomize without adding air. Some sophisticated sprayers, both conventional and airless, heat the paint before it's atomized.

Spray painting is much faster than brushing or rolling. My manhour formulas later in the book reflect this increased efficiency. Unfortunately, it's easier to make a major mistake when spray painting. The paint viscosity, the air-paint ratio, the pressure, and the spray pattern have to be exactly right. That's why spray painters earn more than brush or roller painters. And spray painting isn't appropriate for every surface. You have to match the application method to the job to get good production.

When spraying is appropriate, here are some suggestions for maximizing production:

• Airless spray tips which are worn can use twice as much paint as new tips. Make sure your painters check and replace tips frequently.

• Be sure the spray painter knows how to use the equipment and how to keep it in good working order.

• Keep spare parts on hand for each pump. I also keep a few new tips and an extra hose handy. Be ready for the most likely breakdowns.

• Sometimes you'll need more than a few spare parts. Know a repair shop where spray equipment can be repaired quickly and economically.

• Keep a back-up pump on the job so work can continue while repairs are being made.

Chapter 15

PARTS OF AN ESTIMATE: EQUIPMENT

Whether you're using rented or company-owned equipment, it's easy to figure the equipment costs into your estimate.

If you're estimating a short-term job, a job that uses only small quantities of materials, or a repaint job, base your equipment costs on what it costs you to rent the equipment, or what it *would* cost to rent if you didn't own it. Your rental yard will quote daily, weekly and monthly equipment rental rates. Figure 15-1 shows some typical rental costs. Of course, your costs will be different. But if you make up a table like this showing your actual rental costs, it can save you hours of calling around to rental yards.

In Chapter 18, estimating repaint jobs, I'll show you how to apply these equipment costs in a repaint estimate. For new construction projects, the equipment costs are included in my estimating formulas. There's not a separate line for equipment costs in the new construction estimate. I'll explain them in Chapter 19.

Equipment Inventory

In many painting companies the estimator takes responsibility for maintaining an inventory of company-owned equipment. I recommend that you identify each piece of equipment with a stamped inventory number or code. Keep track of your equipment on an equipment inventory checklist like Figure 15-2. Hold your foremen responsible for any equipment assigned to them on the checklist.

Subcontracts

Painting contractors don't hire many subcontractors. But once in a while you'll need a specialist for sandblasting, waterblasting, wallcovering, scaffolding or pavement marking jobs. When you hire a subcontractor, make sure the quoted price includes all the labor, material (with tax, if applicable), equipment, overhead and profit. There should be no added costs after the subcontractor's original price is submitted. Include the subcontractor's quote in your bid, then add your overhead and profit percentage.

Figure 15-3 shows some typical rates quoted by sandblasting subcontractors. Figure 15-4 is a checklist for pavement marking subcontractors. Figure 15-5 shows some representative prices for that type of work.

	Purchase	Rental		
		$/day	$/week	$/month
Air compressors				
150 CFM - gas		61.00	200.00	475.00
185 CFM - diesel		98.00	295.00	690.00
250 CFM - diesel		140.00	447.00	1225.00
600 CFM - diesel		224.00	700.00	1790.00
Air hose with coupling, 50' lengths				
¼" I.D.		3.00	6.00	12.00
½" I.D.		5.00	10.00	25.00
Boomlifts - 3' x 4' to 3' x 8' basket				
20' two wheel drive		125.00	475.00	1300.00
30' two wheel drive		150.00	600.00	1800.00
40' four wheel drive		200.00	800.00	2450.00
50' 1,000 lb.		330.00	1000.00	3020.00
¾" I.D.		7.00	16.00	35.00
1" I.D.		9.00	21.00	48.00
1¼" I.D.		11.00	25.00	60.00
1½" I.D.		13.00	32.00	74.00
2" I.D.		15.00	40.00	110.00
3" I.D.		18.00	43.00	117.00
Ladders, extension				
16' to 36' fiberglass only	128.00	9.00	27.00	65.00
40' to 60' fiberglass only	227.00	18.00	56.00	165.00
Ladder jacks (purchase only because of safety, no guardrail)				
Short body	70.00/pair			
Long body	80.00/pair			
Masking paper dispenser		10.00	40.00	120.00
Pics - walkboards: no guardrail (Also known as airplane planks, toothpicks, painters pics and banana boards)				
16'	285.00		20.00	40.00
20'	375.00		25.00	52.00
24'	467.00		30.00	60.00
28'	550.00		40.00	80.00
32'	630.00		45.00	90.00
Planks				
Plain end microlam scaffold plank				
9"			4.00	
12"			5.00	
Rolling ladders				
30" wide, 2 step with rails	175.00			
30" wide, 7 step with rails	360.00			
Rolling platforms, self-propelled, OSHA & ANSI approved				
15'		65.00	195.00	565.00
25'		90.00	350.00	1050.00
35'		120.00	480.00	1440.00
Rolling towers				
Manual, adjustable scissor type to:				
15'				475.00
25'				790.00
5' wide, 9' high, 7' long	880.00			
Add 5' high sections	170.00			
Complete with wheels & railings to 20' high				99.00

	Purchase	Rental		
		$/day	$/week	$/month
Safety nets, stock sizes, purchase only, price per SF				
Nylon ½" mesh	1.65/SF			
¾" mesh for debris	1.50/SF			
Nylon 4" mesh	1.45/SF			
Polypropylene, 6" mesh	1.20/SF			
Combined 4" + ¾" mesh	1.45/SF			
Sandblast units complete				
Portable without hood (open top)				
3 CF capacity		42.00	133.00	265.00
6 CF capacity		50.00	147.00	390.00
Sandblast machines				
150 lb		31.00	82.00	240.00
300 lb		45.00	130.00	325.00
600 lb		53.00	154.00	390.00
Sandblast hoses - 50' lengths				
¾" I.D.		8.00	18.00	45.00
1" I.D.		12.00	27.00	65.00
1¼" I.D.		15.00	35.00	78.00
1½" I.D.		17.00	42.00	94.00
Sandblast hoses - 10' length whip lines				
¾" I.D.		5.00	11.00	35.00
1" I.D.		8.00	18.00	48.00
1¼" I.D.		11.00	27.00	65.00
1½" I.D.		13.00	40.00	95.00
Sandblast hoods				
Aluminum air-fed		12.00	30.00	90.00
Canvas air-fed		8.00	22.00	64.00
Canvas helmet, standard		5.00	15.00	45.00
Helmet supply hoses		4.00	10.00	27.00
Sandblast nozzles, Venturi style				
Short barrel		9.00	27.00	74.00
Long barrel		11.00	30.00	86.00
Sandblast accessories				
Remote control valve		19.00	37.00	93.00
1 sack sand pot only		35.00	64.00	185.00
3 sack sand pot only		55.00	90.00	262.00
Remote control with sand pot		74.00	140.00	380.00
Water tap		7.00	21.00	57.00
Silica sand abrasive	25.00/ton			
Sanders				
Belt - 7"		13.00	50.00	150.00
Disc - 4" x 24"		14.00	56.00	168.00
Scaffolding: rolling stage, caster mounted, 2'0" to 10'8" high				
4' to 6' reach			30.00	60.00
7' to 11' reach			40.00	80.00
12' to 16' reach			46.00	92.00
17' to 21' reach			66.00	132.00
22' to 26' reach			70.00	140.00
27' to 30' reach			74.00	148.00
Casters - each			4.00	8.00

Typical equipment purchase and rental prices
Figure 15-1

Scaffolding: stationary, running footage

Complete including planks, erection and dismantling, based on erection on level ground. Add for unlevel ground.

	Rental $/week
2 frames high will reach from 15' to 20':	
Square footage: per face footage of reach:	.44/SF
Unlevel ground add:	.04/SF
Lineal footage: per running foot of scaffolding:	8.00/LF
Unlevel ground add:	.75/LF
3 frames high will reach from 21' to 26':	
Square footage: per face footage of reach:	.45/SF
Unlevel ground add:	.03/SF
Lineal footage: per running foot of scaffolding:	10.50/LF
Unlevel ground add:	.75/LF
4 frames high will reach from 28' to 33':	
Square footage: per face footage of reach:	.46/SF
Unlevel ground add:	.03/SF
Lineal footage: per running foot of scaffolding:	14.00/LF
Unlevel ground add:	.75/LF
5 frames high will reach from 34' to 39':	
Square footage: per face footage of reach:	.48/SF
Unlevel ground add:	.02/SF
Lineal footage: per running foot of scaffolding:	17.50/LF
Unlevel ground add:	.75/LF
6 frames high will reach from 41' to 46':	
Square footage: per face footage of reach:	.50/SF
Unlevel ground add:	.02/SF
Lineal footage: per running foot of scaffolding:	21.75/LF
Unlevel ground add:	.75/LF
7 frames high will reach from 47' to 52':	
Square footage: per face footage of reach:	.52/SF
Unlevel ground add:	.01/LF
Lineal footage: per running foot of scaffolding:	25.75/LF
Unlevel ground add:	.75/LF
8 frames high will reach from 53' to 58':	
Square footage: per face footage of reach:	.54/SF
Unlevel ground add:	.01/SF
Lineal footage: per running foot of scaffolding:	30.00/LF
Unlevel ground add:	.75/LF

Example: If a building has a perimeter of 120 LF with a height of 36'0", the scaffolding costs are:

Per lineal foot: 120 LF x $17.50 = $2,100.00

Per square foot: 120 LF x 36' =

4,320 SF x $.48 = $2,074.00

Scaffolding erection

Frames and cross braces	
One laborer:	12/day
Planks	
One laborer:	65/day
Accessories (brackets, jacks, etc.)	
One laborer:	100/day

Spray line - airless: ⁵⁄₁₆", 3000 PSI w/couplings

GRACO #210-54	85-1.00/LF
Wagner #8802	.80-.95/SF

Spray rigs: airless pumps, complete with gun and 50' of line

	Purchase	Rental $/day	Rental $/week	Rental $/month
GRACO:				
EM 490 (.44 gal/min)	40.00			
Ultra #400 (.45 gal/min)	40.00			
Ultra #433 (.45 gal/min)	55.00			
Ultra #333 (.85 gal/min)	55.00			
Wagner:				
1250 (½ gal/min)	35.00			
2250 (¾ gal/min)	45.00			
Rental, average		50.00	200.00	600.00

Spray rig: emulsion pumps

	Purchase	Rental $/day	Rental $/week	Rental $/month
65 gal, 5 HP engine		21.00	59.00	191.00
200 gal, 5 HP engine		38.00	115.00	345.00

Spray rig: conventional pumps, gas, portable

	Purchase	Rental $/day	Rental $/week	Rental $/month
8 CFM, complete		35.00	94.00	275.00
17 CFM, complete		45.00	148.00	395.00
85 CFM, complete		55.00	220.00	775.00
150 CFM, complete		88.00	359.00	1324.00

Storage containers

	Purchase	Rental $/day	Rental $/week	Rental $/month
11' x 8' x 7'				65.00
21' x 8' x 7'				90.00
26' x 8' x 8'				100.00
Based on SF floor space of the storage container				.42-.50

Add: move on & move off $25.00 to $60.00 one time charge.

Striper, paint (parking lot striping)

	Purchase	Rental $/day	Rental $/week	Rental $/month
Aerosol		10.00	40.00	120.00
Pressure regulated		15.00	60.00	160.00

Swing stage-

Any length drop, motor operated, excluding safety gear and installation or dismantling. Note: must be set up by a professional to ensure safety.

	Purchase	Rental $/day	Rental $/week	Rental $/month
Swing stage			290.00	850.00
Basket			150.00	450.00
Bosun's chair			150.00	450.00
10' complete motor operated	1150.00			

Swing stage safety gear, purchase only

	Purchase
Safety belt, single D-ring and 3" pad	28.00
4' lanyard with locking snap at each end	25.00
DBI rope grab for ¾" safety line	58.00
Komet rope grab for ¾" safety line	75.00

Trailers, office with 8' ceilings

	Purchase	Rental $/day	Rental $/week	Rental $/month
4' x 4' trailer		11.00	21.00	31.00
4' x 8' trailer		16.00	30.00	58.00
8' x 12' trailer		21.00	41.00	75.00
Car or tractor trailer		38.00		

Add: (move on-off) $26.00 to $74.00

Typical equipment purchase and rental prices
Figure 15-1 (continued)

Inventory number	Equipment description	Model number	Foreman/sprayman	Check out date	Return date
QPD 1	Masking machine	448			
QPD 2	Masking machine	448			
QPD 3	Masking machine	448			
QPD 4	10' wood ladder	W-10			
QPD 5	10' wood ladder	W-10			
QPD 6	10' metal ladder	M-10			
QPD 7	25' wood ladder	W-25			
QPD 8	40' metal ladder	M-40			
QPD 9	25' pick	P-25			
QPD 10	30' pick	P-30			
QPD 11	Ladder jacks	LJ-24			
QPD 12	Ladder jacks	LJ-24			
QPD 13	Pump	GH-433			
QPD 14	Pump	GH-433			
QPD 15	Pump	SW-8000			
QPD 16	Pump	SW-8000			
QPD 17	Spray gun - GRACO	Silver			
QPD 18	Spray gun - GRACO	SWG-10			
QPD 19	Spray gun - GRACO	SWG-10			
QPD 20	Spray gun - GRACO	Pole			
QPD 21	Spray gun - GRACO	Pole			
QPD 22					
QPD 23					
QPD 24					
QPD 25					

Equipment inventory log
Figure 15-2

Minimum charges: $275.00, scaffolding not included

Additional insurance: May be required to cover adjacent personal and real property which may not be protected.

Sandblasting water soluble paints	$ .45 to .55/SF
Sandblasting oil paints	.50 to .60/SF
Sandblasting heavy mastic (depends on coating thickness)	.75 to .85/SF
Sandblasting brick - light blast	.45 to .55/SF
Sandblasting masonry block walls	
Clean up & remove grime - light	.40 to .50/SF
- heavy	.80 to .90/SF
Sandblasting structural steel	
Pricing rules of thumb:	
Pipe up to 12" O.D.	.80 to 1.30/SF
Structural steel up to 2 SF/LF	.70 to .80/SF
Structural steel from 2 to 5 SF/LF	.90 to 1.00/SF
Structural steel over 5 SF/LF	*(depends on shape)*
Tanks and vessels up to 12'0" O.D.	1.25 to 1.50/SF
Tanks and vessels over 12'0" O.D.	1.25 to 1.50/SF
Brush off blast - light blast (Loose mill scale)	
Field welded, new, uncoated	
ground runs	.25 to .40/SF
above ground	.40 to 1.00/SF

Previously painted surfaces - add	.25 to .55/SF
Epoxy coated - add	.55 to .70/SF
With portable equipment - add	.30 to .35/SF
Commercial blast - 67% white stage	
Field welded, new, uncoated	
ground runs	.50 to .65/SF
above ground	.70 to 1.25/SF
Previously painted surfaces - add	.25 to .55/SF
Epoxy coated - add	.55 to .70/SF
With portable equipment - add	.30 to .45/SF
Near white blast - 95% white stage	
Field welded, new, uncoated	
ground runs	.65 to .80/SF
above ground	.80 to 1.35/SF
Previously painted surfaces - add	.25 to .55/SF
Epoxy coated - add	.55 to .70/SF
With portable equipment - add	.30 to .45/SF
White blast - 100% uniform white stage	
Field welded, new, uncoated	
ground runs	1.10 to 1.40/SF
above ground	1.25 to 1.55/SF
Previously painted surfaces - add	.25 to .55/SF
Epoxy coated - add	.55 to .70/SF
With portable equipment - add	.30 to .45/SF

Sandblasting pricing table
Figure 15-3

Preparation operations
- ☐ Sweeping
- ☐ Sandblastng
- ☐ Layout
- ☐ Cleanup

Striping and graphics
- ☐ Company name
- ☐ Individual name
- ☐ Employees only
- ☐ Visitors only
- ☐ Suite number
- ☐ Reserved
- ☐ Guests
- ☐ Exit
- ☐ Entry
- ☐ Double line striping
- ☐ No parking
- ☐ Arrows
- ☐ Bike lanes
- ☐ Cross walks
- ☐ Cross hatch
- ☐ Radius markings
- ☐ Red curbs
- ☐ No parking fire lane symbol
- ☐ Handicap symbol
- ☐ Walkways (crosswalks)
- ☐ Trash enclosure area
- ☐ Speed bump markings

Parking lot sealing
- ☐ Number of coats
- ☐ Type of sealer
- ☐ Prepare cracks and depressions

Asphalt repairs
- ☐ Layout and mark areas (eroded, sunken, cracked or broken)
- ☐ Excavate
- ☐ Root repairs
- ☐ Trash area repairs
- ☐ Trench repairs
- ☐ Street repairs

Concrete products
Wheel stops
   Size: ☐3' ☐4' ☐5' ☐6'
   Attachment: ☐ Glued
              ☐ Pinned
              ☐ Drilled (concrete)

Signs and poles
Sign type: ☐ Stop
             ☐ Fire lane
             ☐ Handicap access
             ☐ No parking

Standard size: ☐ 12" x 18"
Pole type: ☐ Round
              ☐ U channel
Installed: ☐ Concrete base
              ☐ Compacted earth

Barricades and guard posts
Number of posts: ☐ Single
                  ☐ Double
                  ☐ Triple

Road markings
☐ Double or ☐ Single
Solid: ☐ 4" yellow
       ☐ 4" white
       ☐ 8" white
       ☐12" white stop bar
Broken: ☐ 4" yellow
       ☐ 4" white
       ☐ 8" white

Traffic logos
- ☐ Stop
- ☐ Yield
- ☐ Slow
- ☐ Ahead
- ☐ Ped
- ☐ Xing
- ☐ School
- ☐ Left
- ☐ Right
- ☐ Turn
- ☐ Only
- ☐ Straight

Pavement markers
- ☐ Remove existing
- ☐ Layout
- ☐ White ceramic
- ☐ Yellow ceramic
- ☐ 1 way clear
- ☐ 2 way clear
- ☐ 1 way amber
- ☐ 2 way amber
- ☐ 2 way blue

Estimating considerations
- ☐ Quality of paint products related to the dry time
- ☐ Weather affecting dry time
- ☐ Template investment costs
- ☐ Number of coats of paint (one or two)
- ☐ Width of each stripe
- ☐ Size of graphic letters or numerals

Pavement marking operations checklist
Figure 15-4

Pricing rules of thumb:
Number of parking spaces: Figure one space per 300 SF of pavement

Single line striping with light graphics apply	$ 5.00 per space
Single line striping with heavy graphics apply	10.00 per space
Single striping, light graphics and 3' wheel stop	15.00 per space
Single striping, heavy graphics and 3' wheel stop	20.00 per space

Equipment pricing:

Simple "inverted spray can" approximate cost	$150.00
Professional striping machine cost range	$3,200 to 3,500
Professional road/highway striper	$175,000.00

Subcontractor pricing:

Move on:	$100.00 to 125.00

Striping prices:

Single line striping	$ .25 to .35 per lineal foot
Bike lane striping	$ .35 to .45 per lineal foot
Fire lane, red curb	$ .25 to .35 per lineal foot

Symbol pricing:

Templates - 8'0" template	$125.00 to 150.00 each
Arrows	25.00 to 30.00 each
Handicap symbol, one color	10.00 to 15.00 each
two color	20.00 to 25.00 each
No parking fire lane stencil	2.00 to 2.50 each

Wheel stops:

3'0" stops	$15.00 to 20.00 each if pinned on asphalt
	20.00 to 25.00 each if glued and pinned
6'0" stops	25.00 to 30.00 each if pinned on asphalt
	30.00 to 35.00 each if glued and pinned
	(add for wheel stops pinned to concrete)

Signs and posts:

Sign only 12" x 18"	$35.00 to 50.00
Post mounted 12" x 18"	90.00 to 125.00

Pavement markers:

One way pavement markers	$6.00 each
Two way pavement markers	8.00 each

Pavement marking pricing table
Figure 15-5

```
┌─────────────────────────────────────────────────────────────────────┐
│                                                                       │
│   Minimum charges:    $275.00, scaffolding not included               │
│                                                                       │
│   Additional insurance:   May be required to cover adjacent           │
│   personal and real property.                                         │
│                                                                       │
│   Pricing rules of thumb:                                             │
│     Up to 5,000 psi blast        - 3 hour minimum $ 60.00/hour        │
│      5,000 to 10,000 psi blast   - 8 hour minimum $ 95.00/hour        │
│     10,000 psi                   - 8 hour minimum $115.00/hour        │
│     Wet sandblasting             - 3 hour minimum $ 75.00/hour        │
│                                                                       │
└─────────────────────────────────────────────────────────────────────┘
```

Waterblasting pricing table
Figure 15-6

Hiring a waterblasting sub may be the best choice if you don't need the service often. Figure 15-6 shows some typical rates for waterblasting. Make up a table like this based on quotes from subcontractors in your area. But if you're in the repainting business, you'll probably need a waterblaster on most jobs. If you decide to buy a waterblaster, base your equipment cost on what rental yards are getting for similar equipment.

Receiving Subcontractor Bids

Use the telephone bid form, Figure 15-7, when you're soliciting price quotes from subcontractors. The only part that isn't self-explanatory is the line labeled *firm status*. Here's what the abbreviations mean:

SBE — Small Business Enterprise
MBE — Minority Business Enterprise
WBE — Women's Business Enterprise
NON — None of the above

You won't need this part of the form unless you're bidding subcontracted work for public projects.

Commissions and Bonuses

Painting contractors rarely have a sales staff, so there won't be commissions to pay on most jobs. There's one exception, however. Most room addition and remodeling contractors do have salespeople. And many of their remodeling projects *exclude* painting. Their contracts often specify that the painting will be done by the owner. These may be a good source of leads for a paint contractor who develops a relationship with the sales staff (with the remodeling contractor's approval, of course). If you have a relationship like this, you'll probably have to pay a commission to the salesperson who gave you the lead. Just add this commission into the estimate.

Some painting contractors pay their estimators a bonus of 1% to 3% per job in addition to their salary. If you have an incentive like this, add the percentage to your estimate.

Escalation

A clause that allows for specific increases for material costs and cost-of-living raises for workers is usually called *an escalator*. If costs increase between the time you bid the job and the time the work is done, you should recover the difference — especially if there was an unreasonable delay through no fault of yours. An escalation clause in the contract can give you a claim for increases in both labor and material costs. But owners and general contractors don't like to see escalation clauses.

Painting contractors seldom include an escalation clause in their bids because lengthy delays aren't common. But you should always include an expiration date on your bids. If the contract award is delayed beyond your expiration date, you'll have the opportunity to review your costs and make any necessary adjustments. But be careful here. If you increase your bid, you might lose the contract. So raise your bid only if necessary, and then only by the amount of the actual cost increases. Don't see it as an opportunity to make a killing.

QUALITY PAINTING & DECORATING
777 Main Street, Yourtown, USA 77777 (515) 555-1512

Project: *THE COURTYARD*

Company ___ABC WALL COVERING___

Contact: ___JAMES___   Telephone: (619) 555-1111

Trade/CSI Division _____

Total Bid: ___$ 4,322.00___

Per Plans & Specs: YES	Addenda Noted: A & B
Installed Complete: YES	F.O.B. Jobsite: —
Tax Included: YES	Add Freight: 0
Written Bid Requested: YES	Lead Time: 1 WEEK
Firm Status: SBE (MBE) WBE NON	Premium Wages: N/A
Bond Included: Yes [ ] No [✓]	Bond Rate: N/A

Includes: ___WALLCOVER MATERIAL ALLOWANCE OF $12.00 /ROLL___

Excludes: ___GYPBOARD SEALER PRIOR TO WALLCOVER APPLICATION___

Notes: _____

Date: ___5-10-88___   By: ___Jim___

Telephone bid form
Figure 15-7

If the work is rescheduled after you've received the contract, you may be able to receive compensation for the delay. This is more likely on public projects than on private jobs. If there's a significant delay due to weather, you may have a good argument for adjusting the contract amount.

In Chapter 14 I recommended that you add 10% to material prices to cover sundries. This allowance can also serve as a cushion to absorb minor increases in labor or material costs. But don't rely on it to absorb major inflationary cost increases. Plan ahead if prices are rising. Look for an escalation clause in contracts you are offered.

Of course, I can't predict what inflation will do in the future. But here's what the trends have been in the recent past, according to professional construction estimators:

1983	5%	1986	8%
1984	7%	1987	4%
1985	7%	1988	3%

Expiration Dates

An expiration date on your proposals helps protect you against labor or material cost increases. Include an expiration date on *every* proposal. If you anticipate significant cost increases, consider using two sets of prices with different expiration dates:

	Expiration dates	
	7-1-89	**10-1-89**
Plan A	$1,100	$1,160
Plan B	1,200	1,275
Plan C	1,250	1,310

Or add this qualifying statement to the proposal: "This bid is subject to a 2% increase as an escalation charge for labor and material increases if not accepted by . . . (date)."

Contingency

Painting estimators often add a contingency allowance in repaint projects. But it's rare in new construction work. When a contingency allowance is added, it's usually from 3% to 5%. It can go higher, however, if there are unusual conditions that make an accurate estimate more difficult. Include an amount for contingency if you have reason to expect:

- An uncertain scope of work

- An inexperienced owner or general contractor

- Incomplete drawings

- Possible delays in beginning the project

- Owner involvement in supervision

- Below-standard working conditions

Don't use contingency allowances as substitutes for accurate estimates. Include all your costs in every estimate. Estimate everything that can be estimated. Include a contingency allowance to cover only what can't be estimated (by anyone) and can't be foreseen.

Chapter 16

PARTS OF AN ESTIMATE: OVERHEAD AND PROFIT

What is overhead? It's usually defined as indirect expenses — costs that aren't related to any particular job. And that's correct as far as it goes. Most overhead is *indirect,* like your office rent and a secretary's salary. But there are also some *direct* overhead expenses, like a bond which is required for a specific job. I'll show you how to estimate both indirect and direct overhead in this chapter.

Estimating overhead isn't as clear-cut as labor and material. That's why it's too often underestimated. Don't make that mistake in your estimates. Underestimating your overhead is like throwing away part of your profit on every job. After all, those expenses have to be paid, even if you forgot to include some of them in your estimate.

In large painting companies, management accumulates overhead costs and translates them into a percentage that the estimator can add to the costs of each job. In smaller companies, the estimator should maintain a record of overhead expenses and calculate the overhead costs for each day, week, month and year. That makes it easy to add overhead costs into the estimate based on the length of the job.

Here's one case where larger companies may have an advantage. A large company working many projects at the same time can spread their overhead costs over all the projects — charging a smaller percentage of overhead to each job. The more jobs, the lower the overhead per job — assuming overhead doesn't increase faster than business volume.

On the other hand, a small business may be able to compete by keeping the overall overhead low. But even painting contractors who work out of their homes have overhead expenses. And there's one overhead expense that you might overlook: the cost of doing the estimate itself. That's part of the salary expense of whatever staff member does the estimate.

Indirect Overhead

Indirect overhead is often referred to as *general and administrative* (G&A) expenses. Here are a few examples:

Salaries— All salaries (except craftsmen), including the employer's burden: officers or owners, estimators, clerical staff and field superintendents.

Office expenses— Rent or mortgage payment, utilities (gas, electric water and telephone), furniture and equipment, maintenance, office supplies (including stationery and printing), postage and so on.

Vehicles— Expenses include lease or purchase payments, maintenance, repairs and fuel.

Field equipment— This includes rental expense, maintenance, repairs and fuel for equipment not directly charged against a job.

Yard expense— Storage sheds, warehouses or fences.

Sales promotion— Advertising is included here, and perhaps entertainment and travel.

Taxes— Property tax if you own your building, income tax, and sales tax on all materials except paint products included in your estimates.

Licenses— Including your contractor's license and business license.

Insurance— General liability, auto liability and damage, and operations liability.

Interest expense— Include any interest on loans and other bank charges. Also consider loss of interest on payments retained by the general contractor until the job is done.

Miscellaneous expenses— These include depreciation and amortization on building and vehicles, bad debts, legal and accounting fees, educational expenses and job photographs.

Direct Overhead

Direct overhead can be applied *directly* to the job. You'll usually list each direct overhead cost as a separate line item in your estimate.

Insurance

Most of your insurance is included in the indirect overhead category. But there are two exceptions. If the owner, builder or general contractor requires you to increase the limits of your insurance coverage through an umbrella policy, the extra cost

for that coverage is a direct overhead expense. And if your insurance company charges you to add the owner or general contractor as an "additional insured," pass that cost along also.

Bonds

When required, performance and bid bonds are bought for individual jobs. That makes them direct overhead. You can get these bonds from your insurance company or through one of their affiliates specializing in bonds. Bonds protect the building owner. There are several types:

Bid bonds— A bid bond guarantees the owner that if the painting contractor is low bidder, he will enter into a contract with the owner for the amount of the bid. The bonded amount will usually be between 3% and 5% of the bid price. The fee for bid bonds is small because any company that's issuing a bid bond is also ready to supply a performance bond.

Performance bonds— A painting contractor, if he's the prime contractor or bidding on a large, formal bid project, may be required to furnish a performance bond. This bond is a guarantee that the painting contractor will finish the project. If the contractor doesn't complete the work, the bond underwriter has to hire another contractor to do what the first agreed to do. That protects the owner. Performance bonds are sometimes bought by the builder or general contractor to reassure the owner that the entire project will be completed.

Payment bonds (labor and material bonds)— A payment bond guarantees that a contractor will pay all employees, suppliers, and subcontractors on the job when payment is due. That reduces the risk of liens being filed against the job.

The cost of payment and performance bonds together is usually 1% of the contract amount. Add this cost to your estimate. These bonds are usually posted at the time the contract is signed, and returned to the contractor when work has been completed and accepted.

Maintenance bonds— Maintenance bonds guarantee that the contractor will return to repair or repaint defective painting for a warranty period, usually one or two years. The cost of these bonds is usually included with the payment and performance bonds.

Safety Affects Overhead

While we're talking about insurance and bonds, I'd like to digress a little to cover a subject that's too important to be ignored. And that's *safety*. There are two good reasons to stress safety on your jobs. The first, and most important, is to protect the health and lives of your employees and the property of the owners you work for. The second is that safety is good business. Insurance rates are higher for companies with poor accident records. If your estimator has to include extra high insurance rates in the estimates he writes, your bid price will have to be higher, and you're going to win fewer of them.

To save lives *and* reduce your overhead, follow the safety tips in Figure 16-1 on every job. A sample safety letter is shown in Figure 16-2.

Safety meetings— Depending on the size of the project, safety meetings may be required of all contractors by the Occupational Safety and Health Administration (OSHA). Even if they're not required, hold a safety meeting once in a while. There was at least one instance where an accident occurred on a job, followed, naturally, by a lawsuit. When the contractor admitted, on being examined by the prosecutor, that he hadn't held even one safety meeting, the case was pretty much wrapped up — with the contractor on the losing end. Figure 16-3 is a safety meeting report form.

Accident reports— Assign your foreman on each job the responsibility for completing accident reports. That cuts down on confusion when an accident happens. Make sure he has accident report forms and understands how to complete those forms:

• Record the time, place, and cause of the accident.

• Describe the conditions at the scene of the accident. Include photographs.

• Record your insurance policy number on every report.

• Record the employee's full name. No initials or nicknames.

• Record the Social Security number accurately.

• Avoid abbreviations, especially anything about the injury.

• Be as complete and accurate as possible in describing the injury.

• Specify *the employee's* right or left for injuries involving eyes, hands, arms, or legs.

• In injuries involving hands or feet, specify which fingers or toes.

• Always include the names of any witnesses.

Lower Overhead by Reducing Theft and Vandalism

If theft and vandalism are common on your jobs, your insurance costs will be high. Keep your insurance rates and overhead down by following the suggestions in Figure 16-4. Give each employee a copy of a theft and vandalism warning letter like Figure 16-5.

Overhead Percentage Calculation

Here are my recommendations for figuring your overhead and allocating it among your jobs. Start with a complete list of overhead expenses for at least the last six months or the last year. You need overhead cost information that goes back far enough to eliminate the effect of seasonal changes in business volume.

Here's the formula for calculating the overhead percentage:

$$\frac{\text{Indirect overhead}}{\text{Job cost expenses}} = \text{overhead \%}$$

Your job cost expenses include all labor, supervision, material, equipment, subcontracts, commissions and contingency expenses.

✔ Never spray paint in unvented areas. Fumes can cause serious illness or injury. Spontaneous combustion can also cause an explosion if ignition occurs in a confined area.

✔ Supply every vehicle with a first aid kit and fire extinguisher.

✔ Report all accidents, defective or unsafe equipment or unsafe working conditions.

✔ Use protective equipment such as face masks, respirators, sock hats, and hard hats.

✔ Inspect safety equipment and gear frequently.

✔ Wear protective clothing.

✔ No horseplay or throwing tools or materials in the shop/office or job site.

✔ Keep working area free of litter, debris, dirt and dust.

✔ Post a code of safe practices and procedures. Require all employees to follow these rules.

✔ Issue a safety letter (Figure 16-2) to existing and new employees.

✔ Railing and toeboard safety:
Railings must be on all elevations above 7.5 feet
Top rail 42" to 45" high with midrail at halfway point
Toeboards 3.5" minimum at roof or shaft openings where craftsmen pass under or work below

✔ Stairway and ladder safety:
One stairway up to three stories. Two stairways over three stories.
Use single (double) cleat ladders up to 30 feet.
Use ladders, secured against sliding or falling, for climbing or descending the scaffold. Climbing on scaffolding frames is prohibited.
Use only heavy-duty ladders and wood ladders with metal wire supports below each rung.
When using metal ladders, stay clear of power lines.
Place ladders on firm, level ground with the proper angle to the wall or surface before climbing.
Move the ladder periodically so you are always at a comfortable reach.
Don't stand on the top two steps or on the fold-out shelf. Secure your paint can to the ladder while painting.

✔ Inspect the condition of your ladders regularly.

✔ Scaffold safety:
Planking to be 2' x 10' nominal structural plank

✔ Split or unsafe planks must be removed

✔ All scaffold frames shall have x-braces on one length.
Base plates shall be installed on all scaffold legs.
All scaffold legs shall be placed on firm sills.
Provide solid support for sills which extend over trenches.
Platform slope not to exceed 2 feet in 10 feet with secured planks.
Erection of scaffolds to be supervised by qualified personnel.

✔ Conduct safety meetings every other week (once in ten working days).

Safety tips
Figure 16-1

MEMO TO: All employees

FROM: The management

RE: Safety

Your safety is our highest priority. Safe working conditions are a major concern to the management of this company and to our insurance carrier.

When we are safe and accident free, our insurance rates are lower, our overhead expense is lower and we will win more jobs to keep you employed. When we're not safe, our costs go up and we win less work.

Safe working conditions must be enforced and maintained by each member of our field crews. Always follow safe practices when using equipment, especially ladders, scaffolding, heavy lifting, spray painting, spray rigs, roller poles and working in areas which are not well ventilated.

In addition, the use or possession of alcohol or drugs is strictly prohibited in the shop/office or on any job site at any time. Any employee found using drugs or alcohol of any kind will be terminated on the spot. Furthermore, pets of any kind are not allowed in the shop/office or on any job site at any time.

Safety meetings will be held every Thursday at 4:00 PM. All employees are required to attend.

Your cooperation in these matters will allow the company to run more smoothly and will contribute to your continued employment.

Thank you for cooperating with your management staff.

The Management

Safety letter
Figure 16-2

SAFETY MEETING REPORT

Date: _7-15-88_

Job # _88-029_

Builder _JOHN DOE CONST._

Foreman _GEORGE BURNS_

Items Discussed: _LADDER SAFETY - PROPER ANGLE TO THE WALL_
SCAFFOLDING FOOTINGS
CLEAN UP EMPTY CANS; DEPOSIT IN DUMPSTERS
KEEP PAINT SHOP ORGANIZED

Recommendations For Improvements In Accident Prevention: _____
LOOK FOR AND AVOID OR CORRECT
UNSAFE CONDITIONS

Employees Present: _KEVIN REYNOLDS_ _STEVE RICE_
HOWARD SMITH _DENNIS JOHNSON_
TERRY SNYDER _ROBERT CLARK_
GEORGE KIRBY _JAMES JONES_

Comments: _NEXT MEETING - 8-1-88_

Signature of Foreman: _George Burns_

Safety meeting report
Figure 16-3

✔ Install a fence with barbed wire around your yard.

✔ Lock or guard yard gates when not in use.

✔ Provide night lighting for your yard.

✔ Install dead bolts and bars on windows of all storage sheds.

✔ Assign yard and shop keys only to responsible employees.

✔ Use **Warning** signs to discourage theft and vandalism, including "No trespassing, violators will be prosecuted," and "Alarm system installed."

✔ Install alarm system on office and storage areas.

✔ Ask assistance from neighbors to keep an eye on your yard and equipment.

✔ Inventory all material, tools and equipment and keep it up to date.

✔ Photograph all vehicles, spray rigs and other large equipment and keep a record of their replacement value.

✔ Secure all material, tools and equipment when not in use.

✔ Chain all spray rigs, hoses and ladders to trucks.

✔ Mark all materials and company-owned equipment with two sets of permanent identification numbers, one in an obvious location and one in an inconspicuous location.

✔ Encourage craftsmen to mark their own tools and equipment.

✔ Sign for all deliveries.

✔ Encourage security suggestions from your employees.

✔ Promptly report theft and vandalism to the police.

✔ Issue a letter detailing the company's position on theft and vandalism to each new employee, and periodically to all employees.

✔ Provide employee parking separate from storage areas.

✔ Never purchase stolen material or equipment.

Theft and vandalism prevention tips
Figure 16-4

MEMO TO: All employees

FROM: The management

RE: Theft and vandalism

This letter is intended to remind you of a problem we all know exists on job sites - theft. Theft increases insurance rates and increases construction costs. With these increased costs, the company is not as competitive and will not win as much work. Theft and vandalism affect the company and your continued employment.

We all know about theft on construction sites. Copper, lumber and equipment losses are frequently mentioned in the newspaper. To fight these thefts, we are working closely with the police. We ask your assistance by reporting any suspicious activity to us.

How often have you seen a fellow employee take home a "5" of paint, a brush or two, or other company owned supplies or equipment? Small items you say! Taken individually, you are right. But when you add all these small thefts together, and add the time lost when supplies run out unexpectedly, the bill is in the thousands. In fact these small thefts usually cost more than the big thefts - and they're usually not covered by insurance.

Because this is an on-going problem, we have to take firm measures against theft and vandalism. *If you are caught stealing, you will lose your job and be reported to the police for prosecution.* In addition, anyone proven to have knowledge of a theft or vandalism and failing to report it will be dismissed immediately. *This is a serious matter.*

Remember, this is a common problem. If your "buddy" steals from us, he'll steal from you. And if it goes far enough, he may just take all our jobs home with him.

Thank you for your cooperation.

The Management

Theft and vandalism letter
Figure 16-5

Let's look at an example. Assume a painting company completed 40 new housing projects in the last year. Average revenue per project was $25,000. Gross receipts were $1,000,000.

$1,000,000.00	=	Gross income
50,000.00	=	Profit realized at 5%
950,000.00	=	Gross expenses
- 848,214.39	=	Total job cost expenses
101,785.61	=	Overhead

$$\frac{\$101,785.61 \text{ (total annual overhead)}}{\$848,214.39 \text{ (total annual job costs)}} = .12 \text{ or } 12\%$$

If your company is new, you won't have accurate overhead figures for the last year. Your best estimate will have to do. If you don't have any other estimate, assume that overhead will be 15% of direct job cost. But after six months, as you've begun to accumulate actual cost figures, use actual costs, not estimates, to calculate the overhead percentage. Keep adjusting it every six months to be sure your overhead calculations are realistic.

When you've calculated overhead as a percentage of direct job cost, apply that percentage to all of your estimates. Without this overhead percentage, your estimates aren't complete. You haven't included all your costs.

Your Profit

The average annual profit for U.S. construction contractors ranges from 1.5% to 2.0% of gross. Nearly one-third of all construction contractors don't show any profit at all. Many of those companies are unprofitable because of unexpected cost overruns and poor estimating procedures.

Contracting is a risky business. And your profit should be directly proportional to your risk. The more risk, the greater profit. But how do you define risk?

Here's my definition. Risk is the *headache factor:* the number of potential problems you could face in completing the project. Repaint jobs have more unknowns, so they're a greater risk. And dealing with an indecisive or picky homeowner can be the greatest headache of all.

The scope of work is usually clearly defined when painting new construction projects. That makes them less risky. And the general contractor is generally better organized than the homeowner.

It's usually safe to charge a lower percentage of profit on new construction jobs.

Several times in this book, I've talked about the *standard base bid*. That's your usual price for labor, material, equipment, overhead and your usual profit markup. By using your usual profit markup, you can compare costs from one project to another. But before you submit any bid, consider whether you want to make adjustments to your standard prices.

You might adjust prices either up or down because of unusual labor productivity, material requirements, equipment costs, or overhead considerations. Also consider the bidding variables when you're deciding how to adjust your standard costs. Review the bidding variables in Chapter 7 if you don't remember all of them.

But here's the point you must remember: You never make adjustments to profit. When you adjust the base bid, it's because you expect your crews to be more or less efficient on this project, or you expect overhead to be higher or lower on this job. There's some logical reason to modify the standard base bid you would usually use.

Of course, your profit may be affected by a bad guess about adjustments or by some estimates that are inaccurate. The profit you take away from a job will rarely be exactly the same as the profit you estimated — but don't give the profit away before the job starts. Don't make adjustments in your standard prices just to win a job. Make adjustments because there's something in the job that's unusual and demands special consideration.

Risk Factors

Based on your assessment of the difficulty of the job, assign a *risk factor* that you'll use to modify your profit percentage. The higher the risk, the higher the factor. Here are my suggestions:

Risk factor	Normal profit (assume 10%)		Difficulty factor		Result
High risk	10%	x	1.5 to 2.5	=	15% to 25%
Average risk	10%	x	1.3 to 1.6	=	13% to 16%
Moderate risk	10%	x	1.0	=	10%
Low risk	10%	x	.6 to .9	=	6% to 9%

As you might expect, these difficulty factor adjustments can vary greatly. There's a lot of judgment involved. Your experience and good instincts are needed to apply these factors.

Profit Margins

Your profit margin depends on the way you do business, the kind of work you do, and the competition you face. Only you can decide what percentage is right for your bids. This subject is too important to take anyone's advice. Use your own judgment. But here are some typical profit margins for the work most painting contractors do.

Repaints:	custom	20% to 35%
	average	15% to 20%
Commercial or industrial		10% to 15%
New residential: 1 to 4 units		10% to 12%
	5 or more	5% to 7%
Government work		5% to 7%

The Profit Formula

When you've won the bid and started work, the estimator's job isn't finished. It's just beginning. Even if your estimate was right on the money, a lot can go wrong before that last brush is cleaned. Keep tabs on the profit as the job progresses. Otherwise your profit is likely to slip away.

Here's a formula I use to estimate the actual profit to date. First, find the costs incurred to date and total cost to complete the job.

Cost incurred to date (direct costs and overhead)

	= CITD	$	20,000.00
Total estimated job cost	= TEJC		100,000.00
Total cost to complete	= CITD - TEJC = CC		80,000.00
Total contract amount	= TCA		105,000.00
Expected total profit	= TCA - TEJC = ETP		5,000.00

When you have these figures, use this formula to find the amount of profit recognized to date:

$$\text{Profit recognized to date} = \frac{CITD}{CC} \times ETP = PRTD$$

$$\text{Profit recognized to date} = \frac{\$20,000.}{\$80,000.} \times \$5,000. = \$1,250.$$

To use this profit formula, you need current records of all direct job costs (labor, material and equipment costs) and an accurate accounting of your overhead costs. By plugging in these variables for any particular job, you can tell whether your costs are in line with your estimate. If any costs are out of line, there's time to make corrections in the field to cut your losses and salvage your profit.

There's another, less complicated way to determine if a job in progress is going to be profitable. Look back to the progress reporting system in Chapter 11. That method focuses on the most critical element of the job, the manhours. If labor costs are running over or under the estimate, the potential for profit is probably changing.

That completes our look at the five parts of every estimate (labor, material, equipment, overhead and profit). In the next chapter we get down to the nuts and bolts: estimating preparation work.

$\mathscr{Chapter}$
17

ESTIMATING PREPARATION WORK

Preparation is one of the hardest parts of the job to estimate accurately. Any painter who's done a few projects can make reasonably good estimates of the quantity of paint needed on a job, and how long it will take to apply it. But the amount of prep work needed will vary widely — especially for repaint jobs. Some will need very little work. Others will take more time for prep than for painting. Let's begin this chapter with a look at the easiest type of prep work to estimate: new construction.

Estimating Prep for New Construction

Preparation work for new construction jobs is relatively easy to estimate. You'll have to mask cabinets before spraying sealer on wet area walls (Figure 17-1), caulk at the baseboards (Figure 17-2), putty the nail holes in wood trim, and occasionally use a wire brush to smooth and clean a surface. The time required for this work is fairly predictable. I've included normal preparation work on unpainted surfaces in the painting manhour estimates in Chapter 19. If you don't use my painting formulas, you'll have to estimate the surface prep time separately. You can use my preparation estimating formulas later in this chapter.

The cost of materials for normal surface preparation on unpainted surfaces will be covered by the 10% sundries allowance I recommend adding to the cost of paint. But if more than normal surface prep work is needed, estimate the manhours and materials you'll need.

Estimating Repaint Preparation

The preparation work on a repaint project can range from practically none to more than half the job. No two repaint jobs are identical. That makes your task as estimator very difficult. To make accurate estimates, you need to bring to the job the kind of judgment that usually comes with experience. A misjudgment in estimating preparation work can cost you your profit on a job.

But I don't agree with the claim that it's impossible to estimate surface preparation time for repaint jobs. It *is* possible. There are good estimates and bad estimates for surface preparation. After reading this chapter, you should be able to make good estimates on nearly any type of job.

Some paint estimators bid surface preparation by the hour, using their shop rate or some other specified hourly rate. That protects them against cost overruns if the preparation takes longer than

**Masking cabinets before
spraying wet area walls
Figure 17-1**

anticipated. But there's a danger here. The owners may be angry about the cost because they don't understand what's involved in preparation and why it takes so long. You can avoid this with a "not to exceed" bid for the prep work, or for the entire job. Set a maximum price for a well-defined scope of work with specific inclusions and exclusions.

Since estimating preparation work is a big subject, I'll break it down into two parts: estimating materials and estimating manhours.

Estimating Preparation Materials

For repaint jobs with minimal prep, the 10% sundry charge added to the paint cost will cover the prep materials. But most repaint jobs need more preparation than that. There are two ways to estimate the cost of the preparation materials in excess of the 10% sundry charge. You can add a lump sum to cover those costs, or make a detailed take-off of the materials required. Although the detailed method is the most accurate, it takes more time because many low-cost items are needed in prep work: cans of putty, masking paper, tubes of caulking, and so on.

When you're new at estimating materials for preparation work, I recommend making a detailed take-off of these materials. After you've had some experience doing that, you'll develop judgment

**Caulking at paint-grade baseboards
Figure 17-2**

about the cost of prep materials for different types of jobs. Then you can start adding a lump sum cost, and save the time of taking off the prep materials.

My preparation manhour and material chart a little later in this chapter includes some recommendations for prep materials.

Estimating Preparation Manhours

Here's how I estimate the time my crews will spend on prep work on repaint jobs: *SURRPTUCU*. No, that's not a typo. That's my acronym for the operations included in prep work: Setup (SU), remove and replace (RR), protection (P), Touchup (TU) and Cleanup (CU). Each of these operations must be considered for each repaint estimate.

Setup— Setup time includes the 20 to 30 minutes spent each day getting ready to paint. It starts when your crew gets out of the truck and ends when they start preparing surfaces or begin to apply paint. Setup time includes unloading the vehicle, spreading the tarp and setting up the tools — in short, everything that has to be done before prep or painting can begin.

Remove and replace— This is the time required to remove and replace the items that would interfere with the painting; door hardware, cabinet hardware, the contents of cabinets, light fixtures, bathroom accessories, switch covers and outlet plates, among others.

Protection— This includes the time and excess materials needed to protect furniture and adjacent surfaces: floors, cabinets, plumbing or electrical fixtures, windows, doors, and the like. Protection methods include masking, applying visqueen, drop cloths, and protecting windows. Of course, this time and excess material must be included in your repaint estimate.

Touchup— The time necessary for touchup depends on the speed and quality of the painting job, and how fussy the owner is. Of course, the more careful the painters, the less touchup time needed. You can only estimate touchup time accurately when you know how your crews perform on the job. In my new construction estimating tables, I allocate 12% of the total manhours for the interior operations to touching up both the interior and the exterior.

Cleanup— Cleanup time is usually about the same as setup time: about 20 to 30 minutes each day for repaint jobs. It's the time from the end of painting to the time the crew's back in the truck and ready to go home. It includes cleaning the tools, dismantling the paint shop and loading the vehicle.

The Preparation Manhour and Material Tables

Figure 17-3 shows the manhour and material figures I use for estimating the prep work for repaint jobs. Of course, no estimate of prep work is possible until you've seen the job. Then you'll use your judgment and experience to estimate the time and materials needed. Finally, use my tables to confirm your estimates. You can also use them as a handy summary of preparation operations.

There are a couple of categories that require a little explanation: burn off and waterblasting.

Burn Off

Heat softens and blisters the paint to allow easy removal by scraping. Both electric and propane-powered appliances are available for paint removal. Since this is a dangerous operation, the painting contractor must always notify the homeowner's insurance company and get permission to proceed. Also, equipment should be ready to extinguish any fire.

Waterblasting

Although this process is commonly called waterblasting in the construction trades, it's better to call it *power washing* or *pressure washing* in your advertising and when talking to homeowners. These terms make it clear to them that it's not just washing their house down with an ordinary garden hose.

The typical waterblaster uses about 1,500 to 1,700 pounds per square inch of pressure. A nozzle lets the operator restrict the stream to a small area or open up to cover a larger area. Waterblasting is a fast and easy way to remove flaking, peeling or cracking paint and to clean large surfaces quickly. Waterblasting, along with scraping and sanding,

Preparation Estimating Tables
Definition of Terms

Manhour rates: These tables show manhour production rates in square feet of surface per hour. They are divided into three classifications: slow, medium and fast work. Use the rate that applies to your job. Here are the three classifications:

Slow	Medium	Fast
Good quality	Average quality	Minimum quality
High difficulty	Average difficulty	Low difficulty
Poor conditions	Average conditions	Good conditions
Small job	Medium size job	Large projects
Low production	Average production	High production
(single units, repaints)	(2 to 4 units)	(5 or more units)
Unskilled painters	Semiskilled painters	Skilled crews

Material usage rates: The material usage rates are in square feet per gallon, with minimum mixing preparation. The rates show a range of coverages in two classifications: heavy and light. Here's what they mean:

Heavy usage	Light usage
Standard paint	Production paint
New construction	Repaint
(high absorption)	(low absorption)
Heavy application	Light application
Heavy coverage	Light coverage
Heavy usage	Light usage
High waste factor	Low waste factor
No thinning	Production thinning
Unskilled painters	Skilled painters

Acid wash gutters & downspouts	LF per hour			Muriatic acid LF per gallon	
	Slow	Med	Fast	Hvy	Lt
Gutters	80	95	110	400	425
Downspouts	70	80	90	400	425

Burning-off paint	SF per hour			SF per gallon	
	Slow	Med	Fast	Hvy	Lt
Exterior: Exterior trim	20	25	30	--	--
Plain surfaces	35	45	55	--	--
Beveled wood siding	25	35	45	--	--
Interior: Interior trim	15	20	25	--	--
Plain surfaces	20	30	40	--	--

Note: Because surfaces and the material being removed vary widely, it's best to quote prices for burning-off existing finishes on a time-and-material or cost plus fee basis with a preset hourly rate. All widths less than 12" are to be considered as 12" wide.

Prep work for repaint jobs
Figure 17-3

Caulking

	LF per hour			LF per fluid oz	
	Slow	Med	Fast	Hvy	Lt
1/8″ gap	60	65	70	12	14
1/4″ gap	50	55	60	3.0	3.5
3/8″ gap	40	45	50	1.3	1.5
1/2″ gap	33	38	43	.75	1.0

Caulking that's part of normal surface preparation is included in the painting manhour tables. When extra caulking is required, use this guide. It's based on oil or latex base, silicone or urethane caulk.

Cutting cracks

	SF per hour			SF per gallon	
	Slow	Med	Fast	Hvy	Lt
Varnish or hard oil and repair cracks	120	130	140	Nominal	
Gloss painted walls and fix cracks	125	135	145	Nominal	

Filling wood floors

	SF per hour			SF per gallon	
	Slow	Med	Fast	Hvy	Lt
Fill and wipe wood floors	45	60	75	135	155

Airblast, compressed air

	SF per hour			SF per gallon	
	Slow	Med	Fast	Hvy	Lt
Average production	150	175	200	--	--

Putty application

	SF per hour			SF per pound	
	Slow	Med	Fast	Hvy	Lt
Good condition, 1 coat	60	90	120	120	150
Average condition, 1 coat	35	65	95	60	90
Poor condition, 1 coat	15	30	45	20	40

Flat trim or sash: Estimate 1 linear foot of trim as 1 square foot of surface. These figures will apply to either spackle or swedish putty.

Sandblasting

Sandblasting production rates vary widely. Use these figures as a reference for estimating and to establish performance data for your company. The abrasive material used in sandblasting is usually white silica sand. Slags have recently gained in popularity. Material consumption varies with several factors:
1) Type of finish required
2) Condition of the surface
3) Quality of abrasive material (i.e. sharpness, cleanliness and hardness).
4) Nozzle size
5) Equipment arrangement and placement
6) Operator skill

All material consumption values are based on three uses of a 25 to 35 mesh white silica sand abrasive at a cost of $30.00 to $35.00 per ton. (Check the current price in your area.)

Prep work for repaint jobs
Figure 17-3 (continued)

Sandblast, brush off blast	SF per hour			Lbs per SF	
	Slow	Med	Fast	Hvy	Lt
Surface condition basis - Large projects & surface areas					
Remove cement base paint	150	175	200	3.0	2.0
Remove oil or latex base paint	100	125	150	4.0	3.0
Surface area basis					
Pipe up to 12" O/D	125	150	175	5.0	4.0
Structural steel					
Sizes up to 2 SF/LF	150	175	200	5.0	4.0
Sizes from 2 to 5 SF/LF	200	225	250	4.0	3.0
Sizes over 5 SF/LF	250	275	300	4.0	2.0
Tanks and vessels					
Sizes up to 12'0" O/D	200	225	250	4.0	3.0
Sizes over 12'0" O/D	250	275	300	4.0	2.0

Sandblast, commercial blast **(67% white)**	SF per hour			Lbs per SF	
	Slow	Med	Fast	Hvy	Lt
Surface condition basis - Large projects & surface areas					
Loose mill scale & fine powder rust	150	175	200	5.0	4.0
Tight mill scale & little or no rust	125	150	175	6.0	5.0
Hard scale, blistered, rusty surface	75	100	125	8.0	6.0
Rust nodules and pitted surface	50	60	70	11.0	8.0
Surface area basis					
Pipe up to 12" O/D	45	60	75	7.0	5.0
Structural steel					
Sizes up to 2 SF/LF	70	85	100	7.0	5.0
Sizes from 2 to 5 SF/LF	80	95	110	6.0	5.0
Sizes over 5 SF/LF	85	100	115	6.0	5.0
Tanks and vessels					
Sizes up to 12'0" O/D	80	95	110	7.0	6.0
Sizes over 12'0" O/D	75	100	125	6.5	6.0

Sandblast, near white blast **(95% white stage)**	SF per hour			Lbs per SF	
	Slow	Med	Fast	Hvy	Lt
Surface condition basis - Large projects & surface areas					
Loose mill scale & fine powder rust	125	150	175	7.0	5.0
Tight mill scale & little or no rust	75	100	125	9.0	7.0
Hard scale, blistered, rusty surface	50	75	100	13.0	9.0
Rust nodules and pitted surface	35	50	65	17.0	12.0
Surface area basis					
Pipe up to 12" O/D	30	45	60	10.0	8.0
Structural steel					
Sizes up to 2 SF/LF	40	55	70	10.0	7.0
Sizes from 2 to 5 SF/LF	45	60	75	9.0	7.0
Sizes over 5 SF/LF	55	70	85	9.0	8.0
Tanks and vessels					
Sizes up to 12'0" O/D	65	80	95	8.0	6.0
Sizes over 12'0" O/D	70	85	100	8.0	6.0

Prep work for repaint jobs
Figure 17-3 (continued)

Sandblast, white blast (100% uniform white stage)

	SF per hour			Lbs per SF	
	Slow	Med	Fast	Hvy	Lt
Surface condition basis - Large projects & surface areas					
Loose mill scale & fine powder rust	50	75	100	10.0	7.0
Tight mill scale & little or no rust	40	60	80	11.0	8.0
Hard scale, blistered, rusty surface	30	45	60	15.0	10.0
Rust nodules and pitted surface	25	35	45	20.0	15.0
Surface area basis					
Pipe up to 12″ O/D	30	40	50	13.0	10.0
Structural steel					
Sizes up to 2 SF/LF	40	50	60	12.0	9.0
Sizes from 2 to 5 SF/LF	45	55	65	11.0	8.0
Sizes over 5 SF/LF	50	60	70	11.0	8.0
Tanks and vessels					
Sizes up to 12′0″ O/D	60	70	80	11.0	8.0
Sizes over 12′0″ O/D	70	80	90	11.0	8.0

Sanding, medium (before first coat)

	SF per hour			SF per gallon	
	Slow	Med	Fast	Hvy	Lt
Interior flatwall areas	275	300	325	--	--
Interior enamel areas	250	275	300	--	--

Sand & putty (before second coat)

	SF per hour			SF per gallon	
	Slow	Med	Fast	Hvy	Lt
Interior flatwall areas	190	200	120	--	--
Interior enamel areas	110	125	140	--	--
Exterior siding & trim-plain	180	200	220	--	--
Exterior trim only (LF measurement)	100	110	120	--	--
Bookshelves	100	125	150	--	--
Cabinets	125	150	175	--	--

Consider all exterior trim to be one foot wide (even if it is less than 12″).
High grade work - Use the manhours equal to one coat of paint.
Medium grade work - Use half (50%) of the manhours for one coat of paint.

Sanding, light (before third coat)

	SF per hour			SF per gallon	
	Slow	Med	Fast	Hvy	Lt
Interior flatwall areas	335	345	355	--	--
Interior enamel areas	130	140	150	--	--
Exterior siding and trim -plain	250	275	300	--	--
Exterior trim only (LF measurement)	150	175	200	--	--
Bookcases	175	225	275	--	--
Cabinets	200	250	300	--	--

Sanding, extra fine flat surfaces, varnish

	SF per hour			SF per gallon	
	Slow	Med	Fast	Hvy	Lt
Sand or steel wool	50	85	125	--	--

Prep work for repaint jobs
Figure 17-3 (continued)

Strip, remove or bleach

	SF per hour			SF per gallon	
	Slow	Med	Fast	Hvy	Lt
Remove wallcover					
Old wallpaper up to 3 layers	50	70	90	--	--
Stripping flat varnished surfaces					
Varnish with liquid remover					
Light duty	25	35	45	140	175
Heavy duty	20	30	40	125	150
Stripping floors					
Paint removal	20	30	40	170	180
Varnish removal	30	40	50	175	185

Note: Because the type of surface and type of material being stripped or removed will alter rates, it's best to strip, remove or bleach existing finishes on a time and material or cost plus basis with a preset hourly rate.

Taping gypsum wallboard

	LF per hour				
	Slow	Med	Fast	Hvy	Lt
Preparation					
Bead, spot nail heads & sand	85	100	115	--	--
Taping					
Hand operation	125	150	175	--	--
Mechanical tools	200	225	250	--	--
Tape 250 LF per roll	--	--	--	550	650
Joint cement (premixed) per 75-lb bag	--	--	--	550	650

Unsticking windows

On repaint jobs, test all windows during your estimating walk-through and allow approximately 15 minutes (.25 hours) for each stuck window. But don't price yourself out of the job with this extra time.

Washing

	SF per hour			SF per gallon	
	Slow	Med	Fast	Hvy	Lt
Interior flatwall (smooth surfaces)					
Wash only	175	200	225	--	--
Wash & touchup	135	160	185	--	--
Interior flatwall (rough surfaces)					
Wash only	125	150	175	--	--
Wash & touchup	55	100	135	--	--
Interior enamel (wall surfaces)					
Wash only	190	220	240	--	--
Wash & touchup	85	110	140	--	--

Prep work for repaint jobs
Figure 17-3 (continued)

Washing (continued)	SF per hour			SF per gallon	
	Slow	Med	Fast	Hvy	Lt
Interior enamel trim					
Wash only	100	150	200	--	--
Wash & touchup	90	125	150	--	--
Interior varnish trim					
Wash only	150	190	240	--	--
Wash & touchup	120	140	160	--	--
Interior varnish floors					
Wash only	160	210	260	--	--
Wash & touchup	130	155	175	--	--
Interior plaster (smooth)					
Wash only	150	175	200	--	--
Wash & touchup	125	155	190	--	--
Interior plaster (sand finish)					
Wash only	110	135	160	--	--
Wash & touchup	85	110	140	--	--

Note: Because the type of surface and type of material being removed will alter rates, it's best to remove calcimine deposits on a time and material basis with a preset hourly rate.

Waterblasting	SF per hour			SF per gallon	
	Slow	Med	Fast	Hvy	Lt
	450	500	550	--	--

Use an hourly or daily rate depending on the quantity of work involved. Waterblast to remove deteriorated, cracked flaking paint from accessible concrete, block, brick, wood, plaster or stucco surfaces. Rates assume a ¼" diameter nozzle with 100 lbs. pressure.

Window protective coating (paraffin wax)	SF per hour			SF per gallon	
	Slow	Med	Fast	Hvy	Lt
Hand application per window	90	100	110	300	325

Wire brushing	SF per hour			SF per gallon	
	Slow	Med	Fast	Hvy	Lt
Pipe up to 12" O/D	50	75	100	--	--
Structural steel					
Sizes up to 2 SF/LF	90	110	125	--	--
Sizes from 2 to 5 SF/LF	100	120	140	--	--
Sizes over 5 SF/LF	110	130	150	--	--
Tanks and vessels					
Sizes up to 12'0" O/D	110	130	150	--	--
Sizes over 12'0" O/D	120	140	160	--	--

Prep work for repaint jobs
Figure 17-3 (continued)

leaves a smooth, clean surface. That makes for a high quality, long-lasting paint job. Use waterblasting on any job where a quality finish is needed. Figure 17-4 shows a waterblaster in use.

If you're in the repainting business, a waterblaster is a good investment. If you won't be using it often enough to justify the purchase price, rent one when you need it.

Surface Prep Techniques and Materials

To estimate prep work accurately, you've got to know what needs to be done and how to do it. The rest of this chapter describes surface prep techniques and materials — beginning with exterior wood preparation.

The waterblaster in use
Figure 17-4

Exterior Wood: Preparation for Paint

New construction— All wood surfaces must be dry, free of grease, mildew, dirt, and mortar and asphalt splatters. Knots and sappy spots must be sealed with a sealer. Rough surfaces must be sanded smooth, with all nail holes and cracks puttied. All window and door trim joints must be caulked.

Repaint jobs— All blistered, peeling and scaling paint must be removed down to a stable surface by sanding, wire brushing or scraping. Remove chalk deposits by waterblasting, hand scraping or wire brushing. Remove or replace all loose or split caulking. Putty all cracks, crevices and nail holes. Use a commercial mildew remover if mildew is present.

Use a waterblaster on exterior wood surfaces if you can wait several days after blasting for the wood to dry. After waterblasting, finish up with light sanding or wire brushing. Enlarge expansion cracks with a putty knife until they're large enough to provide a firm anchor for the preparation material. These patches must be primed and sealed

prior to paint application. But before applying the first coat of primer or paint to a surface which has been waterblasted, allow it to dry *completely*. This may take as long as a week. Waterblasting forces water deep into the surface.

Exterior Wood: Preparation for Stain

New construction— All surfaces must be clean and free of foreign material. Roughen the surface with a stiff wire brush to remove loose fibers and splinters.

Repaint jobs— It's possible to restain a wood surface, but only after it's been cleaned down to raw wood. All loose, split or otherwise defective caulking or putty must be removed and replaced. Mildew must be killed.

Figure 17-5 is a primer and paint selection guide for painting exterior wood. Figure 17-6 is a selection guide for staining exterior wood.

Exterior Galvanized Metal

Galvanized sheet metal, such as gutters and downspouts, must be treated with acid or a specialized paint before receiving the prime coat. All metal that's to be painted should get a prime coat to prevent rust.

Exterior Ferrous Metals (Iron and Steel)

Structural steel, doors and frames, metal trim, fire escapes, ornamental iron, handrails and other iron or steel surfaces must be free from oil and grease before they're painted. Washing metal surfaces with solvent or emulsion cleaner is best. Surfaces with rust or scale should be cleaned by scraping and wire brushing, or by sandblasting. These surfaces must be recoated with primer within 24 hours.

The amount of preparation on ferrous metal surfaces depends on how much deterioration or damage there is. Follow these preparation stages for progressively worse surface conditions.

Hand and power tool cleaning— Light oxidation, rust, oil and grease can be removed with wire brushes or small power tools such as sanders and grinders.

Surfaces	Primer selection	Type	Finish coating selection	Finish	Type
Painted: Clapboard siding, hardboard siding, shingles, shakes, framing, trim, doors, fascia	Primer	Long-oil alkyd	Latex house paint Eggshell finish house paint Latex house & trim paint House paint	Low lustre Eggshell Soft gloss High gloss	Latex Long-oil alkyd Latex Long-oil alkyd
Enameled: Window/door framing trim, sash, doors	Primer	Long-oil alkyd	High gloss enamel Industrial enamel	High gloss	Alkyd
Porches steps, platforms, decking, railings	Porch & floor enamel thinned	Alkyd	Porch & floor enamel, as packaged	High gloss	Alkyd

Primer and paint selections for painted exterior wood
Figure 17-5

Surfaces	Primer selection	Type	Finish coating selection	Finish	Type
Stained: Clapboard siding, shakes, shingles textured or rough sawn siding, trim, primer fencing, decking	None. If necessary to suppress bleeding, use latex exterior primer	Latex	Exterior stain Solid colors Exterior stain semi-transparent Vinyl acrylic latex stains	Flat Penetrating Flat	Alkyd Latex
Clear finish: Doors, trim & misc.	Spar varnish, thinned	Phenolic-modi-fied tung oil	Spar varnish, as packaged	High gloss	Phenolic-modi-fied tung oil
Clear finish: Clapboard siding shakes, shingles textured or rough sawn siding, fencing decking, trim	None			Penetrating clear wood finish	Penetrating	Phenolic tung oil Modified linseed oil

Primer and stain selections for stained exterior wood
Figure 17-6

Surfaces	Primer selection	Type	Finish coatings selection	Finish	Type
Ferrrous: Structural steel, Storage tanks, doors, trim, sash fire escapes, ornamental iron catwalks, railings	Metal primer Zinc chromate primer	Alkyd	Optional Optional Enamel Quick dry industrial enamel Enamel	Stain Soft gloss High gloss	Alkyd Latex Alkyd Epoxy ester
Galvanized iron: Gutters, leaders vents, doors ducts, framing siding	Galvanized metal primer Zinc chromate primer	Latex Alkyd Alkyd Alkyd	Latex house paint Latex house & trim paint House paint Enamel Quick dry industrial enamel Aluminum	Low lustre Soft gloss Bright	Latex Long-oil Alkyd Epoxy ester Linseed- coumarone indene
Aluminum metal	Zinc chromate primer	Alkyd	Aluminum	Bright	Linseed- coumarone indene
Factory finshed aluminum siding	If required base primer	Long oil alkyd	Latex house paint Latex house & trim paint Eggshell house paint House paint	Low lustre Soft gloss Eggshell High gloss	Latex Alkyd
Factory finished steel buildings	If required, metal primer	Alkyd	Enamel Quick dry industrial enamel	High gloss	Akyd

Primer and paint selections for metal surfaces
Figure 17-7

Brush-off sandblast— The brush-off blast is a light sandblast that will prepare ferrous metal surfaces when hand and small power tools won't do the job. The brush-off blast will remove light mill scale or well-bonded paint.

Commercial sandblast— Sandblasting is needed when the surface has a non-uniform dull gray color. It removes most old paint, mill scale and rust that's visible to the naked eye.

Near-white metal blast— The term *near-white* is used to describe the appearance of a variety of metals such as high strength structural steel. Sandblasting typically leaves these metals spotty — not a uniform gray color. The time and material required for the near-white blast and the white blast are very similar.

White metal blast— The *white blast* is used to remove *all* mill scale, old paint and other foreign matter visible to the naked eye. The surface has a uniform gray color almost like polished aluminum.

It's good painting practice to pretreat or preprime the metal surfaces with a zinc oxide or zinc chromate primer before applying the finish coats of paint. And remember, the Underwriter's Laboratory fire labels on fire doors and frames must always be visible. Don't paint over them. Mask them off before painting.

Figure 17-7 is a primer and paint selection guide for metal surfaces.

Concrete and Masonry Surfaces
New construction— Ideally, concrete and masonry will cure for 60 to 90 days before preparation or painting. Remove all loose particles and mortar by scraping or with a wire brush. Form-oil compound and salts on a concrete surface can be cleaned off with a 10% solution of muriatic acid. Then rinse

thoroughly and let it dry. Before masonry is painted or sealed, the surface must be treated with a mixture of T.S.P. and water. After cleaning, any remaining residue should be removed with a wire brush. Otherwise the paint will flake off.

All grout or concrete splatters must be removed, and all holes, cracks, crevices and voids should be pointed, scraped, cleaned and caulked.

The new construction estimating formulas in Chapter 19 include normal preparation time and material.

Repaint jobs— Surfaces that are peeling, scaling or have started to chalk must be cleaned by scraping, wire brushing, waterblasting or with a mechanical grinder. All mildew must be killed. All loose caulking and grout must be removed from cracks and crevices, and the cracks cleaned and filled with a patching compound.

Remove dirt, oil and grease from unpainted surfaces (walls and floors) with a grease-dissolving compound. Then the surface can be painted with paint designed for concrete and masonry. Figure 17-8A and 17-8B is a primer selection guide for concrete and masonry.

Interior Wood: Preparation for Paint
New construction— The surface must be dry, sand-

ed smooth, and free from dust, dirt and grit. Nailholes, cracks and blemishes must be puttied. Knotholes should be coated with a primer or sealer before the prime coat operation. Each coat must be completely dry and lightly sanded before applying the next coat. Doors must have a primer undercoat on all six sides. The new construction formulas in Chapter 19 include normal preparation time and material.

Repaint jobs— All surfaces must be clean and free from wax, oil, grease and grime. Sand glossy surfaces and remove all loose, peeling or flaking paint by scraping or sanding. Holes, cracks, chips, gouges and crevices must be repaired with patching compound and sanded flush with the surface, matching the original texture if possible. Surfaces stained with marking pens, crayons or lipstick must be washed with solvent and primed with a stain killer to control bleeding. Figure 17-9 is a primer and paint selection guide for painted interior wood.

Interior Wood: Preparation for Stain
New construction— All surfaces must be dry, sanded smooth, free from dirt, dust or grit. All nail holes, cracks, crevices and blemishes must be repaired with a filler tinted to match the color of the wood. Open-grained wood such as oak or

Surfaces	Primer selection	Type	Finish coatings selection	Finish	Type
Poured and precast concrete, cement and cinder block	Block filler except under satin. Where required for repaint, use primer	Latex	Latex house paint Latex house & trim paint Satin	Low lustre Soft gloss Satin	Latex
Stucco, brick, unglazed asbestos-cement siding/shingles, flexboard, concrete	None. Where required for repaint, use primer	None	Latex house paint (2 coats) Latex house & trim paint (2 coats) Satin	Low lustre Soft gloss Satin	Latex
Concrete floors, platforms	Porch and floor enamel, thinned	Alkyd	Porch & floor enamel, as packaged	High gloss	Alkyd

Primer and paint selections for masonry and concrete - exterior
Figure 17-8A

Surfaces	Primer selection	Type	Finish coatings selection	Finish	Type
Poured/precast concrete, cement, and cinder block walls and ceilings	Block filler	Latex	Wall satin		Latex
			Alkyd flat	Flat	Alkyd
	Latex, quick dry prime seal*	Latex	Optional	Eggshell	
			Satin enamel	Satin	Latex
			Optional	Semi-gloss	Alkyd
	Waterproofing masonry paint**	Vinyl toluene-butadiene	Enamel		Alkyd
			Quick dry enamel	High gloss	Epoxy ester
			Enamel		Epoxy polyester
			Tile-like enamel		
			Ceilings: Sweep-up spray finishes	Flat or eggshell	Alkyd
			Texture: Texture paint	Sand/rough Spanish	Latex
Fire retardant (new unpainted block). New unpainted smooth surfaces or repaint	Block filler, Latex enamel underbody	Latex	Latex fire retardant paint	Flat	Latex
Concrete floors, platforms, stairs	Same as finish coat. (First coat thinned)		Porch & floor enamel	High gloss	Alkyd
			Enamel		Epoxy ester
			Latex floor & patio finish	Satin	Latex epoxy modified

*   For smooth surfaces or repaint priming.

**   For new unpainted wall surfaces subject to excessive moisture. Particularly effective under solvent thinned coatings and primer for the tile-like enamel

**Primer and paint selections
for masonry and concrete - interior
Figure 17-8B**

walnut can be filled with a suitable wood filler. Tops and bottoms of doors must be sealed with at least one finish coat.

Repaint jobs— Surfaces which have been treated with a wax or oily furniture polish should be cleaned with a solvent. Wiping cloths must be changed regularly so the oil or wax isn't wiped back into the surface. Scaling paint can be removed by scraping and sanding with fine grit paper. Glossy surfaces must be dulled with fine grade steel wool or sandpaper. Use a power sander or paint remover on surfaces that require complete restoration. Figure 17-10 is a primer and stain selection guide for stained interior wood.

Surfaces	Primer selection	Type	Finish coatings selection	Finish	Type
Painted/enameled:			Wall satin	Flat	Latex
Doors, trim	Alkyd enamel	Alkyd	Flat	Eggshell	Alkyd
cabinets,	underbody		Optional	Satin	Latex
ceilings,	or		Optional	Semi-gloss	
paneling,	Latex enamel	Latex	Enamel		Alkyd
framing, sash	underbody		Industrial enamel	High gloss	
Fire retardant	Alkyd enamel underbody	Alkyd	Latex fire retardant paint	Flat	Latex

Primer and paint selections for painted interior wood
Figure 17-9

Surfaces	Primer selection	Type	Finish coatings selection	Finish	Type
Stain/clear finish:			Stain/penetrating stain*	Flat	Alkyd
Doors, trim,			Coating finishes	Gloss/low luster/flat*	Urethane
cabinets,	See		Urethane finishes	Satin	Alkyd
open roof decking,	product		Stain finish varnish	Gloss/low luster*	Vinyl toluene
trusses,	descriptions		One hour clear finishes		alkyd
paneling,			Latex finishes**	Gloss/satin	Latex
framing,			Sealer finishes		Vinyl toluene
floors			Sanding sealer***	Satin	Castor rosin
			Oil finish		ester
* Fill open-grained wood before staining, if desired.					
** Not recommended for floors.					
*** Do not use as finish on floors.					

Primer and stain selections for stained interior wood
Figure 17-10

Interior Plaster or Drywall

New construction— All plaster surfaces must cure for 30 days and be dry and clean before painting. Cracks and voids must be filled to match the texture of the surface. Repairs must be spot primed with a latex quick-dry primer seal before applying the overall coat of primer.

Gypsum drywall surfaces must be scribed at the intersection of the wall and ceiling, and bladed on the wall surface (if required). The surfaces must also be free from sanding dust and dirt. All texture and joint compound must be completely dry before painting.

Surfaces	Primer selection	Type	Finish coating selection	Finish	Type
Keene's	Alkyd primer sealer*	Alkyd	Wall satin	Flat	Latex
cement plaster,			Flat	Eggshell	Alkyd
texture/sand finish	or latex prime seal	Latex	Optional	Satin	Latex
plaster,			Optional	Semi-gloss	Alkyd
drywall,	Latex prime seal		Enamel		Epoxy ester
composition/wood pulp	or	Latex	Enamel	High gloss	Epoxy
board	latex enamel underbody		Tile-like enamel		polyester
Fire retardant	Latex enamel under-body	Latex	Latex fire retardant paint	Flat	Latex
*Not for new drywall/composition board					

Primer and paint selections for interior plaster or drywall
Figure 17-11

Repaint jobs— All peeling and scaling paint must be removed and the edges of repaired areas must be feathered smooth. All holes, cracks, crevices and blemishes must be filled and sanded flush, then spot primed with stain killer to control residual bleeding. Ceilings with water stains must also be spot primed with stain killer before painting. Wash greasy or waxy areas, and dull glossy surfaces by sanding. Figure 17-11 is a primer and paint selection guide for interior plaster and drywall.

Repaint Symptoms and Remedies

You can only make an accurate estimate of the time it will take to repair paint problems if you know what is required. Here are the common paint defects and their remedies.

Alligatoring— This is caused by incompatible types of paint, like oil paint on an undercoat of bituminous paint. Remove the defective paint surface by scraping, or using a belt sander or paint remover. Apply two coats of primer prior to the finish coat.

Bleeding— Stain or natural wood resins (sap and pitch) ooze through the surface finish coat. Sand the surface and seal with stain killer primer, aluminum paint, white pigmented shellac or all-

purpose primer. Test the solubility of the stain. (Does it dissolve in oil or water?) Finish the surface with either oil- or water-base paint. But don't use water-base paint over shellac.

Blisters— Blisters (Figure 17-12) can occur when moisture is trapped below the finish coat. When the sun heats the trapped moisture, it rises and causes bubbles in the top coat. To repair it, scrape the blisters and allow time for the moisture to evaporate. Sand the dried surface and spot prime the damaged areas.

Cat's eyes— These are spots with circles around them on freshly painted surfaces, caused by oil under the surface. To avoid them, clean all oil and grease from surfaces and keep all spray equipment clean. Touch up spots while the surface is wet.

Chalking— The powdering effect shown at Figure 17-13 is called chalking. It's caused by a breakdown of the paint, which releases pigment particles. Excessive chalking occurs when paint dries too fast, usually because of sunlight falling on fresh paint. To remedy the problem, wash off the chalk and recoat with a nonchalking latex paint.

Paint blistering
Figure 17-12

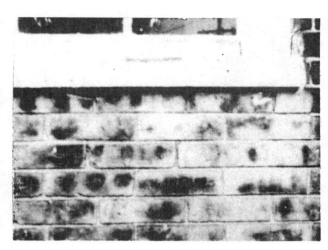

Excessive chalking indicates paint breakdown
Figure 17-13

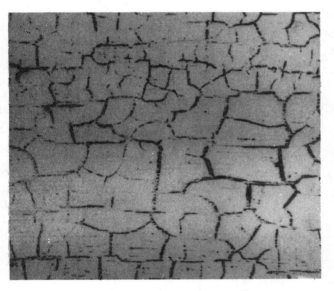

Checking has irregular cracks
Figure 17-14

Cracking from paint buildup
Figure 17-15

Checking— Checking occurs when the top coat of paint is too thin. The surface is irregularly cracked as shown at Figure 17-14. Remove the top coat by scraping, sanding or paint remover. Apply two coats of primer prior to the finish coat. Be sure to add for this when you're estimating preparation time.

Cracking— The cracking at Figure 17-15 is caused by paint buildup after several repaints. Scrape or burn thick layers or use paint remover and sand to finish. Fixing checking and cracking both require considerable preparation time.

Discoloration— Brownish stains (Figure 17-16) can appear in redwood or cedar siding. The stains are caused when moisture dissolves the natural staining agents in the wood and brings them to the surface. Carefully apply a coat or two of primer tinted to the color of the finish coat and let dry for several

**Surface discoloration
Figure 17-16**

**Paint peeling
Figure 17-17**

days. Reprime remaining spots and apply one or two finish coats of solid color stain. Don't go telling the customer that this job will be done in two days.

Flaking— Expansion and contraction of the surface causes moisture to be absorbed. When it dries, the paint becomes brittle and cracks and pulls away from the wood. To repair it, first identify and stop the source of the moisture. Scrape the surface to raw material and let it dry. Spot prime and apply finish coat.

Mildew— Mildew is a fungus or mold that can live in or on the paint in warm, humid conditions. It looks like dirt. To remove it, scrub with a mixture of 2/3 cup T.S.P., 1/3 cup detergent and 1 quart bleach in 3 quarts of water. Rinse with clean water.

Peeling— Peeling (Figure 17-17) can occur when a finish coat isn't bonded to the previous coat. This can be caused by a waxy or oily undercoat, or salts which attract moisture under the finish coat. Moisture can also migrate through the siding from inside the house. First locate the moisture source and vent to allow moisture to escape. Caulk around flashing, eaves, and vents, scrape, sand, spot prime and paint with a latex paint which will allow the surface to breath.

Peeling metal— Galvanized gutters and downspouts will peel because of poor surface preparation or poor choice of paint. Clean to bare metal by scraping or wire brushing and sanding. Prime with a latex metal primer and finish.

Rust stains— Rust stains from nails can cause streaks on the surface. Remove paint and existing rust from the nail heads, then seal the cleaned heads with shellac or a stain killer before repainting. Another remedy is to clean nail heads, set them with a countersink and cover with putty before prime and finish coats.

Wrinkling— The wrinkling at Figure 17-18 is caused by a paint film that dries more rapidly on the surface than underneath, probably because of hot sun shining on the surface. Remove wrinkled paint by sanding, scraping, burning, or paint remover, and repaint under favorable temperature conditions. Avoid painting a surface that's exposed to direct sunlight.

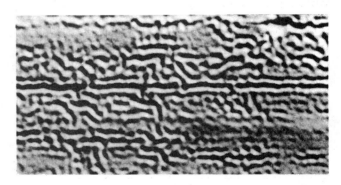

**Wrinkling needs to be removed before repainting
Figure 17-18**

Chapter 18

Estimating Repaint Jobs

The repaint business can be profitable — but it's also risky. You don't make a dime until you find the work, estimate it accurately, satisfy the customer and then collect what's due. None of those steps is easy. But of the four, the hardest one is making an accurate estimate.

Being an experienced painting contractor doesn't automatically make you a good estimator. Even the most experienced painters can't estimate costs accurately without making a detailed labor and material take-off. Some painters can evaluate job costs with reasonable accuracy just by looking at what has to be painted. But I don't recommend it. The only way to improve your estimating accuracy is by figuring the area to be covered and calculating the labor and material needed to paint that area. If you want to make a good living in the painting business, take the time to figure each job accurately.

Of course, it takes a lot longer to produce a detailed estimate based on a complete take-off. But if you invest that time, you know your estimate is "on the money." You can concentrate on doing a quality job and still make an honest profit. I recommend doing a detailed take-off for any job large enough to keep a crew busy for more than a day or two. Remember, there's no substitute for an accurate, detailed estimate.

The Detailed Repaint Estimate

When estimating repaint jobs, watch out for those hidden headaches that are common in the repainting business. Just a few unforeseen problems can suck the profit out of the entire job. And you're not in the business to do charity work.

The flow chart in Figure 18-1 shows the estimating process. The hardest part is figuring the manhours required for preparation. That's a special challenge to your estimating abilities. But it's not the only variable to watch out for. Here are some other parts of the job that are easy to underestimate or leave out entirely:

1) Daily setup (SU)

2) Removing and replacing (RR) hardware, electrical plates and the contents of cabinets

3) Protecting (P) adjacent surfaces

4) Touchup (TU)

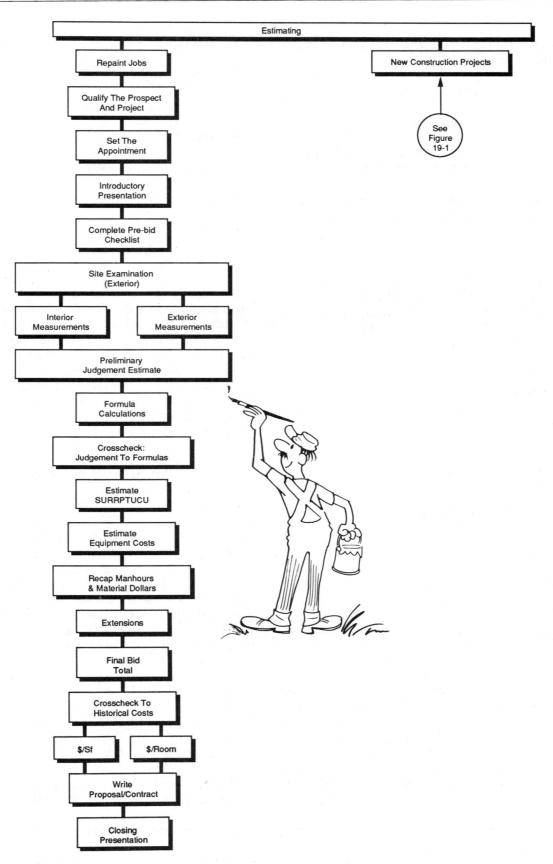

Repaint estimating flow chart
Figure 18-1

5) Daily cleanup (CU) and removal of trash and rubbish

6) Amounts due your subcontractors

7) Commissions due others

8) Escalation factor (time delays which cause increases in labor or material costs)

9) Problems with the owner (attitude, in the way, supervising work, etc.)

Estimating Repaint Work

First, we'll look at the estimating process for repaint jobs. Then I'll walk you through a complete sample estimate. Let's begin with the tools you'll need to do the estimate.

Your Estimating Tools

For estimating repaint jobs, you have to take measurements in the field. You'll need:

- Tape measure (at least 25'0'')

- Two sharp pencils

- Small pencil sharpener

- Stapler

- Hand calculator

- Architect's scale

- This estimating book

- A folder or binder to hold your forms.

Don't confuse the estimating folder with the sales presentation binder. They're two different things. Your estimating book doesn't have to be a three-ring binder. You can use a folder with a pocket and clip for holding loose papers. Use whichever you prefer, as long as it keeps everything you need together. Your estimating kit should contain:

- Repaint take-off sheets

- Repaint recap sheets

- Estimating checklists

- Repaint manhour/material formulas

- A manhour conversion table

- Material price list

- Table of room sizes

- Blank paper

- Proposal/contract forms

- Carbon paper

It's a good idea to keep some door hangers and flyers in your kit, along with some letters of introduction. You can distribute them around the neighborhood after you've finished your estimate. You'll find blank copies of my take-off and recap forms in the back of the book. A print shop can make copies of these and bind them into handy pads at a reasonable cost. Now, armed with a pencil, a tape measure and your estimating kit, you're ready to meet the owner.

The Site Examination

Begin the *site examination* by looking at the other homes in the neighborhood. What's their general condition? What's the community standard for paint quality? These homes are a good indicator of the quality of work the homeowner will expect.

Now look closely at the house you're going to paint and its surroundings. Consider how these items will affect the cost of doing the job:

- Is there good access for painters all around the building?

- Are there shrubs or trees to cut back or tie back?

- Are there other houses or cars near enough to be hit by overspray?

- What's the travel distance from the shop and the material suppliers?

- Is there room for a paint storage area?

- What about roof access and roof type? If

there's a tile roof, your painters will have to be careful not to break the tile, or to slip off, when painting roof jacks, vents and flashing.

Now it's time for a close look at the house. What's the condition of the exterior surfaces? While you're checking the surfaces, make a sketch of the building's shape. There's room for this sketch on the repaint recap sheet later in this chapter. Make this sketch as large as possible and as close to scale as you can. Write in the dimensions as you make the sketch. You may want to use the back of the recap sheet or a separate sheet of graph paper for your sketch or for additional notes or specifications.

As you sketch the shape of the building, identify each wall with a number. The wall facing the street is number 1. Continue in a counterclockwise direction until all the walls are labeled. Be sure to number the walls at the entry or patio indentations.

While you're doing your sketch, take notes on the preparation required. During your walk around the building, have the owner point out areas he's concerned about. Note his comments on your take-off sheet when you itemize the preparation requirements for each wall.

Sketch the Interior

Now move into the house. Complete your sketch by adding the interior walls. Start in the living room and move counterclockwise through the other rooms. Measure each room. Mark the location of each door and window opening, labeling them A, B, C and so on until all are identified. Label each room: LIV (living room), KIT (kitchen), UTIL (utility), BA (bath) and BR1 (bedroom #1) for example.

As you walk through the building, fill out a separate take-off sheet for each room. Have the owner point out damage, defects and areas he's particularly concerned about. Mark each damaged area with an X on your sketch and list all the preparation requirements on the take-off sheet. Finally, staple all the take-off sheets together.

Estimate the Preparation Work

Next, retrace your steps through each room. Thoroughly review the preparation work. Estimate and list the materials and manhours needed to do the preparation work for each room on the take-off sheet. I've listed typical prep requirements on the completed take-off sheets later in this chapter.

Estimate the Painting Operations

After you've estimated the prep work for each room, begin your take-off for the painting itself. Start at the ceilings of each room and work down to the floor. Always work top-to-bottom. Use the checklists in Chapter 5 to make sure you don't miss anything.

Here's the top-to-bottom order I use to estimate repaint jobs. This is the order I'll follow in the sample estimate later in this chapter.

Interior	Exterior
Ceiling	Roof
Beams	Fascia & overhang
Walls	Walls
Doors	Doors
Windows	Windows
Trim	Wood trim
Baseboards	Metal trim
Floors	Patios, decks

Examine each surface in order, then estimate the manhours, material and equipment you'll need for each of the painting operations. This systematic approach in the field will give you an accurate, detailed estimate — *if* you have the experience to be able to visualize the work that needs to be done.

The Repaint Take-Off Form

I designed the repaint take-off form to use when listing room and wall dimensions in the field. In the sections headed Manhours and Materials, there are columns to record your preliminary judgment estimates of the time and gallons of paint the job will take. Fill out these columns while you're doing the take-off in the house. Use a separate form for each room. There's a blank copy in the back of the book and filled-out forms later in this chapter.

Using the Repaint Formulas

After you've finished the take-off and made your preliminary judgments, calculate the manhour and material quantities using your repaint formulas. Then compare both sets of results.

You can use my repaint formulas if you don't have any of your own — but make up your own formulas based on your cost records as soon as possible. No figures from a book will be as accurate as the figures you compile from your own jobs. Where possible, do these calculations back in the privacy of your office. If you have to make a quick estimate on the site, go out to your truck so there's some privacy while you're calculating. When you're finished, enter the results of your calculations in the formula columns under manhours and materials.

Compare Judgment to Calculations

Next, compare your detailed labor and material estimate with your original judgment estimate of the cost. If the two figures are more than 15% apart, something may be wrong. Go over the numbers again. This crosschecking will help eliminate most major mistakes. It's better than relying on either your judgment or your formulas alone. When you combine the advantages of the intuitive approach and the objective approach, it's almost like getting a second opinion.

Estimate SURRPTUCU

Now your manhour and material calculations are done. Use the SURRPTUCU section of each take-off form to estimate SetUp, Remove and Replace, Protection, TouchUp and CleanUp. Evaluate the manhour and material needs for each of these requirements and enter the totals on the take-off form.

Estimating Equipment Costs

Start the equipment estimate by listing the equipment needed and how long you'll need it. Use monthly rental rates to calculate the daily rate, then multiply this rate by the number of days you'll need each piece of equipment. There's space for your estimated equipment costs on the recap sheet later in this chapter.

Recapping and Extending the Totals

The next step in the repaint estimating process is to recap your totals. Use the recap form to summarize the manhours, materials and equipment costs for the entire project.

Now you're ready for the *extensions.* You'll extend the manhours into labor costs, then

add all the other itemized costs on the recap sheet to find the total bid price.

Note that by *total* bid price I don't necessarily mean *final* bid price. There's one more step to take. The bottom section of the recap sheet is called "Crosscheck to historical costs." Use this section to compare both price per square foot ($/SF) for the entire project and price per room ($/room) to a range of your actual costs on similar projects. If your estimated costs are within the range of historical costs, your estimate is done. The final step is to prepare your proposal for presentation to the owner.

That's my entire detailed repaint estimating system. In my opinion, it's the best way to produce an accurate, moneymaking estimate for repaint work. Now let's see how the system works on a sample project.

The Interior Repaint Take-Off

We'll begin with the living room of the sample plan in Appendix A. Figure 18-2 is my estimating table for repaint manhours and materials. Figure 18-3 is my price list. Obviously, these prices won't be accurate for your estimates. Just use these prices for the sample estimate and as a guide for making up your own price list. For the sample estimate, we'll use these figures in the same way you'd use your own prices and estimating formulas in actual estimates.

Following the rule that we estimate in the same order as we paint, move from top to bottom. Begin the estimate with the ceiling and move to the walls, doors and windows. The final step is the baseboard and floor, if they'll be painted.

Use a take-off sheet for each room. Figure 18-4 is the take-off sheet for the living room in the sample estimate. Identify the room and its dimensions in the heading, as well as the job name, estimate number and date.

Use the room dimensions to calculate the floor area. Enter the square feet of floor area in the SF section at the top of the form. Notice that there are 14 numbered lines in each of those sections. Make sure you enter the living room ceiling — and all the other operations you're estimating — on the same numbered line in the manhour and material sections.

Repaint Estimating Tables

Use this table to estimate the time and material needed for repainting exterior and interior surfaces on existing homes and apartments. Production rates are in manhours per square foot (SF) or per linear foot (LF) of area coated. Material coverage is in square feet or linear feet covered per gallon of coating. Paint material types are identified in Figure 18-3, the material price list. These tables do not include time needed for setup, removal, replacement, protection, touchup or cleanup (SURRPTUCU) except as noted. Abbreviations in parentheses in these tables are the same as the abbreviations used in the sample estimates.

Baseboard, per LF of baseboard Single coat applications	LF per hour	LF per gallon	Material type
Paint, roll with walls	2500	1500	3
Enamel, roll with walls	1800	1000	4
Enamel, brush and cut in	100	700	4

Baseboard, per SF of floor Single coat applications	SF per hour	SF per gallon	Material type
Paint, roll with walls	2500	1500	3
Enamel, brush and cut in	500	1000	4

Beams Single coat applications	LF per hour	LF per gallon	Material type
Heights to 13'	35	50	8
Over 13' to 17'	24	50	8
Over 17' to 19'	16	50	8
Over 19' to 21'	12	50	8

These figures will apply when a roller and brush are used to paint beams from 4" x 8" to 6" x 14". Labor and material are per linear foot of beam. *High time difficulty factors* are included in these rates.

Repaint estimating tables
Figure 18-2

Cabinets Per SF of cabinet face	SF per hour	SF per gallon	Material type
Paint grade, one coat, roll and brush application			
Undercoat application	75	260	2
Enamel application	85	300	4
Paint cabinet backs (wall behind the cabinet)			
Roll and brush, one coat, flat or enamel	150	300	3
Stain, seal and lacquer, including the seven steps			
listed below:	40	40	--
Step 1, sand and putty	--	--	--
Step 2, spray 1 coat of stain	--	--	5a
Step 3, wipe with a rag	--	--	--
Step 4, spray 1 coat of sanding sealer	--	--	5b
Step 5, sand lightly to a soapy film		--	-- --
Step 6, spray 1 coat of lacquer	--	--	5c
Step 7, spray final coat of lacquer	--	--	5c

The figures above include painting or staining the cabinet face, back of doors, stiles and rails. For the seven step stain and lacquer process, the figures include a fog coat of stain on the shelves and cabinet back (the wall behind the cabinet).

Carport canopy   For wood canopy, see *Overhang (eaves)*. Metal carport canopy is usually prefinished corrugated material.

Ceilings, gypsum wallboard One coat applied by roller	SF per hour	SF per gallon	Material type
Flat wall paint and orange peel or			
knockdown (medium) texture	300	300	3
Sealer or enamel (in wet areas) and orange peel or knockdown (medium) texture			
Seal wet area ceilings	325	275	1
Enamel wet area ceilings	275	285	4

For ceilings over 8 feet high, apply *High time difficulty factors*. Do not make deductions for openings in the ceiling area that are under 100 SF.

Ceilings, tongue and groove wood Semi-transparent stain	SF per hour	SF per gallon	Material type
Roll on 1 coat	200	275	7
Spray on 1 coat	300	220	7

Repaint estimating tables
Figure 18-2 (continued)

Closets
One coat applied by brush

	LF per hour	LF per gallon	Material type
Molding, enamel applied over flat wall primer to molding going around the perimeter			
of a closet, brush on 1 coat	70	225	4
Poles, stained before pole is installed			
Brush and rag wipe, 1 coat	40	225	5a or 8
Shelf and pole, enamel applied over flat wall primer after shelf			
installation, brush on 1 coat	15	80	4
Shelves, enamel applied over flat wall primer			
brush on 1 coat	25	100	4

Measurements are based on the linear feet of molding, pole or shelf painted and include coating all exposed surfaces.

Corbels
Up to 4" by 8"

	LF per hour	LF per gallon	Material type
Brush on 1 coat	15	50	8

See Figure 19-14 for a picture of rafter tails and corbels.

Cornice   See *Overhang*

Decks   See *Siding* for deck surface and *Overhang* for deck overhang.

Doors, exterior

	Hours per door	Doors per gallon	Material type
French (F)	1.0	12	10
Louvered (L)	1.4	7	10
Entry doors (E)			
Paint grade, exterior enamel	1.4	4	10
Stain grade, marine spar varnish	1.4	4	9
Stain grade, polyurethane	1.4	4	9
Other exterior doors (X)	.5	7	10

These figures include finishing all six sides of the door, jamb and trim. Paint grade doors get two coats of exterior enamel. Stain grade doors get a coat of stain, sealer, and the finish.

Doors and casing, interior

	Hours per opening	Gallons per opening	Material type
Undercoat using roller or spray	.4	.10	2
Enamel on trim using roller or spray	.4	.10	4

These figures apply to painting all six sides of interior doors, jambs and trim, and pullman and linen closet doors. It's usually much faster (and nearly as accurate) to count the openings and estimate time and materials from Figures 18-9 and 18-10 than it is to estimate each opening separately. Use this table if you elect not to use Figures 18-9 and 18-10. This table shows labor and materials required per opening.

Repaint estimating tables
Figure 18-2 (continued)

Eaves See *Overhang*

Fascia Brush and roll one coat	LF per hour	LF per gallon	Material type
2" x 4"	180	140	8
2" x 6" to 2" x 10"	150	120	8
2" x 12"	110	90	8

Fencing Standard wood plank up to 6' high	SF per hour	SF per gallon	Material type
Roll, 1 coat	100	200	7 or 8
Spray, 1 coat	400	150	7 or 8

For good neighbor fence, multiply the surface area by 1.5 and use these rates.

Fireplace trim Single coat applications	LF per hour	SF per hour	Material type
Mantels, rough sawn wood to 4" x 12", brush	15	50	8
Plant-on interior trim, roll and brush	75	135	8

Fireplaces and adjacent siding Single coat applications	SF per hour	SF per gallon	Material type
Masonry fireplace, brush application	70	140	8
Siding, interior wood, roll and brush	90	100	8

Firewood boxes Single coat applications	Hours each	Gallons each	Material type
Based on a rough-sawn wood box up to 3'0" x 3'6" x 3'6" deep, brush application	.4	.20	8

Flashing See *Sheet metal*

Gutters & downspouts	LF per hour	LF per gallon	Material type
Gutters, brush, 1 coat	80	400	8
Downspouts, brush, 1 coat	30	250	8

Rule of thumb: Use 0.2 manhours plus $1 for material for each 8' of gutter or downspout painted.

Repaint estimating tables
Figure 18-2 (continued)

High time difficulty factors
Painting takes longer when heights above the floor exceed 8 feet. Add the following percentages to your labor estimates:

Over 8' to 13'	Add 30% (multiply the area by 1.3)
Over 13' to 17'	Add 60% (multiply the area by 1.6)
Over 18' to 19'	Add 90% (multiply the area by 1.9)
Over 20' to 21'	Add 120% (multiply the area by 2.2)

Mailbox structures Take off each board and use the manhours and materials given for *Trellis* or *Plant-on trim*

Masonry block walls Concrete masonry units (CMU)	SF per hour	SF per gallon	Material type
Precision (smooth face) block			
Roll, 1st coat	300	240	11
Roll, 2nd coat	350	300	11
Spray, 1 coat	725	190	11
Split face block, spray, 1 coat	600	100	11
Fluted block, spray, 1 coat	600	100	11
Slump block, spray, 1 coat	550	75	11

Measurements are based on the square feet of surface painted

Overhang (eaves) Spray one coat	SF per hour	SF per gallon	Material type
At rake or eaves	350	95	8
Over an entry or deck	475	95	8
At wood carports	550	95	8

For standard overhang, measure the area (length times width) and then multiply by 1.5 to allow for painting rafter tails and outriggers.

Pass-through shelves (P/T) Per linear foot of shelf	LF per hour	LF per gallon	Material type
Brush, 1 coat	30	125	6 & 8

Allow at least 0.2 manhours plus $1 for materials on pass-through shelves.

Repaint estimating tables
Figure 18-2 (continued)

Plant-on trim Roll on one coat	LF per hour	LF per gallon	Material type
2" x 2" to 2" x 4"	80	310	8
2" x 6" to 2" x 8"	70	210	8
2" x 10" to 2" x 12"	60	150	8

For work more than 8 feet above ground level, apply *High time difficulty factors.*

Pot shelves, exterior (P/S) Per linear foot of shelf, 12" to 18" wide	LF per hour	LF per gallon	Material type
Roll and brush, 1 coat	75	40	8

Protective coating   See *Stucco.*

Railing, decorative handrail, interior Coating wood handrail only	LF per hour	LF per gallon	Material type
Stain, seal and lacquer, including the seven steps listed below.	55	100	--
Step 1, light sanding	--	--	--
Step 2, spray 1 coat of stain	--	--	5a
Step 3, wipe with rag	--	--	--
Step 4, spray on sanding sealer	--	--	5b
Step 5, light sanding	--	--	--
Step 6, spray on 1 coat of lacquer	--	--	5c
Step 7, spray on 1 coat of lacquer	--	--	5c
Paint grade, undercoat or enamel coats Brush on each coat	30	120	2 or 4

Use these figures to estimate the cost of coating decorative wood interior handrail. Measurements are per linear foot of handrail.

Railing, decorative wood, interior Coating all surfaces	LF per hour	LF per gallon	Material type
Paint grade, undercoat or enamel coats Brush, per coat	10	50	2 or 4
Stain, seal and lacquer, including the seven steps listed below.	8	30	--
Step 1, light sanding	--	--	--
Step 2, spray 1 coat of stain	--	--	5a
Step 3, wipe with rag	--	--	5b
Step 4, spray on sanding sealer	--	--	5b
Step 5, light sanding	--	--	--
Step 6, spray on 1 coat of lacquer	--	--	5c
Step 7, spray on 1 coat of lacquer	--	--	5c

Use these figures to estimate the cost of coating decorative interior wood railing including all vertical and horizontal members. Measurements are per linear foot of rail and include the coating described above for all vertical and horizontal surfaces.

Repaint estimating tables
Figure 18-2 (continued)

Railing, wood, exterior

	LF per hour	LF per gallon	Material type
Rough sawn, 42" high with 2" x 2" verticals each 6"			
Brush, 1 coat	16	20	8
Decorative, based on one coat of stain, two coats of sanding sealer, sanding, putty, and two coats of varnish. 36" to 42" high with spindles each 12"			
First coat	22	100	9
Added coats	30	120	9

These figures include coating the rail cap, balusters, newels and spindles. The minimum preparation time for varnishing will usually be 80 square feet per hour for a steel wool buff and 80 square feet per hour for application of wax. The figures in this table assume no jobs with no more than 50 linear feet of rail per living unit.

Railing, wrought iron, interior/exterior
Prime coat applied by others

	LF per hour	LF per gallon	Material type
1/2" x 1/2" verticals, 42" high with bars each 6" to 9"			
No wood cap, brush 1 coat	20	110	6
With wood cap, brush, 1 coat	15	90	6
1/2" x 1/2" verticals, 60" to 72" high with bars each 6" to 9"			
Brush, 1 coat	10	90	6

These figures will apply on either exterior or interior work and are based on less than 50 linear feet of rail per living unit.

Registers, HVAC

	SF floor area per hour	SF floor area per spray can	Material type
Spray bomb, 1 coat	1000	700	Spray can

HVAC registers are usually painted with aerosol spray (bomb) paint to match the walls. Rather than figure the register area to be painted, base your labor and material estimates on the square feet of floor area in the home or apartment. As a *rule of thumb*, figure 6 minutes of labor for each 100 square feet of floor. These estimates include the time needed to remove, paint and replace registers and grilles.

Roof jacks (RJ)
Brush on one coat

	Hours per roof	Gallons per roof	Material type
One story home or multiple units with attached roof area			
Brush 1 coat	.7	.5	8
Two story home, brush 1 coat	.9	.7	8

These figures are minimums based on 1500 square feet of roof and assume that the jacks were primed by others.

Repaint estimating tables
Figure 18-2 (continued)

Sheet metal See also *Vents and flashing*	LF per hour	LF per gallon	Material type
Rain diverters and gravel stops, widths to 2"			
Flat paint, brush, 1 coat	230	600	8
Galvanized iron flashing and parapet wall cap, widths from 2" to 8"			
Flat paint, brush, 1 coat	215	525	8

Shutters Painting all sides	Shutters per hour	Shutters per gallon	Material type
Undercoat, brush, one coat	2.5	12	2
Enamel, brush, each coat	2.0	15	4

These figures assume assembled shutters measuring 2' by 4'.

Siding One coat applications	SF per hour	SF per gallon	Material type
Shingles, sprayed on			
Clear sealer	400	150	12
Semi-transparent stain	300	200	7
Wood siding, solid body or semi-transparent stain applied on a smooth surface			
Up to 500 SF job			
Roller application	125	200	7 or 8
Spray application	450	125	7 or 8
Over 500 to 1000 SF job			
Roller application	200	175	7 or 8
Spray application	500	150	7 or 8
Over 1000 SF job			
Roller application	250	200	7 or 8
Spray application	600	200	7 or 8

For work over 8 feet above ground level, use *High time difficulty factors*.

Stair stringers, exterior	LF per hour	LF per gallon	Material type
Rough sawn wood to 2" x 12" each side			
Roll and brush, 1 coat	40	70	8
Metal shapes up to 14" each side			
Roll and brush, 1 coat	50	120	6

Use these figures when estimating the cost of painting stringers that support open stair treads. Measurements are based on the linear feet of each stringer.

Repaint estimating tables
Figure 18-2 (continued)

Stair stringers, interior	LF per hour	LF per gallon	Material type
Rough sawn wood to 2" x 12" each side			
Roll and brush, 1 coat	35	60	8
Metal shapes up to 14" each side			
Roll and brush, 1 coat	45	110	6

Use these figures when estimating the cost of painting stringers that support open stair treads. Measurements are based on the linear feet of each stringer.

Stair treads and steps, wood Measure the surface area of rise and run and use the manhour and material figures listed under *Siding*.

Stairs, wood Measure the surface area of rise and run and use the estimates listed under *Siding*.

Steel, miscellaneous Single coat application by brush	LF per hour	LF per gallon	Material type
1/2" to 3" widths	200	400	6
3" x 3" to 8" widths	75	225	6
10" to 18" widths	50	150	6

Use these figures for smaller steel members such as corner guards or small posts. For large steel shapes, see the tables in Chapter 20. These figures assume the steel has been primed by others and are based on the linear foot of member painted.

Stucco	SF per hour	SF per gallon	Material type
Textured surface, painted one coat			
Roller application	245	250	11
Sprayed application	550	200	11
Waterproofing, clear hydro sealer, per coat			
Sprayed application	650	200	12

When calculating the stucco area, make no deductions for openings less than 100 SF. If wax protective coating is sprayed on windows before stucco is painted, figure 1/10th manhour per window. A gallon of protective wax (material type 13) will cover about 325 square feet of window. For heights above 8 feet, use *High time difficulty factors*. See Window protective coating in Figure 17-3.

Touchup	% of total interior labor	% of total interior material	Material type
Brush as required	20%	2%	As needed

Touchup will be required on nearly all interior jobs. The skill of your paint crews and the type of job will determine the time needed. The time and materials shown here are generous allowances. The actual time required will usually be less. Figure the touchup time and material needed and then add the appropriate amounts to your estimate.

Repaint estimating tables
Figure 18-2 (continued)

Trellis or lattice
Per LF, brushed and rolled, one coat

	LF per hour	LF per gallon	Material type
2" x 3" to 2" to 6"	120	130	8
2" x 8" to 4" x 12"	100	100	8

This table is based on the linear feet of trellis or lattice member painted.

Trellis or lattice
Per SF, sprayed, one coat

	SF per hour	SF per gallon	Material type
2" x 2" lumber spaced at 3" with 2" x 8" supports	50	60	8

These figures are based on the overall (width times length) area painted.

Valance, light
Roll and brush one coat

	LF per hour	LF per gallon	Material type
Rough-sawn wood, 2" x 6" or 2" x 8"	30	100	8

These figures include time and material to paint all exposed surfaces. Figure a minimum of 0.3 hour hours plus 1/10th gallon of paint for even the smallest valance. Measurements are based on the linear feet of valance including side returns.

Vents and flashing (V & F)
Brush on one coat

	Hours per home	Gallons per home	Material type
1 story home	.7	.4	8
2 story home	.9	.5	8
Multiple units with attached roofs, per 1500 SF of roof area			
Brush, 1 coat	.6	.3	8

These figures assume all work can be done from the roof surface and that the vents and flashing have been pre-primed or pre-treated by others.

Walls, concrete tilt-up
One coat applications

	SF per hour	SF per gallon	Material type
Roller applications	275	280	11
Spray applications	500	260	11

See the tables in Chapter 20 for more information on concrete coatings. For heights over 8 feet, use *High time difficulty factors*.

Repaint estimating tables
Figure 18-2 (continued)

Walls, gypsum wallboard
Per SF of wall coated

	SF coated per hour	SF coated per gallon	Material type
Flat wall paint and orange peel or knockdown texture			
Roll on 1st coat	400	300	3
Roll on 2nd coat	500	325	3
Sealer or enamel (in wet areas) and orange peel or knockdown texture (medium texture) with cabinets and pullmans in place			
Roll on 1 coat	225	250	1
Enamel wet area walls (kitchens and baths) with cabinets and			
pullmans in place, roll on 1 coat	300	285	4

When measuring wall area, don't deduct for wall openings of less than 100 square feet. For heights over 8 feet, use *High time difficulty factors*.

Walls, gypsum wallboard
Per SF of floor area

	SF floor per hour	SF floor per gallon	Material type
Flat wall paint and orange peel or knockdown texture			
Roll on 1st coat	250	175	3
Roll on 2nd coat	300	200	3
Sealer or enamel (in wet areas) and orange peel or knockdown texture (medium texture), with cabinets and pullmans in place--*walls and ceilings*			
Roll on 1 coat	125	100	1
Enamel wet area walls (kitchens and baths) with cabinets and			
pullmans in place--*walls and ceilings*, roll on 1 coat	150	100	4

It's usually quicker (though somewhat less accurate) to estimate wall painting from the floor area. If you want to estimate by the square feet of floor rather than the square feet of wall painted, use the figures in this table. For heights above 8 feet, apply *High time difficulty factors*.

Window seats, wood
Paint grade, brush

	LF per hour	LF per gallon	Material type
Prime coat	20	45	2
Finish coat	25	55	4

These estimates are based on painting exposed surfaces on a window seat up to 24" wide.

Window sills, wood
Paint grade, brush

	LF per hour	LF per gallon	Material type
Prime coat	40	140	2
Finish coat	50	175	4

These figures are per linear foot of sill painted.

Windows, wood   See Appendix B.

Wine racks   See *Cabinets*.

Repaint estimating tables
Figure 18-2 (continued)

ID# Material type	Retail price guide	Contractor price at a 20% discount	Add 10% sundries & escalation	Estimating prices (without tax)
Interior materials				
1 - Sealer, off-white	$ 9.25	$ 7.40	$ 8.14	round to $ 8.10
2 - Undercoat	$13.80	$11.00	$12.14	round to $12.10
3 - Flat wall (production)				
Walls & paint grade base	$10.33	$ 8.25	$ 9.09	round to $ 9.10
4 - Enamel (production)				
K&B walls & openings	$14.50	$11.60	$12.76	round to $12.80
5 - Stain, seal & lacquer system				
Cabinets				
5a - Lacquer stain	$11.00	$ 8.80	--	--
Stain grade base				
5b - Sanding sealer	$12.50	$10.00	--	--
5c - Lacquer (x 2 coats)	$13.00	$10.40	--	--
Average cost for 5a, b & c		*$ 9.90*	*$10.89*	*round to $10.90*
6 - Zinc oxide	$20.75	$16.60	$18.26	round to $18.30
(Railing & pass-through shelf support - use minimum requirement.)				
Exterior materials				
7 - Semi-transparent	$13.00	$10.40	$11.44	round to $11.40
T & G ceiling				
8 - Solid color	$12.00	$ 9.60	$10.56	round to $10.60
Beams				
Light valance				
Fascia				
Overhang				
Siding				
Plant-on trim				
Pot shelf (use minimum requirement)				
Pass-through shelf (use minimum requirement)				
Vents & flashings (use minimum requirement)				
9 - Marine spar varnish	$27.00	$21.00	$23.76	round to $23.80
Entry doors				
10 - Exterior enamel	$17.00	$13.60	$14.96	round to $15.00
French, louvered, exterior doors				
11 - Exterior vinyl	$14.00	$11.20	$12.32	round to $12.30
Masonry, concrete & stucco				
12 - Clear hydro-sealer	$14.20	$11.36	$12.50	use $12.50
Stucco seal and waterproof				

Sample discount material price list
Figure 18-3

Interior room __LIVING ROOM__   Size __14.5 x 17.5__   Job name: __GLEASON__

Exterior _____   SF __254__   Estimate number: __89-045__

Manhours

Operation	Dimension	LF/ SF	Method	Coats	Judgment hours	Formula Feet/hr	Formula hour	Final hours
1. T&G CEILING	17.5 x 15.3 x 1.3	348	R&B	1	2.0	200	1.8	2.0
2. SAND	"	"	"		1.0	300	1.16	1.2
3. BEAMS	17.5 x 1 + 15.3 x 7	125	BRUSH	1	3.0	35	3.6	3.6
4. WIRE BRUSH	" "	"			2.0	75	1.67	1.7
5. WALLS - FLAT	512+67+58.7+38	675	ROLL	1	2.0	400	1.7	1.7
6. PREP					.5	—	.5	.5
7. ALL OPENINGS	ALL	14	ROLL	1	5.6	—	5.6	5.6
8. SAND					1.0		1.0	1.0
9. BASEBOARD	17.5 x 2 + 14.5 x 2	64	R&B	1	.1	900	.1	.1
10.								
11. W.I. RAIL	36" HIGH	4	BRUSH	1	.5	15	.3	.5
12.								
13.								
14.								

Crosscheck: Manhour totals __17.7__   vs. __17.37__

Manhour bid total __17.9__

Material

Operation	LF/ SF	Color	Coats and type	Judgment gallons	Formula Ft/gal	Formula gallons	Price per gallon	Final cost
1. T&G CEILING	268	CEDAR	1-ST	1.0	275 SF	1.0	$ 11.40	$ 11.40
2. SAND PAPER							$	$ 2.00
3. BEAMS	125	RUSTIC	1-HB	2.0	50 LF	2.5	$ 10.60	$ 26.50
4. WIRE BRUSH							$	$ —0—
5. WALLS - FLAT	675	NAVAJO	1-FLAT	2.5	300 SF	2.3	$ 9.10	$ 20.90
6.							$	$
7. OPENINGS	14	NAVAJO	1-ENAMEL	2.0	.1 EA	2.0	$ 12.80	$ 25.60
8.							$	$
9. BASEBOARD	64	NAVAJO	1-FLAT	.2	400	.16	$ 9.10	$ 2.00
10.							$	$
11. W.I. RAIL	4	BLACK		.1	90 LF	.1	$ 18.30	$ 2.00
12.							$	$
13.							$	$
14.							$	$

Crosscheck: Gallons __7.8__   vs. __8.33__

Total material cost $ __90.40__

SURRPTUCU

Operation	Description	Labor hours	Labor cost (at $ 20.25)		Material cost		Totals
Setup		.25	5.—	+	2.—	=	$ 7.—
		.25	5.—	+	1.—	=	$ 6.—
Remove/replace	OPENING HARDWARE	.75	15.—	+	0	=	$ 15.—
	OUTLET & SWITCH PLATES	.5	10.—	+	0	=	$ 10.—
				+		=	$
Protection	FURNITURE	.5	10.—	+	0	=	$
	VISQUEEN FLOOR			+		=	$
	MASKING TAPE			+		=	$
Touchup		.25	5.—	+	1.00	=	$ 7.—
				+		=	$
Cleanup		.25	5.—	+	0	=	$ 5.—
				+		=	$

SURRPTUCU total $ __50.—__

Living room take-off sheet
Figure 18-4

Here's the calculation for the floor area of the living room on the sample plan:

$$14.5 \times 17.5 = 253.75 \text{ or } 254 \text{ SF}$$

Now let's use the room size table (Figure 18-5) to double-check the floor area calculation. The dimensions of our living room are closest to the 14 x 18 dimensions on the table. The 252 square feet from the table is very close to our answer of 254 square feet. That checks.

Living Room Ceiling

Imagine that you're standing in the living room shown on the sample plan. The first thing you'd notice is the cathedral ceiling with exposed tongue and groove wood and beams. So your first step is to estimate the preparation manhours and materials. The ceiling prep will include sanding before a finish coat of varnish. The exposed rough-sawn beams will need to be wire brushed before a finish coat of solid body stain. Enter your preliminary judgments about manhours and materials in the appropriate columns.

The Ceiling Measurement

Ordinarily, in rooms with flat ceilings, the floor area is the ceiling area. With a cathedral or vaulted ceiling like the one in the sample plan, however, the ceiling area is greater than the floor area because the ceiling is at an angle. The plan shows that the ceiling rises to 12 feet at the ridge beam. Look at Figure 18-6. To calculate the actual length of the ceiling line, you have to use the formula for a right triangle:

$$A^2 \quad + \quad B^2 \quad = \quad C^2$$

A is the height, B is the base and C is the hypotenuse of the triangle (or the length of the ceiling line). These calculations are easy with a hand-held calculator. First we'll figure the hypotenuse of the small triangle to the left of the beam in Figure 18-6. A is 1 foot and B is 3 feet:

$$
\begin{array}{llll}
1^2 & + & 3^2 & = & C^2 \\
1 & + & 9 & = & 10 \\
& & \sqrt{10} & = & 3.16
\end{array}
$$

For the larger part of the ceiling, A is 4 feet and B is 11.5 feet:

$$
\begin{array}{llll}
4^2 & + & 11.5^2 & = & C^2 \\
16 & + & 132.25 & = & 148.25 \\
& & \sqrt{148.25} & = & 12.17
\end{array}
$$

Now we know the width of the ceiling: 15.33 feet (3.16 feet on one side of the beam and 12.17 feet on the other side). So the area of the ceiling is 17.5 feet times 15.33 feet, or 268.28 square feet. I'll round it to 268 square feet.

The next step is to multiply the actual surface area by a *high time difficulty factor* since the ceiling is over 8 feet high. We use this factor to allow for ladder time. The difficulty factors I use are shown in Figure 18-7.

Since the ridge beam is 12 feet high, add 30% to the 268 square feet of surface area. The easy way to do that is to multiply 268 by 1.3:

$$268 \quad \times \quad 1.3 \quad = \quad 348 \text{ SF}$$

Look at line 1 in both the manhour and material sections of Figure 18-4. I've entered 348 square feet for the T&G living room ceiling. We'll use that 348 square feet as the basis for our manhour calculations. But we'll use 268 for the material quantity calculations since the difficulty factor only applies to labor. Use the estimating formulas in Figure 18-2 and material prices from Figure 18-3.

Manhours:

$$\frac{348 \text{ SF}}{200 \text{ SF/hour}} = 1.74 \text{ or } 1.8 \text{ hours}$$

Material quantity:

$$\frac{268 \text{ SF}}{275 \text{ SF/gallon}} = .97 \text{ or } 1 \text{ gallon}$$

Material cost:

1 gallon @ $11.40/gallon = $11.40

Wall length (in feet)

Wall width (in feet)	6	8	10	12	14	16	18	20	22	24	26	28	30
6	F 36 W 192	F 48 W 224	F 60 W 256	F 72 W 288	F 84 W 320	F 96 W 352	F 108 W 384	F 120 W 416	F 132 W 448	F 144 W 480	F 156 W 512	F 168 W 544	F 180 W 576
8	F 48 W 224	F 64 W 256	F 80 W 288	F 96 W 320	F 112 W 352	F 128 W 384	F 144 W 416	F 160 W 448	F 176 W 480	F 182 W 512	F 198 W 544	F 224 W 576	F 240 W 608
10	F 60 W 256	F 80 W 288	F 100 W 320	F 120 W 352	F 140 W 384	F 160 W 416	F 180 W 448	F 200 W 480	F 220 W 512	F 240 W 544	F 260 W 576	F 280 W 608	F 300 W 640
12	F 72 W 288	F 96 W 320	F 120 W 352	F 144 W 384	F 168 W 416	F 192 W 488	F 216 W 480	F 240 W 512	F 264 W 544	F 288 W 576	F 312 W 608	F 336 W 640	F 360 W 672
14	F 84 W 320	F 112 W 352	F 140 W 384	F 168 W 416	F 196 W 448	F 224 W 480	F 252 W 512	F 280 W 544	F 308 W 576	F 336 W 608	F 364 W 640	F 392 W 672	F 420 W 704
16	F 96 W 352	F 128 W 384	F 160 W 416	F 192 W 448	F 224 W 480	F 256 W 512	F 288 W 544	F 320 W 576	F 352 W 608	F 384 W 640	F 416 W 672	F 448 W 704	F 480 W 736
18	F 108 W 384	F 144 W 416	F 180 W 448	F 216 W 430	F 252 W 512	F 288 W 544	F 324 W 576	F 360 W 608	F 396 W 640	F 432 W 672	F 468 W 704	F 504 W 736	F 540 W 768
20	F 120 W 416	F 160 W 448	F 200 W 480	F 240 W 512	F 280 W 544	F 320 W 576	F 360 W 608	F 400 W 640	F 440 W 672	F 480 W 704	F 520 W 736	F 560 W 768	F 600 W 800
22	F 132 W 448	F 176 W 480	F 220 W 512	F 264 W 544	F 308 W 576	F 352 W 608	F 396 W 640	F 440 W 672	F 484 W 704	F 528 W 736	F 572 W 768	F 616 W 800	F 660 W 832
24	F 144 W 480	F 182 W 512	F 240 W 544	F 288 W 576	F 336 W 608	F 384 W 640	F 432 W 672	F 480 W 704	F 528 W 736	F 576 W 768	F 624 W 800	F 672 W 832	F 720 W 864
26	F 156 W 512	F 198 W 544	F 260 W 576	F 312 W 608	F 364 W 640	F 416 W 672	F 468 W 704	F 520 W 736	F 572 W 768	F 624 W 800	F 676 W 832	F 728 W 864	F 780 W 896
28	F 168 W 544	F 224 W 576	F 280 W 608	F 336 W 640	F 392 W 672	F 448 W 704	F 504 W 736	F 560 W 768	F 616 W 800	F 672 W 832	F 728 W 864	F 784 W 896	F 840 W 928
30	F 180 W 576	F 240 W 608	F 300 W 640	F 360 W 672	F 420 W 704	F 480 W 736	F 540 W 768	F 600 W 800	F 660 W 832	F 720 W 864	F 780 W 896	F 840 W 928	F 900 W 960

Example: A 14' x 20' room has 280 square feet of floor and 544 square feet of wall area.

F = Floor (or ceiling) area in square feet.

W = Wall area in square feet.

**Room size table
Figure 18-5**

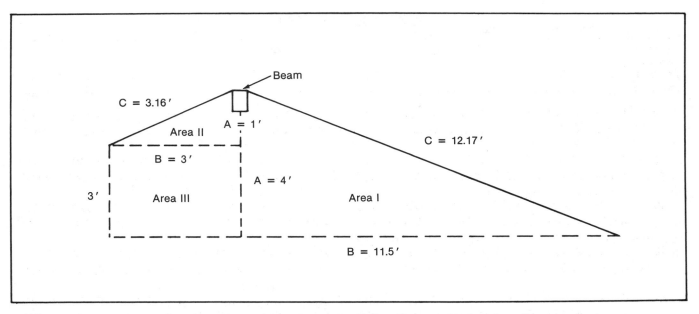

Calculating the area of a cathedral ceiling and related walls
Figure 18-6

Notice that the answers for both the manhours and the material cost have been rounded off. I'll round manhours to the nearest tenth of an hour and material cost to the nearest dime. Look at these figures on the take-off sheet for the living room ceiling (Figure 18-4). Then consider the ceiling preparation. In this case, we'll have to include sanding. The measurement for sanding is 348 square feet, including the high time difficulty factor. My preparation formulas in Chapter 17 give a production rate of 300 square feet per hour for sanding and puttying:

$$\frac{348 \text{ SF}}{300 \text{ SF/hour}} = \quad 1.16 \text{ or } 1.2 \text{ hours}$$

Enter 1.2 hours on line 2 of the take-off sheet. That finishes the living room ceiling — except for the beams. They're next.

Living Room Beams

The beams in the sample living room are identified on the floor plan by dotted lines. The length of the ridge beam is 17.5 feet. You can take that measurement directly from the floor plan. But the rafter beams run away from the ridge beam at the same angle as the ceiling. Measure these beams directly from the section view of the sample plan because

they aren't parallel to the plane of the floor. They run at the same angle, or pitch, as the ceiling. The length of these rafters is the same as the width of the ceiling: 3.16 feet and 12.17 feet, or a total of 15.33 feet each.

The next step is to count the number of rafter beams. At first glance, it looks like there are five — but look again. There are dotted lines at each end of the living room. These indicate beams that are only partially exposed at each end of the room. They must be painted and cut in at the walls. Although only the exposed parts need to be painted, count them as two full beams to allow for the additional time needed for cutting in.

Height	Percent to add to surface area	Multiply by
8'0" to 13'0"	30%	1.3
Over 13'0" to 17'0"	60%	1.6
Over 17'0" to 19'0"	90%	1.9
Over 19'0" to 21'0"	120%	2.2

High time difficulty factors
Figure 18-7

So there are seven rafter beams, each 15.33 feet long. Calculate the total beam length:

Ridge beam:	1 @ 17.5′	=	17.5 LF
Rafter beams:	7 @ 15.33′	=	107.31 LF
	Total		124.81 or 125 LF

The formulas in Figure 18-2 for preparing and painting beams include all beams up to 13'0" ceiling height. The difficulty factor is figured in, so just use the 125 linear feet for your preliminary judgment estimate and to calculate the manhours and material for rolling and brushing stain on the living room beams.

Manhours: $\dfrac{125 \text{ LF}}{35 \text{ LF/hour}}$ = 3.57 or 3.6 hours

Material quantity: $\dfrac{125 \text{ LF}}{50 \text{ LF/gallon}}$ = 2.5 gallons

Material cost: 2.5 gallons x $10.60 = $26.50

Before they can be stained, the beams must be prepared by wire brushing. Use the same 125 linear feet and the rate of 75 linear feet per hour to estimate the time it will take:

$\dfrac{125 \text{ LF}}{75 \text{ LF/hour}}$ = 1.67 or 1.7 hours

These figures for staining and wire brushing the beams are on lines 3 and 4 of Figure 18-4.

Living Room Walls

Find the gross wall area by multiplying the room perimeter by the 8-foot ceiling height. Then add the area under the vaulted ceiling above the 8-foot line. Deduct any openings in the walls (doors or windows, for example) which are larger than 100 square feet.

Begin with the gross wall area calculation:

$$17.5' + 14.5' + 17.5' + 14.5' = 64' \text{ long}$$
$$\underline{\text{x} \quad 8' \text{ high}}$$

Gross wall area up to 8': 512 SF

Next, add the triangular and rectangular wall areas above the 8-foot ceiling line at the vault. Look at Figure 18-6 to see the area involved. To find the area of a rectangle, multiply length by width. For a triangle, multiply 1/2 times base times height. Here's our calculation for the living room wall under the vaulted ceiling:

Area I (triangle)	1/2 x 11.5 x 4 =	23.0
Area II (triangle)	1/2 x 3 x 1 =	1.5
Area III (rectangle)	3 x 3 =	9.0
		33.5 SF
		x 2 walls
		67.0 SF

There's another wall area above the 8-foot ceiling line: the rectangular area between the living room and the kitchen. You can see it best in the section view of the sample plan. The height of this wall is 11 feet (3 feet above the ceiling line). The length is 17.5 feet — so the area is 3 times 17.5, or 52.5 square feet. There's also a 6-inch dropped ceiling in the kitchen, so the ceiling height is 7.5 feet. You'll have to paint the strip that's 6 inches high and 12 feet long (6 SF). That's a total of 58.5 square feet.

Deduct openings— Next, deduct any openings over 100 square feet. First measure and record the sizes of all windows, doors and other openings on your sketch. My list for the sample house is shown in Figure 18-8. You can see that there are no openings over 100 square feet, so no deductions are necessary for this sample estimate.

Apply the difficulty factor— Finally, apply the high time difficulty factor from Figure 18-7 to the areas above 8 feet:

$$67 \text{ SF} + 58.5 \text{ SF} = 125.5 \text{ SF}$$

$$125.5 \times 1.3 = 163.15 \text{ or } 163 \text{ SF}$$

Opening	Dimensions	Area
A. Entry door	3'0" x 6'8"	21 sf
B. Window	5'0" x 5'0"	25 sf
C. Sliding glass door	6'0" x 6'8"	40 sf
D. Window	4'0" x 3'6"	14 sf
E. Bifold doors, 4 each	1'6" x 6'8"	40 sf
F. Opening at kitchen	10'0" x 7'6"	75 sf
G. Water heater door	2'0" x 6'8"	13 sf
H. Bathroom window	3'0" x 1'6"	5 sf
I. Bathroom door	2'0" x 6'8"	13 sf
J. Bedroom door	2'6" x 6'8"	17 sf
K. Bedroom window	6'0" x 4'0"	24 sf
L. Bedroom window	3'0" x 3'0"	9 sf
M. Wardrobe doors, 2 each	3'6" x 8'0"	56 sf
N. Bedroom door	2'6" x 6'8"	17 sf
O. Wardrobe doors, 2 each	3'6" x 8'0"	56 sf
P. Bedroom window	3'0" x 3'0"	9 sf
Q. Bedroom window	6'0" x 4'0"	24 sf

Opening deduction calculations in sample plan
Figure 18-8

Now let's summarize the total wall area we'll use in our calculations for manhours and material quantities:

Wall area up to 8'0":	512
High area:	163
	675 SF

Use this 675 square feet for your judgment estimate and for calculating the rolling and brushing of the living room walls.

Manhours:

$$\frac{675 \text{ SF}}{400 \text{ SF/hour}} = 1.69 \text{ or } 1.7 \text{ hours}$$

Material quantity:

$$\frac{675 \text{ SF}}{300 \text{ SF/gallon}} = 2.25 \text{ or } 2.3 \text{ gallons}$$

Material cost:

2.3 gallons x $9.10 = $20.93 or $20.90

These totals are on line 5 in both the manhour and material sections in Figure 18-4.

The Opening Count

Opening count is a term I use for counting the paint grade doors, windows, pullmans, linens and other surfaces which require an undercoat or enamel coat of paint. Don't confuse this with deducting openings larger than 100 square feet. You could estimate these paint grade surfaces by the square foot, but the opening count is easier.

The opening count begins with counting all the paint grade interior and exterior doors, pullmans, linens, windows (which require paint or stain), shelves and poles. Use the opening count allowance table in Figure 18-9 to calculate the number of openings to count for each.

The sample plan shows louvered bifold doors at the utility area entrance. These doors take a lot of time to refinish properly. Examine them carefully and count each section of each bifold door as one opening. The wardrobe doors in each bedroom only require one opening count because there's no jamb or casing. They're relatively easy to paint.

Pay special attention to the shelf and pole arrangement. Shelves and poles typically receive flat paint. But in this case they require enamel. Include the shelves and poles for each bedroom in the opening count for one coat of enamel and minor preparation. If any openings require extensive preparation or added coats of paint or stain, you might count them as two openings.

Item		Count
Closets	Molding at closet perimeter	1 per 25′0″ length
	Poles, stain	1 per 10′0″ length
	Shelf & pole (undercoat or enamel)	1 per 6′0″ length
	Shelves (undercoat or enamel)	1 per 10′0″ length
Doors	Bifold doors and frames	1 per door
	Dutch doors and frames	2 per door
	Entry doors and frames	1 per door
	FAU (forced air unit)	
	doors and frames	1 per door
	French doors and frames	1.5 per door
	Linen doors with face frame	1 per 2′0″ width
	Louvered bifold doors and frames;	
	false	1 per door panel
	real	1 per door panel
	Louvered doors and frames;	
	false	1 per door
	real	1 per door or per 1′6″ width
	Passage doors and frames;	
	flush	1 per door
	paneled	1.25 per door
	Wardrobe doors	1 per door
	Split coat operation;	
	doors and frames	1 per opening
	Tip-off operation (doors only)	½ per opening
Pullman cabinets		1 per lavatory or per 4′0″ width
Windows, wood		1 per 6 SF of window

Interior opening count allowance table
Figure 18-9

The windows on the sample house are aluminum, but wood windows can be either counted with the openings or estimated by the square foot. My general manhour and material tables in Appendix B include a range of rates for finishing wood windows.

Here's my list of openings to count:

Entry door	1
Utility room doors	4
Water heater	1
Pullman	1
Bathroom door	1
Bedroom 1 entry door	1
Bedroom 1 wardrobe door	1
Enamel shelf and pole	1
Bedroom 2 entry door	1
Bedroom 2 wardrobe door	1
Enamel shelf and pole	1

Openings	Manhours per opening per coat	Undercoat gallons (based on 13 openings/gal.)	Enamel gallons (based on 12 openings/gal.)
1	.4	.08	.08
2	.8	.16	.17
3	1.2	.23	.25
4	1.6	.31	.33
5	2.0	.38	.42
6	2.4	.46	.50
7	2.8	.54	.58
8	3.2	.62	.67
9	3.6	.69	.75
10	4.0	.77	.83

Use for doors, frames, jambs, pullmans and other openings based on Figure 18-9. Roll and brush each coat.

Repaint undercoat and trim table
Figure 18-10

There are 14 openings. Now look at the undercoat and trim table in Figure 18-10 to find the manhours and material costs to apply to your estimate. If there are more than 10 openings, just add to find the total. For example, if there are 12 openings, add 4.0 manhours (for 10 openings) and

0.8 manhours (for 2 openings). Count 4.8 manhours for 12 openings. For the enamel, add 0.83 gallons plus 0.17 gallons, for a total of 1.0 gallon.

These values include a minimum of preparation time and one coat of enamel, since most repaint jobs don't need an undercoater. Always round up the enamel quantity to the next full gallon. Here are the calculations for one coat of enamel on the openings on the sample plan:

Manhours:
14 openings (10 + 4 openings) = 4.0 + 1.6 = 5.6 manhours

Material quantity:
.83 + .33 = 1.16 or 2 gallons

Material cost:
2 gallons x $12.80 = $25.60

The totals for the openings are shown on line 7 in both sections of Figure 18-4. When using the opening count method, you don't need to do a preliminary judgment estimate since the openings are so easy to count and estimate.

Living Room Baseboard

The baseboard length is simply the sum of the perimeter wall measurements. To simplify the process, just measure continuously with no deductions for door openings where there is no baseboard. So there are 64 linear feet of baseboard in the living room that will be rolled with the walls and touched up with a brush. Look at line 9 of the living room take-off sheet.

Manhours:
$$\frac{64 \text{ LF}}{900 \text{ LF/hour}} = .07 \text{ or } .1 \text{ hour}$$

Material quantity:
$$\frac{64 \text{ LF}}{400 \text{ LF/gallon}} = .16 \text{ gallon}$$

Material cost:
.16 gallon x $9.10 = $1.46 or $2.00

Next, refer to the room finish schedule in Appendix A to identify the floor finishes. In this case, all the floors are covered with carpet, vinyl or tile, so there's no hardwood refinishing here.

When you reach the baseboard and floors, it's a good time to review the checklists in Chapter 5 (which should be with you in your binder) to see if you've missed anything. There's one other item on the sample plan which should be included: the wrought iron railing at the entry.

Railing, Wrought Iron

The wrought iron railing is 36 inches high with vertical bars at 6 inches on center and a wood cap. It's only 4 feet long. Since it's so small, you could probably use your judgment to estimate the time and materials needed. But let's do the manhour and materials calculations anyway, just to see how these figures compare to the preliminary estimate. Notice that I'll round up the labor to 0.5 hour. That's the minimum figure I use for any painting operation. I won't round up the paint to a full gallon because you can use black wrought iron paint on many other jobs. As usual, I'll use the estimating formulas and price list in this chapter.

Manhours:
$$\frac{4 \text{ LF}}{15 \text{ LF/hour}} = .267 \text{ or } .5 \text{ hour}$$

Material quantity:
$$\frac{4 \text{ LF}}{90 \text{ LF/gallon}} = .04 \text{ or } .1 \text{ gallon}$$

Material cost:
.1 gallon x $18.30 = $1.83 or $2.00

SURRPTUCU

Now it's time to estimate time and material for setup, remove and replace, protection, touchup and cleanup. Itemize the time and material needed to remove and replace the door and pullman hardware (knobs and latches) and to protect the floor covering in each room on the living room take-off sheet under SURRPTUCU. List the time and material to protect the cabinets on the kitchen take-off sheet. I've used one hour at $20.25 for the labor. That's based on an hourly wage of $15 for journeymen plus the employer's tax and insurance burden at 35%. Of course, you'll use your actual labor cost here.

There's no substitute for good judgment and experience when compiling estimates. But don't rely on judgment and experience alone. Take the time to do it right. Practice using the formulas in the detailed estimating process until it becomes second nature. Good estimating procedure can save you a lot of grief, not to mention money.

Kitchen

Because we're moving in a counterclockwise direction, the kitchen is the next room to estimate. The finish schedule shows how cabinets will be finished. Using this schedule, we'll make a systematic estimate from top to bottom. Figure 18-11 is my kitchen take-off sheet.

Kitchen Cabinets

Before estimating the kitchen ceiling, let's first look at the cabinets. Do they need to be refinished? Ours don't. But remember, when you do have to strip previously finished cabinets, hardwood floors or other woodwork down to raw wood, *be careful!* The stripping process can be very slow. If possible, bid the job on a time and material basis at a set hourly rate. And make sure your painters don't damage the floor covering or other adjacent surfaces during the stripping.

If you're refinishing the cabinets on a particular job, be sure to include ample SURRPTUCU time to remove and replace the hardware, dishes and food in the cupboards.

Kitchen Ceiling

When painting the kitchen ceiling, consider the time necessary to cut in around the cabinets. Compensate for this cut-in time by measuring the entire ceiling area and the entire wall areas as though there were no cabinets, windows or doors. Adding in this additional square footage covers the time needed to paint around the cabinets. And it's easier to do this than to measure the exact ceiling and wall area exposed around the cabinets. Now begin your kitchen take-off by calculating the ceiling area:

$$9.5' \times 8'0'' = 76 \text{ SF}$$

Use 76 square feet for your preliminary estimate and for calculating the manhours and material needed to roll and brush the kitchen ceiling.

Manhours: $\dfrac{76 \text{ SF}}{275 \text{ SF/hour}} = .27$ or .3 hour

Material quantity: $\dfrac{76 \text{ SF}}{285 \text{ SF/gallon}} = .27$ or .3 gallon

Material cost: .3 gallon x $12.80 = $3.84 or $3.80

You'll find these figures on line 1 of the manhour and material sections in Figure 18-11. But before you can paint the kitchen ceiling, it'll have to be washed with TSP. The formula for washing ceilings is in the preparation table in Chapter 17.

Manhours: $\dfrac{76 \text{ SF}}{190 \text{ SF/hour}} = .4$ hour

Kitchen Walls

To find the wall area, just take the length of each wall and multiply by the ceiling height. Deduct for any openings over 100 square feet, but don't deduct for areas covered with cabinets. First, find the gross wall area:

$$8' + 9.5' + 8' + 9.5' \quad = \quad 35' \text{ long}$$
$$\qquad\qquad\qquad\qquad\qquad \times \quad \underline{8' \text{ high}}$$
$$\text{Gross wall area} \qquad\quad 280 \quad \text{SF}$$

There are no openings larger than 100 square feet to deduct, so use 280 square feet for your estimate for rolling the kitchen walls.

Manhours: $\dfrac{280 \text{ SF}}{300 \text{ SF/hour}} = .93$ or .9 hour

Material quantity: $\dfrac{280 \text{ SF}}{285 \text{ SF/gallon}} = .98$ or 1 gallon

Material cost: 1 gallon x $12.80 = $12.80

Interior room __KITCHEN__   Size __9.5 x 8__   Job name: __GLEASON__
Exterior _____   SF __76__   Estimate number: __89-045__

Manhours

Operation	Dimension	LF/SF	Method	Coats	Judgment hours	Formula Feet/hr	Formula hour	Final hours
1. CEILING	9.5 x 8	76	ROLL	1	.5	275	.3	.3
2. WASH w/TSP	"	76	TSP	—	.25	190	.4	.3
3. WALLS	8x2+9.5x2x8	280	ROLL	1	1.0	300	.9	.9
4. WASH w/TSP	" " "	280	TSP	—	1.0	190	1.47	1.0
5.								
6. BASE		0						0
7.								
8.								
9.								
10.								
11.								
12.								
13.								
14.								

Crosscheck: Manhour totals __2.75__   vs. __3.07__ = _____

Manhour bid total __2.5__

Material

Operation	LF/SF	Color	Coats and type	Judgment gallons	Formula Ft/gal	Formula gallons	Price per gallon	Final cost
1. CEILING	76	NAVAJO	1-ENAM	.25	285	.3	$ 12.80	$ 3.80
2. WASH	76	—					$	$
3. WALLS	280	NAVAJO	1-ENAM	1.0	285	1.0	$ 12.80	$ 12.80
4. WASH	280	—					$	$ —
5.							$	$
6. BASE	0						$	$ 0
7.							$	$
8.							$	$
9.							$	$
10.							$	$
11.							$	$
12.							$	$
13.							$	$
14.							$	$

Crosscheck: Gallons __1.25__   vs. __1.3__

Total material cost $ __16.60__

SURRPTUCU

Operation	Description	Labor hours	Labor cost (at $20.25)		Material cost		Totals
Setup	U.SQUEEN	.25	5.—	+	2.—	=	$ 7.—
				+		=	$
Remove/replace	SCRUB MOULDING AT CABINETS	.5	10.—	+	0	=	$ 10.—
				+		=	$
Protection	MASK CABINETS	.25	5.—	+	1.—	=	$ 6.—
	FLOOR	.25	5.—	+	0	=	$ 5.—
				+		=	$
Touchup		.25	5.—	+	0	=	$ 5.—
				+		=	$
Cleanup		.25	5.—	+	0	=	$ 5.—
				+		=	$

SURRPTUCU total $ __38.—__

Kitchen take-off sheet
Figure 18-11

Look at line 3 in the manhours and material sections of Figure 18-11. The time for washing the ceiling is on line 4. Most of the baseboard is attached to the cabinets and won't be refinished. The small amount of baseboard that's left can be painted along with the base in the utility room and bathroom. Don't allow any extra time or material for the kitchen baseboard.

Kitchen SURRPTUCU

When painting the ceiling and walls of the kitchen, the cabinet faces, edges and countertops must be protected. Your estimate must include the manhours needed to remove and replace any trim around the cabinets and to protect the kitchen cabinets.

Utility Room Ceiling

The area of the utility room ceiling is 15 square feet (3'0'' x 5'0''). Here are the costs to roll that ceiling.

Manhours: $\dfrac{15 \text{ SF}}{275 \text{ SF/hour}}$ = .05 or .1 hour

Material quantity $\dfrac{15 \text{ SF}}{285 \text{ SF/gallon}}$ = .05 or .1 gallon

Material cost: .1 gallon x $12.80 = $1.28

Look at both lines 1 in Figure 18-12. The ceiling will have to be washed before it's painted, along with the kitchen walls and ceiling. The area is so small, don't waste time using the formula to calculate the time. Just make a judgment estimate of 0.1 hour. See line 2 in the manhour section.

Utility Room Walls

You need to estimate the cost of rolling the utility room walls. The gross area is:

$$3' + 5' + 3' + 5' = \quad 16' \text{ long}$$
$$\text{x} \quad 8' \text{ high}$$
$$\text{Total wall area} \quad 128 \text{ SF}$$

Manhours: $\dfrac{128 \text{ SF}}{300 \text{ SF/hour}}$ = .43 or .5 hour

Material quantity: $\dfrac{128 \text{ SF}}{285 \text{ SF/gallon}}$ = .45 or .5 gallon

Material cost: .5 gallon x $12.80 = $6.40

To estimate the time to wash the walls, divide 128 square feet by 190 square feet per hour. That comes out to 0.67 hour. That's a little more than the judgment estimate, but I'll use the judgment estimate of 0.6 hours. Now move on to the utility room baseboard since the doors have already been estimated and the floors don't require paint.

Utility Room Baseboard

The utility room has baseboard at only three walls, a total of 11 linear feet.

Manhours: $\dfrac{11 \text{ LF}}{600 \text{ LF/hour}}$ = .02 or .1 hour

Material quantity: $\dfrac{11 \text{ LF}}{350 \text{ LF/gallon}}$ = .03 or .1 gallon

Material cost: .1 gallon x $12.80 = $1.28 or $1.30

These figures are on line 6 of the manhour and material sections of Figure 18-12. Now look at the SURRPTUCU section. It includes time for disconnecting, removing, replacing and reconnecting the washer and dryer.

Bathroom Ceiling

Begin your estimate for the bathroom by calculating the ceiling area: 5.0' times 8.0' equals 40.0 square feet. Use it for both the judgment estimate and the calculations.

Manhours: $\dfrac{40 \text{ SF}}{275 \text{ SF/hour}}$ = .15 or .2 hour

Material quantity: $\dfrac{40 \text{ SF}}{285 \text{ SF/gallon}}$ = .14 or .2 gallon

Material cost: .2 gallon x $12.80 = $2.56 or $2.60

Interior room __UTILITY__   Size __3x5__   Job name: __GLEASON__
Exterior _____   SF __15__   Estimate number: __89-045__

Manhours

	Operation	Dimension	LF/ SF	Method	Coats	Judgment hours	Formula Feet/hr	Formula hour	Final hours
1.	CEILING	3'x 5'	15	ROLL	1	.1	275	.1	.1
2.	WASH w/TSP	—	15	TSP	—	.1	190	.1	.1
3.	WALLS	3x2+5x2 x8	128	ROLL	1	.3	300	.43	.4
4.	WASH w/TSP	—	128	TSP	—	.6	190	.67	.6
5.									
6.	BASE	3x2+5	11	ROLL	1	.1	600	.1	.1
7.									
8.									
9.									
10.									
11.									
12.									
13.									
14.									

Crosscheck: Manhour totals __1.2__   vs.   __1.4__

Manhour bid total __1.3__

Material

	Operation	LF/ SF	Color	Coats and type	Judgment gallons	Formula Ft/gal	Formula gallons	Price per gallon	Final cost
1.	CEILING	15	NAVAJO	1-ENAM	.1	285	.1	$ 12.80	$ 1.30
2.	WASH	15	—					$	$ 0
3.	WALLS	128	NAVAJO	1-ENAM	.5	285	.5	$ 12.80	$ 6.40
4.	WASH	128	—					$	$ 0
5.								$	$
6.	BASE	11	NAVAJO	1-ENAM	.1		.1	$ 12.80	$ 1.30
7.								$	$
8.								$	$
9.								$	$
10.								$	$
11.								$	$
12.								$	$
13.								$	$
14.								$	$

Crosscheck: Gallons __.7__   vs.   __.7__

Total material cost $ __9.00__

SURRPTUCU

Operation	Description	Labor hours	Labor cost (at $20.25)	Material cost		Totals
Setup _____	_____	_____	_____	+ ____	=	$ _____
_____	_____	_____	_____	+ ____	=	$ _____
Remove/replace ___	DISCONNECT WASH/DRY	.25	5.—	+ 0	=	$ 5.—
_____	RECONNECT " "	.25	5.—	+ 0	=	$ 5.—
_____	_____	_____	_____	+ ____	=	$ _____
Protection _____	FLOOR	_____	_____	+ ____	=	$ _____
_____	_____	_____	_____	+ ____	=	$ _____
Touchup _____	MINIMAL	_____	_____	+ ____	=	$ 0
_____	_____	_____	_____	+ ____	=	$ _____
Cleanup _____	MINIMAL	_____	_____	+ ____	=	$ 0
_____	_____	_____	_____	+ ____	=	$ _____

SURRPTUCU total $ __10.—__

Utility room repaint take-off sheet
Figure 18-12

Enter the values on line 1 of each section in Figure 18-13. You'll also estimate the time to wash the bathroom ceiling. At 190 square feet per hour, estimate 0.2 hours for labor.

Bathroom Walls

Use the entire bathroom wall area because there's a small quantity of work with a high difficulty factor (cutting in around the pullman, mirrors, light valance and tub). The room is 5 by 8, so use the gross wall area (208 square feet) for your manhour and material calculations.

Manhours: $\dfrac{208 \text{ SF}}{300 \text{ SF/hour}}$ = .69 or .7 hours

Material quantity: $\dfrac{208 \text{ SF}}{285 \text{ SF/gallon}}$ = .73 gallon

Material cost: .73 gallon x \$12.80 = \$9.34 or \$9.30

Also estimate the cost for washing those walls. At 190 square feet per hour, the calculation is 1.1 hours. I'll use 1 hour for the final figure. See line 4 in Figure 18-13. That leaves the bathroom valance. Remember, the pullman was included in your opening count for minor preparation and one coat of paint.

Bathroom Valance

You can see the light valance best in the interior elevations and details of the sample plan. The valance is the trim surrounding the fluorescent light fixture. It's common in more expensive residential units. This one is 36 inches long and 12 inches deep on one side. That's a total of 4 linear feet.

Manhours: $\dfrac{4 \text{ LF}}{30 \text{ LF/hour}}$ = .13 or .3 hour

Material quantity: $\dfrac{4 \text{ LF}}{100 \text{ LF/gallon}}$ = .04 or .1 gallon

Material cost: .1 gallon x \$10.60 = \$1.06 or \$1.10

Also allow 0.1 hour for sanding the valance. See lines 6 and 7 in Figure 18-13.

Bathroom Baseboard

Most bathrooms only have baseboard on three walls because the tub covers one wall. Measure the three walls (over the doorway) unless there is baseboard at the bathtub. In the sample plan, the three walls total:

$$5.5' + 5.0' + 5.5' = 16.0 \text{ LF}$$

Use 16 linear feet for both the preliminary estimate and the calculations for brushing the bathroom baseboard.

Manhours: $\dfrac{16 \text{ LF}}{600 \text{ LF/hour}}$ = .03 or .1 hour

Material quantity: $\dfrac{16 \text{ LF}}{350 \text{ LF/gallon}}$ = .05 or .1 gallon

Material cost: .1 gallon x \$12.80 = \$1.28 or \$1.30

These are on line 8 in both the manhour and material sections of Figure 18-13. Now move on to the bathroom SURRPTUCU since the door's already been estimated.

Bathroom SURRPTUCU

In the bathroom, you'll need SURRPTUCU time for removing and replacing towel racks, paper holders and hardware on the pullman.

Bedroom 1 Ceiling

The bedroom ceilings in the sample plan will take one coat of flat paint. The ceiling measurement must include the closet:

$$11.5' \times 11.0' = 126.5 \text{ SF}$$

Use 126.5 square feet for both types of estimate. Here are the calculations for rolling the ceiling in bedroom 1:

Manhours: $\dfrac{126.5 \text{ SF}}{400 \text{ SF/hour}}$ = .32 or .3 hour

Material quantity: $\dfrac{126.5 \text{ SF}}{300 \text{ SF/gallon}}$ = .43 gallon

Material cost: .43 gallon x \$9.10 = \$3.91 or \$3.90

Interior room __BATH__   Size __5 X 8__   Job name: __GLEASON__

Exterior _____   SF __40__   Estimate number: __89-045__

Manhours

	Operation	Dimension	LF/ SF	Method	Coats	Judgment hours	Formula Feet/hr	Formula hour	Final hours
1.	CEILING	5 X 8	40	ROLL	1	.25	275	.15	.2
2.	WASH w/TSP		40	TSP	—	.25	190	.2	.2
3.	WALLS	5x2+8x2x8	208	ROLL	1	.75	300	.69	.7
4.	WASH w/TSP		208	TSP	—	1.0	190	1.1	1.0
5.									
6.	VALANCE	4	4	BRUSH	1	.25	30	.3	.3
7.	SAND								.1
8.	BASE	5.5 x 2 + 5	16	ROLL	1	.1	600	.1	.1
9.									
10.									
11.									
12.									
13.									
14.									

Crosscheck: Manhour totals __2.6__   vs. __2.54__

Manhour bid total __2.6__

Material

	Operation	LF/ SF	Color	Coats and type	Judgment gallons	Formula Ft/gal	Formula gallons	Price per gallon	Final cost
1.	CEILING	40	NAVAJO	1-ENAM	.25	285	.2	$ 12.80	$ 2.60
2.	WASH w/TSP							$	$ 0
3.	WALLS	208	NAVAJO	1-ENAM	.75	.300	.73	$ 12.80	$ 9.30
4.	WASH w/TSP							$	$ 0
5.								$	$
6.	VALANCE	4	RUSTIC	1-HB	.1	100	.1	$ 10.60	$ 1.10
7.								$	$
8.	BASE	16	NAVAJO	1-ENAM	.1	350	.1	$ 12.80	$ 1.30
9.								$	$
10.								$	$
11.								$	$
12.								$	$
13.								$	$
14.								$	$

Crosscheck: Gallons __1.2__   vs. __1.13__

Total material cost $ __14.30__

SURRPTUCU

Operation	Description	Labor hours	Labor cost (at $20.25)		Material cost		Totals
Setup		—		+		=	$ 0
				+		=	$
Remove/replace	TOWEL RACK & TP HOLDER	.2	4.—	+		=	$ 4.—
				+		=	$
				+		=	$
Protection	MASK MEDICINE CAB	.1	2.—	+		=	$ 2.—
	MASK TUB	.1	2.—	+		=	$ 2.—
	FLOOR	.1	2.—	+		=	$ 2.—
Touchup				+		=	$
				+		=	$
Cleanup		.1	2.—	+		=	$ 2.—
				+		=	$

SURRPTUCU total $ __14.—__

Bathroom take-off sheet
Figure 18-13

The results go on the bedroom 1 take-off sheet, Figure 18-14.

Bedroom 1 Walls

You'll roll the bedroom walls with one coat of flat paint. To find the surface area of the walls, first add the wall lengths to find the perimeter length. Be sure to include the closet walls.

$$11.5' + 11.0' + 11.5' + 11.0' + 2.0' + 2.0' = 49 \text{ LF}$$

Then multiply 49 times the ceiling height (8.0 feet). Use the total area, 392 square feet, for the judgement estimate and to calculate the manhours and material:

Manhours: $\dfrac{392 \text{ SF}}{400 \text{ SF/hour}} = .98 \text{ or } 1 \text{ hour}$

Material quantity: $\dfrac{392 \text{ SF}}{300 \text{ SF/gallon}} = 1.31 \text{ gallons}$

Material cost: 1.31 gals x $9.10 = $11.92 or $11.90

Remember that the closet shelf and pole are painted with enamel. They're included in the opening count.

Bedroom 1 Baseboard

The length of the baseboard is the same as the bedroom perimeter, 49 linear feet. Here are my calculations for the baseboard:

Manhours: $\dfrac{49 \text{ LF}}{900 \text{ LF/hour}} = .05 \text{ or } .1 \text{ hour}$

Material quantity: $\dfrac{49 \text{ LF}}{400 \text{ LF/gallon}} = .12 \text{ or } .2 \text{ gallon}$

Material cost: .2 gallon x $9.10 = $1.82 or $1.80

Figure 18-14 shows the baseboard in both the manhour and material sections.

Bedroom 1 SURRPTUCU

The time needed for setup, removing and replacing door hardware, protecting the floor covering,

touching up and cleaning up for bedroom 1 is included on the bedroom take-off sheet in Figure 18-14.

Bedroom 2

Conveniently, bedroom 2 is the same size as bedroom 1, so all the figures are the same. See Figure 18-15.

Final Interior Check

After you've finished the interior estimate, go back and compare your preliminary estimates with the detailed estimate to choose the final figures for your bid. Then total the manhours and material costs for each operation (including SURRPTU-CU). Transfer the totals, in order to the recap sheet. My recap sheet is Figure 18-16.

That winds up the interior estimate. Next we'll look at the exterior work.

The Exterior Repaint Take-Off

We'll estimate the exterior systematically, from top to bottom, from roof to the ground. Begin with the preparation work.

Exterior Preparation Work

The first step in estimating the exterior is to determine if the surface needs waterblasting. The area measurements for the waterblasting are:

Manhours:

Fascia	125 SF	(use 1 LF = 1 SF)
Overhang	210 SF	(no addition for rafters)
Siding	108 SF	
Stucco	918 SF	
	1,361 SF	

The total area for the exterior includes the plant-on trim. Don't deduct for openings less than 100 square feet. Calculate the manhours needed for waterblasting using the preparation formulas in Chapter 17:

Manhours:

$$\dfrac{1,361 \text{ SF}}{450 \text{ SF/hour}} = 3.02 \text{ or } 3 \text{ hours}$$

Interior room _BEDROOM #1_   Size _11.5 x 11 + CLOSET_   Job name: _GLEASON_

Exterior ___   SF _127_   Estimate number: _89-045_

Manhours

Operation	Dimension	LF/ SF	Method	Coats	Judgment hours	Formula		Final hours
						Feet/hr	hour	
1. CEILING	11.5 x 11	127	ROLL	1	.3	400	.32	.3
2. CLEAN								0
3. WALLS	11.5 x 2 + 11 x 2 x 8	392	ROLL	1	1.0	400	1.0	1.0
4. CLEAN			WIPE	—	.1	—	—	.1
5.								
6. BASE	11.5 x 2 + 11 x 2 } +2 x 2 }	49	ROLL	1	.1	900	.1	.1
7.								
8.								
9.								
10.								
11.								
12.								
13.								
14.								

Crosscheck: Manhour totals _1.5_   vs. _1.42_

Manhour bid total _1.5_

Material

Operation	LF/ SF	Color	Coats and type	Judgment gallons	Ft/gal	Formula gallons	Price per gallon	Final cost
1. CEILING	127	NAVAJO	1-FLAT	.5	300	.43	$ 9.10	$ 3.90
2. CLEAN							$	$ 0
3. WALLS	392	NAVAJO	1-FLAT	1.25	300	1.31	$ 9.10	$ 11.90
4. CLEAN							$	$
5.							$	$
6. BASE	49	NAVAJO	1-FLAT	.2	400	.2	$ 9.10	$ 1.80
7.							$	$
8.							$	$
9.							$	$
10.							$	$
11.							$	$
12.							$	$
13.							$	$
14.							$	$

Crosscheck: Gallons _1.95_   vs. _1.94_

Total material cost $ _17.60_

SURRPTUCU

Operation	Description	Labor hours	Labor cost (at $20.25)	Material cost			Totals
Setup		.2	4.—	+	0	=	$ 4.—
				+		=	$
Remove/replace				+		=	$
				+		=	$
				+		=	$
Protection	FLOOR	.2	4.—	+	2	=	$ 4.—
				+		=	$
Touchup		.1	2.—	+	0	=	$ 2.—
				+		=	$
Cleanup		.1	2.—	+		=	$ 2.—
				+		=	$

SURRPTUCU total $ _12.—_

Bedroom 1 take-off sheet
Figure 18-14

Interior room _BEDROOM #2_   Size _11.5 x 11 + CLOSET_   Job name: _GLEASON_
Exterior _____   SF _____127_____   Estimate number: _89-045_

Manhours

Operation	Dimension	LF/ SF	Method	Coats	Judgment hours	Formula Feet/hr	hour	Final hours
1.								
2.								
3.								
4.								
5.								
6.								
7.								
8.								
9.								
10.								
11.								
12.								
13.								
14.								

SAME AS BEDROOM #1

Crosscheck: Manhour totals _____ vs. _____ = _____

Manhour bid total _1.5_

Material

Operation	LF/ SF	Color	Coats and type	Judgment gallons	Formula Ft/gal	gallons	Price per gallon	Final cost
1.							$ ___ $	
2.							$ ___ $	
3.							$ ___ $	
4.							$ ___ $	
5.							$ ___ $	
6.							$ ___ $	
7.							$ ___ $	
8.							$ ___ $	
9.							$ ___ $	
10.							$ ___ $	
11.							$ ___ $	
12.							$ ___ $	
13.							$ ___ $	
14.							$ ___ $	

SAME AS BEDROOM #1

Crosscheck: Gallons_____ vs. _____

Total material cost $ _17.60_

SURRPTUCU

Operation	Description	Labor hours	Labor cost (at $20.25)	Material cost			Totals
Setup _____				+ _____	=	$ _____	
				+ _____	=	$ _____	
Remove/replace ___				+ _____	=	$ _____	
_____				+ _____	=	$ _____	
_____				+ _____	=	$ _____	
Protection _____				+ _____	=	$ _____	
_____				+ _____	=	$ _____	
_____				+ _____	=	$ _____	
Touchup _____				+ _____	=	$ _____	
_____				+ _____	=	$ _____	
Cleanup _____				+ _____	=	$ _____	
				+ _____	=	$ _____	

SAME AS BEDROOM #1

SURRPTUCU total $_12.—_

Bedroom 2 take-off sheet
Figure 18-15

Date _____ 5-11-89 _____
Customer ____ DAN GLEASON _____
Address _____ 3333 A STREET _____
City/State/Zip __ YOURTOWN, USA 77777 __
Phone _____ (619) 555-1212 _____
Estimated by ____ CHS _____

Due date _____ 5-12-89 _____
Job name _____ GLEASON _____
Job site _____ RESIDENCE _____
Estimate # _____ 89-045 _____
Total square footage ___ 720 _____
Checked by _____ JACK _____

Sketch

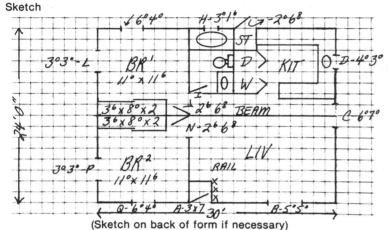

(Sketch on back of form if necessary)

Specifications

1- COAT - NAVAJO
EXT - RUSTIC & TAN
NO CABINETS
UTILITY - ENAMEL
RAILING - 1 COAT

Notes and comments

TRIM 3 TREES
3 DAYS- 2 MEN
NO PAINT STORAGE
AREA

Equipment

Equipment description	Rental days	Daily cost	Total cost
WATERBLASTER	1	$ 50.—	$ 50.—
AIRLESS PUMP	1	50.—	50.—
LADDERS	1 x 2 EA.	5.—	10.—
SANDER, BELT	1	14.—	14.—
		Equipment total	124.—

Recap

Exterior or room	Final hours	Material costs	SURRPTUCU costs
Exterior	19.9	$ 144.20	$ 52.—
LIV	17.9	90.40	50.—
KIT	2.5	16.60	38.—
UTIL	1.3	9.—	10.—
BATH	2.6	14.30	14.—
BR #1	1.5	17.60	12.—
BR #2	1.5	17.60	12.—
Totals	47.2	$ 309.70	$ 188.—
	Hours	Material	SURRPTUCU

Extensions

Rate $ _____ 15.— _____ /hour
Hours __ 47.2 __ x rate = $ ___ 708.— __
Supervision ___ 1 ___ Hrs ___ 16.— __
Subtotal _____ 724.—

Burden __ .35 __ % _____ 253.—
Material _____ 310.—
Equipment _____ 124.—
SURRPTUCU _____ 188.—
Subcontract _____ % _____ 0

Commissions _____ % _____ 0
Contingency _____ % _____ 0
Subtotal _____ 1599.

Overhead __ 15 __ % _____ 240.—
Direct cost _____ 1839.—

Profit __ 10 __ % _____ 184.—
Base bid total _____ 2023.
Adjustment __ 2 __ % + (−) __ 40.
Final bid total _____ 1983.
Price/SF _____ 2.75
Price/room _____ 400.—

Crosscheck to historical costs:
    This project $/SF $ _____ 2.75
    Historical costs ($/SF) range from $ __ 1.50 __ to $ __ 2.90 __

    This project $/room $ _____ 400.—
    Historical costs ($/room) range from $ __ 250.— __ to $ __ 450.— __

Repaint recap
Figure 18-16

Enter 3 hours on the exterior take-off sheet (Figure 18-17). Then consider the waterblaster rental cost. I've used a typical daily rental rate (from Chapter 15) on the recap sheet.

Preparation by Wire Brush
Next, calculate the manhours needed to wire brush the wood surfaces to remove loose scale and peeling paint after the waterblasting operation. Here's the total area of the wood surfaces:

Fascia	125 SF
Overhang	210 SF
Siding	108 SF
	443 SF

Here's the calculation based on the preparation formulas in Chapter 17:

$$\text{Manhours:} \quad \frac{443 \text{ SF}}{75 \text{ SF/hour}} = 5.9 \text{ hours}$$

Exterior Painting Operations
We'll begin at the roof in our top-to-bottom estimating system. The shingles don't need painting, so we'll go on to the rain diverter.

Rain Diverter
The rain diverter on the roof over the entry door measures about 4 feet long. Ordinarily, for this small quantity of sheet metal, you wouldn't bother using the formulas. Your judgment call will probably be more accurate. But for this example, we'll do the calculation.

$$\text{Manhours:} \quad \frac{4 \text{ LF}}{230 \text{ LF/hour}} = .02 \text{ or } .2 \text{ hour}$$

$$\text{Material quantity:} \frac{4 \text{ LF}}{600 \text{ LF/gallon}} = .006 \text{ or } .1 \text{ gallon}$$

Material cost: 1 gallon x $10.60 = $1.06 or $1.10

The figures are on line 3 of the manhour and material sections of the exterior take-off sheet, Figure 18-17. Now move on to the roof jacks.

Roof Jacks
Roof jacks usually require about the same time and material for all one-story or two-story homes. My estimating formulas (Figure 18-2) and price list (Figure 18-3) show the manhours and material quantities for painting the roof jacks on a one-story house:

Manhours: .7 hour minimum

Material quantity: .5 gallon minimum

Material cost: .5 gallon x $10.60 = $5.30

Vents and Flashing
The vents and flashings also require about the same time and material for all one-story or two-story homes. Here's my formula for a one-story home:

Manhours: .7 hour minimum

Material quantity: .4 gallon

Material cost: .4 gallon x $10.60 = $4.24 or $4.20

They're on the exterior take-off sheet (Figure 18-17).

Fascia
We estimate from top to bottom because we paint that way — so newly painted surfaces aren't damaged by overspray or spillage from higher surfaces.

The easiest way to measure the fascia is to measure the building perimeter and add the length of the fascia that extends beyond the building. To measure our sample building, add the length of the overhang (1.5') at each end to the width of the building (30'0''), then multiply by 2 for the front and rear:

$$30' + 1.5' + 1.5' = 33' \times 2 = 66 \text{ LF}$$

Interior room		Size 30'0" x 24'0"		Job name: GLEASON
Exterior ✓		SF		Estimate number: 89-045

Manhours

	Operation	Dimension	LF/ SF	Method	Coats	Judgment hours	Formula Feet/hr	Formula hour	Final hours
1.	WATERBLAST 125/210/108/918		1361	—	—	3.0	450	3.0	3.0
2.	WIRE BRUSH/PATCH 125/210/108		443	—	—	6.0	75	5.9	5.9
3.	DIVERTER	—	4	BRUSH	1	.2	230	.02	.2
4.	ROOF JACKS	1 STORY	—	BRUSH	1	.7	1-STORY	.7	.7
5.	VENTS & FLASH	1 STORY	—	BRUSH	1	.7	1-STORY	.7	.7
6.	FASCIA	66+59	125	R&B	1	.75	150	.8	.8
7.	OVERHANG	198 x 1.5	312	SPRAY	1	1.0	350	.9	1.0
8.	SIDING	24/2 x 9.5 x 2	108	SPRAY	1	1.0	125	.9	.9
9.	STUCCO	255x2+204x2	918	SPRAY	1	1.75	550	1.7	1.7
10.	PROTECT COAT	8 EA.	8 EA	SPRAY	1	.8	.1 EA	.8	.8
11.	DOORS	1 ENT. + 1 EXT.	2 EA	ROLL	1	.5 + .3	—	.5 + .3	.8
12.	PLANT-ONS	66+62+52	180	R&B	1	2.5	70	2.57	2.6
13.	POT SHELF	—	27	R&B	1	.5	50	.54	.6
14.	PASS-THROUGH	1 EA	1 EA	R&B	1	.2	—	.2	.2

Crosscheck: Manhour totals 19.9 vs. 19.53

Manhour bid total 19.9

Material

	Operation	LF/ SF	Color	Coats and type	Judgment gallons	Formula Ft/gal	Formula gallons	Price per gallon	Final cost
1.	WATERBLAST	—	—	—	—	—	—	$	$ 0
2.	WIREBRUSH	—	—	—	—	—	—	$	$ 0
3.	DIVERTER	4	RUSTIC	1-HB	.1	600	.1	$ 10.60	$ 1.10
4.	ROOF JACKS	—	"	1-HB	.5	1-STORY	.5	$ 10.60	$ 5.30
5.	VENTS & FLASH	—	"	1-HB	.4	1-STORY	.4	$ 10.60	$ 4.20
6.	FASCIA	125	"	1-HB	1.0	120	1.0	$ 10.60	$ 10.60
7.	OVERHANG	312	"	1-HB	4.0	95	3.3	$ 10.60	$ 35.00
8.	SIDING	108	"	1-HB	.5	200	.54	$ 10.60	$ 5.70
9.	STUCCO	918	TAN	1-MASON	4.5	200	4.59	$ 12.30	$ 56.40
10.	PROTECT COAT	144	—	1-WAX	.5	325	.44	$ 16.10	$ 7.10
11.	DOORS	2 EA	RUSTIC	1-ENAM	.1 + .1	—	.1 + .1	$ 15.00	$ 3.00
12.	PLANT-ONS	180	"	1-HB	.75	210	.86	$ 10.60	$ 9.10
13.	POT SHELF	27	"	1-HB	.5	50	.54	$ 10.60	$ 5.70
14.	PASS-THROUGH	1 EA	"	1-COAT	—	—	—	$ —	$ 1.00

Crosscheck: Gallons 12.95 vs. 12.47

Total material cost $ 144.20

SURRPTUCU

Operation	Description	Labor hours	Labor cost (at $20.25)	Material cost		Totals
Setup		.5	10.—	+	=	$ 10.—
				+	=	$
Remove/replace				+	=	$ 0
				+	=	$
				+	=	$
Protection	PROTECTIVE COATING — SEE ABOVE			+	=	$
	MASKING DOORS	.5	10.—	+	=	$ 10.—
				+	=	$
Touchup		1.0	22.—	+ 2.—	=	$ 22.—
				+	=	$
Cleanup		.5	10.—	+	=	$ 10.—
				+	=	$

SURRPTUCU total $ 52.—

Exterior repaint take-off sheet
Figure 18-17

But there's something else to consider. When you're figuring the length of the fascia on the sides of the house, don't forget the pitch of the roof. On our sample house, it's a 4 and 12 pitch. Just like the vaulted ceiling inside the house, the actual length of the fascia is longer than the width of the building plus the overhang. The 4 and 12 roof pitch means that for every 4 inches (or feet) in rise, the run is 12 inches (or feet). To find the true length of the fascia on the sides, we'll again use the formula for finding the length of the hypotenuse:

$$
\begin{array}{rclcl}
A^2 & + & B^2 & = & C^2 \\
4^2 & + & 12^2 & = & C^2 \\
16 & + & 144 & = & 160 \\
\sqrt{160} & & & = & 12.65
\end{array}
$$

That means the fascia is actually 12.65 inches long for each 12 inches of apparent length. What percentage do we use to increase the fascia length?

$$\frac{12}{12.65} = .9486 - 1.0 = .051 \text{ or } 5\%$$

That makes it easy. To find the true length of the fascia, just multiply the measured length by 1.05. The actual length of the fascia at the side is:

$$24' + 2' + 2' = 28 \times 2 = 56 \times 1.05 = 58.8 \text{ or } 59 \text{ LF}$$

Now add the front and rear length to the side lengths to find the total fascia length:

$$66' + 59' = 125 \text{ LF}$$

Use 125 linear feet for your preliminary estimate and for the calculations to brush and roll the 2 x 8 fascia:

Manhours: $\dfrac{125 \text{ LF}}{150 \text{ LF/hour}} = .83 \text{ or } .8 \text{ hour}$

Material quantity: $\dfrac{125 \text{ LF}}{120 \text{ LF/gallon}} = 1.04 \text{ or } 1 \text{ gallon}$

Material cost: 1 gallon x $10.60 = $10.60

We entered these values on the exterior take-off sheet (Figure 18-17).

Overhang

Begin by finding the length of the front and rear overhang. Use the fascia length of 33'0'' multiplied by the width of the overhang (2'0''):

$$33' \times 2' \times 2 \text{ (front and rear)} = 132 \text{ SF}$$

To calculate the overhang area at the sides, use the width of the building (24'0'') multiplied by the roof pitch factor (1.05 for this 4 in 12 roof) times the two sides. But don't overlap your measurement where the overhang extends beyond the building at the left and right elevations. This area has already been included in your measurements of the building front and back.

$$24' \times 1.05 \times 1.5' \text{ wide} \times 2 = 75.6 \text{ SF}$$

And don't forget to include the rafter tails. They have to be painted too. Increase the overhang area by a factor of 1.5 to account for the rafter tails. Just add the front, back and side measurements and multiply by 1.5:

$$132 \text{ SF} + 76 \text{ SF} = 208 \text{ SF} \times 1.5 = 312 \text{ SF}$$

Use 312 square feet for the preliminary estimate and the calculations based on the repaint formulas:

Manhours: $\dfrac{312 \text{ SF}}{350 \text{ SF/hour}} = .89 \text{ or } .9 \text{ hour}$

Material quantity: $\dfrac{312 \text{ SF}}{95 \text{ SF/gallon}} = 3.28 \text{ or } 3.3 \text{ gallons}$

Material cost: 3.3 gallons x $10.60 = $34.98 or $35.00

The overhang figures are on line 7 in both sections of Figure 18-17.

Siding

On our sample house, there's siding at each end of the building under the gable ends. Calculate this area using the formula for the area of a triangle, and double the answer because there are two ends:

$$1/2 \times 24' \text{ wide} \times 4.5' \text{ high} \times 2 \text{ ends} = 108 \text{ SF}$$

Calculate the manhours and materials needed to roll one coat on 108 square feet of this smooth wood siding.

Manhours: $\dfrac{108 \text{ SF}}{125 \text{ SF/hour}} = .86 \text{ or } .9 \text{ hour}$

Material quantity: $\dfrac{108 \text{ SF}}{200 \text{ SF/gallon}} = .54 \text{ gallon}$

Material cost: $.54 \text{ gallon} \times \$10.60 = \$5.72 \text{ or } \$5.70$

Finally, enter the totals on the take-off sheet (Figure 18-17).

Stucco

When calculating the area of stucco, I'll use the overall surface area, deducting only for openings larger than 100 square feet. Our sample plan doesn't have any openings that large, so the area calculation is easy:

Front	30' wide	x 8.5' high =	255 SF
Rear	30' wide	x 8.5' high =	255 SF
Right	24' wide	x 8.5' high =	204 SF
Left	24' wide	x 8.5' high =	204 SF
		Total	918 SF

Estimate 918 square feet of stucco to paint.

Material: $\dfrac{918 \text{ SF}}{550 \text{ SF/hour}} = 1.67 \text{ or } 1.7 \text{ hours}$

Material quantity: $\dfrac{918 \text{ SF}}{200 \text{ SF/gallon}} = 4.59 \text{ gallons}$

Material cost: $4.59 \text{ gallons} \times \$12.30 = \$56.44 \text{ or } \$56.40$

Figure 18-17 shows the totals for painting the stucco.

Protective Coating

When spray painting stucco, you have to mask the doors and protect the windows with a paraffin-based wax coating. The time and material for masking the two exterior doors are shown in the SURRPTUCU section of Figure 18-17. The protective coating operation is item #10 in the manhour and material sections of Figure 18-17. Use a window count to find the time needed to spray on the protective coating. There are seven windows and sliding glass doors on our sample house:

Door 7	5'0" x 6'8" =	33.75
Window A	5'0" x 5'0" =	25.00
Window B	4'0" x 3'6" =	14.00
Window C	3'6" x 1'6" =	5.25
Window D (2)	6'0" x 4'0" =	48.00
Window E (2)	3'0" x 3'0" =	18.00
Total area	=	144.00 SF

Use 144 square feet for calculating time and materials for spraying the protective coating on the windows. The results are on line 10 on the exterior take-off sheet.

Manhours: $8 \text{ windows} \times .1 \text{ hour} = .8 \text{ hour}$

Material quantity: $\dfrac{144 \text{ SF}}{325 \text{ SF/gallon}} = .44 \text{ gallon}$

Material cost: $.44 \text{ gallon} \times \$16.10 = \$7.08 \text{ or } \$7.10$

Exterior Doors

Exterior doors need a good coating of exterior-quality paint to prevent weathering. Our house has only two exterior doors, the entry and the water heater door. To finish the entry door:

Manhours: .5 hours

Material quantity: .1 gallon

Material cost: .1 gallon x $15.00 = $1.50

Here are the figures to finish the water heater door:

Manhours: .3 hours

Material quantity: .1 gallon

Material cost: .1 gallon x $15.00 = $1.50

After you've used the estimating tables a few times, you'll remember the manhours and materials needed for doors and won't have to do any calculations. Just put the totals on the take-off sheet (Figure 18-17).

Plant-on Trim

The plant-on trim is the 2 x 6 trim that's attached to (or planted on) the building. It's shown on the exterior elevations. The measurements are:

Front	$24' + 18' + 24' = 66$
Right	$21' + 17' + 24' = 62$
Left	$14' + 14' + 24' = 52$
Total plant-on trim	$= \overline{180\ LF}$

So you'll use 180 linear feet for your calculations:

Manhours: $\dfrac{180\ LF}{70\ LF/hour} = 2.57$ or 2.6 hours

Material quantity: $\dfrac{180\ LF}{210\ LF/gallon} = .86$ gallon

Material cost: $.86$ gallon x $\$10.60 = \$9.12$ or $\$9.10$

Look at the totals for plant-on trim on Figure 18-17.

Pot Shelf (P/S)

The pot shelves are 27'0'' long.

Manhours: $\dfrac{27\ LF}{50\ LF/hour} = .54$ or .6 hour

Material quantity: $\dfrac{27\ LF}{50\ LF/hour} = .54$ gallon

Material cost: $.54$ gallon x $\$10.60 = \$5.72$ or $\$5.70$

These totals are on line 13 of the take-off sheet.

Pass-Through Shelf

A pass-through shelf is usually a 3- or 4-foot shelf outside the kitchen window for passing food through to a patio. On the sample plan, it's a wood shelf with metal supports. You'd instruct your painters to paint the supports the same time they painted the interior railing.

Since most pass-through shelves are about the same size, I've used a fixed figure for manhours and material costs in my formula. It's easy to memorize the figures, so you don't have to do any calculating:

Manhours: .2 hour

Material cost: $1.00

Look at these totals on the take-off sheet. That finishes the painting operations for this house. All that's left is the SURRPTUCU.

SURRPTUCU

For most jobs, you'll allow one-half hour per day for setup and cleanup. I usually allow one hour on the exterior for touchup. Larger jobs or high quality projects will take more touchup time. Estimates for removing and replacing (RR) and protection (P) will vary. Use your judgment to estimate the time they'll take.

To estimate the cost of SURRPTUCU, use the hourly rate of your average painter. I'll use $15.00 per hour plus employer's burden at 35%. That totals $20.25. But this hourly rate doesn't include overhead and profit. Don't confuse it with your shop rate.

Repaint Take-Off Sheet Totals

For most repaint estimates, you'll walk the job, record your measurements and make a preliminary estimate right on the spot. Then, back in the privacy of your office, you'll use your repaint formulas to develop a detailed estimate. Work neatly so it's easy to check the figures later. And *always* double-check the estimate before submitting it.

Then compare your detailed estimate with the judgment estimate. If there's a big difference, check your figures carefully.

Finally, accumulate all of the manhour totals, all of the material totals and all of the SURRPTUCU totals for each room and the exterior on the repaint take-off sheets. Figure 18-16 has these figures in the recap section of the recap sheet.

Equipment Costs

The next step is to estimate equipment costs. Use current rental rates to determine the cost of the equipment needed for the project. Even if you own the equipment, use rental rates that show what a rental yard would charge. Your actual cost probably isn't much less than what a rental yard would charge for the same equipment.

Notice on the recap sheet that the equipment description, rental allowance and totals are all listed. That makes it a simple job to calculate the total equipment costs. Then transfer the total to the equipment line in the extension column.

Recap Manhours and Material

Take the time to double-check the accuracy of all manhour, material and SURRPTUCU figures transferred from the take-off sheets to the recap sheet. If they're correct, accumulate all of the manhours, material costs, and SURRPTUCU costs for the entire project. Then put the totals in the appropriate line in the extension column on the recap sheet.

Extensions

To extend the total manhours into labor costs, multiply them by the hourly rate of $15.00 and enter the result:

$$\$15.00 \text{ x } 47.2 \text{ hours} = \$708$$

Every job requires supervision. That's non-productive time. List on your estimate the time your working foreman will spend supervising rather than working. I've used one hour of supervision for this sample estimate at a pay rate of $1.00 more than the average painter, or $16.00 per hour.

The Base Bid

Prepare the labor cost subtotal and apply the employer's burden at 35%. Then add material, equipment, SURRPTUCU, subcontract, commission and contingency costs to arrive at a subtotal. For this job, we'll add 15% for indirect overhead. Next, add a 10% profit margin to the direct cost to arrive at the base bid total shown on the sample recap sheet.

The Final Bid Amount

If the base bid seems high or low compared to the historical costs, you may want to adjust the final bid amount. Our sample estimate includes a 2% deduction because the base bid was high compared to our historical costs. You might also adjust the base bid because of the competition, site conditions or any of the other bidding variables discussed in Chapter 7.

Cross-Checking

You have your base bid — but you're not finished yet. Don't consider the estimate finished until you've checked the totals against your actual costs on similar jobs. I call these your *historical costs*. Are the square foot price and the per room price within the range of your previous jobs? If so, your estimate is probably right. If not, do some more checking. See if you can find some errors in your take-off.

Remember, your objective is to develop a profitable and successful painting business. You won't be able to do that with my painting formulas alone. No formulas you find in a book are as accurate as your own historical cost information. Use my figures as a guide until you have your own formulas and historical costs. Those are going to be the best estimates for your jobs.

If the bid matches historical costs, your estimate is done. Now we move on to the next step.

The Repaint Proposal

The next step is to prepare your proposal and contract. Whether you fill it out on the spot or take it back to the office and have it typed, make sure you use the repaint proposal outline in Figure 7-5, Chapter 7, as a guide or checklist. That's the only way to be sure you don't leave anything out. The key to writing a good proposal is to ask enough of the right questions while you're estimating to have the scope of work clearly understood and well defined. Then check the proposal outline when you're selecting the scope of work to be included or excluded. Also look for other items that should be noted or qualified. If you're having the proposal typed, you can use the abbreviations in the outline to compose a rough draft for your typist. That can save you a lot of time.

Figure 18-18 shows my draft proposal and contract, using the abbreviations from the proposal outline in Chapter 7. That's what it looks like when the typist gets it. Of course, this only works if the typist is trained to translate your notes into complete sentences. But it's still your responsibility to proofread the proposal and get the mistakes out

Proposal and Contract

  Quality Painting & Decorating
777 Main Street
Yourtown, USA 77777
License – 123456

Proposal submitted to

DAN GLEASON   Phone (619) 555-1212   Date 5-11-89

Street

3333 A STREET   Job name GLEASON

City, State and Zip Code

YOURTOWN, USA 77777   Job location RESIDENCE

RP-1
RP-3 d
RP-4 a, b c
II A, B, F, G, H, J, K-1, L, M
RP-6A – NAVAJO WHITE

III A, B, C, C-1
RP-7   #F-49, TAN STUCCO, #F 55, CHOCOLATE BROWN TRIM

IV b, c . . . .
VI RP-8 . . . 5 . . .

We propose hereby to furnish material and labor — complete in accordance with above specifications, for the sum of:

NINETEEN HUNDRED EIGHTY THREE ___ dollars ($ _____ ($1983.00)

Payment to be made as follows:

VIII a, b

All material is guaranteed to be as specified. All work to be completed in a workmanlike manner according to standard practices. Any alteration or deviation from above specifications involving extra costs will be executed only upon written orders, and will become an extra charge over and above the estimate. All agreements contingent upon strikes, accidents or delays beyond our control. Owner to carry fire, tornado and other necessary insurance. Our workers are fully covered by Workmen's Compensation Insurance.

**Authorized
Signature** _____

**NOTE: This proposal may be withdrawn by us
if not accepted within_____30_____days.**

--------- **Notice to owner** ---------

Under the Mechanics' Lien Law, any contractor, subcontractor, laborer, materialman or other person who helps to improve your property and is not paid for his labor, services or material, has a right to enforce his claim against your property.

Under the law, you may protect yourself against such claims by filing, before commencing such work of improvement, an original contract for the work of improvement or a modification thereof, in the office of the

county recorder of the county where the property is situated and requiring that a contractor's payment bond be recorded in such office. Said bond shall be in an amount not less than fifty percent (50%) of the contract price and shall, in addition to any conditions for the performance of the contract, be conditioned for the payment in full of the claims of all persons furnishing labor, services, equipment or materials for the work described in said contract.

Acceptance of Proposal - The above prices, specifications and conditions are satisfactory and are hereby accepted. You are authorized to do the work specified. Payment will be made as outlined above.

Date of Acceptance _____

Signature _____

Contractors are required by law to be licensed and regulated by the Contractor's State License Board. Any questions concerning a contractor may be referred to the registrar of the board whose address is:
Contractor's State License Board
1020 N Street
Sacramento, California 95814

You the buyer may cancel this transaction at any time prior to midnight of the third business day after the date of this transaction.

**Repaint proposal rough draft
Figure 18-18**

Proposal and Contract

Quality Painting & Decorating
777 Main Street
Yourtown, USA 77777
License – 123456

Proposal submitted to	Phone	Date
Dan Gleason	619-555-1212	5-11-89

Street: 3333 A Street

Job name: Gleason

City, State and Zip Code: Yourtown, USA 77777

Job location: Residence

Interior: Prepare as required

    1 coat throughout to match existing surface

    heat registers: 1 coat paint

    All paint to be Navajo white

Exterior: Prepare by power wash - complete - 1600 PSI

    1 coat on exterior surfaces

    2 colors: tan with chocolate brown trim

    Exclusions: Kitchen cabinets, fencing, roof metal

We propose hereby to furnish material and labor — complete in accordance with above specifications, for the sum of:

Nineteen hundred eighty three _____ dollars ($ _____ $1,983.00 _____)

Payment to be made as follows:

    30% upon move-on for materials and preparation work.

    Balance upon completion.

All material is guaranteed to be as specified. All work to be completed in a workmanlike manner according to standard practices. Any alteration or deviation from above specifications involving extra costs will be executed only upon written orders, and will become an extra charge over and above the estimate. All agreements contingent upon strikes, accidents or delays beyond our control. Owner to carry fire, tornado and other necessary insurance. Our workers are fully covered by Workmen's Compensation Insurance.

Authorized Signature _____

NOTE: This proposal may be withdrawn by us if not accepted within _____ 30 _____ days.

Notice to owner

Under the Mechanics' Lien Law, any contractor, subcontractor, laborer, materialman or other person who helps to improve your property and is not paid for his labor, services or material, has a right to enforce his claim against your property.

Under the law, you may protect yourself against such claims by filing, before commencing such work of improvement, an original contract for the work of improvement or a modification thereof, in the office of the county recorder of the county where the property is situated and requiring that a contractor's payment bond be recorded in such office. Said bond shall be in an amount not less than fifty percent (50%) of the contract price and shall, in addition to any conditions for the performance of the contract, be conditioned for the payment in full of the claims of all persons furnishing labor, services, equipment or materials for the work described in said contract.

Acceptance of Proposal - The above prices, specifications and conditions are satisfactory and are hereby accepted. You are authorized to do the work specified. Payment will be made as outlined above.

Date of Acceptance _____

Signature _____

Contractors are required by law to be licensed and regulated by the Contractor's State License Board. Any questions concerning a contractor may be referred to the registrar of the board whose address is:

Contractor's State License Board
1020 N Street
Sacramento, California 95814

You the buyer may cancel this transaction at any time prior to midnight of the third business day after the date of this transaction.

The final repaint proposal and contract
Figure 18-19

Notice To Customer Required By Federal Law

You have entered into a transaction on _____ which may result in a lien, mortgage, or other security interest on your home. You have a legal right under federal law to cancel this transaction, if you desire to do so, without any penalty or obligation within three business days from the above date or any later date on which all material disclosures required under the Truth in Lending Act have been given you. If you so cancel the transaction, any lien, mortgage, or other security interest on your home arising from this transaction is automatically void. You are also entitled to receive a refund of any down payment or other consideration if you cancel. If you decide to cancel this transaction, you may do so by notifying

_____
(Name of creditor)

at _____
(Address of Creditor's Place of Business)

by mail or telegram sent not later than midnight of _____ . You may also use any other form written notice identifying the transaction if it is delivered to the above address not later than that time. This notice may be used for the purpose by dating and signing below.

I hereby cancel this transaction.

_____   _____
(Date)   (Customer's signature)

Effect of rescission. When a customer exercises his right to rescind under paragraph (a) of this section, he is not liable for any finance or other charge, and any security interest becomes void upon such a rescission. Within 10 days after receipt of a notice of rescission, the creditor shall return to the customer any money or property given as earnest money, downpayment, or otherwise, and shall take any action necessary or appropriate to reflect the termination of any security interest created under the transaction. If the creditor has delivered any property to the customer, the customer may retain possession of it. Upon the performance of the creditor's obligations under this section, the customer shall tender the property to the creditor, except that if return of the property in kind would be impracticable or inequitable, the customer shall tender its reasonable value. Tender shall be made at the location of the property or at the residence of the customer, at the option of the customer. If the creditor does not take possession of the property within 10 days after tender by the customer, ownership of the property vests in the customer without obligation on his part to pay for it.

Rescission notice
Figure 18-20

before a client sees it. Always check to be sure an expiration date is included.

Figure 18-19 shows the completed proposal and contract. It's a specific written statement that qualifies your bid and identifies the scope of work you intend to perform. It also lists specific items *not* included in the price.

As the name implies, the proposal and contract is a proposal when you present it. But when it's signed by both the homeowner and the painting contractor, it becomes a contract. You're also required by federal law to give the customer a rescission notice like the one in Figure 18-20. The owner has the right to cancel the contract within three business days. But if you've done a good job of selling and estimating the job, there won't be any cancellation.

ESTIMATING NEW CONSTRUCTION PROJECTS

It's far easier to estimate painting in new construction than it is to estimate repainting — even if the new building has many units. Usually you can figure each new construction floor plan on a single estimate sheet instead of using a sheet for each room.

In this chapter we'll do a sample estimate for a new project of fifteen homes. We'll include a complete take-off, manhour and material calculations, material pricing, and a full set of extensions. We'll base our estimate on the sample plan in Appendix A.

The flow chart in Figure 19-1 shows my system for estimating high-volume, new construction work. I designed it for use on residential projects with five or more units. But you can also use it for light commercial projects where many rooms, units or buildings are similar.

New Construction Estimating Formulas

Figure 19-2 shows the new construction estimating formulas I'll use in the sample estimate. Use these figures until you have better estimates of what your crews can do. Your painters may be much faster — or slower — than the production rates I'm using here.

Painting larger jobs in new construction usually goes fast because there's less surface preparation and little need to protect adjacent surfaces from overspray. But you'll use more material because new surfaces are highly absorbent. That's why the formulas here assume high production rates and low material coverage rates. I've expressed my manhour production rates in terms of square feet or linear feet completed per hour for most of the painting operations.

My estimating system is about as good as I can make it for the type of work my company handles. It might work well for your company if you work on high production projects with skilled production painters. I recommend that you follow the estimating system outlined here for that kind of work. But I also suggest that you be a little skeptical about the production and coverage rates I use. Your company and painters may have very different experience. But even if your production and coverage rates don't match mine — and that's likely — use my estimating *system*. Simply substitute your own manhour and material coverage figures.

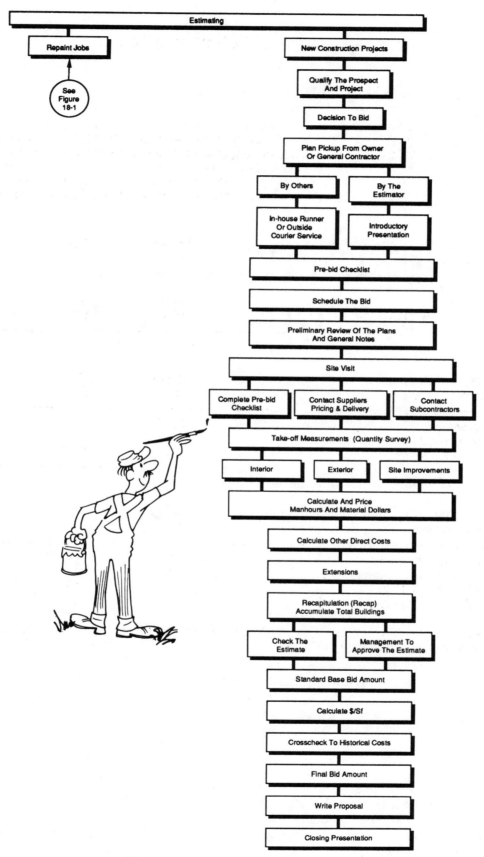

New construction estimating process
Figure 19-1

New Construction Estimating Tables

Use this table to estimate the time and material needed for painting exterior and interior surfaces on new residential construction. Production rates are in manhours per square foot (SF) or per linear foot (LF) of area coated. Material coverage is in square feet or linear feet coated per gallon of coating. Paint material types are identified by number in Figure 19-9. These tables do not include time needed for setup, removal, replacement, protection, touchup or cleanup (SURRPTUCU) except as noted. Abbreviations in parentheses in these tables are the same as the abbreviations used in Figure 19-5.

Baseboard, per LF of baseboard Single coat applications	LF per hour	LF per gallon	Material type
Paint, roll with walls	1000	700	3
Enamel, brush and cut in	140	650	4
Stain, sprayed in a boneyard	1500	1200	5a or 8

Baseboard, per SF of floor Single coat applications	SF per hour	SF per gallon	Material type
Paint, roll with walls	3000	1300	3
Enamel, brush and cut in	600	1200	4
Stain, sprayed in a boneyard	5000	4000	5a or 8

Beams Single coat applications	LF per hour	LF per gallon	Material type
Heights to 13', roller and brush	45	40	8
Over 13' to 17', roller and brush	30	40	8
Over 17' to 19', roller and brush	20	40	8
Over 19' to 21', roller and brush	16	40	8

These figures will apply on beam sizes from 4" x 8" to 6" x 14" and are per linear foot of beam. *High time difficulty factors* are included in these rates.

New construction estimating tables
Figure 19-2

Cabinets	SF per hour	SF per gallon	Material type
Paint grade, one coat, roll and brush application			
Undercoat application	110	240	2
Enamel application	120	275	4
Paint cabinet backs (wall behind the cabinet)			
Roll and brush, one coat	200	250	3
Stain, seal and lacquer, including the seven steps			
listed below:	60	21	--
Step 1, sand lightly	--	--	--
Step 2, spray 1 coat of stain	--	--	5a
Step 3, wipe with a rag	--	--	--
Step 4, spray 1 coat of sanding sealer	--	--	5b
Step 5, sand lightly	--	--	--
Step 6, spray 1 coat of lacquer	--	--	5c
Step 7, spray final coat of lacquer	--	--	5c

The figures above include painting the cabinet face, back of doors, stiles and rails. For the seven step stain and lacquer process, the figures include a fog coat of stain on the shelves, cabinet back and wall behind the cabinet. For wine racks, measure the face area and multiply by three to find the equivalent surface area. Then use the figures for cabinet faces. For wine racks, measure the face area and multiply by three to find the equivalent surface area. Then use the figures for cabinet faces.

Carport canopy   For wood canopy, see *Overhang (eaves)*. Metal carport canopy is usually prefinished corrugated material.

Ceilings, gypsum wallboard Medium texture (orange peel or knockdown)	SF per hour	SF per gallon	Material type
Flat wall paint, roll 1 coat	350	250	3
Seal wet area ceilings, spray 2 coat	800	225	1
Enamel wet area ceilings, spray 1 coat	600	200	4

For ceilings over 8 feet high, use *High time difficulty factors*. Do not make deductions for openings in the ceiling area that are under 100 SF.

Ceilings, tongue and groove wood Semi-transparent stain	SF per hour	SF per gallon	Material type
Roll on 1 coat	280	250	7
Spray on 1 coat	400	180	7

New construction estimating tables
Figure 19-2 (continued)

Closets One coat applied by brush	LF per hour	LF per gallon	Material type
Molding, enamel applied over flat wall primer to molding going around the perimeter of a closet, brush on 1 coat	100	200	4
Poles, stained before pole is installed Brush and rag wipe, 1 coat	60	200	5a or 8
Shelf and pole, enamel applied over flat wall primer after shelf installation, brush on 1 coat	30	60	4
Shelves, enamel applied over flat wall primer brush on 1 coat	40	80	4

Measurements are based on the linear feet of molding, pole or shelf painted and include coating all exposed surfaces.

Corbels Up to 4" by 8"	LF per hour	LF per gallon	Material type
Brush on 1 coat	25	45	8

See Figure 19-14 for a picture of rafter tails and corbels.

Cornice See *Overhang*.

Decks See *Siding* for deck surface and *Overhang* for deck overhang.

Doors, exterior Brush one coat	Hours per door	Doors per gallon	Material type
French (F)	.6	8	9 or 10
Louvered (L)	.7	5	9 or 10
Entry (panel) (E)			
Paint grade, exterior enamel	.8	2	10
Stain grade, marine spar varnish	.8	2	9
Stain grade, polyurethane	1.0	2	9
Exterior (X)	.3	5	10

These figures include finishing all six sides of the door, jamb and trim. Paint grade doors get two coats of exterior enamel. Stain grade doors get a coat of stain, sealer, and finish.

Doors and casing, interior	Hours per opening	Gallons per opening	Material type
Undercoat using roller or spray	.2	.09	2
Enamel on trim using roller or spray	.2	.10	4

These figures apply to painting all six sides of interior doors, jambs and trim, and pullman and linen closet doors. It's usually much faster (and nearly as accurate) to count the openings and estimate time and materials from Figures 19-6 and 19-8 than it is to estimate each opening separately. Use this table if you elect not to use Figures 19-6 and 19-8. This table shows labor and materials required per opening.

Eaves See *Overhang*.

New construction estimating tables
Figure 19-2 (continued)

Fascia Per LF painted or stained
Brush and roll one coat

	LF per hour	LF per gallon	Material type
2" x 4"	230	120	8
2" x 6" to 2" x 10"	200	100	8
2" x 12"	150	60	8

Fencing
Standard wood plank, to 6' high

	SF per hour	SF per gallon	Material type
Roll, 1 coat	150	100	7 or 8
Spray, 1 coat	600	75	7 or 8

For good neighbor fence, multiply the surface area by 1.5 and use rates for plank fence.

Fireplace trim
Single coat applications

	LF per hour	SF per hour	Material type
Mantels, rough sawn wood to 4" x 12", brush	20	40	8
Plant-on interior trim, roll and brush	85	125	8

Fireplaces and adjacent siding
Single coat applications

	SF per hour	SF per gallon	Material type
Masonry fireplace, brush application	80	120	8
Siding, interior wood, roll and brush	100	90	8

Firewood boxes
Single coat applications

	Hours each	Gallons each	Material type
Based on a rough-sawn wood box up to 3'0" x 3'6" x 3'6" deep, brush application	.3	.25	8

Flashing See *Sheet metal.*

Garage door backs, seal coat
Spray one coat

	Hours per door	Gallons per door	Material type
1 car garage	.2	.6	8
2 car garage	.3	1.0	8
3 car garage	.5	1.2	8

Use the figures for siding when estimating the cost of painting garage door fronts. These figures assume a one-car garage door measures 7' x 8' and a two-car garage door measures 7' x 16'. A three-car garage has one single and one double door. Government funded projects (FHA, VA, HUD) usually require sealing the garage door back. They're usually spray painted along with the cabinets or exterior trim.

New construction estimating tables
Figure 19-2 (continued)

Gutters & downspouts	LF per hour	LF per gallon	Material type
Gutters, brush, 1 coat	100	350	8
Downspouts, brush, 1 coat	40	200	8

Rule of thumb: Use 0.2 manhours plus $1 for material for each 8' of gutter or downspout painted.

High time difficulty factors
Painting takes longer when heights above the floor exceed 8 feet. Add the following percentages to your labor estimates:

Over 8' to 13'	Add 30% (multiply the area by 1.3)
Over 13' to 17'	Add 60% (multiply the area by 1.6)
Over 18' to 19'	Add 90% (multiply the area by 1.9)
Over 20' to 21'	Add 120% (multiply the area by 2.2)

Mailbox structures Take off each board and use the manhours and materials given for *Trellis* or *Plant-on trim*.

Masonry block walls Concrete masonry units (CMU)	SF per hour	SF per gallon	Material type
Precision (smooth face) block			
Roll, 1st coat	390	215	11
Roll, 2nd coat	450	300	11
Spray, 1 coat	850	240	11
Split face block, spray, 1 coat	800	55	11
Fluted block, spray, 1 coat	750	60	11
Slump block, spray, 1 coat	700	55	11

Measurements are based on the square feet of surface painted

Overhang (eaves) Spray one coat	SF per hour	SF per gallon	Material type
At rake or eaves	400	85	8
Over an entry or deck	520	85	8
At wood carports	650	85	8

For standard overhang, measure the area (length times width) and then multiply by 1.5 to allow for painting rafter tails and outriggers.

Pass-through shelves (P/T) Per linear foot of shelf	LF per hour	LF per gallon	Material type
Brush on 1 coat	40	100	6 & 8

Allow at least 0.2 manhours plus $1 for materials on pass-through shelves.

New construction estimating tables
Figure 19-2 (continued)

Plant-on trim Roll on one coat	LF per hour	LF per gallon	Material type
2" x 2" to 2" x 4"	140	240	8
2" x 6" to 2" x 8"	140	140	8
2" x 10" to 2" x 12"	110	80	8

For work more than 9 feet above ground level, apply *High time difficulty factors*.

Pot shelves, exterior (P/S) Per linear foot of shelf, 12" to 18" wide	LF per hour	LF per gallon	Material type
Roll and brush, 1 coat	75	40	8

Protective coating   See *Stucco*.

Railing, decorative handrail, interior Coating wood handrail only	LF per hour	LF per gallon	Material type
Stain, seal and lacquer, including the seven steps listed below.	65	75	--
Step 1, light sanding	--	--	--
Step 2, spray 1 coat of stain	--	--	5a
Step 3, wipe with rag	--	--	--
Step 4, spray on sanding sealer	--	--	5b
Step 5, light sanding	--	--	--
Step 6, spray on 1 coat of lacquer	--	--	5c
Step 7, spray on 1 coat of lacquer	--	--	5c
Paint grade, undercoat or enamel coats			
Brush on each coat	40	100	2 or 4

Use these figures to estimate the cost of coating decorative wood interior handrail. Measurements are per linear foot of handrail.

Railing, wood, exterior	LF per hour	LF per gallon	Material type
Rough sawn, 42" high with 2" x 2" verticals each 6"			
Brush, 1 coat	20	15	8
Decorative, based on one coat of stain, two coats of sanding sealer, sanding, putty, and two coats of varnish. 36" to 42" high with spindles each 12"			
First coat	26	80	9
Added coats	34	100	9

These figures include coating the rail cap, balusters, newels and spindles. The minimum preparation time for varnishing will usually be 80 square feet per hour for a steel wool buff and 80 square feet per hour for application of wax. The figures in this table assume jobs with no more than 50 linear feet of rail per living unit.

New construction estimating tables
Figure 19-2 (continued)

Railing, decorative wood, interior Coating all surfaces	LF per hour	LF per gallon	Material type
Paint grade, undercoat or enamel coats			
Brush, per coat	16	40	2 or 4
Stain, seal and lacquer, including the seven steps listed below.	12	20	--
Step 1, light sanding	--	--	--
Step 2, spray 1 coat of stain	--	--	5a
Step 3, wipe with rag	--	--	--
Step 4, spray on sanding sealer	--	--	5b
Step 5, light sanding	--	--	--
Step 6, spray on 1 coat of lacquer	--	--	5c
Step 7, spray on 1 coat of lacquer	--	--	5c

Use these figures to estimate the cost of coating decorative interior wood railing including all vertical and horizontal members. Measurements are per linear foot of rail and include the coating described above for all vertical and horizontal surfaces.

Railing, wrought iron, interior/exterior Assuming a prime coat applied by others	LF per hour	LF per gallon	Material type
1/2" x 1/2" verticals, 42" high with bars each 6" to 9"			
With wood cap, brush, 1 coat	20	80	6
1/2" x 1/2" verticals, 60" to 72" high with bars each 6" to 9"			
Brush, 1 coat	20	80	6

Figures are based on less than 50 linear feet of rail per living unit.

Registers, HVAC	SF floor area per hour	SF floor area per spray can	Material type
Spray bomb, 1 coat	3000	700	5a & 5c

HVAC registers are usually painted with aerosol spray (bomb) paint to match the walls. Rather than figure the register area to be painted, base your labor and material estimates on the square feet of floor area in the home or apartment. As a rule of thumb, figure 2 minutes of labor for each 100 square feet of floor. These estimates include the time needed to remove, paint and replace registers and grilles.

Roof jacks (RJ) Brush on one coat	Hours per roof	Gallons per roof	Material type
One story home or multiple units with attached roof area			
Brush 1 coat	.5	.6	8
Two story home, brush 1 coat	.7	.8	8

These figures are minimums based on 1500 square feet of roof and assume that the jacks were primed by others.

New construction estimating tables
Figure 19-2 (continued)

Sheet metal
See also *Vents and flashing*

	LF per hour	LF per gallon	Material type
Rain diverters and gravel stops, widths to 2"			
Flat paint, brush, 1 coat	250	500	8
Galvanized iron flashing and parapet wall cap, widths from 2" to 8"			
Flat paint, brush, 1 coat	240	475	8

Shutters
Painting all sides

	Shutters per hour	Shutters per gallon	Material type
Undercoat, brush one coat	3.5	10	2
Enamel, brush each coat	3.0	13	4

These figures assume assembled shutters measuring 2' by 4'.

Siding
One coat applications

	SF per hour	SF per gallon	Material type
Shingles, sprayed on			
Clear sealer	600	75	12
Semi-transparent stain	275	150	7
Wood siding, solid body or semi-transparent stain applied on a smooth surface			
Up to 500 SF job			
Roller application	150	100	7 or 8
Spray application	500	100	7 or 8
Over 500 to 1000 SF job			
Roller application	225	150	7 or 8
Spray application	600	125	7 or 8
Over 1000 SF job			
Roller application	300	160	7 or 8
Spray application	700	160	7 or 8
Clear sealer, sprayed on smooth wood	600	150	12

For work over 8 feet above ground, use *High time difficulty factors.*

Stair stringers, exterior

	LF per hour	LF per gallon	Material type
Rough sawn wood to 2" x 12" each side			
Roll and brush, 1 coat	50	60	8
Metal shapes up to 14" each side			
Roll and brush, 1 coat	60	110	8

Use these figures when estimating the cost of painting stringers that support open stair treads. Measurements are based on the linear feet of each stringer.

New construction estimating tables
Figure 19-2 (continued)

Stair stringers, interior	LF per hour	LF per gallon	Material type
Rough sawn wood to 2" x 12" each side			
Roll and brush, 1 coat	45	50	8
Metal shapes up to 14" each side			
Roll and brush, 1 coat	55	100	8

Use these figures when estimating the cost of painting stringers that support open stair treads. Measurements are based on the linear feet of each stringer.

Stair treads and steps, wood   Measure the surface area of rise and run and use the manhour and material figures listed under *Siding*.

Stairs, wood   Measure the surface area of rise and run and use the estimates listed under *Siding*.

Steel, miscellaneous Single coat application by brush	LF per hour	LF per gallon	Material type
1/2" to 3" widths	260	350	6
3" x 3" to 8" widths	100	175	6
10" to 18" widths	75	100	6

Use these figures for smaller steel members such as corner guards or small posts. For large steel shapes, see the tables in Chapter 20. These figures assume the steel has been primed by others and are based on the linear foot of member painted.

Stucco Per coat	SF per hour	SF per gallon	Material type
Textured surface (spraying is recommended)			
Roller application	300	200	11
Sprayed application	650	150	11
Waterproofing, clear hydro sealer			
Sprayed application	800	100	12

When calculating the stucco area, make no deductions for openings less than 100 SF. If wax protective coating is sprayed on windows before stucco is painted, figure 1/10th manhour per window. A gallon of protective wax (material type 13) will cover about 325 square feet of window. For heights above 8 feet, use *High time difficulty factors*. See *Window protective coating* in Figure 17-3.

Touchup	% of total interior labor	% of total interior material	Material type
Brush as required	15%	1%	As needed

Touchup will be required on nearly all interior jobs. The skill of your paint crews and the type of job will determine the time needed. The time and materials shown here are generous allowances. The actual time required will usually be less. Figure the touchup time and material needed and then add the appropriate percentage to your estimate.

New construction estimating tables
Figure 19-2 (continued)

Trellis or lattice
Per LF, brushed and rolled, one coat

	LF per hour	LF per gallon	Material type
2" x 3" to 2" to 6"	130	110	8
2" x 8" to 4" x 12"	120	80	8

This table is based on the linear feet of trellis or lattice member painted.

Trellis or lattice
Per SF, sprayed, one coat

	SF per hour	SF per gallon	Material type
2" x 2" lumber spaced at 3" with 2" x 8" supports	60	50	8

These figures are based on the overall (width times length) area painted.

Valance, light
Roll and brush one coat

	LF per hour	LF per gallon	Material type
Rough-sawn wood, 2" x 6" or 2" x 8"	40	90	8

These figures include time and material to paint all exposed surfaces. Figure a minimum of 0.3 hour hours plus 1/10th gallon of paint for even the smallest valance. Measurements are based on the linear feet of valance including side returns.

Vents and flashing (V & F)
Brush on one coat

	Hours per home	Gallons per home	Material type
1 story home	.5	.5	8
2 story home	.7	.6	8
Multiple units with attached roofs, per 1500 SF of roof area			
Brush, 1 coat	.4	.4	8

These figures assume all work can be done from the roof surface and that the vents and flashing have been preprimed or pretreated by others.

Walls, concrete tilt-up or floors
One coat applications

	SF per hour	SF per gallon	Material type
Roller applications	300	200	11
Spray applications	600	175	11

See the tables in Chapter 20 for more information on concrete coatings. For heights over 8 feet, use *High time difficulty factors.*

New construction estimating tables
Figure 19-2 (continued)

Walls, gypsum wallboard Per SF of wall coated	SF coated per hour	SF coated per gallon	Material type
Flat wall paint and orange peel or knockdown (medium) texture			
Roll on 1st coat	675	250	3
Roll on 2nd coat	700	300	3
Sealer or enamel (in wet areas) and orange peel or knockdown texture (medium texture) with cabinets and pullmans not in place			
Roll on 1 coat	500	200	1
Enamel wet area walls (kitchens and baths) with cabinets and			
pullmans in place, roll on 1 coat	600	240	4

When measuring wall area, don't deduct for openings in wall area that are less than 100 square feet. For heights over 8 feet, use High time difficulty factors.

Walls, gypsum wallboard Per SF of floor area	SF floor per hour	SF floor per gallon	Material type
Flat wall paint and orange peel or knockdown texture			
Roll on 1st coat	400	140	3
Roll on 2nd coat	500	125	3
Sealer or enamel (in wet areas) and orange peel or knockdown texture (medium texture), with cabinets and pullmans *not* in place--*walls and ceilings*			
Roll on 1 coat	240	75	1
Enamel wet area walls (kitchens and baths) with cabinets and pullmans			
in place--*walls and ceilings*, roll on 1 coat	135	80	4

It's usually quicker (though somewhat less accurate) to estimate wall painting from the floor area. If you want to estimate by the square feet of floor rather than the square feet of wall painted, use the figures in this table. Apply the *High time difficulty factors*.

Window seats, wood Paint grade, brush application	LF per hour	LF per gallon	Material type
Prime coat	30	40	2
Finish coat	35	50	4

These estimates are based on painting exposed surfaces on a window seat up to 24" wide.

Window sills, wood Paint grade, brush application	LF per hour	LF per gallon	Material type
Prime coat	60	120	2
Finish coat	70	150	4

These figures are per linear foot of sill painted.

Windows, wood See Appendix B.

Windows, protective coating See *Stucco* in this table and in Figure 17-3.

New construction estimating tables
Figure 19-2 (continued)

A good working environment promotes accurate, reliable bids

The New Construction Take-Off Sheet

The new construction take-off sheet helps organize your estimate into a logical order. But that's not all. It's also a checklist that will help prevent an expensive oversight. There's a blank copy in the back of the book and a completed copy in the sample estimate later in this chapter. As usual, we'll take off the quantities in the same order as the painting is done. I've arranged the take-off sheet with this step-by-step procedure in mind.

The take-off sheet is divided into two sections, interior and exterior. The exterior section has room for three different elevations. Finally, there's a recap section.

The Decision to Bid

Don't start estimating until you've evaluated the job and made the decision to bid. Let's briefly review the bidding variables you'll consider in deciding whether a project fits within your niche.

Project type and size— The project of 15 single-family detached homes is a comfortable size for your company.

Location— The tract is within your geographical boundaries. It won't require travel time or per diem payments to the painters. It's also near supply sources.

Storage— All materials, tools and equipment can be stored on site at no expense to the company.

Manpower— Your production painters are experienced in projects of this size, and have proven their ability to finish jobs like this at a profit.

Reputations— The *owner* is reasonable, with a reputation for excellent planning and for making few changes during construction. The *architect* is known for producing a complete set of plans with very few revisions and corrections. The *general contractor* is organized, respects his subcontractors and pays invoices on time. All members of the design and construction team have good reputations.

Competition— There are only two other qualified painting contractors bidding this project. Each has similar overhead expenses and other costs. The number and quality of competitors is acceptable.

Picking Up the Plans

You could have an employee or outside courier service pick up the plans. But when a builder asks you to bid for the first time, I recommend that you pick up the plans yourself. Make an appointment, if possible, so you can meet one or more key employees of the general contractor. Try to meet the person who's in charge of projects and writes the subcontracts. Introduce yourself so you establish credibility for your company.

The Pre-Bid Checklist

Use a pre-bid checklist for *all* estimates — whether for a new or established customer. There's a sample pre-bid checklist back in Chapter 6. The checklist fills in for the painting specifications — which are often incomplete and inaccurate. Many plan sets include only boilerplate specifications in the general notes. They may not accurately reflect the owner's or general contractor's specific painting requirements. Fill out the pre-bid checklist at the introductory presentation with new prospects, or at the office after your preliminary review of the plans. The pre-bid checklist for the sample new construction estimate is shown in Figure 19-3.

Schedule the Bid

As soon as any plan set arrives in your office, note the bid deadline on your bid log. The turnaround time for our sample bid is one week, so there's time to complete it without rushing.

Review every sheet in the plans, but concentrate on the general notes or specifications that relate to painting. Get familiar with the entire project while you identify any conditions which require special attention.

Review the sample plans in Appendix A and you'll notice some items which require special attention: the tongue and groove ceiling with exposed beams in the living room, the stain grade kitchen cabinets, the details of the pot shelf and pass-through shelf, the exterior siding, the stucco painting, and the stucco seal operations.

During your preliminary review of the plans, you may find other special items that aren't listed on the pre-bid checklist. If you do, note them on the take-off sheet. Use the section called *Notes-Options-Alternates-Exclusions.*

The Site Visit

There are two good reasons to visit the site. First, find out if there's adequate access to all areas that need to be painted. In most cases, access problems have been solved for other trades by the time your painters arrive on the job. But if access to the buildings is limited, the site visit can be critical to your estimate. You may have to include labor to move materials, run additional spray lines, install scaffolding or use other specialized equipment.

Second, get to know the superintendent. Find out if he's experienced and easy to work with. A competent super will know how to schedule work so each trade can get in and out without conflicting with other trades. A few minutes of conversation will tell you plenty about the superintendent's competence. The ability of the superintendent may influence your bid price.

New Construction Estimating Process

O.K. You've decided to bid and you've looked over the job site. You know the plans like the back of your hand. Now where do you start the take-off? Here's an outline of the step-by-step system I recommend:

• First, fill in the name of the project and rest of the information called for in the heading.

• Next, take the measurements for each painting operation from the plans and identify each unit of measurement.

• Use your new construction formulas (or mine) to calculate the manhours and material quantities.

• Price the materials from the volume discount price list.

• List the manhours and material costs on the take-off sheet and extend them for the standard base bid.

• Finally, make any necessary adjustments to the standard base bid. Then you're ready to write your proposal.

Now let's get started on the sample estimate. Review the sample plan, the formulas and the take-off sheet before you begin. And be sure to have a calculator handy so you can follow along with the math as we walk through the estimate.

PROJECT NAME: _Vista Park_   **DATE:** _6-5-89_

PROJECT LOCATION: _Main at Broadway_   **BUILDER:** _John Doe Const._

Interior

Paint brand: _Glidden / Navajo white_

	Pre-finished	Paint grade	Stain seal lacquer
Kitchen cabinets			✓
Pullmans		✓	
Linen closet		✓	
Forced air unit	0	0	0
Passage doors		✓	
Wardrobe doors		✓	
Other _____			

Wet area walls and ceilings:
- Undercoat + 1 coat ____✓____
- Undercoat + 2 coats _____

Pullmans, linens, doors and casings:
- Undercoat + 1 coat ____✓____
- Undercoat + 2 coats _____
- Split coat _____
- Brush coat _____
- Other _____

Walls:
- 1 coat flat ___TO COVER___
- 2 coats flat _____
- 1 coat sealer _____

Interior wood (mantel, siding, etc.)
- 1 coat ___✓ BEAMS / LIGHT VALANCE___
- 2 coats _____
- Other _____

Tongue & groove (T&G) ceiling:
- Finish _SEMI-TRANSPARENT STAIN_

Fireplace masonry ___N/A___

Base:
- Stain ____✓____
- Paint _____

Exterior

Paint brand: _Glidden / per contractor_

Exterior wood (plant ons, overhang, fascia):
- 1 coat ____✓____
- 2 coats _____
- Clear seal per FHA _____

Siding:
- Heavy body stain ____✓____
- Semi-transparent stain _____

Shingles:
- Clear sealer ___N/A___
- No finish _____

Stucco:
- Paint ___N/A___
- Sealer _UP TO 4"0" & AROUND OPENINGS_

Fireplace masonry: ___N/A___

Fencing: ___BY OWNER___

Other: _NO MASONRY PAINT OR LIGHT POSTS_

****

Total number of units ___15___

Number of phases ___1___

Painting start date ___7-15-89___

Completion date ___8-15-89___

Price expiration date ___8-7-89___

Present painter _PACIFIC PAINTING_

Customer's phone _(619) 555-1212_

Purchasing agent _John Doe_

Pre-bid checklist
Figure 19-3

New construction take-off sheet form

Company _John Doe Construction_ **Project** _Vista Park_

Plan # _1_ **# units** _15_

Sq. Ft. _720_ **Stories** _1_ **Plan date** _6-7-89_ **Plan set** _#7_

Prepared by: _Jeff Jones_ **Checked by:** _JDG_

Interior

High ceiling _Liv to 13'0"_

Kitchen	_85_	Util. _15_	140 S.F.	
Bath	_40_			
Walls	_720_	– _140 = 580_	656 S.F.	
Clip	_254_	x _.3 = 76_		

Seal	(_140_)		_.6_ +	_11.40_
U/C	(_12_)		_2.0_ +	_10.00_
Cabs	(_90_)		_1.5_ +	_35.30_
Walls	(_656_)		_1.6_ +	_29.70_
K & B	(_140_)		_1.4_ +	_16.80_
Trim	(_12_)		_2.0_ +	_11.50_
Beams _122.5 LF/4"x8"/13'0"_			_2.7_ +	_19.40_
T & G ceiling	(_330_)		_.8_ +	_15.70_
Rail	(_4_) _36"w/w.cap_		_.3_ +	_1.00_
Stringers	( )		_0_ +	—
Valance	(_3'0"_)		_.3_ +	_1.00_
Fireplace	( )		_0_ +	—
Base P E (S)			_.4_ +	_1.50_

Subtotal	_13.6_ +	_153.30_	
T/U _15%+1% 2.0_ +		_1.53_	
_6%_ Tax		_9.29_	
Totals	_15.6_ +	_164.12_	

Notes - Options - Alternatives - Exclusions

_P/S_

_P/T_

S/S + Stucco Seal

Exclude: Fencing

Masonry

Recap	Manhours	+	Material cost
Elevation A	_22.8_	+	_327_
Elevation B	_23.6_	+	_339_
Elevation C	_24.1_	+	_359_
Option #		+	
Option #		+	

Exterior

Elevation A

Fascia	(_124_)	_2x8_		_.7_ +	_9.80_
O/H	(_207_)	x 1.5 = _311_		_.8_ +	_29.20_
Side	(_108_)	(ST) HB		_.7_ +	_11.60_
P/O	(_180_)	_2x6_		_1.2_ +	_9.70_
Doors F L E /X/				_1.3_ +	_11.50_
V & F				_.5_ +	_6.00_
RJ & BGD				_.5_ +	_4.00_
	_P/S_	_27_		_.4_ +	_5.40_
	_P/T_	_1_		_.2_ +	_1.00_
	_S/S_	_692_		_.9_ +	_65.10_
Subtotals				_7.2_ +	_153.30_

Tax (_6%_)		_9.20_
Totals	_7.2_ +	_163.00_

Elevation B

Fascia	( )		+	
O/H	( )	x 1.5 =	+	
Side	( )	ST HB	+	
P/O	( )		+	
Doors F L E X			+	
V & F			+	
RJ & BGD			+	

Subtotals		+

Tax		
Totals	_8.0_ +	_175.00_

Elevation C

Fascia	( )		+	
O/H	( )	x 1.5 =	+	
Side	( )	ST HB	+	
P/O	( )		+	
Doors F L E X			+	
V & F			+	
RJ & BGD			+	

Subtotals		+

Tax		
Totals	_8.5_ +	_195.00_

New construction take-off sheet
Figure 19-4

The New Construction Take-Off

Begin by filling in the heading of the new construction take-off sheet. (The take-off sheet for this sample estimate is Figure 19-4. Figure 19-5 is a list of the abbreviations used on the take-off sheet.) Then begin counting the openings.

BGD	Back of the garage door
Base	Baseboard
	P = painted (flat)
	E = enameled
	S = stained
Clip	Portion of a wall which extends above 8 feet
	(vaulted, cathedral or high ceiling)
Doors	F = French
	L = Louvered
	E = Entry
	X = Exterior
HB	Heavy (solid) body stain
HVY	Heavy
K & B	Kitchen and bath walls and ceiling enamel operation
Kit	Kitchen area
LF	Linear feet
LT	Light
NR	Not recommended
O/B Ceil	Open beam ceiling, tongue and groove portion
O/C	On center
O/H	Overhang
P/O	Plant-on
P/S	Pot shelf
P/T	Pass-through shelf
Recap	Recapitulation, a summary of calculation totals
RJ	Roof jacks
S & L	Stain and lacquer
Seal	Kitchen and bath wall and ceiling sealer operation
SF	Square feet
S/S	Stucco seal operation
ST	Semi-transparent stain
T/U	Touchup
Trim	Opening enamel operation for doors, pullmans, linens, etc.
U/C	Opening undercoat operation for doors, pullmans, linens, etc.
Util	Utility area
V & F	Vents and flashing
WI	Wrought iron

Abbreviations for new construction take-off sheet
Figure 19-5

The Opening Count

I introduced my system for counting and estimating openings in the last chapter. We'll use the same system for the new construction estimate. This opening count includes all paint grade doors with frames and casings, all paint grade pullman cabinets, linen closet doors, casings, frames, and shelving. And don't forget paint grade bookcases and wine racks. These openings will take one coat of enamel undercoater and one coat of enamel trim paint.

Follow a system when counting these openings.

Item		Count
Closets:	Molding at closet perimeter	1 per 25'0" length
	Poles, stain	1 per 10'0" length
	Shelf & pole (undercoat or enamel)	1 per 6'0" length
	Shelves (undercoat or enamel)	1 per 10'0" length
Doors:	Bifold doors and frames	1 per door
	Dutch doors and frames	1.5 per door
	Entry doors and frames	1 per door
	FAU (forced air unit) doors and frames	1 per door
	French doors and frames	1.5 per door
	Linen doors with face frame	1 per 2'0" width
	Louvered bifold doors and frames;	
	false	1 per door panel
	real	1 per door panel or per 1'6" length
	Louvered doors and frames;	
	false	1 per door
	real	1 per 1'6" width
	Passage doors and frames;	
	flush	1 per door
	paneled	1.25 per door
	Wardrobe doors	1 per door
	Split coat operation; doors and frames	1 per opening
	Tip-off operation (doors only)	½ per opening
Pullman cabinets		1 per lavatory or per 4'0" width
Windows, wood:		1 per 6 SF of window

Opening count
Figure 19-6

Begin in one corner of the building and move counter-clockwise from room to room. Mark each opening with a red pencil as you count it. Assign each opening a value based on the opening count allowance table in Figure 19-6. The values in this table are based on *flush interior passage doors* (Figure 19-7A) which count as one opening. Other openings are assigned values that are a multiple of the time needed to paint that flush door. For example, *paneled interior passage doors* are harder to paint. They count as 1.25 openings each.

Many *entry doors* are solid core, natural wood and paneled (Figure 19-7B). Even if they take a stain and varnish finish or a polyurethane coating, include them as one opening. They need extra care and that takes extra time. We'll add more time and material for painting the outside of the entry door in the exterior section.

A single *French door* (Figure 19-7C) is counted as one and one-half openings, and a pair of French doors is counted as three openings.

Real louvered doors (Figure 19-7D) are more difficult to finish than any other type of door. That's

why you count one opening for each 1'6'' width of a louvered door. For a louvered bifold door, count one opening for each panel or section of the door. The most efficient method of painting doors with real louvers is to spray both the undercoater and enamel. Remember, real louvered doors take a lot of time to do right.

False louvered doors have louvers either pressed into the door or applied to the door. The difference is that false louvers don't go all the way through the door, so air can't pass through. These doors can be sprayed or rolled and brushed as easily as an interior passage door. Count them as one opening.

Dutch doors (Figure 19-7E) count as 1.5 openings. *Wardrobe* doors may be vinyl coated, mirrored, natural wood finish or standard flush hardboard (Masonite). Refer to the door schedule for a description of all door sizes and types.

The paint grade wardrobe doors in the sample plan are made of hardboard. Wardrobe openings with bipass doors usually don't include door casings. The perimeter of these openings is generally enclosed in drywall and painted with the walls. So count only one opening for each pair of bipass

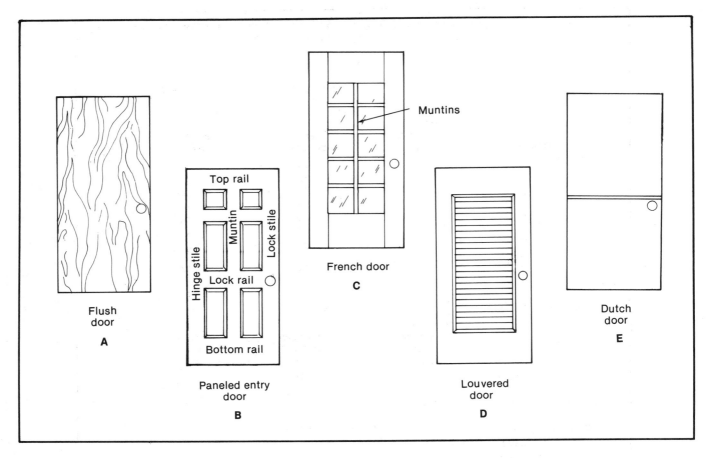

Door types
Figure 19-7

wardrobe doors for up to a 7-foot opening. But first be sure there's no casing or molding which requires paint.

Bifold doors, such as those at the utility room in the sample plan, are counted as one opening for each section of door. For the sample plan, that's four openings.

Most *pullmans* or bathroom vanities have a single lavatory, although some of the larger ones have two. For paint grade pullmans, count one opening for each sink or for each 4'0'' width of pullman cabinet.

If there are stain grade doors, pullmans or linens with the same stain, seal and lacquer finish as the kitchen cabinets, measure them along with the cabinets.

Linens may be closets with hollow core doors, or they may be assembled with cabinet doors and a face frame. These linen cabinets are called knockdown assemblies because they're "knocked down"

after fabrication to be shipped to the site and reassembled. The opening count for these cabinet doors and face frames is one opening for each 2'0'' in width.

Shelves that will be rolled and brushed separately must be included in the opening count. Use your judgment to estimate the time involved. Then increase the opening count by one for each 10 minutes of additional time required.

When the shelves can be sprayed along with the walls, they don't take any extra time. So don't allow extra openings for the shelves and poles in the closets of the sample house.

Figure 19-8 shows the time and material values I use for both undercoat and enamel painting for these openings. I've allowed about 10 minutes for each opening, and 10 to 11 openings per gallon. This includes the time and material needed to paint pullmans, linens, or all six sides of doors, along with the frames and jambs.

Doors, frames, jambs, pullmans & other interior paint grade openings based on the interior opening count allowance table

Roll and brush each coat

Openings	Manhours per opening per coat	Undercoat based on 11 openings/gallon — Undercoat gallons	Enamel based on 10 openings/gallon — Enamel gallons
1	.2	.09	.10
2	.3	.18	.20
3	.5	.27	.30
4	.7	.36	.40
5	.9	.45	.50
6	1.0	.54	.60
7	1.2	.64	.70
8	1.4	.73	.80
9	1.5	.81	.90
10	1.7	.90	1.00

Example: 12 openings = 10 openings + 2 openings

	Manhours per opening per coat	Undercoat gallons	Enamel gallons
10 each	1.7	.90	1.00
2 each	.3	.18	.20
12 each =	2.0	1.08	1.20

Note: 10 minutes per coat = .167 hours rounded to .2 hours
15 minutes per coat = .25 hours
20 minutes per coat = .3 hours

New construction undercoat and trim table
Figure 19-8

The Split Coat Operation

In addition to the undercoat and trim coat, some general contractors may require a *split coat*. That's an equal mixture of undercoater and enamel that's applied after the undercoat. It's the second of three coats. When a split coat is required, just treat it as another line item, with the same time and material as the enamel trim operation. The sample estimate doesn't include a split coat.

The Tip-Off Operation

Some general contractors may require the painters to *tip off* all doors and cabinets. (The term comes from using the tip of the paint brush for the final coat.) That takes more time than rolling or spraying. Treat it as a separate line item and allow an additional one-half opening for each door or cabinet to be tipped off. No tip-off is included in the sample estimate.

Now you're ready to count the openings on the floor plan of the sample plan. You probably remember from the last chapter that there are 12 openings. But it's a good idea to double-check by recounting the openings. Then enter the correct count on the take-off sheet in the parentheses after *U/C* and after *Trim*. That covers both the undercoat and enamel trim coats for each opening. Look at my completed take-off sheet in Figure 19-4.

But don't calculate the manhours and material dollars yet. While you're going over the plans to take off the rest of the interior operations, you might come across an opening you missed. It's easy to overlook an opening in a concealed location, such as a storage door under the stairs.

High Ceilings

After you've recorded the openings on the take-off sheet, look for any high ceilings in the floor plan.

The section drawing in our sample plan shows that the living room has a vaulted ceiling. We'll put *Liv to 13'0"* on Figure 19-4 on the *High ceiling* line.

Other plans may have vaulted ceilings in several rooms, all with different ceiling heights. List the ceiling height for each room separately so you can calculate the added wall space in each room.

Wet Area Walls and Ceilings

Now let's consider the item called *Seal* on the take-off sheet. We'll use the formula for sealing wet area walls from the estimating formulas in Figure 19-2. There are three wet area rooms in our plan. The kitchen (10 by 8.5 feet) has 85 square feet. The bath (5 by 8 feet) has 40 square feet. And the utility room is only 2.5 by 6 feet, or 15 square feet.

Write in all of these floor areas on the take-off sheet in the section below *High ceilings* and total them to the right. Then write in the total (140 SF) in the parentheses beside *Seal* and *K & B*. We'll use the total floor area for the labor and material calculations for wet area walls and ceilings.

Sealer at Walls and Ceilings

The seal coat on the wet area walls and ceilings protects the drywall from moisture. These calculations are simple. We know there are 140 square feet of floor area. And we know the manhour formula for sealing wet areas — 240 square feet of wet area per hour.

$$\frac{140 \text{ SF}}{240 \text{ SF/hour}} = .6 \text{ hour}$$

Enter the result on the take-off sheet to the left of the plus sign on the *Seal* line. That's the manhour column.

To the right of the plus sign is the material cost column. It says $11.40. Here's how to find it. According to the formulas in Figure 19-2, the coverage rate for the sealing is 75 square feet of floor area for each gallon of material used:

$$\frac{140 \text{ SF}}{75 \text{ SF/gallon}} = 1.87 \text{ gallons}$$

Multiply 1.867 gallons by the cost for PVA sealer on the price list in Figure 19-9. It costs $6.10 a gallon including 10% sundries and escalation.

Here's the calculation:

$$1.8 \text{ gallons} \times \$6.10 = \$11.40$$

Enamel Walls and Ceilings

There's a line on the take-off sheet called *K & B*. That's where you put the manhours and material cost for painting the wet area walls and ceilings with enamel. We've already written in the floor area — 140 square feet. Now look at the formulas in Figure 19-2. The manhour production rate for K & B is only 135 square feet of floor space per hour. That's much slower than the sealer operation, because the sealer is sprayed on and the enamel is brushed and rolled. Here's the calculation for manhours:

$$\frac{140 \text{ SF}}{135 \text{ SF/hour}} = 1.0 \text{ hour}$$

Here are the material quantity and cost calculations:

$$\frac{140 \text{ SF}}{80 \text{ SF/gallon}} = 1.75 \text{ gallons}$$

$$1.75 \text{ gallons} \times \$9.60 = \$16.80$$

Walls

The remaining walls of the sample plan will be rolled with a latex flat wall paint. The estimating formulas (Figure 19-2) allow for minor preparation and protection. The calculations for the manhours and material cost for the flat wall area are also based on the floor area. Look at the line called *Walls* on the take-off sheet. I found the floor area of the flat wall rooms by taking the total construction square footage of the house (720 SF) and deducting the wet area floor space (140 SF). That leaves 580 square feet of floor area for the flat wall rooms in the sample house.

But that's not the final figure. That's just walls to 8 feet high. Remember that high ceiling in the living room? The wall above the 8-foot level is commonly called the *clip* area. You have to add it in or your flat wall calculations won't be accurate. You're adding the cost of painting that section of wall, plus additional time for using a ladder or an extended roller pole to reach the clip area.

ID # Material type	Retail price guide	Contractor price at a 40% discount	Add 10% sundries & escalation	Estimating prices (without tax)
Interior materials				
1 - Sealer, off-white Wet area walls	$ 9.25	$ 5.55	$ 6.11	round to $ 6.10
2 - Undercoat openings	$13.80	$ 8.25	$ 9.11	round to $ 9.10
3 - Flat wall (production) Walls & paint grade base	$10.30	$ 6.20	$ 6.82	round to $ 6.80
4 - Enamel (production) K&B walls & openings	$14.50	$ 8.70	$ 9.57	round to $ 9.60
5 - Stain, seal & lacquer system Cabinets				
5a - Lacquer stain Stain grade base	$11.00	$ 6.60	$ 7.26	round to $ 7.30
5b - Sanding sealer	$12.50	$ 7.50	--	--
5c - Lacquer (x 2 coats)	$13.00	$ 7.80	--	--
Average cost for 5a, b and 5c	--	*$ 7.43*	*$ 8.17*	*round to $ 8.20*
6 - Zinc oxide	$20.75	$12.45	$13.70	use $13.70
(Railing & pass-through shelf support - use minimum requirement.)				

ID # Material type	Retail price guide	Contractor price at a 40% discount	Add 10% sundries & escalation	Estimating prices (without tax)
Exterior materials				
7 - Semi-transparent T & G ceiling	$13.00	$ 7.80	$ 8.58	round to $ 8.60
8 - Solid color Beams Light valance Fascia Overhang Siding Plant-on trim Pot shelf (use minimum requirement) Pass-through shelf - (use minimum requirement) Vents & flashings - (use minimum requirement)	$12.00	$ 7.20	$ 7.92	round to $ 7.90
9 - Polyurethane or marine spar varnish Entry doors	$27.00	$16.20	$17.82	round to $17.80
10 - Exterior enamel French, louvered, exterior doors	$17.00	$10.20	$11.22	round to $11.20
11 - Exterior vinyl Masonry, concrete & stucco	$14.00	$ 8.40	$ 8.90	use $ 8.90
12 - Clear hydro-sealer Stucco seal and waterproof	$14.20	$ 8.52	$ 9.37	round to $ 9.40

Volume discount price list for new construction estimate
Figure 19-9

I figure the manhours and material for the clip area by applying the high time difficulty factor only to the floor area of the room or rooms with high ceilings. Since the living room is 17.5 feet by 14.5 feet, there are 254 square feet of floor area. So let's figure the area to add to the take-off sheet:

254 SF x 30% (.3) = 76.2 or 76 SF

That makes the total floor area for flat wall painting 656 square feet. That's 580 square feet plus 76 square feet. That's the total in the parentheses on the *Walls* line on the take-off sheet. Now we're ready to figure the manhours and material cost for painting those flat walls:

$$\frac{656\ SF}{400\ SF/hour} = 1.64\ or\ 1.6\ hours$$

$$\frac{656\ SF}{150\ SF/gallon} = 4.37\ gallons$$

4.37 gallons x $6.80 = $29.72 or $29.70

My formulas for painting walls are based on floor area instead of wall area. They came from my actual historical costs. Floor-area formulas are useful for production painting of houses, apartments or condominiums from 700 square feet to 3,000 square feet. But before using these formulas, make sure they're consistent with your company's costs for similar projects.

If you use the formulas, you may want to double-check the accuracy of your wall area calculations. Here's a rule of thumb for converting floor areas to wall surface areas:

Apartments or condos:
floor area x 3.0 = wall area

Single family homes:
floor area x 2.5 = wall area

If the ceilings will be painted, use these conversion factors:

Apartments or condos:
floor area x 4.0 = wall and ceiling area

Single family homes:
floor area x 3.5 = wall and ceiling area

Cabinets

The sample plan has stain grade cabinets. My stained cabinet formulas are based on a seven-step finish process:

1) Lightly sand before staining.

2) Spray application of one coat of stain.

3) Hand wipe stain.

4) Spray application of one coat of sanding sealer.

5) Lightly sand smooth, leaving a fine dust with a soapy appearance.

6) Spray application of the first coat of lacquer.

7) Spray application of the second coat of lacquer.

The second coat of lacquer dramatically increases the quality of the cabinet finish. You might consider adding this coat as a bonus, since many competitors will include only one coat. It could make a difference when the bids are compared. My manhour and material coverage rates allow for the large amounts of time and material required for high-quality staining.

The pullman cabinet in the bathroom isn't included in this operation. We put it in the opening count because it'll be painted, not stained.

Find the measurements of the kitchen cabinets in the interior elevations. For estimating purposes, separate them into three horizontal rows — the upper, the middle and the lower, or base, cabinets. Assume each row is 36 inches high, although there may be some variation in the upper and middle sections. Unless there's a floor-to-ceiling pantry, there probably won't be any cabinets in the middle section.

To take off the cabinet measurements, start with the interior elevation at the top left corner of the plan sheet. Using the 1/8'' = 1'0'' scale on your measuring tape, make a continuous measurement of the upper, middle and lower cabinets, including vertical banks of drawers. Pass over the spaces for the refrigerator, range and the dishwasher. Then move from left to right across the plan sheet to each of the other interior elevations and measure the kitchen cabinet faces until you've included them all in your take-off. You'll accumulate a total of 90 in the 1/8'' scale.

The next step is to convert the measurement in 1/8'' scale to the scale of the interior elevations (3/8'' = 1'0''). You need to divide the measurement by 3/8. Remember, to divide by a fraction, you convert the measurement to a fraction, then invert the fraction and multiply:

$$90 \text{ LF} \times 1/8 = 90/8$$

$$90/8 \div 3/8 = 90/8 \times 8/3 = 90/3 = 30 \text{ LF}$$

To find the square footage of the cabinets, multiply the 30 linear feet by the cabinet height of 36 inches. That's easy: 30 times 3 is 90 square feet.

Notice that the 90 square feet is the same as the original measurement in 1/8'' scale. This measurement almost converts itself! You can use this short cut as long as the scale of the interior elevations is 3/8'' = 1'0''.

Look at Figure 19-4 again. The 90 square feet is in parentheses beside the line called *Cabs*. Look up the formulas for cabinets in Figure 19-2 and do the calculations.

$$\frac{90 \text{ SF}}{50 \text{ SF/hour}} = 1.8 \text{ hours}$$

$$\frac{90 \text{ SF}}{15 \text{ SF/gallon}} = 6 \text{ gallons}$$

$$6 \text{ gallons} \times \$8.20 = \$49.20$$

Opening Count Review and Calculation

The next step is to check and review the opening count. If it's accurate, look up the openings in the undercoat and trim table (Figure 19-8). The table only goes up to 10 openings, but it's a simple matter to find the manhours and materials for larger numbers. For 12 openings, just add the values for 10 and 2 openings. There's an example at the bottom of Figure 19-8. For our 12 openings, allow 2.0 manhours for the undercoat and 2.0 manhours for the trim painting.

You can also look up the material quantities in Figure 19-8 and the material prices in Figure 19-9. For 12 openings, you need 1.1 gallons of undercoater at $9.10 a gallon. That's $10.00. For the enamel, use 1.2 gallons at $9.60. The cost is $11.50. You'll find these manhour figures and costs on the take-off sheet on the lines called *U/C* and *Trim*.

Beams

The exposed beams in the living area are indicated by dotted lines on the floor plan. There's one ridge beam, five interior rafter beams and two end rafter beams. Count them all as complete beams, although some are only partially exposed. This helps compensate for the extra time it takes to cut in at the wall.

Measure the 17.5-foot ridge beam directly from the floor plan. For the rafter beams that run at an angle to the vaulted ceiling, measure from the section drawings, not the floor plan. They're each 15 feet long. The total length of all beams is 122.5 linear feet. On the take-off sheet, it looks like this: 122.5 LF/4'' x 8''/13'0''. There are 122.5 lineal feet of 4 x 8 beams, 13 feet above the floor.

In Figure 19-2, the formula for beams up to 13'0'' includes the difficulty factor. Here are the calculations:

$$\frac{122.5 \text{ LF}}{45 \text{ LF/hour}} = 2.7 \text{ hours}$$

$$\frac{122.5 \text{ LF}}{50 \text{ LF/gallon}} = 2.45 \text{ gallons}$$

$$2.45 \text{ gallons} \times \$7.90 = \$19.36 \text{ or } \$19.40$$

Tongue and Groove Ceilings

Along with exposed beams, there's a tongue and groove (T&G) ceiling that requires a semi-transparent stain finish. It's also called an open beam ceiling.

The manhour and material cost calculations for the vaulted T&G ceiling are based on the floor area of the room multiplied by a high time difficulty factor. The factor compensates for the height and for the increased area of the vaulted ceiling. The factor for a height of 13 feet is 30%. We already know the floor area of the living room is 254 square feet. To increase that by 30%, multiply by 1.3:

$$254 \text{ SF} \times 1.3 = 330 \text{ SF}$$

On the *T&G ceiling* line, the area is 330 square feet, the time is 0.8 manhour, and the material cost is $15.70.

$$\frac{330 \text{ SF}}{400 \text{ SF/hour}} = .825 \text{ or } .8 \text{ hour}$$

$$\frac{330 \text{ SF}}{180 \text{ SF/gallon}} = 1.83 \text{ gallons x } \$8.60 = \$15.70$$

Interior Railings

There's a wrought iron railing with a wood cap in the entry of the sample house. It's shown on the floor plan and in a detail drawing. On the floor plan, you can take off the length of 4 feet. It's in the parentheses next to *Rail* on the take-off sheet. Finish the pre-primed rail with one coat of zinc oxide paint. The finish for the wood cap is two coats of polyurethane or marine spar varnish. Find the time and material cost for the railing:

$$\frac{4 \text{ LF}}{20 \text{ LF/hour}} = .2 \text{ hour}$$

$$\frac{4 \text{ LF}}{80 \text{ LF/gallon}} = \begin{array}{l} .05 \text{ gallon x } \$13.70 = \\ \$.69 \text{ or } \$1.00 \end{array}$$

Since there's such a small amount of railing, you'll have to be flexible and use your judgment. Establish minimum values for manhours and material cost for small quantities of work like this. The minimum time for the painter must include setup and cleanup time in addition to the actual painting. If there's only one home, a reasonable estimate would be 0.5 hour and $2.00 for material. Since there are 15 homes with railings, I'd allow 0.3 hour and $1.00 for each home. That's the figure on the take-off sheet.

Here's something else to consider. Whenever there's an ornamental iron railing in the scope of work, contact the general contractor or the iron subcontractor to make sure that it will be preprimed the same color as the finish coat. Otherwise it might take more than one coat to cover. That's not too significant for these 15 homes, but in a 100-home project, putting a second coat on 400 linear feet of railing could be expensive.

Other Interior Railings

Decorative wood railing is common in interior entry areas, staircases and balconies in expensive homes. It usually includes smooth balusters and a railing cap with eased edges or smooth routed sides. If you're using the seven-step staining system, there will be a lot of overspray. This is slow work with low coverage rates.

Although there are no decorative wood railings in the sample plan, you'll find formulas for them in Figure 19-2. There are also *wood handrails* built against the wall on most staircases. *Rough sawn wood railing* is rare in interiors, but if you do find it, use the exterior formula for rough sawn wood railing.

Stringers

Stair stringers support the stair treads and risers. Staircases may be closed (Figure 19-10A) or open (Figure 19-10B). If an interior wood staircase is *closed*, stair treads and stair risers are usually carpeted. The notched stringers which support the treads and risers are usually covered with drywall on one or both sides, but the wood may be exposed inside next to the tread. You may have to paint these *kickboards* with enamel. Don't assume they can be painted along with the wall. Check the stairway details.

In an *open* interior wood staircase, the stringers are usually made of 2 x 10 or 2 x 12 rough sawn wood, with carpeted wood treads attached with metal angles. One of the stringers is probably attached to the wall. Even though it's only partially exposed, measure it as though you had to paint it on both sides. After all, cutting in will take some time. Add the length of this attached stringer and the suspended stringer for the total length.

Stair treads and *wood risers* aren't included in the stringer formulas. For painting treads and risers, measure the total surface area of the top and bottom of each tread. Then use the siding formula to calculate the manhours and material.

Steel stair stringers are usually fabricated and preprimed in the shop. You'll seldom find them on the interior.

There are no stairs on the sample plan.

Light Valances

Light valances are a decorative frame for bathroom light fixtures. You may also find one over the kitchen sink. In the interior elevations on the sample plan, you can see that the light valance is rough sawn wood that needs to be painted. Take off the face measurement directly from the bathroom interior elevation. Most light valances return from 18 inches to 24 inches to the wall. My calculations are based on a front length of 3 feet and a 24-inch return, for a total of 5 feet. The calculations are:

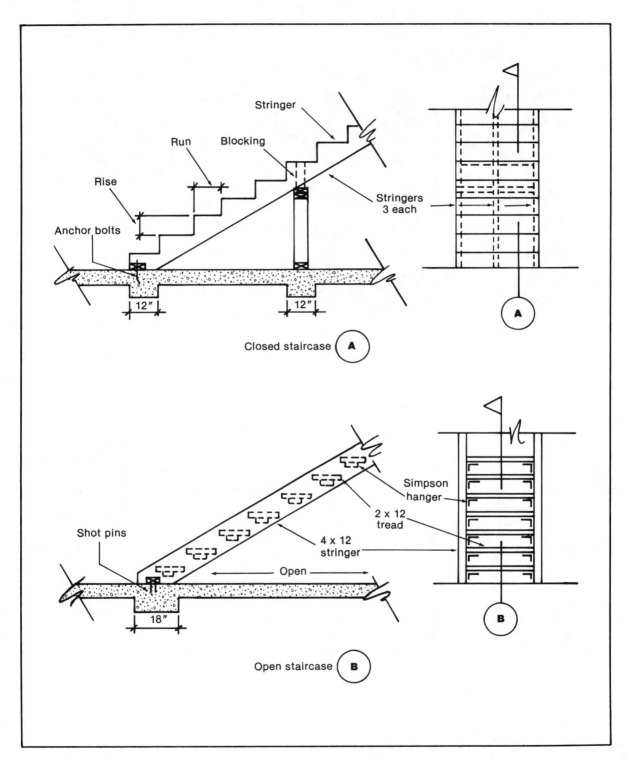

Closed and open staircases
Figure 19-10

Interior boneyard
Figure 19-11

$$\frac{5\ LF}{40\ LF/hour} = .125\ hour$$

$$\frac{3\ LF}{60\ LF/gallon} = .005\ gallon \times \$7.90 = \$.04$$

Since this is a small area, I'll use minimum figures of 0.3 hour and $1.00. They're on the take-off sheet on the *Valance* line.

Fireplaces

The sample plan doesn't include a fireplace, but there's a line for fireplaces on the take-off sheet. Let's look at some of the common fireplace features found in new tract homes.

Fireplace mantels are usually 5 to 6 feet long. Many are 4 x 12 rough sawn wood finished with a heavy-bodied stain. In more expensive homes, mantels may be decorative wood finished with a stain, seal and urethane process. Take them off along with the kitchen cabinets.

Fireplace siding is sometimes used in expensive houses. It usually runs from the mantel to the ceiling and is finished with a semi-transparent stain to accent the natural qualities of the wood. Estimate it using exterior siding formulas. Set minimum figures for this siding if you won't use the same stain anywhere else. If it's a decorative wood finished with stain, seal and lacquer, take it off along with the kitchen cabinets.

Fireplace masonry is occasionally painted with an accent color. Measure the surface area to be painted and use the fireplace masonry formula. Again, use minimum figures if that's the only place you'll use masonry paint.

Fireplace wood boxes are becoming more common in residential units with fireplaces. My formulas are based on applying stain to a box that's 2 feet wide, 3 feet high and 3 feet deep.

Baseboard

Baseboard is the molding, either wood or vinyl, that's installed at the base of the walls. Only wood baseboard needs to be painted or stained.

Painted base is installed before painting. It takes more time to finish than stained baseboard because it's brushed after the walls are painted.

Stained base is finished before it's installed. To save time, spread it out in a *boneyard* and spray large quantities at a time. Figure 19-11 shows a boneyard setup. You can save even more time by staining the base the same color and at the same time as the cabinets or along with the exterior wood siding. Of course, after the stained base is installed, the nail holes must be filled with putty dipped in matching stain.

Builders are using more stained base because it costs less to finish and it's easy to maintain. Scratches are easily touched up and marks and scuffs don't show.

The baseboard on the sample plan will be stained, so I circled *S* on the take-off sheet next to the *Base* line. The formulas are based on the square feet of construction floor area. Using a total of 720 square feet, here are the calculations:

$$\frac{720 \text{ SF}}{5000 \text{ SF/hour}} = .14 \text{ hour}$$

$$\frac{720 \text{ SF}}{4000 \text{ SF/gallon}} = .18 \text{ gallon} \times \$7.30 = \$1.32$$

There are two reasons why I chose a small house for our sample estimates. First, the pages of this book aren't big enough to show a large, complex house plan. Second, I wanted my sample estimate to be simple and easy to follow. But my formulas assume larger floor areas, more like the houses you'll actually be painting. That means my formulas for baseboard may not be accurate for a job this small.

Set minimums for manhours and material costs if the area is too small for accurate calculations. To establish your minimum values, consider the work that needs to be done. For staining base, that includes handling the material during layout, setting up the boneyard and spray rig, applying the stain and putting the nail holes. I'll use 0.4 manhours per unit and $1.50 for materials as a minimum.

Miscellaneous Interior Operations

My estimating formulas in Figure 19-2 show several miscellaneous interior operations that aren't included in the sample plan. Look through the formulas and make yourself familiar with all of these:

• Cabinet backs: Painting the wall behind stain grade cabinets.

• Closet poles: Accent stain applied before installation.

• Closet shelves: Enamel application is based on the linear footage.

• Closet perimeter molding: Counted along with the openings.

• HVAC registers: Painted with spray bombs to match the walls.

• Pot shelves or planters: Use the exterior stain formulas.

• Window seats, wood: Paint grade formula based on linear footage.

• Window sills, wood: Paint grade formula based on linear footage.

• Windows, wood: Pane dividers (muntins) make finishing difficult.

Interior Subtotals

The next step is to accumulate the interior subtotals for both manhours and material costs. Look at my subtotals on Figure 19-4. I calculate 13.6 manhours and $153.30 in material costs.

Touchup

Touchup is the last item in the interior section of the take-off sheet. Look for *T/U* right under the subtotal line.

There are two phases of touchup included in the estimating formulas. The first phase is the *production touchup*. It's started after the floor covering has been laid and the other trades have finished their work. Production touchup includes picking up holidays, skippers, cat's eyes, smudges, nicks, scratches and gouges. It's intended to leave the interior and exterior of each unit clean and ready to move into.

The second and final phase is the *customer service touchup*. The touchup painter corrects any flaws discovered during the walk-through by the general contractor and the homeowner.

Look at my touchup formulas in Figure 19-2. For the production touchup for both the interior and exterior, I use a percentage of the interior manhour and material totals: 15% of the manhours and 1% of the material cost. Here are the calculations for the sample plan.

13.6 hours x 15% (.15) = 2.04 or 2 hours

$153.30 x 1% (.01) = $1.53

You'll find these on the *T/U* line about midway down the interior column.

Tax

In most cases, you'll include sales tax on materials in your estimate. Sales tax is usually paid by the final consumer. Most states consider painting contractors to be the final consumer, so you'll usually pay the sales tax. In a few states, the general contractor is the final consumer. Find out what your state requires before submitting any bids.

For the sample estimate, we're assuming that the painting contractor will pay the sales tax. The rate is 6%. It's a simple calculation:

$153.30 + $1.53 = $154.84 x 6% = $9.29

Now we're ready to find the totals for the interior work. Just add the subtotals, touchup and tax. For the interior of the sample house, we'll allow 15.6 manhours and $164.12 for materials.

Now it's time to move over to the exterior column.

Estimating New Construction Exteriors

Once again we'll estimate the work in the same order as the work will be done. Of course, your crew may paint the exterior first. Even so, I would estimate the interior first so you get familiar with the floor plan right away.

The Importance of Scheduling

One of the keys to making a profit on new construction projects is to coordinate the scheduling so other trades don't interfere with your painters. That's important. You want to move onto the job, paint, and move off smoothly, with no interruptions.

Don't trust the judgment of the general contractor's superintendent. He'll often call you to the job before it's ready to paint. Always have your field superintendent inspect the job at least one day before sending out any painters. Don't start work until all surfaces to be painted are complete and cleaned by the previous trades.

Don't begin painting the interior until the drywall is finished and the acoustic ceilings are sprayed. The walls must be textured and the ceilings scribed at the perimeter. You'll have to finish the cabinets and pullmans before the counter tops are installed. The floor covering should go in after the interior painting is done, but before the two touchup operations.

On the exterior, the major thing to look for in stucco houses is that the wood trim is free of plaster spills and overspray. The new construction formulas are based on spray painting the trim after the brown coat is applied and cleaned up, but before the color coat goes on. Schedule the fascia painting before the roofing material is applied so overspray doesn't damage the finished roof. This is especially important with concrete or clay tile roofs. Otherwise, the painters will have to mask off the edge course of tile before painting the fascia. That's expensive. Make sure it doesn't happen.

To paint the fascia and overhang on a two-story building, the painters can usually use the scaffolding installed by the plaster crews or siding installers. Your bid will be more competitive if you don't have to include the cost of scaffolding.

Why am I taking the time to talk about scheduling in the middle of our sample estimate? There's one good reason. None of the formulas in this book allow for time lost due to scheduling mistakes. Lost time translates directly into lost profits.

Good scheduling can save you money. So can following good estimating practice on every bid. That includes looking at the roof plan along with the exterior elevations to make sure you don't overlook anything. Some buildings have design features that aren't obvious on the exterior elevations. For example, look at the roof plan in Figure 19-12. There's a recessed entry porch that's not noticeable in the front elevation. If you take it off as though the house has a flat front, you're missing the fascia returns on each side of the entry. This may seem like a small oversight, but if you're painting 40 houses, it can turn into a major cost item.

Some paint estimators work from dimensions written on the plan rather than scaling off areas directly from plan sheets. I prefer to measure directly from the plan sheets and then double-check my figures against written dimensions.

Fascia Board

Although the fascia and overhang are often stained

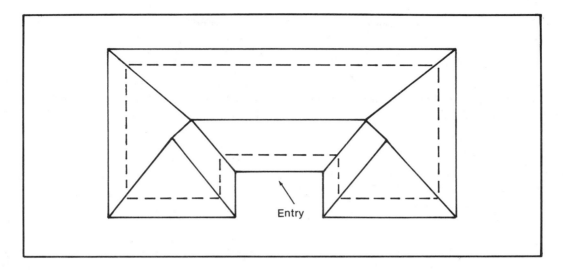

Roof indentation (setback) at entry
Figure 19-12

the same color at the same time, take them off separately in case they're different colors. There's a different formula for each operation. Take off the fascia first. Using the exterior elevations of the sample plan, start measuring the 2 x 8 fascia board at the front elevation. Take off the length of the fascia and mark the distance on the tape with your thumb. Move from elevation to elevation around the perimeter of the house until you've measured the entire length of the fascia. You should get 124 linear feet. Then check the roof plan to make sure you haven't missed any areas that are hidden on the elevations.

Double-check your measurement against the written dimensions. Then write the number in on the take-off sheet. The *Fascia* line is the first line in the exterior section. Look at Figure 19-4. I've written 124 in the parentheses, along with a notation that it's a 2 x 8.

Now look up the manhour and material formulas in Figure 19-2. Calculate the time and material cost for this fascia.

$$\frac{124\ LF}{200\ LF/hour} = .62\ or\ .7\ hour$$

$$\frac{124\ LF}{100\ LF/gallon} = 1.24\ gallons\ x\ \$7.90 = \$9.80$$

This is another situation where you might consider minimum values, since the area to be painted is small. How will it be done? The fascia can be sprayed with a pole gun, and the overhang is the same color. We can allow enough time for each operation by rounding up the 0.62 hour to 0.7 hour. I've written in 0.7 hour and $9.80 for material costs.

Overhang

Notice that the overhang is wider at the front and rear elevations (24 inches at the eaves) than at the side elevations (18 inches at the rake). So you'll measure all the 24-inch overhang separately from the 18-inch overhang. The front elevation measures 33 feet from one end of the overhang to the other. Here's how to figure the total square footage of 24-inch overhang in the front and rear:

$$33\ LF\ x\ 2.0' = 66\ SF\ x\ 2 = 132\ SF$$

Next, measure the overhang on the left elevation. But *don't* overlap at the corners of the building. We included the corner area in the front and rear calculations. Using the bottom of the fascia as a guide, begin the take-off at the outside wall and measure 25'0'' to the opposite outside wall. This measurement, taken directly from the plan sheet, allows for the angle of the roof pitch (the rake). It's the true length of the overhang on the left side. The right side is the same. So there are 50 lineal feet times a width of 18 inches, or 1.5 feet. That's a total area of 75 square feet on the sides.

To find the total overhang area, add 132 and 75. Then write in 207 square feet on the *O/H* line. You'll notice a factor of 1.5 on that line. Since the overhang area isn't just a flat surface, multiply the total by this factor to allow for rafter tails and outriggers that extend through the overhang. That brings the total area to 311 square feet. Now find the time and material cost:

$$\frac{311 \text{ SF}}{400 \text{ SF/hour}} = .78 \text{ or } .8 \text{ hour}$$

$$\frac{311 \text{ SF}}{85 \text{ SF/gallon}} = 3.7 \text{ gallons} \times \$7.90 = \$29.20$$

Siding

The only siding on our sample house is at the gable ends on each side elevation. My formulas for siding are based on surface area. So let's figure the area of the triangles of siding on each end of the house. Remember, the area of a triangle is 1/2 times base times height. The base of the triangular siding area is the 24-foot width of the house. Measure the height from the base up to the ridge of the roof and round it up to the nearest half foot. Rounding up allows for the area of the siding covered by the fascia board at the exterior elevation. The height is 4.5 feet.

Here are the calculations for the area of the siding:

$$1/2 \times 24' \text{ (base)} \times 4.5' \text{ (height)} = 54 \text{ SF}$$

$$54 \text{ SF} \times 2 \text{ (left and right side)} = 108 \text{ SF}$$

So put 108 square feet in the parentheses on the *Side* line and circle *ST* because it's a semi-transparent stain. Now you're ready for the calculations:

$$\frac{108 \text{ SF}}{150 \text{ SF/hour}} = .72 \text{ or } .7 \text{ hour}$$

$$\frac{108 \text{ SF}}{100 \text{ SF/gallon}} = \begin{array}{l} 1.1 \text{ gallons} \times \$10.50 = \\ \$11.55 \text{ or } \$11.60 \end{array}$$

The siding formulas in Appendix B offer a range of manhour rates and material coverage figures that are accurate for painting or staining most siding under average conditions. In unusual situations, use the high time difficulty factors I described in the interior wall section earlier in the chapter.

Garage Door Exteriors

Use the siding formulas to estimate the flat surface area of garage door exteriors. If there's no other siding, this may be the only place you use the siding formulas. Here are typical garage door sizes and surface areas:

Single door: 7'0'' x 8'0'' = 56 square feet

Double door: 7'0'' x 16'0'' = 112 square feet

Triple door: 7'0'' x 24'0'' = 168 square feet

There aren't any garage doors on our sample plan. But most new homes have garage doors. Include their area along with the siding take-off. And take off any plant-on trim separately. That's next.

Plant-Ons

Plant-ons are pieces of wood trim attached to the exterior of a building around windows, doors or as accent trim in other locations. They add appeal to what might otherwise be a plain and unattractive building.

Begin the take-off with the 2 x 6 plant-ons shown in the front exterior elevation. Using your tape, measure each length of plant-on trim, marking each length on the tape with your thumb until you've measured all the plant-ons on the front elevation. Then move clockwise around the other exterior elevations until you've measured the length of all plant-on trim. I'll show the measured lengths of each elevation here, but you can take it off in one continuous measurement.

Front elevation	24 + 18 + 24	=	66 LF
Left elevation	14 + 14 + 24	=	52 LF
Rear elevation			0
Right elevation	21 + 17 + 24	=	62 LF
Total			180 LF

Write the total next to P/O and note the size, 2 x 6. Then look up the formulas. Both the LF per hour and LF per gallon are 140.

$$\frac{180 \text{ LF}}{140 \text{ LF}} = \begin{array}{l} 1.23 \text{ hours and} \\ \text{gallons} \end{array}$$

$$1.23 \times \$7.90 = \$9.72 \text{ or } \$9.70$$

Exterior Doors

The next line on the take-off sheet is *Doors F L E X*. The capital letters are abbreviations for the four common types of doors: *F*rench, *L*ouvered, *E*ntry and e*X*terior. This is where you include the final, weather-resistant finish on all doors exposed to the elements. This time is in addition to the time already allowed in the opening count earlier in the take-off.

French doors are hard to finish because each mullion or muntin dividing the glass panes has to be painted by hand. The formulas allow time to apply polyurethane or varnish over the stain or a coat of exterior enamel on a paint grade door.

A *Dutch door* or a *half glass door* will take about the same amount of time. Use the French door formulas.

Louvered doors on the exterior of a building may be used to ventilate utility rooms. Use this formula for doors that have louvers on their full height. It doesn't apply to the water heater door on the sample plan, which has only two louvered vents in the door.

Entry doors are probably the single most important design feature on a residential unit. A flawless finish gives the buyers or renters a good first impression. The formulas allow enough time and material for a fine finish of exterior enamel or polyurethane.

Exterior doors are flush doors on the exterior of a building. You'll usually find them going into the garage. They're often called "man doors" because they let a person enter the garage without opening the garage door. Flush exterior doors are also common on utility rooms which enclose water heaters, gas or electric meters or telephone circuits.

On our sample plan, the exterior elevations show two doors to include on the exterior take-off sheet: an entry door that takes a polyurethane finish, and an exterior door with an enamel finish. Here are the manhour and material calculations, using the formulas in Figure 19-2:

$$
\begin{array}{lll}
\text{1 entry door} & = & 1.0 \text{ hour} \\
\text{1 exterior door} & = & \underline{.3 \text{ hour}} \\
& & 1.3 \text{ hours}
\end{array}
$$

$$
\text{1 entry door} \quad = \quad \frac{\$17.80/\text{gallon}}{2 \text{ doors/gallon}} \quad = \quad \$\ 8.90
$$

$$
\text{1 exterior door} \quad = \quad \frac{\$11.20/\text{gallon}}{5 \text{ doors/gallon}} \quad = \quad \$\ 2.60
$$

Total material cost = \$11.50

Enter these totals on the line next to *Doors* in the exterior section of the take-off sheet.

Vents and Flashings

Attic *vents* can usually be sprayed with the same color and type of stain as the fascia, overhang or siding. Vents don't require much additional time or material to finish.

Metal *flashing* prevents water or moisture from leaking in where two exterior surfaces meet. Look for flashing at the intersection of the chimney and the roof, at the intersection of a stair stringer and a wall, and at the edge of a deck with a stucco soffit below.

Every building has flashing somewhere. Estimate the time and material required for finishing the vents and flashing with a *per-unit allowance*. If there's more flashing than usual, at a parapet wall cap for instance, use the formula for linear footage for the extra flashing in addition to the normal per-unit formula.

The formulas for vents and flashing allow more time for a two-story building because painting will be from a ladder. On the other hand, each unit in a two-story multi-family building takes less time because the painters can finish the flashing for many units with only one ladder trip. These formulas are based on square feet of roof area. You can also use the roof area formula for light commercial buildings.

Since the sample plan is a one-story building, use the manhours and material cost per vent listed for vents and flashing. That's 0.5 manhours and \$6.00 for materials on the *V & F* line on the take-off sheet.

Roof Jacks

A roof jack is a metal, tube-shaped exhaust vent that sticks up about 8 to 12 inches above the plane of the roof. Most single-family detached homes have at least three roof jacks to paint. Roof jacks can be painted at the same time as the flashing. Most of the labor cost here is for ladder time. The roof jack formulas also allow more time for two-story homes than for single-story homes.

Roof jack time and material costs for multi-family or large commercial buildings are based on square footage of roof area. Since the sample plan is a one-story building, take the manhours and material cost directly from the per-unit roof jack formulas. Write 0.5 manhours and $4.00 on the *RJ* line of the take-off sheet.

Back of Garage Doors

Most government agencies, including the FHA and the VA, require the painters to finish all exposed wood. The back of all garage doors must have at least one coat of sealer or stain to prevent warping and deterioration.

You can include a coat of sealer along with the stain grade cabinets, or a coat of exterior stain with the fascia, overhang or siding. Your take-off for the back of the garage door is included with roof jacks on the *RJ & BGD* line. Since the sample plan doesn't have garage doors, I've crossed out the *BGD*.

Pot Shelves

On the sample plan, there are pot shelves under the front windows. Since they're not as common as the other items on the take-off sheet, they're easy to miss. Take note of them during the preliminary review of the plans or while you're taking off the other exterior operations.

Pot shelves — including the underside — are usually stained along with the other exterior wood trim. On the sample plan, the pot shelf is 27 feet long. That's written on the first blank line, which I've labeled *P/S*. Here are the calculations:

$$\frac{27\ LF}{75\ LF/hour} = .36\ or\ .4\ hours$$

$$\frac{27\ LF}{40\ LF/gallon} = .68\ gallon \times \$7.90 = \$5.37\ or\ \$5.40$$

Pass-Through Shelves

Look for a pass-through shelf under the kitchen windows. It's used for passing food and dishes from the kitchen to the patio area. Unlike the pot shelf, the pass-through shelf is supported by metal braces. They're usually preprimed, so your painters will have to apply one coat of zinc oxide paint to cover. The shelf surface may be wood or ceramic tile.

Pass-through shelves are usually 3 or 4 feet long. Estimate the time and material on a per-shelf basis. On the sample plan, there's one shelf. I've written

1 next to *P/T* on the next blank line. Take the labor and materials directly from the formulas: 0.2 manhours and $1.00 for material.

Stucco Seal

Stucco sealer is a water-repellent coating that's applied over the final color coat. It's usually applied in a 4-foot strip up from the stucco weep screed, near the finished grade, and in a 2-foot wide strip around doors and windows.

Stucco seal protects the building from water stains and saturation caused by sprinkler overspray and rain. To measure for sealer, accumulate the total length of the perimeter of the building, using the dimensions on the sample plan. Multiply the total length by 4 feet, with no deductions for openings or for the pot shelves:

$$30 + 30 + 24 + 24 = 108\ LF \times 4 = 432\ SF$$

Now calculate the 2-foot wide area around each exterior opening. Use the outside dimensions of the seal coat area to calculate the total area. Then deduct the area of the window itself. For example, look at Figure 19-13. The outside dimensions of the seal area are 10 feet by 8 feet. That's an area of 80 square feet. The area of the 4 x 6 window is 24 square feet. When you deduct that from 80 square feet, there's a total of 56 square feet to seal. But some of that is already included in your perimeter calculation. Look again at Figure 19-13. There's a broken line that represents the perimeter line 4 feet up from the finish grade. It overlaps about half of the area that needs to be sealed around the window. So multiply that 56 square feet by 0.5. Add only 28 square feet to the perimeter measurement for that window.

To calculate the area remaining after you deduct the overlap on the other openings, look at the exterior elevations of the sample plan. Estimate the percentage of the area around the openings that *won't* be overlapped by the perimeter application. And remember there's an additional overlap when openings are within 4 feet of each other. Here's how I accumulated the 2-feet wide areas around the openings in the sample plan:

Front Elevation: Area around 6040 window = 56 SF x .5 = 28 SF

Area around 5050 window = 56 SF x .5 = 28 SF

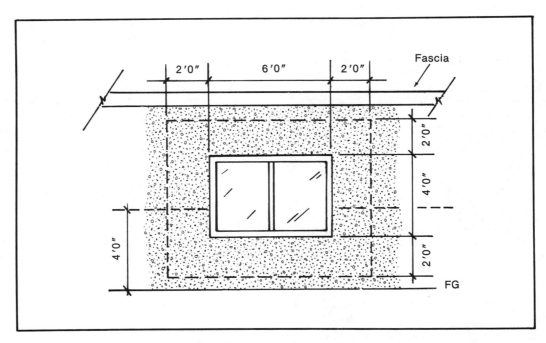

Stucco seal area around window
Figure 19-13

Area around 3068 door =
42 SF x .5 = 21 SF

Left Elevation: Area around 3030 window =
40 SF x .75 = 30 SF

Area around 3030 window =
40 SF x .75 = 30 SF

Rear Elevation: Area around 3016 window =
34 SF

Area around 6050 window =
60 SF x .5 = 30 SF

Area around 2068 door =
40 SF x .3 = 12 SF

Right Elevation   Area around 4036 window =
46 SF x .5 = 23 SF

Area around 6068 SGD =
48 SF x .5 = 24 SF

Total   260 SF

Add the 260 square feet from the openings to the 432 square feet perimeter measurement. That's a total of 692 square feet of area for stucco seal. Look at the line labeled *S/S* on the take-off sheet. Here are the calculations for 692 square feet of surface area:

$$\frac{692 \text{ SF}}{800 \text{ SF/hour}} = .87 \text{ or } .9 \text{ hour}$$

$$\frac{692 \text{ SF}}{100 \text{ SF/gallon}} = \begin{array}{l} 6.92 \text{ gallons x } \$9.40 = \\ \$65.05 \text{ or } \$65.10 \end{array}$$

Be sure to schedule the stucco seal operation before the final cleanup of the exterior windows. If the wax that protects the windows has been cleaned off, your painters will have to mask and protect the windows. My formulas don't include time for this.

Miscellaneous Exterior Operations
Even though they're not used for our sample take-off, look over the formulas for these operations back in Figure 19-2.

Carport canopy

Wood: Use the overhang formula with 1.5 factor.
Metal: Typically prefinished corrugated material.

Corbels

Wood members extending beyond exterior wall surfaces. Look at Figure 19-14.

Rafter tails are estimated as corbels
Figure 19-14

Decks

Overhang: Use the overhang formula with 1.5 factor for joists.
Top surface: Use the siding formula.

Fencing

Solid: Use the siding formula.
Good neighbor: Planks alternating from side to side (Figure 19-15).

Gutters and downspouts

Preprimed or acid etched before finish.

Mailbox structures

Take off individual wood members (overhang, trim, etc.) and use the respective formulas.

Masonry or concrete walls

Consider the absorption factor.

Railing

Wood: Decks, balconies and stairs.
Wrought iron: Preprimed by others, one coat paint.

Stair stringers

Wood: Typically rough sawn 2 x 10 or 2 x 12.
Steel: Preprimed by others, one coat paint.

Steps

Wood: Use siding formula based on surface area to be painted.

Stucco paint

No deductions for areas less than 100 square feet.

Trellis

Use LF of each member or SF if 2 x 2 at 3 inches on center.

Window protection

Apply paraffin wax when exterior is siding.

Windows, wood

Muntins make finishing difficult.

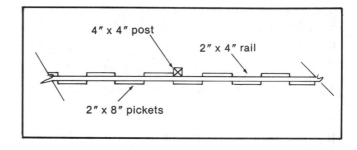

Good neighbor fence (plan view)
Figure 19-15

Exterior Totals

First let's accumulate the subtotals for exterior manhours and material costs on the take-off sheet. Use the section called Elevation A. Look again at Figure 19-4. Our job should take 7.2 manhours for each unit, plus $153.30 in material costs. But that's before sales tax. When we add on the 6% sales tax, the total material cost rises to $163.00.

You'll notice that I have totals for exteriors B and C also. We didn't do a take-off, since we only have one sample plan to work with. But we'll use the totals for all three exteriors in the recap. It's rare for a tract of single family homes to have more than three exterior elevations for each floor plan. If there are more than three, use an additional take-off sheet and change the headings to elevations D, E and F.

The buildings in an apartment and condominium complex are usually similar on the outside, but each building type may have a different number of units. Since they're different sizes, you have to estimate each building type separately. Use the exterior side of my take-off sheet, but change the headings from *elevations* A, B and C to *buildings* A, B and C.

Recap

Now add the interior totals to the exterior totals for each elevation. I'll round the material costs to the nearest dollar. Elevation A comes to 22.8 manhours and $327. Assume elevation B is 23.6 manhours and $329, while C is the most expensive at 24.1 manhours and $359. But not all take-offs will be complete at this point. Notice those two little lines called *Option* under the recap lines.

Options

Builders of single family homes may offer *building design options* to home buyers. For example, they might offer to convert an empty bonus room into a den or bedroom by adding a closet. Or they can add a nook off the kitchen or a third garage. These options usually don't require much painting. You can calculate the time and material estimate in the space under *Notes-Options-Alternates-Exclusions.* Then put the totals on the option lines, along with the option number for identification.

Alternates

The owner or general contractor may request an alternate price to see if the budget will allow an upgrade or require a downgrade in the quality of the work. They might want to know how it would affect your bid to:

- Use a higher or lower quality of paint

- Increase or decrease the number of colors used

- Paint the garage walls

- Paint the heat registers

- Do a split coat or tip-off on all openings

- Apply one or two coats on all exterior wood trim

You can also submit alternate prices for the entire project based on the starting date. If it might not start until after scheduled increases for labor costs take effect, include an alternate price for each building.

Exclusions

During the take-off, use this area to list any operations which you're excluding. That might include stucco, masonry, fencing, prefinished cabinets or garage walls. There's a list of standard exclusions in the proposal outline in Chapter 7, Figure 7-4.

Notes

During the preliminary review of the plans, you made notes about items that require special attention. If you discover other special items during the take-off, note them in this part of the take-off sheet. That'll remind you to mention them in the proposal.

That's the last thing that goes on the take-off sheet. The final calculations go on the extension sheet.

The Extension Sheet

The next step is to extend the manhours and material costs into a standard base bid. Look at the extension sheet in Figure 19-16. Here are the steps:

1) Multiply manhour totals by hourly rate

2) Add supervision for the working foreman

3) Compute employer's burden

4) Add material cost totals

5) Compute percentage of overhead

6) Compute percentage of profit

7) Arrive at standard base bid total

Project *Vista Park* **Builder** *John Doe* **Date** *6-7-89*
Prepared by *JJ* **Checked by** *DDG*

PLAN #1

	A	B	C	
Rate $ _15.00_ /hour				
Hours _22.8_ × Rate =	$ _342_	23.6 $ _354_	24.1 $ _362_	$ ___
Supervision _1_ Hrs	_16_	_16_	_16_	
Subtotal	_358_	_370_	_378_	
Burden _35_ %	_125_	_130_	_132_	
Material	_327_	_339_	_359_	
Subtotal	_810_	_839_	_869_	
Overhead _15_ %	_122_	_126_	_130_	
Direct cost	_932_	_965_	_999_	
Profit _5_ %	_47_	_48_	_50_	
Base bid total	_979_	_1013_	_1049_	
Price/SF _720 SF_	_1.36_	_1.41_	_1.46_	
Adjustment _2_ % + (−)	_20_	_20_	_21_	
Final bid total	_959_	_993_	_1028_	
Final price/SF	_1.33_	_1.38_	_1.43_	

Rate $ ___ /hour				
Hours ___ × Rate =	$___	$___	$___	$___
Supervision ___ Hrs				
Subtotal				
Burden ___ %				
Material				
Subtotal				
Overhead ___ %				
Direct cost				
Profit ___ %				
Base bid total				
Price/SF				
Adjustment ___ % + −				
Final bid total				
Final price/SF				

Rate $ ___ /hour				
Hours ___ × Rate =	$___	$___	$___	$___
Supervision ___ Hrs				
Subtotal				
Burden ___ %				
Material				
Subtotal				
Overhead ___ %				
Direct cost				
Profit ___ %				
Base bid total				
Price/SF				
Adjustment ___ % + −				
Final bid total				
Final price/SF				

New construction extension sheet
Figure 19-16

8) Analyze bidding variables

9) Make adjustments to the bid

10) Arrive at final bid total

That's a complete list of the steps I recommend. But do you notice what's *missing* from that list? There's no mention of equipment, escalation, miscellaneous costs, subcontractors, commissions or contingency. My new construction estimating system includes equipment costs in the overhead. You cover escalation when you mark up the material to include tools and price increases. The rest of them just don't apply to new construction painting.

Let's do the extensions and finish the estimate. First, fill in the headings: project, builder, date, prepared by and checked by. Then identify the plan and elevations. I've written in Plan 1 and elevations A, B and C.

Rate
The first item on the extension sheet is the hourly pay rate. Enter your rate for a brush or roller journeyman. Depending on the project and your company's labor practices, base this rate on the union rate, prevailing rate (Davis-Bacon) or the open shop rate. For this sample estimate, we'll use $15.00 per hour.

Hours
Write in the 22.8 manhours for elevation A, and multiply by the labor rate. It comes to $342. Elevations B and C are $354 and $362.

Supervision
The supervision line accounts for the nonproductive time spent by the working foreman to organize the crews, troubleshoot, and inspect the quality of workmanship with the field superintendent. It does *not* include the field superintendent's time on the job. That's included in overhead.

Every project will include some supervision time. In Chapter 13, I suggested guidelines for estimating supervisory time. For this relatively simple job, let's assume supervision will take one hour per house. The foreman usually makes $1 an hour more than the journeyman, so we'll add $16 to each unit for super-

vision. The total labor cost, including supervision, appears on the first *Subtotal* line.

Burden
The *employer's burden* includes taxes, insurance and benefits paid by the employer on wages earned by the painter and office staff. We covered them in Chapter 13. Here are the values we'll use for the painters in this estimate:

Fixed burden

FICA (Social Security)	7.15%
Unemployment insurance	5.60%
Workers' Compensation	10.60%
Variable burden	11.65%
Total burden percentage	35.00%

So we'll write in 35% and multiply the labor cost for each elevation by 0.35. We'll add from $125 to $132 to each elevation for the employer's burden.

Material
You can take the material costs directly from the take-off sheet and write them on this line. For our estimate, material costs range from $327 to $359. Just add the material cost to the labor subtotal and employer's burden to arrive at the subtotal. For elevation A, the subtotal is $810.

Overhead
The next line is for *indirect overhead*. That includes the general and administrative costs — mostly office expenses. We'll use 15%. That's a typical overhead percentage. Increase the labor and material subtotal by 15% to find the total direct cost for each elevation. For elevation A, multiply 0.15 by $810. It comes to $121.50. We'll round it up to $122.

Direct Cost
The actual cost of the job is listed on the *Direct cost* line. It ranges from $932 for elevation A to $999 for elevation C.

Profit

We discussed profit in Chapter 16. For this project, we have 15 similar homes. That's enough to consider it a high production project. We'll add a 5% profit to the direct costs. Look at the *profit* line on Figure 19-16.

Base Bid Total and Price/SF

The standard base bid is $979 for elevation A, $1,013 for elevation B and $1,049 for elevation C. That's the price we would be comfortable with if all the bidding variables were normal. To double-check, we'll divide the base bid by the square footage to find the price per square foot. Ours vary from $1.36 to $1.46. Let's assume our historical costs range from $.60 to $1.00 per square foot for economy tract homes, and from $.90 to $1.40 for quality homes. Our sample plan is a small home, but it has many more amenities than most houses this small. This unique design makes it an exception to the rule. Our square foot price seems acceptable in these circumstances.

The Adjustment

Now we've reached the end of the estimating process and the beginning of the bidding process. We have our standard base bid. Do we want to adjust it up or down? To help us make that decision, we'll review the bidding variables. We want to make the best possible offer to do the painting, and still make a fair profit.

We've already considered the historical costs, and decided that our bid is acceptable even though it's higher than some of our average costs. The historical costs suggest that we can expect a 4% to 7% profit.

But what about the bidding variables? We considered the variables when we made the decision to bid. But now let's reconsider them to see if they affect the need to adjust the bid. There's a complete list of bidding variables in Chapter 7.

In our sample project, the type, size and location fall within our niche. The general contractor has a good reputation for making payments on time, and the competition isn't too strong. All areas to be painted are accessible. It looks like the scheduling is good for the project. In short, all the bidding variables are favorable. That leaves only two things to consider — your company's desire for the work, and your gut feeling about the job. We'll assume that our company needs this job to help it reach growth projections. That justifies a 2% reduction in the bid to help make sure we get the job.

I've written the 2% on the *Adjustment* line, and have circled the minus sign to show that we'll adjust it downward rather than upward. That means we'll deduct $20 or $21 for each elevation.

Final Bid Total and Price/SF

After deducting the 2%, fill in the final bid totals. Then divide each by 720 square feet to find the final price per square foot. Then compare that final square foot price with historical costs again.

Building Recap

The next step is the building recap. You use it to summarize the building mix and accumulate the final bid amounts for all the work included in your proposal. If there are site improvements or support buildings (recreation rooms, bathrooms, etc.) in the project, include them here.

Do your recap on a separate sheet of paper and leave plenty of space between the figures to avoid confusion or mistakes. Don't take short cuts here. Leaving out a building at this stage could be a financial disaster.

Our recap is simple. There's just one floor plan with three elevations in this project. List the three plans. Round the total bid for each plan to the nearest $5, then multiply by the number of units of that plan. There are five 1As, four 1Bs and six 1Cs:

Plan 1A: $ 959 rounded to $ 960 x 5 = $4,800

Plan 1B: $ 993 rounded to $ 995 x 4 = $3,980

Plan 1C: $1,028 rounded to $1,030 x 6 = $6,180

Don't accumulate the total project cost. Leave that to the owner or general contractor.

The Bid Proposal

With the bid proposal, you *make the offer* to do the painting according to the plans and specifications at the bid price.

The first step in preparing the proposal is to review your pre-bid checklist and the specifications or general notes on the plans. Confirm that you've included all painting requirements in your estimate. Check the specifications or general notes for general qualifications, the pre-bid checklist for the contractor's specific requirements, and the *Notes-Alternates-Options-Exclusions* section of the take-off sheet for items that must be included in your proposal. After you've reviewed them all, you can start writing your proposal.

The Proposal Rough Draft

Writing the proposal begins with the *rough draft*. Use the abbreviations from Chapter 7 to save time here. Start by filling in the heading information on a photocopy of your proposal letterhead. Then, step by step, pencil in each letter on the proposal outline that defines the scope of work you're including in your estimate.

Figure 19-17 shows my proposal rough draft. Here's what the abbreviatons mean:

I C: "We propose to furnish labor, material and equipment to paint the referenced project as follows:" This is your *Statement of Intent*.

II A: Interior: "Enamel areas, doors & casings; prime and one coat enamel." The term *prime* includes both the wall sealer and undercoat for the trim items. This satisfies the specification requirements.

B: "Flat wall areas, one coat flat wall." This entry will satisfy the term "other walls" used in the specifications.

C: "Kitchen cabinets; stain, seal and two coats lacquer." The two coats of lacquer will satisfy the specifications.

F: "Pullmans & linens; prime and one coat enamel." Since pullmans and linens might be stain grade in some projects, these items are on a different line than doors and casings.

G: "Rough sawn wood, one coat heavy bodied stain." This item is for the exposed ceiling beams in the living room.

H: "Tongue and groove ceiling; one coat semi-transparent stain." The open ceiling area with stain grade wood will usually receive a light stain in contrast to the dark stained beams.

J: "Metal; preprimed by others, one coat paint." This item includes the wrought iron handrail at the entry. It's important to include the term "preprimed by others" because we didn't allow any time for priming this railing.

K: "Base to stain." This will satisfy the specifications.

L: "Handrail caps; two coats of polyurethane." This finish will be durable enough to withstand all the traffic at the entry door.

N: "Figured for one basic off-white color throughout." This line item should appear in all of your new construction proposals unless otherwise specified. The formulas don't allow time for changing colors.

III A: Exterior: "Wood; one coat heavy bodied stain." Even though only one coat is specified, a second light coat is often required to touch up after the other trades. My formulas allow time for this light second coat.

B: "Metal; preprimed by others, one coat paint." This item is for the vents, flashings and roof jacks.

C-1: "Stucco; one coat clear hydro sealer to 4'0" and 2'0" around openings." This line will satisfy the specifications.

IV a, b, c, g, h: Exclusions: "Stucco paint, masonry, fencing, light posts and mailbox structures are not included."

V a: Notes: "Bid based on plans dated 2-7-89. Plan set #7." Be sure to include the plan date and plan set number. You may have to identify the series or exact set of plans used in your estimate to prove the validity of your inclusions and exclusions. Any addenda, cost-saving recommendations, clarifications, corrections or comments will also appear in this section of your proposal.

VI: Prices: Here you write in the totals from your recap sheet, which you've double-checked for accuracy. Remember, this is the most important section in the proposal. Have your typist double- and triple-check it for accuracy. And proof it yourself before submitting the proposal.

If there are any options or alternates, include the prices here. When estimating multi-family or commercial projects with common areas, include all the site improvements in your estimate. The formulas for site improvements are included in the general manhour and material formulas in Appendix B.

777 Main Street,
Yourtown, U.S.A. 77777
Contractors License Number 77777

Quality
Painting & Decorating
555-1212

Proposal for _John Doe Construction_
Address _797 Fifth Avenue_
City and State _Yourtown, USA 77777_
Project _Vista Park_

Phone _(619) 222-1515_

Date _6-7-89_
Location _Main at Broadway_

Proposal

I C   WE PROPOSE

II   A, B, C, F, G, H, J, K, L-1, N

III   A, B, C-1

IV   a, b, c, g, h

V a   2-7-89 #7

VI   PLAN 1A - 5 EACH @ $960 — = $4800 —
           1B - 4 EACH @   995 — = 3980 —
           1C - 6 EACH @   1030 — = 6180 —

VII   9-7-89

Accepted by _____
Date _____

Quality Painting & Decorating
By _____

Contractors are required by law to be licensed and regulated by the Contractors' State License Board. Any question concerning a contractor may be referred to the registrar of the board whose address is: P.O. Box 26000, Sacramento, California 95826.

Quality Painting & Decorating shall be entitled to recover its attorney's fees and costs in collecting any amount due it under this proposal.

Rough draft of proposal
Figure 19-17

Remember, you don't want to present a lump sum total for your bid. On your proposal, always give the price for each plan or building type and multiply times its quantity. If your plans aren't itemized, you could be stuck with painting a building that was added after your proposal was written.

VII: Expiration: "Prices expire 9-7-89" The expiration date should be 30 to 90 days from the date of the proposal.

After the typed proposal is proofed and triple-checked for accuracy, it's ready to sign. Figure 19-18 shows the final proposal for this sample estimate.

777 Main Street,
Yourtown, U.S.A. 77777
Contractors License Number 77777

Quality
Painting & Decorating
555-1212

Proposal for ___ John Doe Construction

Address ___ 797 Fifth Avenue

City and State ___ Yourtown, USA 77777

Project ___ Vista Park

Phone ___ (619) 222-1515

Date ___ 6-7-89

Location ___ Main at Broadway, Yourtown, USA

Proposal

We propose to furnish labor, material and equipment to paint the referenced project as follows:

Interior: Enamel areas, doors & casings; prime and one coat enamel. Flat wall areas, one coat flat wall. Kitchen cabinets; stain, seal and two coats lacquer. Pullmans & linens; prime and one coat enamel. Rough sawn wood, one coat heavy bodied stain. Tongue and groove ceiling; one coat semi-transparent stain. Metal; preprimed by others, one coat paint. Base to stain. Handrail caps; two coats of polyurethane. Figured for one basic off-white color throughout.

Exterior: Wood; one coat heavy bodied stain. Metal; pre-primed by others, one coat paint. Stucco; one coat clear hydro sealer to 4'0" and 2'0" around openings.

Exclusions: Stucco paint, masonry, fencing, light posts and mailbox structures are not included.

Notes: Bid based on plans dated 7-7-89. Plan set #7.

Prices: Plan 1A - 5 each @ $ 960.00 = $4,800.00
Plan 1B - 4 each @ $ 995.00 = $3,980.00
Plan 1C - 6 each @ $1,030.00 = $6,180.00

Expiration: Prices expire 9-7-89.

Accepted by _____

Date _____

Quality Painting & Decorating

By _Jeff Jones_

Final proposal
Figure 19-18

Chapter 20

ESTIMATING COMMERCIAL AND INDUSTRIAL PROJECTS

The system for estimating heavy commercial, industrial and institutional jobs isn't too different from the residential and light commercial jobs we estimated in Chapters 18 and 19. There are many similarities, and many important differences. Let's look at the similarities.

First, the estimating procedure should be the same. Whether you're estimating a small home or a large manufacturing plant, follow your estimating routine faithfully. Estimate in the same order you'll do the work. Make a detailed labor and material take-off for each area that has to be painted. You can use my new construction take-off sheet from Chapter 19. Pay attention to detail. Work carefully in a logical order. Use manhour and material formulas based on your experience. The result should be consistently accurate and profitable estimates.

Now, let's look at the differences:

1) Plans drawn by architects tend to be more accurate and complete.

2) Specifications are more complete and detailed. They're usually bound in a project manual.

3) The bid documents include specific instructions to bidders which define bidding procedures.

4) Higher quality workmanship and materials are usually required. Most painters in this field are skilled professionals.

5) Many projects will use union labor.

6) Material coverage requirements are more specific. You may have to meet mil thickness standards.

7) There are many unique structures, measurement methods and painting techniques.

8) The bid submittal is a semi-formal or formal procedure with little flexibility.

9) The competition is more intense.

10) The competition is likely to be more ethical and experienced.

The Manhour/Material Tables

Your estimating formulas must allow for the higher quality of workmanship and material required. The work will be slower, and you'll use more materials.

Manhours

Even on heavy commercial or industrial jobs, you'll do some residential grade painting. For instance, painting a wall is painting a wall, whether it's in a house or a factory. For that type of work, use the general estimating formulas in Appendix B. Just use the slow or medium manhour production rates. It takes more time to meet higher quality standards.

For painting that's unique to commercial or industrial work, use Figure 20-1 or your own formulas tailored for that work. Figure 20-1 includes operations you just don't find in residential work — like duct work, fire escapes and mechanical equipment. Select the appropriate manhour rate, from slow to fast, depending on your evaluation of the project.

Material Coverage

You'll probably apply more paint per square foot. When you use the general tables on an industrial job, take the figure in the *heavy material coverage* column. For specialized painting, use the material coverage rates in Figure 20-1. Select the coverage rate, either light or heavy, that fits the specifications of the particular job. If the specifications require a minimum mil thickness, calculate the material quantities using the formula in Chapter 14.

The preparation formulas in Chapter 17 will also apply on commercial and industrial jobs.

Painting Operations

Let's look at some structures, surface area calculations, measurement methods and painting techniques unique to heavy commercial jobs.

Ceilings and Walls

In an industrial setting, there are pipes, conduit and other obstructions that usually slow down the wall and ceiling operations. Apply a difficulty factor to allow for the extra time needed to paint around obstructions. Use your judgment for the additional time it might take to mask off or shield obstructions and to paint walls or ceilings where you have limited access in a tight situation.

Conduit, Pipe and Pipe Railing

Take off conduit and pipe by the linear foot and convert to square feet of surface area. Then adjust the square footage to fit the conditions of the job. Consider these conditions before adjusting the area measurement:

- Frequency of weld joints, valves, flanges, fittings and mounting hangers. Typically add 10% to the total area of conduit or pipe.

- Finish color of conduit or pipe compared to adjacent surface.

- Color coding requirements.

My estimating tables in Figure 20-1 are based on the square feet of surface area. To convert linear measurement to square feet, use the conversion factor in Figure 20-2. To calculate the area in square feet for pipes with an outside diameter greater than 30 inches, convert all dimensions to their decimal equivalents in feet and use this formula:

Outside diameter x pi x length = surface area

$$O/D \times \pi \times L = \text{per LF}$$

Let's do a couple of conversions for practice.

Pipe O/D =	Decimal equivalent	x	π	=	Circumference	x L =	SF/LF
3"	.25'	x	3.1416	=	.79	x 1 =	.79 (use 1.0)
4"	.33'	x	3.1416	=	1.05	x 1 =	1.05 (use 2.0)
7"	.58'	x	3.1416	=	1.83	x 1 =	1.83 (use 2.0)
8"	.67'	x	3.1416	=	2.09	x 1 =	2.09 (use 2.5)

There's an easier way to get the same result. Just multiply the outside diameter in inches by 0.2618. Here's how it works:

O/D (in inches)   x .2618

4"   x .2618   = 1.05 SF per LF

Industrial and Commercial Estimating Tables

Use this table to estimate the time and material needed for painting industrial, commercial and institutional structures. Production rates are in manhours per square foot (SF) or per linear foot (LF) of area coated. Material coverage is in square feet or linear feet covered per gallon of coating.

Manhour estimates in this table assume work by journeyman painters. But no time is included for sandblasting, setup, removal, replacement, protection, touchup or cleanup (SURRPTUCU) except as noted. Medium (or average) production rates are most common when semiskilled painters are working on medium-size jobs and doing average quality work without special difficulties. Work will go faster or slower under other conditions. Unless noted otherwise, rates listed in this chapter assume medium production rates. Production rates for *flat paint* will usually range from medium to fast and rates for *enamel paint* will usually range from slow to medium. Where fast, medium and slow production rates are given, the conditions are assumed to be as listed in the table that follows.

Slow	Medium	Fast
Good quality	Average quality	Minimum quality
High difficulty	Average difficulty	Low difficulty
Poor conditions	Average conditions	Good conditions
Small job	Medium size job	Large projects
Low production	Average production	High production
(single units, repaints)	(2 to 4 units)	(5 or more units)
Unskilled painters	Semiskilled painters	Skilled crews

Repainting will usually require about 35% more labor than similar new construction work because extra time is needed to protect adjacent surfaces which aren't painted.

Material coverage rates are listed in square feet (SF) per gallon and assume that minimum time is needed for mixing and preparation. Rates are listed in this chapter by coverage classifications, either heavy or light. Industrial, commercial and institutional jobs usually require heavy coverage. Here's a guide to use when deciding whether material usage on the job you're estimating will be heavy or light.

Heavy	Light
Standard paint	Production paint
New construction	Repaint
(high absorption)	(low absorption)
Heavy application	Light application
Heavy coverage	Light coverage
Heavy usage	Light usage
No thinning	Production thinning
Unskilled painters	Skilled painters

High time difficulty factors should be used for heights above 30 feet. It takes longer to apply paint high above the ground level. Painters have to set up ladders and then ascend and descend ladders, carrying tools and materials with them. The manhour figures in this chapter assume work will be done no more than 30 feet above ground level. When coatings will be applied more than 30 feet but less than 90 feet above ground level, add 20% to the manhours listed. When coatings are applied more than 90 feet above ground level, add 30% to the manhours listed, except as otherwise noted.

Shop painting estimates are *not included* here because this work is usually done by metal fabricators.

Field welds Steel that has to be welded in the field is usually delivered to the jobsite unprimed. A minimum of two coats of red oxide rust inhibitive paint will usually be applied in the field. If steel is to remain exposed after construction is complete, aluminum paint will usually be required.

Industrial and commercial estimating tables
Figure 20-1

Conduit, electric

	SF per hour Slow-Med-Fast	Acid wash coat	Metal primer	Industrial enamel oil base	Epoxy coating
		------------------------------ SF per gallon ------------------------------			
		Heavy-Light	Heavy-Light	Heavy-Light	Heavy-Light
Brush					
1st coat	60- 80-100	600-700	350-400	400-450	375-425
Added coats	100-125-150	--	400-450	450-500	425-475
Roll					
1st coat	175-200-225	600-700	325-375	375-425	350-400
Added coats	225-250-275	--	375-425	425-475	400-450
Spray					
1st coat	350-400-450	500-600	300-325	350-375	325-350
Added coats	450-500-550	--	350-375	375-400	360-385
Mitt or glove					
1st coat	175-200-225	600-700	375-400	425-450	400-425
Added coats	225-250-275	--	425-450	475-500	450-475

Use Figure 20-2 to convert linear feet of pipe of any size to square feet of surface.

Decking and siding, metal

Spray application Per SF coated	SF per hour Slow-Med-Fast	Acid wash coat	Metal primer	Industrial enamel oil base	Epoxy coating
		------------------------------------- SF per gallon -------------------------------------			
		Heavy-Light	Heavy-Light	Heavy-Light	Heavy-Light
Corrugated					
1st coat	700-750-800	400-500	225-275	275-325	250-300
Added coats	850-900-950	--	325-375	375-425	350-400
Flat pan					
1st coat	800- 850- 900	500-600	250-300	325-375	300-350
Added coats	1000-1050-1100	--	325-375	375-425	350-400

The figures in the table above are based on width times length (overall) dimensions. But all decking and siding has corrugations, peaks and valleys that increase the surface that has to be painted. For example, corrugated siding with 2-1/2" center to center corrugations has a surface area 10% greater than the width times length dimension. For corrugated siding with 1-1/4" center to center corrugations, increase the surface area by 15%. For square corner decking, the table that follows shows how much area must be added to allow for peaks and valleys.

Industrial and commercial estimating tables
Figure 20-1 (continued)

Square corner decking factors

C	2C	D	PW	VW	Factor
--	12"	4-1/2"	3"	2"	2.50
--	12"	1-1/2"	3-1/8"	2"	1.50
--	12"	1-1/2"	5-1/16"	1"	1.45
12"	--	3"	9-5/8"	1"	1.50
12"	--	4-1/2"	9-5/8	1"	1.75
24"	--	4-1/2"	12"	12"	1.60
24"	--	6"	12"	12"	1.75
24"	--	8"	12"	12"	1.95

For square corner decking, calculate the overall (width times length) deck area. Then measure the peaks and valleys on the deck. Select the row in the table above that most nearly matches the deck you're painting. Multiply the overall deck area by the number listed in the column headed "factor" to find the actual area you're painting. Use this actual area when calculating labor and material requirements. In the table above, figures in the column headed **C** show the distance between the center of the peaks. Column **2C** shows the distance between every second center of peak (2 centers). Column **D** shows the depth of corrugation. Column **PW** shows the peak width. Column **VW** shows the valley width. If the deck you're painting doesn't match any deck listed in this table, use the factor for the most similar deck in the table.

Doors, hollow metal
Brush application

	SF per hour Slow-Med-Fast	SF per gallon Heavy-Light
First coat	160-180-200	400-425
Added coats	175-195-215	450-475

Duct work Bare duct	SF per hour Slow-Med-Fast	Acid wash coat ------------ Heavy-Light	Metal primer -------SF Heavy-Light	Industrial enamel oil base per gallon--- Heavy-Light	Epoxy coating ---------- Heavy-Light
Brush					
1st coat	80-100-120	650-750	300-350	350-400	300-350
Added coats	90-115-140	--	350-400	400-450	375-425
Roll					
1st coat	225-250-275	600-700	275-325	325-375	300-350
Added coats	275-300-325	--	375-425	425-475	400-450
Spray					
1st coat	550-600-650	450-550	275-300	300-350	300-325
Added coats	700-750-800	--	300-325	325-375	325-350
Mitt or glove					
1st coat	175-200-225	600-700	325-375	375-425	350-400
Added coats	225-250-275	--	375-425	425-475	375-425

Industrial and commercial estimating tables
Figure 20-1 (continued)

Duct, insulated Canvas jacket	SF per hour Slow-Med-Fast	Water base latex Heavy-Light	Oil base paint -------------------- SF per gallon -------------------- Heavy-Light	Epoxy coating Heavy-Light
Brush				
Prime	60- 75- 90	225-250	--	--
2nd coat	85-100-125	250-275	275-300	260-285
Added coats	100-125-150	300-325	325-350	310-335
Roll				
Prime	125-150-175	225-250	--	--
2nd coat	175-200-225	250-275	275-300	250-275
Added coats	225-250-275	375-400	425-450	400-425
Spray				
Prime	450-500-550	175-200	--	--
2nd coat	550-613-700	200-225	225-250	215-235
Added coats	700-750-800	225-250	250-275	240-265

Fire escapes Spray application	Flights per hour	Flights per gallon
Solid (plain) deck	1.0 to 2.0	1.0
Grating deck	2.0 to 3.0	1.5

Fire excapes can also be estimated by the square foot. Calculate the actual area to be coated. For continuous solid (plain) deck, use the rates listed under *Decking and siding.* For continuous grating deck, use the rates listed under *Grates, steel.*

Fire sprinkler systems Use labor and material rates listed for 1" to 4" pipe. For painting sprinkler heads at 12' on center at a ceiling height of 12', figure three minutes per head (20 per hour). Very little paint is needed. Your material estimate for the sprinkler pipe will include enough to cover the heads.

Grates, steel Over 1" thick	SF per hour Slow-Med-Fast	SF per gallon Heavy-Light
Without supports		
Brush, each coat	60- 85-110	125-175
Spray, each coat	190-210-225	100-125
Including painting typical supports		
Brush, each coat	40- 55- 70	100-125
Spray, each coat	120-135-150	75-100

Use these figures when estimating steel grates over 1" thick. The figures will apply when both sides are painted with oil or water base paint. Square foot calculations for grates are based on overall (width times length) dimensions. See the following table for grilles under 1" thick.

Industrial and commercial estimating tables
Figure 20-1 (continued)

Grilles, steel Under 1" thick	SF per hour Slow-Med-Fast	SF per gallon Heavy-Light
Brush, each coat	175-200-225	150-200
Spray, each coat	400-450-500	125-150

Use these figures when estimating plain steel grilles under 1" thick. The figures will apply when both sides are painted with either oil or water base paint. Square foot calculations for grates are based on overall (width times length) dimensions. Add the cost of painting any grille supports.

Ladders   Measure the length of the ladder rungs and vertical members. Then multiply by a difficulty factor of 1.5 (Length x 1.5) to allow for limited access to the back of the ladder. Then use rates in the pipe tables to figure the labor and material required.

Mechanical equipment Per square foot of area covered	SF per hour Slow-Med-Fast	SF per gallon Heavy-Light
Brush on first coat	175-200-225	250-275
Brush on second coat	200-225-250	350-375
Spray on first coat	350-375-400	225-275
Spray on second coat	375-400-425	325-375

Use these figures to estimate the cost of painting mechanical equipment (such as compressors and mixing boxes) with either oil or water base paint. See the following table for boiler room equipment.

Mechanical equipment (boiler room)   Don't bother figuring the exact area of boiler room equipment that has to be coated. Instead, take the area as equal to 1/2 the wall height times the ceiling area in the room. Figure a painter will coat 125 square feet per hour and a gallon of paint will cover 300 square feet. This rate does not include time needed to paint walls, ceiling or floor around mechanical equipment. In any case, judgment will be needed when painting boiler room equipment.

Industrial and commercial estimating tables
Figure 20-1 (continued)

Piping, bare pipe	SF per hour Slow-Med-Fast	Metal primer	Industrial enamel oil base	Epoxy coating
		-------------------- SF per gallon --------------------		
		Heavy-Light	Heavy-Light	Heavy-Light
Brush				
1st coat	75-100-125	310-360	350-400	325-375
2nd coat	90-115-140	350-400	400-450	375-425
Added coats	125-150-175	400-450	450-500	425-475
Roll				
1st coat	175-200-225	--	350-400	--
2nd coat	200-225-250	--	400-450	--
Added coats	250-300-350	--	450-500	--
Spray				
1st coat	300-350-400	150-175	175-200	160-185
2nd coat	375-425-475	160-185	185-210	175-200
Added coats	425-475-525	225-250	275-300	250-275
Mitt or glove				
1st coat	175-200-225	300-325	325-350	335-360
2nd coat	200-225-250	315-340	350-375	350-375
Added coats	275-300-325	340-365	375-400	365-390
			Heat resisting enamel	Aluminum base paint
Brush on each coat	50-75-100		550-600	550-600

Use the pipe conversion factors in Figure 20-2 to convert linear feet of pipe to square feet of surface. Vertical pipe runs require 2 to 3 times the manhours plus 10% more material. Solid color coded piping requires 15% to 25% more labor and material. For color bands on piping at 10' to 15' intervals, add the cost of the additional primer coat.

Industrial and commercial estimating tables
Figure 20-1 (continued)

Pipe, insulated Canvas jacket	SF per hour Slow-Med-Fast	Water base latex ------------------ Heavy-Light	Oil base paint ---------- SF per gallon ---------- Heavy-Light	Epoxy coating Heavy-Light
Brush				
1st coat	60- 80-100	125-150	--	--
2nd coat	75-100-125	275-300	310-335	300-325
Added coats	100-150-175	350-400	425-450	400-425
Roll				
1st coat	135-160-185	125-150	--	--
2nd coat	175-200-225	275-300	310-335	300-325
Added coats	275-300-325	375-400	425-450	400-425
Spray				
1st coat	225-250-275	75-100	--	--
2nd coat	275-300-325	175-200	210-235	200-225
Added coats	375-400-425	275-300	310-335	300-325

Use the pipe conversion factors in Figure 20-2 to convert linear feet of pipe to square feet of surface. Vertical pipe runs require 2 to 3 times the manhours plus 10% more material. Solid color coded piping requires 15% to 25% more labor and material. For color bands on piping at 10' to 15' intervals, add the cost of the additional primer coat.

Radiators	SF per hour Slow-Med Fast	SF per gallon Heavy-Light
Brush, each coat	50- 70- 90	90-100
Spray, each coat	225-250-275	75- 90

Use these figures to estimate the cost of painting both sides of 6" to 18" deep hot water or steam radiators with oil or water base paint. Measurements are per square foot of area measured one side (width times length).

Structural steel fabrication and erection estimates are usually based on the tons of steel. As a paint estimator you need to convert tons of steel to square feet of surface. Of course, the conversion factor depends on the size of the steel members. On larger jobs and where accuracy is essential, use Figure 20-4 to make exact conversions. On smaller jobs where the precise surface area is less important, estimate that there are 225 SF of paintable surface per ton of steel.

Industrial and commercial estimating tables
Figure 20-1 (continued)

Light structural steel

Per SF coated	SF per hour Slow-Med-Fast	Metal primer	Industrial enamel oil base	Epoxy coating
		----- SF per gallon -----		
		Heavy-Light	Heavy-Light	Heavy-Light
Brush				
1st coat	60- 80-100	375-400	425-450	400-425
Added coats	80-100-120	400-425	450-475	425-450
Roll				
1st coat	125-150-175	355-380	400-425	375-400
Added coats	175-200-225	365-390	415-440	400-425
Spray				
1st coat	400-500-600	275-300	310-340	300-325
Added coats	500-600-700	300-325	335-365	325-350

Light structural steel has from 300 to 500 square feet of surface per ton. *Rule of thumb:* When coatings are applied by brush, a journeyman painter will apply a first coat on from 2 to 3 tons per 8-hour day. A painter will apply second and subsequent coats at from 3 to 4 tons per day. When coatings are applied by spray, output and material used should average as follows:

Coating light structural steel

Rule of thumb, per SF coated	Hours per ton	Gallons per ton
Spray, 1st coat	1.6	1.1
Spray, 2nd coat	1.3	1.0
Spray, 3rd coat	1.0	0.9

Medium structural steel

Per SF coated	SF per hour Slow-Med-Fast	Metal primer	Industrial enamel oil base	Epoxy coating
		----- SF per gallon -----		
		Heavy-Light	Heavy-Light	Heavy-Light
Brush				
1st coat	80-100-120	375-400	425-450	400-425
Added coats	100-125-150	400-425	450-475	425-450
Roll				
1st coat	200-225-250	355-380	400-425	375-400
Added coats	225-250-275	365-390	415-440	400-425
Spray				
1st coat	500-600-700	275-300	310-340	300-325
Added coats	600-700-800	300-325	335-365	325-350

Medium structural steel has from 150 to 300 square feet of surface per ton. *Rule of thumb:* When coatings are applied by brush, a journeyman painter will apply a first coat on from 4 to 5 tons per 8-hour day. A painter will apply second and subsequent coats at from 5 to 6 tons per day. When coatings are applied by spray, figure output at 0.6 hours per ton and material use at about 0.6 gallons per ton.

Industrial and commercial estimating tables
Figure 20-1 (continued)

Heavy structural steel

Per SF coated	SF per hour Slow-Med-Fast	Metal primer Heavy-Light	Industrial enamel oil base — SF per gallon — Heavy-Light	Epoxy coating Heavy-Light
Brush				
1st coat	130-150-170	375-400	425-450	400-425
Added coats	175-200-225	400-425	450-475	425-450
Roll				
1st coat	250-275-300	355-380	400-425	375-400
Added coats	275-300-325	365-390	415-440	400-425
Spray				
1st coat	650-750-850	275-300	310-340	300-325
Added coats	750-850-950	300-325	335-365	325-350

Generally heavy structural steel has from 100 to 150 square feet of surface per ton. Extra heavy structural steel has from 50 to 100 square feet of surface per ton. *Rule of thumb:* When coatings are applied by spray, figure output at 0.2 hours per ton and material use at about 0.2 gallons per ton.

Tank, silo, vessel or hopper

Exterior walls only	SF per hour Slow-Med-Fast	Metal primer Heavy-Light	Industrial enamel oil base — SF per gallon — Heavy-Light	Epoxy coating Heavy-Light
Brush				
1st coat	150-175-200	350-400	400-450	375-425
Added coats	200-225-250	375-425	425-475	400-450
Roll				
1st coat	275-300-325	330-380	375-425	375-425
Added coats	375-400-425	350-400	400-450	400-450
Spray				
1st coat	700-750-800	275-300	325-350	300-325
Added coats	850-900-950	300-325	350-375	325-350
			Vinyl coating	
Brush				
1st coat	125-150-175		225-250	
2nd coat	165-190-215		100-150	
Spray				
1st coat	600-625-650		200-225	
2nd coat	725-750-775		80-130	

Use this table when estimating walls only. The table that follows has labor and material requirements for painting the roof of a steel tank, silo, vessel or hopper.

Industrial and commercial estimating tables
Figure 20-1 (continued)

Tank, silo, vessel, or hopper Exterior roof only	SF per hour Slow-Med-Fast	Metal primer -------------------- SF per gallon -------------------- Heavy-Light	Industrial enamel oil base Heavy-Light	Epoxy coating Heavy Light
Brush				
1st coat	175-200-225	350-400	400-450	375-425
Added coats	225-250-275	375-425	425-475	400-450
Roll				
1st coat	325-350-375	330-380	375-425	375-425
Added coats	400-425-450	350-400	400-450	400-450
Spray				
1st coat	850- 900- 950	275-300	325-350	300-325
Added coats	950-1075-1100	300-325	350-375	325-350
Brush			Vinyl coating	
1st coat	125-150-175		225-250	
2nd coat	200-225-250		100-150	
Spray				
1st coat	750-775- 800		200-225	
2nd coat	900-950-1000		80-130	
			Inorganic zinc coating	
Brush, 1 coat	135-160-185		225-250	
Spray, 1 coat	800-850-900		200-225	

Use these figures to estimate labor and materials for painting the exterior surface of a steel roof on a tank, silo, vessel or hopper. *Rule of thumb:* For a vaulted or peaked roof, figure the roof area as though it were flat and add 5%.

Industrial and commercial estimating tables
Figure 20-1 (continued)

Walls, concrete tilt-up SF per hour Slow-Med-Fast		Water base latex -------------------- SF per gallon -------------------- Heavy-Light	Oil base paint Heavy-Light	Epoxy coating Heavy-Light
Brush				
1st coat	150-185- 225	200-310	200-350	250-330
2nd coat	200-225- 250	225-360	250-400	300-380
Roll				
1st coat	275-300- 325	200-280	160-310	210-290
2nd coat	300-338- 375	225-360	250-400	300-380
Spray				
1st coat	500-700- 900	175-260	140-280	235-270
2nd coat	600-800-1000	265-350	175-400	300-375
Brush			Waterproof sealer	
1st coat	150-175-200		120-160	
2nd coat	230-275-295		175-200	
Roll				
1st coat	170-200-245		130-200	
2nd coat	275-300-325		225-325	
Spray				
1st coat	500-700- 900		100-125	
2nd coat	600-800-1000		140-200	
Brush			Industrial waterproofing	
1st coat	90-100-110		90-100	
2nd coat	150-180-195		175-200	
Roll				
1st coat	100-113-125		100-125	
2nd coat	180-198-215		175-200	

Use these figures to estimate the labor and material needed to paint concrete with either a smooth finish (trowel), rough texture, or exposed aggregate finish. For wall heights above 10', increase the computed area by 50%.

Windows, steel factory (storm) sash Brush application	LF per hour Slow-Med-Fast	LF per gallon Heavy-Light
1st coat	100-125-150	750- 850
2nd coat	125-150-175	850- 950
3rd coat	150-175-200	950-1050

These figures will apply when painting steel factory sash but do not include work on the glazing or frame.

Industrial and commercial estimating tables
Figure 20-1 (continued)

Pipe O/D (inches)	Conversion factor (SF per measured LF)
1″ to 3″	1 SF for each 1 LF
4″ to 7″	2 SF for each 1 LF
8″ to 11″	3 SF for each 1 LF
12″ to 15″	4 SF for each 1 LF
16″ to 19″	5 SF for each 1 LF
20″ to 22″	6 SF for each 1 LF
23″ to 26″	7 SF for each 1 LF
27″ to 30″	8 SF for each 1 LF

**Conduit/pipe area conversions
Figure 20-2**

Insulated pipe— Add twice the insulation thickness to the outside diameter of the pipe to find the outside dimension of pipe and insulation. See Figure 20-3.

Pipe railing— The formulas in Figure 20-1 are based on linear feet. I've figured in the difficulty factors. Measure the length of the vertical and horizontal members and use the conversion factors in Figure 20-2 to convert to total surface area in square feet. Then use the bare piping formulas from Figure 20-1 to calculate the manhours and material quantities.

Piping or Conduit Color Code
Painting pipes or conduits according to color codes takes a lot of additional time. Include it as a separate line on your bid. Here's my rule of thumb for color coding: Add a difficulty factor of 15% to 25% to the manhour and material rates in the piping formulas. In the piping section of Figure 20-1, there are rules of thumb for color coding pipes all one solid color and for adding bands or stripes at 10-foot to 15-foot intervals.

Decking: Corrugated Metal
To estimate corrugated metal roof decking and siding, the first step is to find the true surface area. Use the conversion factors in Figure 20-1. Take the measurements for a deck from the plan view and the siding measurements from the elevation view. Multiply the width by the length to find the area. Multiply that area by the conversion factor to find the true surface area:

Measurement (from plan view)   x **Factor**   =   Actual area

10 x 10 = 100 SF   x 1.4   =   140 SF

When you've found the true surface area, you can use the formulas for flat metal surfaces. But remember, most corrugated metal is fabricated on the job site, so it's not preprimed. Figure in a prime coat as the first coat for all job-fabricated metal.

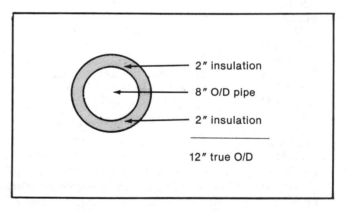

**Outside dimension of insulated pipe
Figure 20-3**

Duct Work
To estimate duct work, calculate the square feet of surface area and apply the formulas in Figure 20-1. If there's limited access and adjacent surfaces must be protected, use your judgment to assign a difficulty factor to allow for the extra time involved.

Fire Escapes, Steel Stairs, Grating and Grills
Use the manhour and material rates from Figure 20-1 for this work. They don't need any adjustments.

Ladders

Measure the length of the ladder rungs and vertical members in the ladder. Then use the pipe conversion table in Figure 20-2 to convert linear feet to square feet. When you have the total area of the ladder surfaces, multiply by a difficulty factor of 1.5 if access to the back of the ladder is limited. Then use the formulas for pipe to find the costs.

Mechanical Equipment and Machinery

The formulas in Figure 20-1 are based on surface area in square feet. The difficulty factors are figured in.

Sprinkler Systems

Use the 1-inch to 4-inch pipe formulas to calculate the manhours and material for the pipe. Add 3 minutes for each sprinkler head (20 per hour). Paint for the sprinklers is included in the pipe material figures.

Structural Steel

You can calculate the paint needed for structural steel by the ton of steel or by the linear foot of beam, girder or column. Calculating by the ton is easier, but it's possible only when the plans or specs show the tonnage.

If you don't have the tonnage, you'll have to measure the length of each steel member. Then use the conversion table in Figure 20-4 to convert tons or linear feet to surface area. For hand cleaning or sandblasting, look up the preparation formulas in Chapter 17. For painting, use the formulas in Figure 20-1.

When estimating structural steel, several major variables will affect the costs. Consider:

1) The weight of the steel: light, medium or heavy. Light steel is less dense, so it has more surface area per ton. Heavy steel, on the other hand, has less surface area per ton.

2) Access to the work area and the height of the building. The preparation estimating tables in Chapter 17 and the formulas in Figure 20-1 allow for work up to 30 feet high. For work over 30 feet, use the high time difficulty factors in Figure 20-1.

3) Application method: brush, roll or spray. The formulas in Figure 20-1 include all three application methods.

Tanks and Spheres

When you're calculating the surface area of cylindrical tanks, don't forget to include the top as well as the sides. Here are the formulas for the entire tank:

Sides of tank:	Pi x diameter x height π x D x H
Flat top of tank:	Diameter squared x .7854 D^2 x .7854
Domed top of tank:	2 x pi x radius squared $2\,\pi\,r^2$
Sphere:	4 x pi x radius squared $4\,\pi\,r^2$

Figure 20-5 shows the surface area of spheres of different sizes. The surface area of a dome is half that of the sphere.

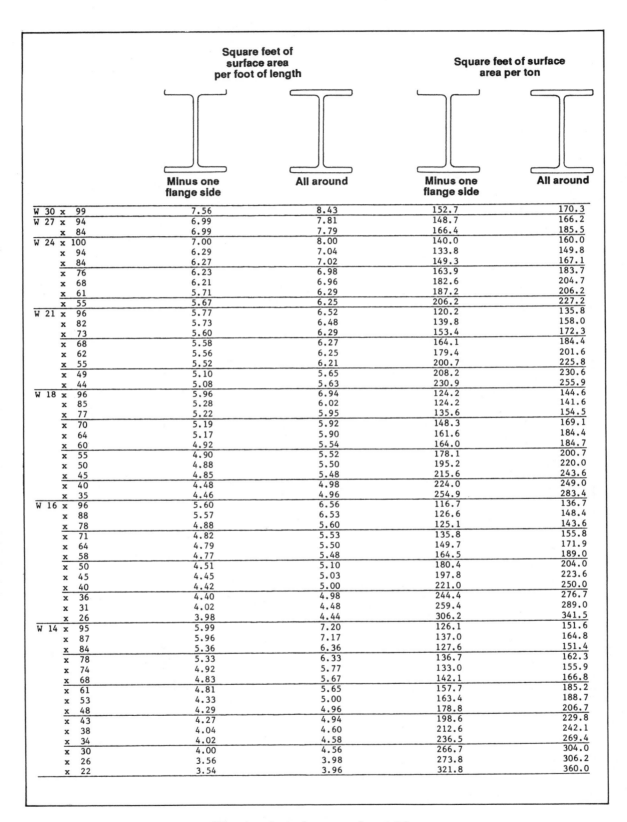

			Square feet of surface area per foot of length		Square feet of surface area per ton	
			Minus one flange side	All around	Minus one flange side	All around
W 30	x	99	7.56	8.43	152.7	170.3
W 27	x	94	6.99	7.81	148.7	166.2
	x	84	6.99	7.79	166.4	185.5
W 24	x	100	7.00	8.00	140.0	160.0
	x	94	6.29	7.04	133.8	149.8
	x	84	6.27	7.02	149.3	167.1
	x	76	6.23	6.98	163.9	183.7
	x	68	6.21	6.96	182.6	204.7
	x	61	5.71	6.29	187.2	206.2
	x	55	5.67	6.25	206.2	227.2
W 21	x	96	5.77	6.52	120.2	135.8
	x	82	5.73	6.48	139.8	158.0
	x	73	5.60	6.29	153.4	172.3
	x	68	5.58	6.27	164.1	184.4
	x	62	5.56	6.25	179.4	201.6
	x	55	5.52	6.21	200.7	225.8
	x	49	5.10	5.65	208.2	230.6
	x	44	5.08	5.63	230.9	255.9
W 18	x	96	5.96	6.94	124.2	144.6
	x	85	5.28	6.02	124.2	141.6
	x	77	5.22	5.95	135.6	154.5
	x	70	5.19	5.92	148.3	169.1
	x	64	5.17	5.90	161.6	184.4
	x	60	4.92	5.54	164.0	184.7
	x	55	4.90	5.52	178.1	200.7
	x	50	4.88	5.50	195.2	220.0
	x	45	4.85	5.48	215.6	243.6
	x	40	4.48	4.98	224.0	249.0
	x	35	4.46	4.96	254.9	283.4
W 16	x	96	5.60	6.56	116.7	136.7
	x	88	5.57	6.53	126.6	148.4
	x	78	4.88	5.60	125.1	143.6
	x	71	4.82	5.53	135.8	155.8
	x	64	4.79	5.50	149.7	171.9
	x	58	4.77	5.48	164.5	189.0
	x	50	4.51	5.10	180.4	204.0
	x	45	4.45	5.03	197.8	223.6
	x	40	4.42	5.00	221.0	250.0
	x	36	4.40	4.98	244.4	276.7
	x	31	4.02	4.48	259.4	289.0
	x	26	3.98	4.44	306.2	341.5
W 14	x	95	5.99	7.20	126.1	151.6
	x	87	5.96	7.17	137.0	164.8
	x	84	5.36	6.36	127.6	151.4
	x	78	5.33	6.33	136.7	162.3
	x	74	4.92	5.77	133.0	155.9
	x	68	4.83	5.67	142.1	166.8
	x	61	4.81	5.65	157.7	185.2
	x	53	4.33	5.00	163.4	188.7
	x	48	4.29	4.96	178.8	206.7
	x	43	4.27	4.94	198.6	229.8
	x	38	4.04	4.60	212.6	242.1
	x	34	4.02	4.58	236.5	269.4
	x	30	4.00	4.56	266.7	304.0
	x	26	3.56	3.98	273.8	306.2
	x	22	3.54	3.96	321.8	360.0

Structural steel conversion table
Figure 20-4

		Square feet of surface area per foot of length		Square feet of surface area per ton	
		Minus one flange side	All around	Minus one flange side	All around
W 12 x	99	5.19	6.21	104.8	125.4
x	92	5.14	6.15	111.7	133.7
x	85	5.12	6.13	120.5	144.2
x	79	5.09	6.10	128.9	154.4
x	72	5.04	6.04	140.0	167.8
x	65	5.02	6.02	154.5	185.2
x	58	4.54	5.38	156.6	185.5
x	53	4.50	5.33	169.8	201.1
x	50	4.07	4.75	162.8	190.0
x	45	4.00	4.67	177.8	207.6
x	40	4.00	4.67	200.0	233.5
x	36	3.70	4.25	205.6	236.1
x	31	3.65	4.19	235.5	270.3
x	27	3.63	4.17	268.9	308.9
x	22	3.04	3.38	276.4	307.3
x	19	3.02	3.35	317.9	352.6
x	16.5	3.00	3.33	363.6	403.6
x	14	2.98	3.31	425.7	472.9
W 10 x	100	4.45	5.31	89.0	106.2
x	89	4.38	5.23	98.4	117.5
x	77	4.33	5.19	112.5	134.8
x	72	4.28	5.13	118.9	142.5
x	66	4.26	5.10	129.1	154.5
x	60	4.24	5.08	141.3	169.3
x	54	4.19	5.02	155.2	185.9
x	49	4.17	5.00	170.2	204.0
x	45	3.69	4.35	164.0	193.3
x	39	3.67	4.33	188.2	222.1
x	33	3.63	4.29	220.0	260.0
x	29	3.15	3.63	217.2	250.3
x	25	3.13	3.60	250.4	288.0
x	21	3.08	3.56	293.3	339.0
x	19	2.71	3.04	285.3	320.0
x	17	2.69	3.02	316.5	355.3
x	15	2.67	3.00	356.0	400.0
x	11.5	2.65	2.98	460.9	518.3
W 8 x	67	3.56	4.25	106.3	126.9
x	58	3.52	4.21	121.4	145.2
x	48	3.45	4.13	143.8	172.1
x	40	3.41	4.08	170.5	204.0
x	35	3.35	4.02	191.4	229.7
x	31	3.33	4.00	214.8	258.1
x	28	2.96	3.50	211.4	250.0
x	24	2.94	3.48	245.0	290.0
x	20	2.67	3.10	267.0	310.0
x	17	2.65	3.08	311.8	362.4
x	15	2.35	2.69	313.3	358.7
x	13	2.33	2.67	358.5	410.8
x	10	2.31	2.65	462.0	530.0
W 6 x	25	2.59	3.10	207.2	248.0
x	20	2.54	3.04	254.0	304.0
x	15.5	2.50	3.00	322.6	387.1
x	16	2.04	2.38	255.0	297.5
x	12	2.00	2.33	333.3	388.3
x	8.5	1.98	2.31	465.9	543.5
W 5 x	18.5	2.10	2.52	227.0	272.4
x	16	2.08	2.50	260.0	312.5
W 4 x	13	1.69	2.02	260.0	310.8

Structural steel conversion table
Figure 20-4 (continued)

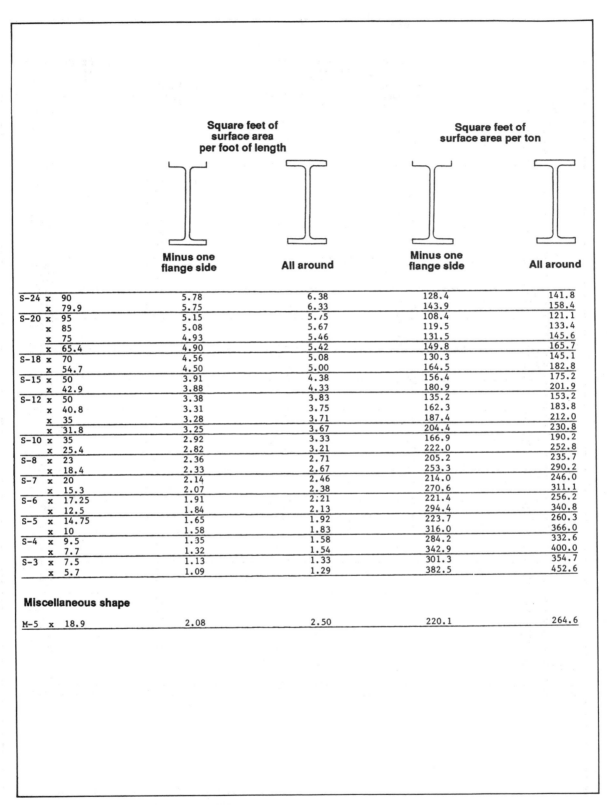

		Square feet of surface area per foot of length		Square feet of surface area per ton	
		Minus one flange side	All around	Minus one flange side	All around
S-24 x	90	5.78	6.38	128.4	141.8
x	79.9	5.75	6.33	143.9	158.4
S-20 x	95	5.15	5.75	108.4	121.1
x	85	5.08	5.67	119.5	133.4
x	75	4.93	5.46	131.5	145.6
x	65.4	4.90	5.42	149.8	165.7
S-18 x	70	4.56	5.08	130.3	145.1
x	54.7	4.50	5.00	164.5	182.8
S-15 x	50	3.91	4.38	156.4	175.2
x	42.9	3.88	4.33	180.9	201.9
S-12 x	50	3.38	3.83	135.2	153.2
x	40.8	3.31	3.75	162.3	183.8
x	35	3.28	3.71	187.4	212.0
x	31.8	3.25	3.67	204.4	230.8
S-10 x	35	2.92	3.33	166.9	190.2
x	25.4	2.82	3.21	222.0	252.8
S-8 x	23	2.36	2.71	205.2	235.7
x	18.4	2.33	2.67	253.3	290.2
S-7 x	20	2.14	2.46	214.0	246.0
x	15.3	2.07	2.38	270.6	311.1
S-6 x	17.25	1.91	2.21	221.4	256.2
x	12.5	1.84	2.13	294.4	340.8
S-5 x	14.75	1.65	1.92	223.7	260.3
x	10	1.58	1.83	316.0	366.0
S-4 x	9.5	1.35	1.58	284.2	332.6
x	7.7	1.32	1.54	342.9	400.0
S-3 x	7.5	1.13	1.33	301.3	354.7
x	5.7	1.09	1.29	382.5	452.6

Miscellaneous shape

M-5 x	18.9	2.08	2.50	220.1	264.6

Structural steel conversion table
Figure 20-4 (continued)

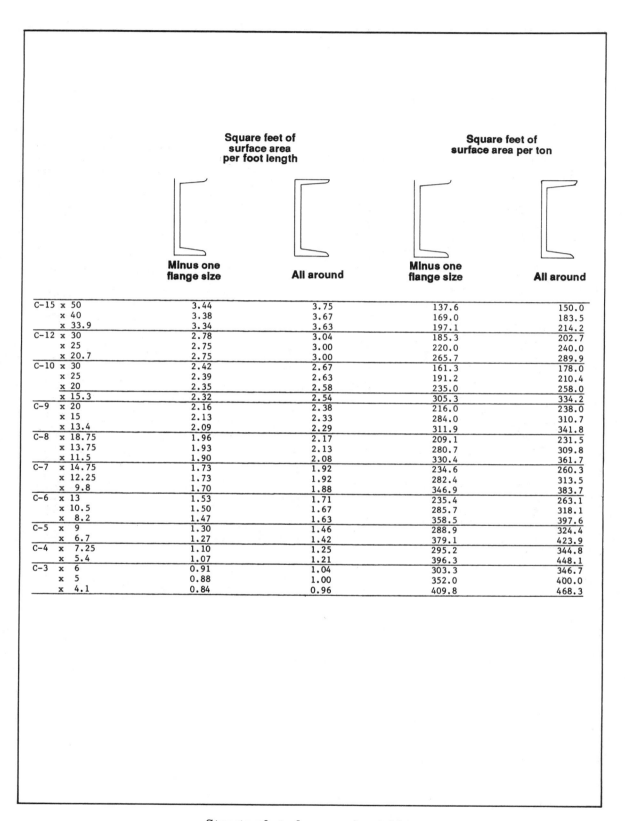

	Square feet of surface area per foot length		Square feet of surface area per ton	
	Minus one flange size	All around	Minus one flange size	All around
C–15 x 50	3.44	3.75	137.6	150.0
x 40	3.38	3.67	169.0	183.5
x 33.9	3.34	3.63	197.1	214.2
C–12 x 30	2.78	3.04	185.3	202.7
x 25	2.75	3.00	220.0	240.0
x 20.7	2.75	3.00	265.7	289.9
C–10 x 30	2.42	2.67	161.3	178.0
x 25	2.39	2.63	191.2	210.4
x 20	2.35	2.58	235.0	258.0
x 15.3	2.32	2.54	305.3	334.2
C–9 x 20	2.16	2.38	216.0	238.0
x 15	2.13	2.33	284.0	310.7
x 13.4	2.09	2.29	311.9	341.8
C–8 x 18.75	1.96	2.17	209.1	231.5
x 13.75	1.93	2.13	280.7	309.8
x 11.5	1.90	2.08	330.4	361.7
C–7 x 14.75	1.73	1.92	234.6	260.3
x 12.25	1.73	1.92	282.4	313.5
x 9.8	1.70	1.88	346.9	383.7
C–6 x 13	1.53	1.71	235.4	263.1
x 10.5	1.50	1.67	285.7	318.1
x 8.2	1.47	1.63	358.5	397.6
C–5 x 9	1.30	1.46	288.9	324.4
x 6.7	1.27	1.42	379.1	423.9
C–4 x 7.25	1.10	1.25	295.2	344.8
x 5.4	1.07	1.21	396.3	448.1
C–3 x 6	0.91	1.04	303.3	346.7
x 5	0.88	1.00	352.0	400.0
x 4.1	0.84	0.96	409.8	468.3

Structural steel conversion table
Figure 20-4 (continued)

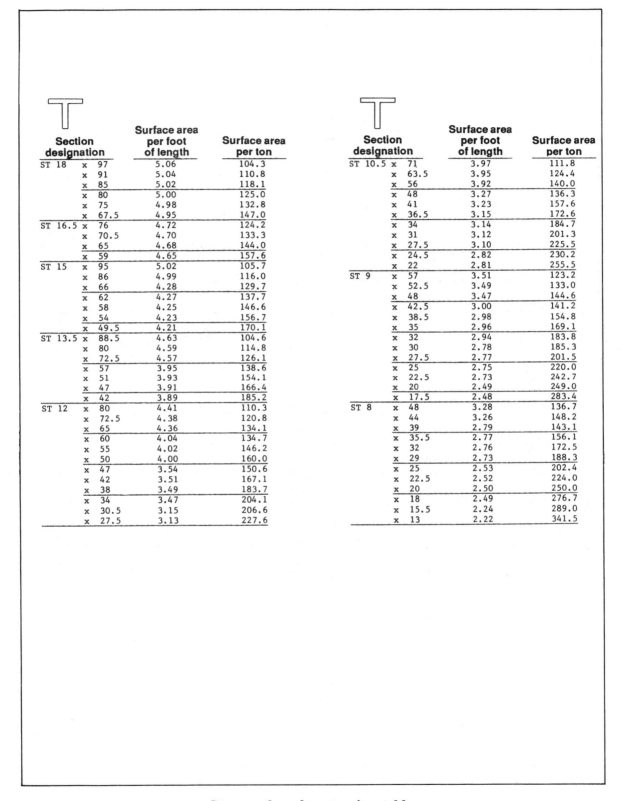

Section designation			Surface area per foot of length	Surface area per ton
ST 18	x	97	5.06	104.3
	x	91	5.04	110.8
	x	85	5.02	118.1
	x	80	5.00	125.0
	x	75	4.98	132.8
	x	67.5	4.95	147.0
ST 16.5	x	76	4.72	124.2
	x	70.5	4.70	133.3
	x	65	4.68	144.0
	x	59	4.65	157.6
ST 15	x	95	5.02	105.7
	x	86	4.99	116.0
	x	66	4.28	129.7
	x	62	4.27	137.7
	x	58	4.25	146.6
	x	54	4.23	156.7
	x	49.5	4.21	170.1
ST 13.5	x	88.5	4.63	104.6
	x	80	4.59	114.8
	x	72.5	4.57	126.1
	x	57	3.95	138.6
	x	51	3.93	154.1
	x	47	3.91	166.4
	x	42	3.89	185.2
ST 12	x	80	4.41	110.3
	x	72.5	4.38	120.8
	x	65	4.36	134.1
	x	60	4.04	134.7
	x	55	4.02	146.2
	x	50	4.00	160.0
	x	47	3.54	150.6
	x	42	3.51	167.1
	x	38	3.49	183.7
	x	34	3.47	204.1
	x	30.5	3.15	206.6
	x	27.5	3.13	227.6

Section designation			Surface area per foot of length	Surface area per ton
ST 10.5	x	71	3.97	111.8
	x	63.5	3.95	124.4
	x	56	3.92	140.0
	x	48	3.27	136.3
	x	41	3.23	157.6
	x	36.5	3.15	172.6
	x	34	3.14	184.7
	x	31	3.12	201.3
	x	27.5	3.10	225.5
	x	24.5	2.82	230.2
	x	22	2.81	255.5
ST 9	x	57	3.51	123.2
	x	52.5	3.49	133.0
	x	48	3.47	144.6
	x	42.5	3.00	141.2
	x	38.5	2.98	154.8
	x	35	2.96	169.1
	x	32	2.94	183.8
	x	30	2.78	185.3
	x	27.5	2.77	201.5
	x	25	2.75	220.0
	x	22.5	2.73	242.7
	x	20	2.49	249.0
	x	17.5	2.48	283.4
ST 8	x	48	3.28	136.7
	x	44	3.26	148.2
	x	39	2.79	143.1
	x	35.5	2.77	156.1
	x	32	2.76	172.5
	x	29	2.73	188.3
	x	25	2.53	202.4
	x	22.5	2.52	224.0
	x	20	2.50	250.0
	x	18	2.49	276.7
	x	15.5	2.24	289.0
	x	13	2.22	341.5

Structural steel conversion table
Figure 20-4 (continued)

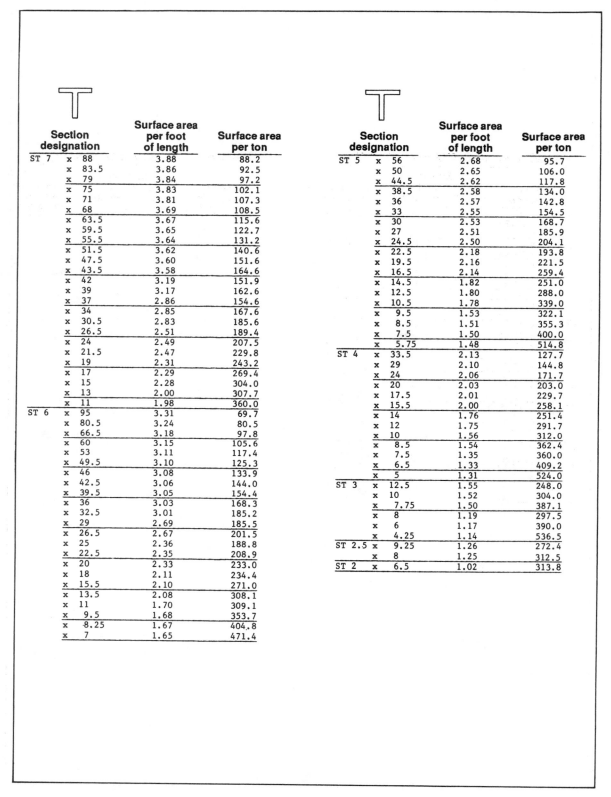

Section designation	Surface area per foot of length	Surface area per ton
ST 7 x 88	3.88	88.2
x 83.5	3.86	92.5
x 79	3.84	97.2
x 75	3.83	102.1
x 71	3.81	107.3
x 68	3.69	108.5
x 63.5	3.67	115.6
x 59.5	3.65	122.7
x 55.5	3.64	131.2
x 51.5	3.62	140.6
x 47.5	3.60	151.6
x 43.5	3.58	164.6
x 42	3.19	151.9
x 39	3.17	162.6
x 37	2.86	154.6
x 34	2.85	167.6
x 30.5	2.83	185.6
x 26.5	2.51	189.4
x 24	2.49	207.5
x 21.5	2.47	229.8
x 19	2.31	243.2
x 17	2.29	269.4
x 15	2.28	304.0
x 13	2.00	307.7
x 11	1.98	360.0
ST 6 x 95	3.31	69.7
x 80.5	3.24	80.5
x 66.5	3.18	97.8
x 60	3.15	105.6
x 53	3.11	117.4
x 49.5	3.10	125.3
x 46	3.08	133.9
x 42.5	3.06	144.0
x 39.5	3.05	154.4
x 36	3.03	168.3
x 32.5	3.01	185.2
x 29	2.69	185.5
x 26.5	2.67	201.5
x 25	2.36	188.8
x 22.5	2.35	208.9
x 20	2.33	233.0
x 18	2.11	234.4
x 15.5	2.10	271.0
x 13.5	2.08	308.1
x 11	1.70	309.1
x 9.5	1.68	353.7
x 8.25	1.67	404.8
x 7	1.65	471.4
ST 5 x 56	2.68	95.7
x 50	2.65	106.0
x 44.5	2.62	117.8
x 38.5	2.58	134.0
x 36	2.57	142.8
x 33	2.55	154.5
x 30	2.53	168.7
x 27	2.51	185.9
x 24.5	2.50	204.1
x 22.5	2.18	193.8
x 19.5	2.16	221.5
x 16.5	2.14	259.4
x 14.5	1.82	251.0
x 12.5	1.80	288.0
x 10.5	1.78	339.0
x 9.5	1.53	322.1
x 8.5	1.51	355.3
x 7.5	1.50	400.0
x 5.75	1.48	514.8
ST 4 x 33.5	2.13	127.7
x 29	2.10	144.8
x 24	2.06	171.7
x 20	2.03	203.0
x 17.5	2.01	229.7
x 15.5	2.00	258.1
x 14	1.76	251.4
x 12	1.75	291.7
x 10	1.56	312.0
x 8.5	1.54	362.4
x 7.5	1.35	360.0
x 6.5	1.33	409.2
x 5	1.31	524.0
ST 3 x 12.5	1.55	248.0
x 10	1.52	304.0
x 7.75	1.50	387.1
x 8	1.19	297.5
x 6	1.17	390.0
x 4.25	1.14	536.5
ST 2.5 x 9.25	1.26	272.4
x 8	1.25	312.5
ST 2 x 6.5	1.02	313.8

Structural steel conversion table
Figure 20-4 (continued)

Tees (cut from American standard shapes)

Section designation		Surface area per foot of length	Surface area per ton
ST 12	x 60	3.34	111.3
	x 52.95	3.31	125.0
	x 50	3.21	128.4
	x 45	3.19	141.8
	x 39.95	3.17	158.7
ST 10	x 47.5	2.87	120.8
	x 42.5	2.84	133.6
	x 37.5	2.73	145.6
	x 32.7	2.70	165.1
ST 9	x 35	2.54	145.1
	x 27.35	2.50	182.8
ST 7.5	x 25	2.19	175.2
	x 21.45	2.17	202.3
ST 6	x 25	1.91	152.8
	x 20.4	1.88	184.3
	x 17.5	1.85	211.4
	x 15.9	1.83	230.2
ST 5	x 17.5	1.66	189.7
	x 12.7	1.61	253.5
ST 4	x 11.5	1.36	236.5
	x 9.2	1.33	289.1
ST 3.5	x 10	1.23	246.0
	x 7.65	1.19	311.0
ST 3	x 8.625	1.09	252.8
	x 6.25	1.06	339.2
ST 2.5	x 7.375	0.96	260.3
	x 5	0.92	368.0
ST 2	x 4.75	0.80	336.8
	x 3.85	0.78	405.2

Miscellaneous tee (cut from M5 x 18.9)

Section designation	Surface area per foot of length	Surface area per ton
MT 2.5 x 9.45	0.83	175.7

Structural steel conversion table
Figure 20-4 (continued)

Section designation			Surface area per foot of length	Surface area per ton
L 8	x 8	x 1-1/8	2.67	93.8
	x 8	x 1	2.67	104.7
	x 8	x 7/8	2.67	118.7
	x 8	x 3/4	2.67	137.3
	x 8	x 5/8	2.67	163.3
	x 8	x 9/16	2.67	180.4
	x 8	x 1/2	2.67	202.3
L 6	x 6	x 1	2.00	107.0
	x 6	x 7/8	2.00	120.8
	x 6	x 3/4	2.00	139.4
	x 6	x 5/8	2.00	165.3
	x 6	x 9/16	2.00	182.6
	x 6	x 1/2	2.00	204.1
	x 6	x 7/16	2.00	232.6
	x 6	x 3/8	2.00	268.5
	x 6	x 5/16	2.00	322.6
L 5	x 5	x 7/8	1.67	122.8
	x 5	x 3/4	1.67	141.5
	x 5	x 5/8	1.67	167.0
	x 5	x 1/2	1.67	206.2
	x 5	x 7/16	1.67	233.6
	x 5	x 3/8	1.67	271.5
	x 5	x 5/16	1.67	324.3
L 4	x 4	x 3/4	1.33	143.8
	x 4	x 5/8	1.33	169.4
	x 4	x 1/2	1.33	207.8
	x 4	x 7/16	1.33	235.4
	x 4	x 3/8	1.33	271.4
	x 4	x 5/16	1.33	324.4
	x 4	x 1/4	1.33	403.0
L 3-1/2	x 3-1/2	x 1/2	1.17	210.8
	x 3-1/2	x 7/16	1.17	238.8
	x 3-1/2	x 3/8	1.17	275.3
	x 3-1/2	x 5/16	1.17	325.0
	x 3-1/2	x 1/4	1.17	403.4

Section designation			Surface area per foot of length	Surface area per ton
L 3	x 3	x 1/2	1.00	212.8
	x 3	x 7/16	1.00	241.0
	x 3	x 3/8	1.00	277.8
	x 3	x 5/16	1.00	327.9
	x 3	x 1/4	1.00	408.2
	x 3	x 3/16	1.00	539.1
L 2-1/2	x 2-1/2	x 1/2	0.83	215.6
	x 2-1/2	x 3/8	0.83	281.4
	x 2-1/2	x 5/16	0.83	332.0
	x 2-1/2	x 1/4	0.83	404.9
	x 2-1/2	x 3/16	0.83	540.7
L 2	x 2	x 3/8	0.67	285.1
	x 2	x 5/16	0.67	341.8
	x 2	x 1/4	0.67	420.1
	x 2	x 3/16	0.67	549.2
	x 2	x 1/8	0.67	812.1
L 1-3/4	x 1-3/4	x 1/4	0.58	418.8
	x 1-3/4	x 3/16	0.58	547.2
	x 1-3/4	x 1/8	0.58	805.6
L 1-1/2	x 1-1/2	x 1/4	0.50	427.4
	x 1-1/2	x 3/16	0.50	555.6
	x 1-1/2	x 5/32	0.50	657.9
	x 1-1/2	x 1/8	0.50	813.0
L 1-1/4	x 1-1/4	x 1/4	0.42	437.5
	x 1-1/4	x 3/16	0.42	567.6
	x 1-1/4	x 1/8	0.42	831.7
L 1	x 1	x 1/4	0.33	443.0
	x 1	x 3/16	0.33	569.0
	x 1	x 1/8	0.33	825.0

Structural steel conversion table
Figure 20-4 (continued)

Section designation			Surface area per foot of length	Surface area per ton
L 9 x 4	x	1	2.17	106.4
x 4	x	7/8	2.17	120.2
x 4	x	3/4	2.17	138.7
x 4	x	5/8	2.17	165.0
x 4	x	9/16	2.17	182.4
x 4	x	1/2	2.17	203.8
L 8 x 6	x	1	2.33	105.4
x 6	x	7/8	2.33	119.2
x 6	x	3/4	2.33	137.9
x 6	x	5/8	2.33	163.5
x 6	x	9/16	2.33	181.3
x 6	x	1/2	2.33	202.6
x 6	x	7/16	2.33	230.7
L 8 x 4	x	1	2.00	107.0
x 4	x	7/8	2.00	120.8
x 4	x	3/4	2.00	139.4
x 4	x	5/8	2.00	165.3
x 4	x	9/16	2.00	182.6
x 4	x	1/2	2.00	204.1
x 4	x	7/16	2.00	232.6
L 7 x 4	x	7/8	1.83	121.2
x 4	x	3/4	1.83	139.7
x 4	x	5/8	1.83	165.6
x 4	x	9/16	1.83	183.0
x 4	x	1/2	1.83	204.5
x 4	x	7/16	1.83	231.6
x 4	x	3/8	1.83	269.1
L 6 x 4	x	7/8	1.67	122.8
x 4	x	3/4	1.67	141.5
x 4	x	5/8	1.67	167.0
x 4	x	9/16	1.67	184.5
x 4	x	1/2	1.67	206.2
x 4	x	7/16	1.67	233.6
x 4	x	3/8	1.67	271.5
x 4	x	5/16	1.67	324.3
x 4	x	1/4	1.67	402.4
L 6 x 3-1/2 x		1/2	1.58	206.5
x 3-1/2 x		3/8	1.58	270.1
x 3-1/2 x		5/16	1.58	322.4
x 3-1/2 x		1/4	1.58	400.0
L 5 x 3-1/2 x		3/4	1.42	143.4
x 3-1/2 x		5/8	1.42	169.0
x 3-1/2 x		1/2	1.42	208.8
x 3-1/2 x		7/16	1.42	236.7
x 3-1/2 x		3/8	1.42	273.1
x 3-1/2 x		5/16	1.42	326.4
x 3-1/2 x		1/4	1.42	405.7

Section designation			Surface area per foot of length	Surface area per ton
L 5 x 3	x	1/2	1.33	207.8
x 3	x	7/16	1.33	235.4
x 3	x	3/8	1.33	271.4
x 3	x	5/16	1.33	324.4
x 3	x	1/4	1.33	403.0
L 4 x 3-1/2 x		5/8	1.25	170.1
x 3-1/2 x		1/2	1.25	210.1
x 3-1/2 x		7/16	1.25	235.8
x 3-1/2 x		3/8	1.25	274.7
x 3-1/2 x		5/16	1.25	324.7
x 3-1/2 x		1/4	1.25	403.2
L 4 x 3	x	5/8	1.17	172.1
x 3	x	1/2	1.17	210.8
x 3	x	7/16	1.17	238.8
x 3	x	3/8	1.17	275.3
x 3	x	5/16	1.17	325.0
x 3	x	1/4	1.17	403.4
L 3-1/2 x 3	x	1/2	1.08	211.8
x 3	x	7/16	1.08	237.4
x 3	x	3/8	1.08	273.4
x 3	x	5/16	1.08	327.3
x 3	x	1/4	1.08	400.0
L 3-1/2 x 2-1/2 x		1/2	1.00	212.8
x 2-1/2 x		7/16	1.00	241.0
x 2-1/2 x		3/8	1.00	277.8
x 2-1/2 x		5/16	1.00	327.9
x 2-1/2 x		1/4	1.00	408.2
L 3 x 2-1/2 x		1/2	0.92	216.5
x 2-1/2 x		7/16	0.92	242.1
x 2-1/2 x		3/8	0.92	278.8
x 2-1/2 x		5/16	0.92	328.6
x 2-1/2 x		1/4	0.92	408.9
x 2-1/2 x		3/16	0.92	542.8
L 3 x 2	x	1/2	0.83	215.6
x 2	x	7/16	0.83	244.1
x 2	x	3/8	0.83	281.4
x 2	x	5/16	0.83	332.0
x 2	x	1/4	0.83	404.9
x 2	x	3/16	0.83	540.7
L 2-1/2 x 2	x	3/8	0.75	283.0
x 2	x	5/16	0.75	333.3
x 2	x	1/4	0.75	414.4
x 2	x	3/16	0.75	545.5
L 2-1/2 x 1-1/2 x		5/16	0.67	341.8
x 1-1/2 x		1/4	0.67	420.1
x 1-1/2 x		3/16	0.67	549.2
L 2 x 1-1/2 x		1/4	0.58	418.8
x 1-1/2 x		3/16	0.58	547.2
x 1-1/2 x		1/8	0.58	805.6
L 2 x 1-1/4 x		1/4	0.54	423.5
x 1-1/4 x		3/16	0.54	551.0
L 1-3/4 x 1-1/4 x		1/4	0.50	427.4
x 1-1/4 x		3/16	0.50	555.6
x 1-1/4 x		1/8	0.50	813.0

Structural steel conversion table
Figure 20-4 (continued)

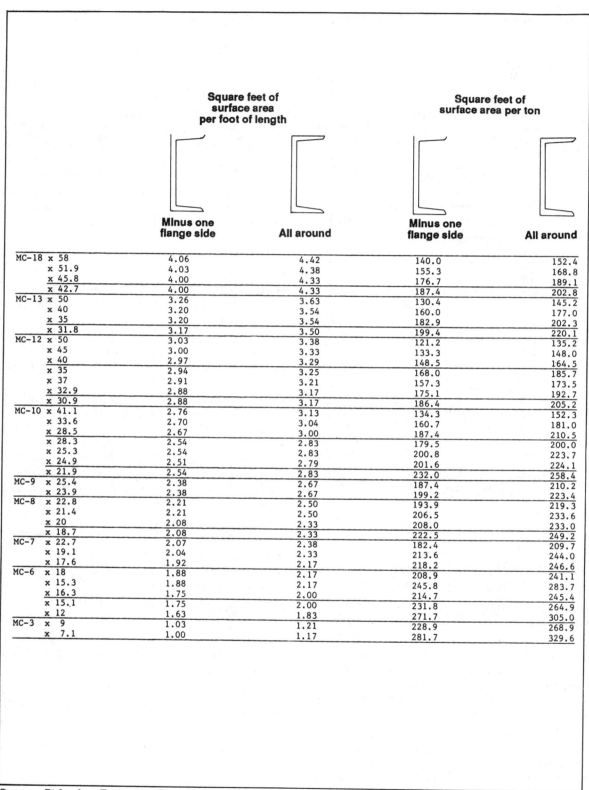

	Square feet of surface area per foot of length		Square feet of surface area per ton	
	Minus one flange side	All around	Minus one flange side	All around
MC-18 x 58	4.06	4.42	140.0	152.4
x 51.9	4.03	4.38	155.3	168.8
x 45.8	4.00	4.33	176.7	189.1
x 42.7	4.00	4.33	187.4	202.8
MC-13 x 50	3.26	3.63	130.4	145.2
x 40	3.20	3.54	160.0	177.0
x 35	3.20	3.54	182.9	202.3
x 31.8	3.17	3.50	199.4	220.1
MC-12 x 50	3.03	3.38	121.2	135.2
x 45	3.00	3.33	133.3	148.0
x 40	2.97	3.29	148.5	164.5
x 35	2.94	3.25	168.0	185.7
x 37	2.91	3.21	157.3	173.5
x 32.9	2.88	3.17	175.1	192.7
x 30.9	2.88	3.17	186.4	205.2
MC-10 x 41.1	2.76	3.13	134.3	152.3
x 33.6	2.70	3.04	160.7	181.0
x 28.5	2.67	3.00	187.4	210.5
x 28.3	2.54	2.83	179.5	200.0
x 25.3	2.54	2.83	200.8	223.7
x 24.9	2.51	2.79	201.6	224.1
x 21.9	2.54	2.83	232.0	258.4
MC-9 x 25.4	2.38	2.67	187.4	210.2
x 23.9	2.38	2.67	199.2	223.4
MC-8 x 22.8	2.21	2.50	193.9	219.3
x 21.4	2.21	2.50	206.5	233.6
x 20	2.08	2.33	208.0	233.0
x 18.7	2.08	2.33	222.5	249.2
MC-7 x 22.7	2.07	2.38	182.4	209.7
x 19.1	2.04	2.33	213.6	244.0
x 17.6	1.92	2.17	218.2	246.6
MC-6 x 18	1.88	2.17	208.9	241.1
x 15.3	1.88	2.17	245.8	283.7
x 16.3	1.75	2.00	214.7	245.4
x 15.1	1.75	2.00	231.8	264.9
x 12	1.63	1.83	271.7	305.0
MC-3 x 9	1.03	1.21	228.9	268.9
x 7.1	1.00	1.17	281.7	329.6

Courtesy: Richardson Engineering Services, Inc.

Structural steel conversion table
Figure 20-4 (continued)

Diameter (in feet)	Area (SF)
10	314
15	707
20	1,257
25	1,963
30	2,827
35	3,848
40	5,027
45	6,362
50	7,854
55	9,503
60	11,310
65	13,273
70	15,394

Surface area of spheres
Figure 20-5

Bidding Heavy Commercial and Industrial Work

Most heavy commercial and industrial construction work is bid on a semi-formal basis. That means you must follow set rules and procedures. In larger cities, you'll see an invitation to bid in a local construction newspaper. Larger projects will be advertised in national publications.

If you want to bid on major commercial, industrial or institutional projects, subscribe to *Dodge Reports.* They'll send you "bidding slips" when major construction projects are ready for bid. The same company maintains plan rooms in many cities where you can check out plans for projects being bid. You might also want to subscribe to *Dodge Scan,* which can transmit plans on microfilm directly to a monitor in your office. Both are available from:

McGraw-Hill Information Systems Co.
2 Coral Circle
Monterey Park, CA 91754-7404

The phone number is (213) 727-0120. For *Dodge Scan,* the phone is (800) 438-7226.

Many general contractors invite selected subcontractors to bid on projects. The best way to find out about new work is to develop a reputation for professionalism and reliability with the general contractors in your area. Then they'll call you when they're bidding, and refer you to other general contractors.

Plan Availability
When an invitation to bid is published, there may be so many subcontractors bidding that plans are in short supply. Often the "major" trades (concrete, steel, framing, plumbing, electric and HVAC) get the first opportunity to bid. They take the plans back to their office to do their take-off. "Minor" trades (including painting) may have to use a plan set that can't leave the plan room, the general contractor's office, or the job site trailer. So be prepared to do take-offs outside of your office.

Even if there are enough plans to go around, you may have to leave a plan deposit of $10.00 to $20.00. That encourages you to return them on time.

Selecting Projects to Bid
How do you choose which projects to bid? We covered bidding variables in Chapter 7, but let's review the variables most important to commercial and industrial work.

1) Budgeted value of the project: Is it within your company's acceptable range?

2) Anticipated length of the construction period.

3) Is it the type of project you do best?

4) Project complexity: Can you handle it?

5) Location of the project: Is it in your geographical range?

6) Reputation of the architects: Are they competent? Have you worked with them before?

7) Reputation of the general contractors bidding the project: Do you work well with them?

8) Competitors: Are they competent and ethical? How many are bidding? What are your odds if five general contractors are bidding and each has requested bids from their seven favorite paint contractors?

9) Time of the year: Is the timing good for your company?

10) Labor status of the project: Is it union or open shop?

11) Insurance and bonding requirements: Are they within your capability?

12) Your desire for the work.

If you carefully consider all of these factors, your decision whether or not to bid should be pretty easy. Some painting contractors assign point values to each item and do a numerical analysis. Others rely on a gut feeling. In doubtful cases, I'll let my intuition override the logical analysis. In other words, if it doesn't feel right, don't do it.

There's one situation that you have to consider even more carefully. What if you have an opportunity to bid on a major project that's larger or more complicated than any of your past projects? I'd suggest doing a detailed take-off and add a little extra profit. And make sure you have enough cash to handle a large project.

The Invitation to Bid
Before you bid to a general contractor, consider the general contractor's history of dealing with subcontractor bids. Some general contractors have favorite subs in each trade. They may solicit bids from a few other painting contractors for each project, but it's the favorite who will be successful. Do you really want to take the time to do an estimate under these conditions?

When a general contractor invites you to bid, don't go by the plans and specifications alone. Consider the general's reputation, and the competition you're facing, before you commit yourself.

Instructions to Bidders
Most commercial or industrial bid documents will include *Instructions to Bidders*. These instructions define all the bid documents and procedures for submitting your bid.

It's important that you read and understand each section of the instructions. If your bid is accepted, you've got to follow these instructions to the letter. Ignorance is no excuse. Failure to comply can be very costly.

Submitting Bids
General contractors usually rush around at the last minute to get their bids in by the deadline. To help them out, submit your bid by phone. And be prepared to follow up with a written proposal the same day. Make sure you have all of this information at your fingertips before you make that phone call:

1) Company name and phone number

2) Agent name (person submitting the bid)

3) Specification number of section bidding

4) Project name

5) Base bid amount

6) Alternates (additional price for alternatives)

7) Bid per plans and specifications

8) Addendum noted (additions to the plans & specs)

9) Specific *exclusions*

10) Specific *inclusions* (other than within section)

The general contractor's estimators will evaluate your bid and call back if they have any questions. Expect to hear from them if:

• The bid is incomplete

• The bid needs explanation or clarification

Make sure your bid is complete and that it follows the Instructions to Bidders. Few general contractors have the time or patience to call about every question they have in a sub-bid. Imagine the problem: calling three bidders for each of the 30 trades in a job. Deadline pressure usually makes that impossible.

On many published bids, the deadline is 2:00 PM and the results are announced by 5:00 PM. The successful general contractor will usually call the subcontractors to let them know they've won the bid. This verbal notification is good news — but don't start buying materials yet. Wait for a contract, or at least a *Letter of Intent* which confirms that a contract is on the way. The Letter of Intent functions like a contract. It's safe to start the job when you have it in hand.

In some cases, there's one last step in the bidding process. The results may have to be published in the same publication that carried the request for bidders. If you've done everything right, you'll see your name in that paper as successful bidder from time to time!

ESTIMATING WALLCOVERING

The broadest definition of *wallcovering* is "any material used to cover either interior or exterior wall surfaces." But in this chapter we'll focus on the narrower, and more familiar, meaning — interior wallcoverings, including wallpaper. We'll consider two categories of wallcoverings, residential and commercial.

Residential and Commercial Wallcoverings

Residential wallcovering is usually packaged and sold in single, double or triple rolls, or in bolts. But most commercial coverings are sold by the linear yard. Let's look at these two general categories of wallcoverings.

Residential Wallcoverings

You'll use residential wallcovering for apartments, condominiums and single-family homes. It comes in widths of 16 to 30 inches. But no matter how wide it is, American rolls will always have 36 square feet and European rolls will have 28.19 square feet. You can get bolts in custom lengths, commonly two to three rolls per bolt.

Commercial Wallcovering Applications

Commercial wallcoverings are used in hotels, motels and offices. You'll find them in widths of 27 and 54 inches, commonly sold by the yard. That's why they're sometimes called *yard goods* or *yardage goods*. A linear yard of 54-inch material will cover 13.5 square feet. You can also buy it in bolts of 30, 60 or 90 yards or any custom length. There's usually an extra charge for this "cut to measure" service.

Wallcovering Contracts
Labor Only Contracts

When the wallcovering material is furnished "by others" (usually the owner), your only responsibility is to furnish the labor for installation. I like "labor only" jobs like that. They help preserve my cash and save the time I would otherwise spend selecting patterns and colors.

Even if you're not involved in the selection process, it's good customer relations to discuss the quantity of material needed, differences in the cost of installing various types of wallcovering, and your material handling charges. If you're installing wallcovering furnished by others, add an extra

10% to 15% to the labor charge for material handling. If your crew damages or loses any wallcover, the 10% or 15% margin will help pay for replacement. And always verify that the right amount of material is supplied.

Labor and Material Contracts

If you buy the wallcover, you'll have cash tied up in inventory before the job starts. The cost of paper may be more than the cost of labor on a wallcovering job. I recommend that you insist on payment for the wallcovering materials when they're delivered to the job site. Make sure your contract provides for this prepayment.

Guarantee Clauses

Your agreement with the general contractor probably sets minimum quality standards for both material *and* your work. A one-year guarantee is most common. But you shouldn't be held responsible if the wallcovering fades or deteriorates during that year. If possible, get guarantees from your material suppliers. Most won't give those guarantees, though some will guarantee a specific application on a specific project.

When you're writing a wallcovering proposal for a building owner, try to avoid making any guarantee of either material or workmanship.

Estimating Forms

Many experienced estimators use a blank sheet of paper to compile wallcovering estimates. I don't recommend that. Instead, use a form appropriate for the estimating system you follow. A form helps you get organized and prevents mistakes. It also serves as a checklist. Use my forms, or design your own. Just make sure the form you use has a place to enter all the parts of the estimate.

Estimating wallcovering is like estimating repaint work. In fact, with a few modifications, you can use the repaint estimating forms from Chapter 18 for your wallcovering estimates. Look back at my repaint take-off sheet (Figure 18-4) and repaint recap form (Figure 18-16). Just revise a few of the title headings, substituting wallcovering for repainting.

Now let's get to the heart of the chapter: how to estimate wallcovering.

Parts of a Wallcovering Estimate

Wallcovering work includes some operations that aren't part of a paint job. You may have to remove old wallcover or prepare the surface with sizing and adhesive. But your wallcovering estimate also includes the sections we've looked at several times — from preparation to profit.

Wallcovering can be expensive. Most of the cost of the job may be materials. That makes your material take-off very important. I'm devoting a large part of this chapter to calculating the material quantity. But first let's look at the parts of a wallcovering estimate, starting with removing the old wallcover.

Removing Wallcovering

If possible, charge by the hour for removing the old wallcover. Use your hourly shop rate. It's hard to know ahead of time just how long the work will take. If you can't charge by the hour, use my formulas back in the preparation estimating table in Chapter 17.

There are three ways to remove that old wallcover: water saturation, steam, or chemical spray. It isn't hard work, but it is messy and tedious. Skilled craftsmen aren't needed. Most wallcovering will peel off if you soak it with water for a few minutes. But some coverings will take more than that. Allow extra time if you find any of the following:

- Water repellant coating on the wallcover

- More than one layer of wallcover

- Paint over old wallcover

- A subsurface that's easily damaged by scraping

When these conditions exist, charging by the hour is the best solution. Also include the cost of protective clothing and goggles for the workers.

Your estimate must also include material and equipment cost for chemicals, spray rigs, or steamers. Estimate the quantity of chemicals you'll need for the job and add the cost to your estimate. Use daily rental rates for any equipment necessary to complete the job.

Surface Preparation

Surface prep is just as important when installing wallcovering as it is when painting. But there's no sure way to estimate the time needed to patch a hole or putty a crack. The best way is to estimate prep on a time and material basis. When your customer insists on a firm bid, use your judgment (and be conservative) to estimate the time and materials needed using the preparation formulas from Chapter 17. Then hope that your crew can do a reasonably professional job in the time and with the material allowed.

For previously painted surfaces, allow time for sanding and washing with TSP (trisodium phosphate). Wallpaper won't stick to a surface that's not clean. Some patching and sanding will probably be needed. The preparation table in Chapter 17 includes labor rates for washing walls, as well as various repairs. As a general rule, figure 100 to 150 square feet per manhour for prepping surfaces for wallcovering under average conditions.

There are some situations, however, where the prep is different. For instance, if you try to remove vinyl wallcovering from drywall, the adhesive may pull off chunks of the drywall. Lots of patching will be needed to make the wall smooth again. You can avoid this by applying new vinyl right over the old. Use a vinyl-to-vinyl sealer adhesive under the new wallcovering to be sure it sticks to the existing cover. But be sure the existing surface is smooth and clean before you apply the new material.

Sizing
Some professionals don't apply sizing under the wallcover. I think that's a mistake. Sizing seals the wall, creates a tacky surface that makes handling easier, and makes removing the wallcovering easier. Sizing the surface is like priming before painting. It's quick and easy and creates a more professional job. I think it's well worth the effort. Labor rates for sizing are in Figure 21-1, the wallcovering estimating tables.

Adhesive
For most commercial wallcovering, you'll have to allow time for spreading adhesive on the wall. Many residential paper-backed wallcoverings just need soaking in water to activate adhesive already there. You'll find spread rates for various adhesive pastes and ready-mix adhesives in Figure 21-1.

Installation Labor
If you don't have your own installation formulas, use my production rates in Figure 21-1. They're arranged according to the Construction Specification Institute (CSI) categories for wallcovering:

Wallcovering	* CSI Division 09950
Vinyl-coated wallcovering	* CSI Division 09955
Vinyl wallcovering	* CSI Division 09960
Cork wallcovering	* CSI Division 09965
Wallpaper	* CSI Division 09970
Wall fabrics	*CSI Division 09975
Flex. wood sheet and veneers	* CSI Division 09980
Prefinished panels	* CSI Division 09985

My formulas include a productivity range from slow to fast. Use the slow figures for working in occupied rooms and the fast figures for vacant rooms. Also consider using a difficulty factor for working in occupied or crowded areas that don't have much elbow room. And don't forget to add time for SURRPTUCU (setup, remove and replace, protection, touchup and cleanup). Review these charges in Chapter 17.

Estimating Material Quantity
Because your manhour estimate will depend on the quantity, estimating material quantities is the most important part of your wallcovering estimate. That's why I'm going to explain several ways to calculate the amount of wallcovering needed. But no matter which method you use, be sure to distinguish between European rolls (28.19 square feet) and American rolls (36 square feet). My formulas in Figure 21-1 are based on American rolls.

Converting Wallcovering Measurements
It's easier to estimate wallcovering materials accurately if you can convert measurements easily from one system to another. For example, you may want to convert American rolls into the equivalent in European rolls. To make this conversion quick and easy, you need a conversion formula:

Wallcover Estimating Tables

Use this table to estimate the time and material needed to cover walls and ceilings with American roll goods (36 square feet per roll). European roll goods have only 28.19 SF per roll and cover only 78% as much area as American rolls. Conversion tables later in this chapter will help you convert from American to European rolls, if that's necessary. Paste coverage rates are listed in square feet (SF) per gallon, yards per gallon or rolls per gallon.

No time is included in the manhour estimates for setup, removal or replacement of hardware, protection of adjacent surfaces, touchup or cleanup (SURRPTUCU) except as noted. Neither do the tables include time needed for preparation of samples for client approval, scaffold erection or rental, or the unloading or loading of vehicles. See the preparation time estimates in Chapter 17 and the equipment pricing tables in Chapter 15.

Production rates in this chapter are in rolls per day and assume work by journeyman paperhangers. Medium (or average) production rates are most common when semiskilled tradesmen are working on medium-size jobs and doing average quality work without special difficulties. Work will go faster or slower under other conditions. The table that follows should help you identify conditions that will affect productivity on the job you're figuring. Production rates in this chapter are classified as slow, medium and fast to reflect job conditions as identified below.

Slow	Medium	Fast
Occupied area	Some obstructions	Vacant rooms
Expensive material	Medium cost material	Low cost material
(good quality)	(average quality)	(minimum quality)
First quality work	Average quality	Production quality
Heavy-weight goods	Medium-weight	Light-weight goods
High difficulty	Medium difficulty	Low difficulty
Poor conditions	Average conditions	Good conditions
Many doors & windows	Average number of openings	Few openings
Over existing	Some re-cover	New construction
Small job	Medium job	Large job
(under 1,000 SF)	(1,000 to 5,000 SF)	(over 5,000 SF)
Single units	2 to 4 units	5 or more units
Unskilled crew	Semiskilled crew	Skilled crew

Adhesive and paste consumption rates will vary from heavy to light, depending on several factors. Here's a guide to deciding whether adhesive or paste usage will be heavy or light on the job you're figuring.

Heavy	Light
Heavy-weight goods	Light-weight goods
Heavy-texture goods	Light-texture goods
High backing absorption	Low absorption
Heavy application	Light application
Heavy coverage	Light coverage
Heavy usage	Light usage
Thick mix	Thin mix
High waste factor	Low waste factor
Unskilled applicators	Skilled applicators
Many openings	Few or no openings

Wallcover estimating tables
Figure 21-1

Waste factors will vary from job to job. Expect more waste of materials where walls over stairways are papered, under dormers or dropped ceilings, in furred areas, in hallways and in smaller rooms such as bathrooms. Waste will be less in long hallways, in hotel or motel rooms and in larger rooms with few openings. There is no consistently reliable way to estimate waste other than measuring the surface and figuring the drops required.

	Number of rolls per day		
Average labor production	Slow	Medium	Fast
Average room size			
Walls	17	19	21
Ceilings	15	17	19
Small rooms			
Walls	7	9	11
Ceilings	6	8	10

Productivity and pricing	Rolls per hour	Yards per hour	Dollars per roll
Residential jobs			
Kitchen or baths	1.5	--	$19.00
Fabric	--	5.0	$8.00
Commercial jobs (motels, large tenant improvement)			
54" vinyl	--	9.0	$5.00
27" vinyl	3.25	--	$14.00

These figures can be used to estimate piece-work production costs. They're based on an hourly cost of $17 for residential work and $14.75 for commercial work. At those rates, a wallcover contractor should charge $300 per day for a qualified residential journeyman paperhanger and $200 per day for a qualified commercial journeyman paperhanger.

	Square feet per hour		
Surface preparation	Slow	Medium	Fast
Rule of thumb, typical preparation	100	125	150
Putty cracks, sand and wash	120	135	150

Rule of thumb: For surface preparation and sizing, allow 1 hour per room, maximum. See also the surface preparation table in Chapter 17.

Sizing · *Rules of thumb*	SF per hour Slow-Med-Fast	SF per gallon Heavy-Light
Brush adhesive size on smooth walls	350-375-400	350-400
Varnish sizing	300-325-350	300-350

Wallcover estimating tables
Figure 21-1 (continued)

Adhesive coverage

Per gallon of liquid Type of adhesive	Size	Adhesive conversion to gallons	SF per gallon Heavy-Light	American rolls per gallon Heavy-Light	Linear yards per gallon Heavy-Light
Ready-mix:					
Light-weight vinyl	gallon	--	225-275	7-8	17 - 20
Heavy-weight vinyl	gallon	--	150-200	5-6	13 - 15
Cellulose	gallon	--	200-250	6-8	16 - 19
Vinyl-to-vinyl	pint	6	175-225	6-7	15 - 17
Powdered cellulose	2 oz	1.75	333-400	10-12	25 - 30
Powdered vinyl	1 lb	1.75	333-400	10-12	25 - 30
Powdered wheat paste	1 lb	1.75	375-425	11-13	28 - 33

The column headed *Conversion to gallons* shows the quantity of vinyl or dry paste required to make one gallon of liquid paste. For example, one pound of powdered wheat makes 1.75 gallons of liquid paste when mixed with about 1-1/2 gallons of cold water.

Vinyl wallcover production

CSI Divisions 09950 to 09965 In single rolls per day	Residential (hand pasted) 18" to 27" width Slow Med Fast			Commercial (machine pasted) 48" or 54" width Slow Med Fast		
Cut-up areas (stairs, halls, landing areas)						
Walls	10	11	12	16	18	20
Ceilings	7	8	9	13	15	17
Small rooms (baths, utility rooms)						
Walls	11	12	13	17	20	22
Ceilings	9	10	11	15	18	20
Medium room (bedrooms, dining rooms)						
Walls	17	19	21	25	30	35
Ceilings	15	17	19	22	27	32
Large rooms (living room, conference rooms)						
Walls	20	23	26	30	35	40
Ceilings	18	20	22	26	31	36
Large wall areas (corridors, long hallways)						
Walls	24	27	30	35	40	45
Ceilings	21	23	25	30	35	40
Paper-backed vinyl on medium room walls						
Bedrooms, dining rooms	8	10	12	17	21	25
Cork wallcovering on medium room walls						
Bedrooms, dining rooms	8	10	12	17	21	25

Vinyl coated wallcovering appears under section 09955 in the CSI indexing system. Vinyl wallcovering appears in section 09960. Cork wallcovering appears in section 09965. The table above assumes that residential rolls are hand pasted and commercial rolls are machine pasted.

Wallcover estimating tables
Figure 21-1 (continued)

Wallpaper production CSI Division 09970 In single rolls per day	Residential (hand pasted) 18" to 27" width Slow Med Fast			Commercial (machine pasted) 48" or 54" width Slow Med Fast		
Blind stock (lining)						
Cut-up areas (above stairs, landings)						
Walls	11	13	14	19	21	23
Ceilings	10	11	12	16	18	20
Small room walls (baths, utility rooms)						
Walls	12	14	16	21	25	29
Ceiling	11	12	14	17	20	22
Medium room walls (bedrooms, dining rooms)						
Walls	20	23	26	29	35	41
Ceilings	18	20	22	25	30	34
Large room walls (living or conference rooms)						
Walls	23	27	31	35	41	47
Ceiling	20	22	24	29	33	38
Large area walls (corridors, long halls)						
Walls	29	33	36	40	45	50
Ceilings	23	25	27	33	38	42
Ordinary pre-trimmed wallpaper or butt joint work						
Medium room walls (bedrooms, dining rooms)						
Walls	18	21	24	26	31	36
Ceilings	16	18	20	23	27	32
Hand-crafted wallpaper						
Medium room walls (bedrooms, dining rooms)						
Walls	12	15	18	20	24	28
Ceilings	10	12	14	18	21	23
Flock wallpaper, medium rooms (bedrooms, dining rooms)						
Walls	10	13	16	14	17	20
Foil wallpaper, medium rooms (bedrooms, dining rooms)						
Walls	9	12	15	13	16	19
Scenic wallpaper, medium rooms (bedrooms, dining rooms)						
Walls	12	14	16	16	18	20

The figures above assume that residential rolls are hand pasted and commercial rolls are machine pasted.

Scenic panels and borders
Hand pasted

	Slow	Med	Fast
Panels, panels per hour	1.3	1.6	2.0
Borders 3" to 8" wide, LF per hour	100.0	112.0	125.0
Canvas wallpaper, single rolls per hour	1.0	1.3	1.5

These figures will apply in medium rooms (such as bedrooms or dining rooms) and on either residential or commercial jobs.

Wallcover estimating tables
Figure 21-1 (continued)

Wall fabric production CSI section 09975 In single rolls per day	Residential (hand pasted) 18" to 27" width Slow Med Fast			Commercial (machine pasted) 48" or 54" width Slow Med Fast		
Coated fabrics						
Cut-up areas (above stairs and landings)						
Walls	12	13	14	23	25	27
Ceilings	8	9	10	14	16	18
Small rooms (bathrooms, utility rooms)						
Walls	13	14	15	24	26	28
Ceilings	10	11	12	16	19	22
Medium rooms (bedrooms, dining rooms)						
Walls	18	20	22	27	32	37
Ceilings	16	18	20	24	29	34
Large rooms (living, conference rooms)						
Walls	22	25	28	34	39	44
Ceilings	19	21	23	27	32	37
Large area walls (corridors or long hall)						
Walls	26	29	32	38	44	50
Ceilings	22	24	26	31	36	41
Canvas sheeting						
Medium rooms (bedrooms, dining rooms)						
Walls	14	16	17	--	--	--
Grasscloth						
Medium rooms (bedrooms, dining rooms)						
Walls	15	20	24	--	--	--
Burlap						
Medium rooms (bedrooms, dining rooms)						
Walls	10	14	18	--	--	--
Natural fabric: silk						
Medium rooms (bedrooms, dining rooms)						
Walls	8	12	15	--	--	--
Natural fabric: felt, linen, cotton						
Medium room walls (bedrooms, dining rooms)						
Walls	7	9	11	--	--	--

Flexible wood sheet and veneer CSI section 09980 Square feet per hour	Residential or commercial Slow Med Fast		
Wood veneer flexwood	14	20	26
Flexi-wall systems	12	18	24

Use these figures to estimate walls in medium rooms (such as bedrooms or dining rooms).

Wallcover estimating tables
Figure 21-1 (continued)

American/European conversion formulas— To convert from American to European single rolls, use a factor of 1.25. Here's where the factor comes from:

$$\frac{36.0 \text{ SF}}{28.19 \text{ SF}} = 1.277 \text{ rounded to a factor of } 1.25$$

To convert American single rolls (ASR) to European single rolls (ESR), multiply by the factor:

$$\text{ASR x } 1.25 = \text{ESR}$$
$$5 \text{ ASR x } 1.25 = 6.25 \text{ rounded to } 7 \text{ ESR}$$

To convert European single rolls to American single rolls, multiply the ESR by 0.75

$$\text{ESR x } .75 = \text{ASR}$$
$$5 \text{ ESR x } .75 = 3.75 \text{ rounded to } 4 \text{ ASR}$$

Metric conversion formulas— To convert domestic to metric measurements, or metric to domestic, use Figure 21-2.

Single roll and bolt conversion formulas— Use Figure 21-3, American single roll conversion table, and Figure 21-4, American bolt conversion table, to covert American goods to linear inches, feet or yards. These tables also show the number of strips per roll or bolt.

Figures 21-5 and 21-6 show the same conversions for European rolls and bolts.

Commercial wallcovering conversion tables— Figures 21-7, 21-8 and 21-9 make it easy to convert American or European rolls to square feet, square yards or linear yards.

Domestic to metric conversions

1 inch	=	2.54 centimeters
1 foot	=	30.48 centimeters
1 yard	=	91.40 centimeters or .914 meters
1 square inch	=	6.45 square centimeters
1 square foot	=	929.03 square centimeters
1 square yard	=	.836 square meters

Metric to domestic conversions

1 centimeter	=	.39 inch or .033 feet
1 meter	=	1.1 yards
1 square centimeter	=	.15 square inches or .001 square feet
1 square meter	=	1.21 square yards

Metric conversion table
Figure 21-2

Roll width (inches)	SF per roll	Linear feet	Linear yards	Linear inches	Number of drops or strips per single roll		
					8 ft	9 ft	10 ft
18	36	24	8	288	3 +	2 +	2 +
20 ½	36	21	7	252	2 +	2 +	2 +
24	36	18	6	216	2 +	2 +	1 +
27	36	16	5 ⅓	192	2 +	1 +	1 +
27	33.8	15	5	180	1 +	1 +	1 +
28	35	15	5	180	1 +	1 +	1 +
36	36	12	4	144	1 +	1 +	1 +

American single roll conversion table
Figure 21-3

Roll width (inches)	SF per bolt	Rolls	Linear feet	Linear yards	Linear inches	Number of drops or strips per single roll		
						8 ft	9 ft	10 ft
18	72.0	2	48	16	576	6 +	5 +	4 +
20½	72.0	2	42	14	504	5 +	4 +	4 +
24	72.0	2	36	12	432	4 +	4 +	3 +
27	72.0	2	32	10.67	384	4 +	3 +	3 +
	108.0	3	48	16	576	6 +	5 +	4 +
27	67.5	2	30	10	360	3 +	3 +	3 +
	101.3	3	45	15	540	5 +	5 +	4 +
28	70.0	2	30	10	360	4 +	3 +	3 +
	105.0	3	45	15	540	5 +	5 +	4 +
36	72.0	2	24	8	288	3 +	2 +	2 +
	108.0	3	36	12	432	4 +	4 +	3 +

American bolt conversion table
Figure 21-4

Roll width (inches)	SF per roll	Linear feet	Linear yards	Linear inches	Number of drops or strips per single roll		
					8 ft	9 ft	10 ft
20	27.5	16′6″	5.5	198	2 +	1 +	1 +
20½	28.2	16′6″	5.5	198	2 +	1 +	1 +
21	28.8	16′6″	5.5	198	2 +	1 +	1 +

Note: European rolls may vary from 20″ wide to 21″ wide depending on the pattern or manufacturer.

European single roll conversion table
Figure 21-5

Roll width (inches)	SF per bolt	Rolls	Linear feet	Linear yards	Linear inches	Number of drops or strips per single roll		
						8 ft	9 ft	10 ft
20	55.0	2	33	11	396	4 +	3 +	3 +
20½	58.4	2	33	11	396	4 +	3 +	3 +
21	57.8	2	33	11	396	4 +	3 +	3 +

European bolt conversion table
Figure 21-6

Basis: One (1) linear yard of 48″ wallcovering	Basis: One (1) lineal yard of 54″ wallcovering
= 12.0 square feet = 1.33 square yards = 1.11 square meters = .333 American single rolls = .426 European single rolls	= 13.5 square feet = 1.53 square yards = 1.254 square meters = .375 American single rolls = .479 European single rolls

Commercial wallcovering conversion table
Figure 21-7

Quantity American single rolls	Total square feet	Total square yards	48″ wide linear feet	48″ wide linear yards	54″ wide linear feet	54″ wide linear yards
1	36	4	9	3	8	2.67
2	72	8	18	6	16	5.33
3	108	12	27	9	24	8.00
4	144	16	36	12	32	10.67
5	180	20	45	15	40	13.33
6	216	24	54	18	48	16.00
7	252	28	63	21	56	18.67
8	288	32	72	24	64	21.33
9	324	36	81	27	72	24.00
10	360	40	90	30	80	26.67
20	720	80	180	60	160	53.33
30	1080	120	270	90	240	80.00
40	1440	160	360	120	320	106.67
50	1800	200	450	150	400	133.33
60	2160	240	540	180	480	160.00
70	2520	280	630	210	560	186.67
80	2880	320	720	240	640	213.33
90	3240	360	810	270	720	240.00
100	3600	400	900	300	800	266.67

Commercial wallcovering conversion table
(American rolls)
Figure 21-8

Quantity American single rolls	Total square feet	Total square yards	48″ wide linear feet	48″ wide linear yards	54″ wide linear feet	54″ wide linear yards
1	28.19	3.13	7.05	2.35	6.27	2.09
2	56.38	6.26	14.10	4.70	12.54	4.18
3	84.57	9.40	21.15	7.05	18.81	6.27
4	112.76	12.53	28.20	9.40	25.08	8.36
5	140.95	15.66	35.25	11.75	31.35	10.45
6	169.14	18.79	42.30	14.10	37.62	12.54
7	197.33	21.93	49.32	16.44	43.89	14.63
8	225.52	25.06	56.37	18.79	50.16	16.72
9	253.71	28.19	63.42	21.14	56.43	18.81
10	281.90	31.32	70.47	23.49	62.70	20.90
20	563.81	62.64	140.94	46.98	125.28	41.76
30	845.70	93.97	211.44	70.48	187.92	62.64
40	1127.60	125.29	281.91	93.97	250.59	83.53
50	1409.50	156.61	352.38	117.46	313.23	104.41
60	1691.40	187.93	422.85	140.95	275.87	125.29
70	1973.30	219.26	493.32	164.44	438.51	146.17
80	2255.20	250.58	563.79	187.93	501.15	167.05
90	2537.10	281.90	634.29	211.43	563.79	187.93
100	2819.00	313.22	704.76	234.92	626.43	208.81

Commercial wallcovering conversion table
(European rolls)
Figure 21-9

Material Waste Factors

There will be waste on every wallcovering job. Short ends of rolls won't be long enough to use. Creases in the wallcovering may make part of the roll unusable. Allow for that with a waste factor.

The standard waste factor for domestic roll goods assumes you'll get 30 square feet of usable material out of a 36 square foot roll. That's a waste factor of 20% (36 divided by 30 is 1.2).

The standard waste factor for European roll goods is about 13%. It assumes that there are 25 usable square feet in a 28.19 square foot on a roll (28.19 divided by 25 is 1.1276).

The actual waste on a job can vary between 5% and 30%. For example, if the pattern in the paper is repeated every 4 feet, there will be a lot more waste. This is because the patterns in adjacent strips have to meet exactly at the seam between strips. Matching pattern at the seam will waste several feet of paper on most strips if the pattern repeats each 4 feet. A pattern that repeats every foot will result in less waste.

There will be waste on every wallcovering job

Here are the factors that influence the amount of waste:

1) The type of material used

2) The size of the room(s)

3) The width of the paper

4) The distance between pattern repeats

5) The length of the rolls or bolts

6) The number of windows, doors, or other obstructions.

7) The skill level of the hangers doing the work

Calculating Material Quantities

Estimates for wallcovering begin with a take-off of the material quantity. That's the basis of both your material and labor calculations. Your material estimate may have very little detail or great detail, depending on the estimating method you use. I'll show four ways to estimate wallcovering quantities. Use the method you like best for the job you're figuring.

To illustrate these methods, we'll go through a take-off for bedroom 1 of the sample plan in Appendix A. Its dimensions are 11 feet by 11.5 feet. Then I'll offer some charts you can use to check the results. I'll start with the standard square foot method.

Square Foot of Wallcovering Method

The square foot method uses the standard 20% waste factor (30 SF per roll usable) for walls and 10% waste (33 SF per roll usable) for ceilings. I recommend this method for jobs that use average cost materials applied to continuous, unbroken surfaces with little cutting and no pattern to match.

Step 1— Find the total square footage of the walls by measuring the perimeter of the room. Multiply the room perimeter by the height of the room:

$$11.5' + 11.0' + 9.0' + 8.0' + 2.5' + 3.0' =$$

$$45.0 \text{ LF} \times 8.0 \text{ high} = 360 \text{ SF}$$

Step 2— Deduct the openings:

Bedroom, door	2'6" x 6'8" =	17 SF
Window	6'0" x 4'0" =	24 SF
Window	3'0" x 3'0" =	9 SF
Wardrobe doors (2)	2'6" x 8'0" =	56 SF
Total deductions		106 SF

Step 3— Apply the standard waste factor to find the number of rolls you'll need. And remember to round up to the next full roll. This example is based on domestic roll goods, so we'll use a 20% waste factor for cutting, matching and fitting. First, find the net wall area, then divide it by 30 square feet per roll:

Gross wall area	360 SF
Deductions	106 SF
Net wall area	254 SF

$$\frac{254 \text{ SF}}{30 \text{ SF/roll}} = 8.47 \text{ or } 9 \text{ rolls}$$

Step 4— For this example, we're also covering the ceiling. To find the ceiling surface, multiply the room length by the width:

$$11.0' \text{ x } 11.5' = 126.5 \text{ or } 127 \text{ SF}$$

Step 5— There's little or no waste on continuous ceilings when pattern matching isn't a problem. To calculate the number of rolls needed for the ceiling, use a 10% waste factor. Divide the area by 33:

$$\frac{127 \text{ SF}}{33 \text{ SF/roll}} = 3.85 \text{ or } 4 \text{ rolls}$$

Step 6— Finally, add the rolls you'll need for the walls and ceiling. You calculated 9 rolls for the walls and 4 for the ceiling. That's a total of 13 rolls.

Square Foot of Surface Area Method

This method is based on adding the percentage of waste in terms of square feet of wall area. It's similar to the method we just used, except you don't use the standard percentage for waste. Use this method for jobs which are more difficult — average to good-quality material, some cutting, some pattern matching and some broken surfaces.

Steps 1 and 2— These are the same as the first method. There are 360 square feet of wall area and deductions of 106 square feet. That's a net wall area of 254 square feet.

Step 3— For this example, assume that the job is a little more difficult. You want to allow 25% for waste on walls instead of the standard 20%.

$$254 \text{ SF x } 25\% = 63.5 \text{ or } 64 \text{ SF}$$
$$254 \text{ SF } + 64 \text{ SF } = 318 \text{ SF}$$

Steps 4 and 5— Again, these steps are the same as the first method. There are 127 square feet of ceiling area, which has little waste. Allow 4 rolls of wallcover, including the closet.

Step 6— To find the total rolls required for the walls, divide the adjusted square feet by 36:

$$\frac{318 \text{ SF}}{36 \text{/SF roll}} = 8.83 \text{ or } 9 \text{ rolls}$$

Once again, you'll need 4 rolls for the ceiling and 9 for the walls, for a total of 13 rolls. Why do I bother with two methods if the end result is the same? So you can choose the one that works best for you. The first method is more common, and you can use the second method to double-check your results.

Square of the Room Method

This shortcut method is handy for quick, approximate estimates for walls only. You can also use it to check your calculations done by other methods. It works best for jobs with little cutting, no pattern matching and unbroken surfaces. And it only works with domestic roll wallcoverings in rooms with standard 8-foot ceilings.

Step 1— Add the length and the width of the room.

11.0'
11.5'
22.5'

Step 2— Divide the answer by 2 to get the gross number of rolls you'll need:

$$22.5' \div 2 = 11.5 \text{ or } 12 \text{ rolls}$$

Step 3— Calculate the square foot area of the openings. We did that back in the first method. The openings in the sample bedroom total 106 square feet.

Step 4— Find the number of rolls to deduct, based on 36 square feet per roll, and round down to the nearest whole roll since this is a deduction from the total:

$$\frac{106 \text{ SF}}{36 \text{ SF/roll}} = 2.94 \text{ or } 2 \text{ rolls}$$

Step 5— Deduct the 2 rolls from the gross number of rolls: 12 minus 2 is 10 rolls for this job. This shortcut method yields an estimate that's 1 roll more than the detailed estimating methods. Don't rely on it for an actual estimate.

Drop or Strip Method

This is the most accurate method of estimating wallcovering. Use it when you're applying fragile, expensive material with a pattern and many drops or strips to cut. To do an accurate estimate, you have to know the width of the material, the length of the roll or bolt, and the distance between each repeat of the pattern.

Step 1— Calculate the number of *full drops*. Find the length in linear feet of the full walls (uninterrupted from floor to ceiling) and divide by the width of the material. Let's use 24 inches (2.0') for this example. Here's the take-off for our sample bedroom:

8.5'	÷	2.0'	=	4.25	or	5
2.5'	÷	2.0'	=	1.25	or	2
2.5'	÷	2.0'	=	1.25	or	2
2.5'	÷	2.0'	=	1.25	or	2
3.5'	÷	2.0'	=	1.75	or	2
2.5'	÷	2.0'	=	1.25	or	2
3.0'	÷	2.0'	=	1.50	or	2
			Full drops			17

Step 2— Calculate the frequency of *repeats*. If the pattern repeats every 18 inches and the wall height is 96 inches, there are 5.33 pattern repeats per drop. Round it up to six pattern repeats per drop. Don't deduct the height of the baseboard in this calculation.

Step 3— Calculate the actual *drop length*. Since there are six pattern repeats at 18 inches each, the total required length for each drop is:

$$6 \times 18" = 108" \text{ or } 9.0' \text{ for each drop}$$

Step 4— Calculate the number of *rolls* required. If there are 36 square feet per single 24-inch roll, each roll is 18 feet long. That means there are two 9-foot drops in each roll. Since you need 17 drops, how many rolls do you need?

$$\frac{17 \text{ total drops}}{2 \text{ drops per roll}} = 8.5 \text{ single rolls}$$

Step 5— Calculate the actual length of the *header drops*. Refer to Figure 21-10. It shows the distance at the headers over the bedroom door and windows. It's 14 inches, the distance between the top of the openings at 6'8'' and the ceiling at 8'0''. According to the door schedule in Appendix A, the wardrobe doors extend to the ceiling, so there's no header here.

Step 6— Since you know that the *pattern repeat* distance is greater than the header drop, find the cut length of the header drop by multiplying the 14-inch distance by 1.5:

$$14" \times 1.5 = 21" \text{ or } 1.75 \text{ LF}$$

Step 7— To find the *number of header drops*, divide the width of each opening by the width of the roll:

Bedroom door	2.5' ÷ 2.0' = 1.25 or	2
Wardrobe door	(no header drops with 8'0" doors)	0
Window	6.0' ÷ 2.0' = 3.0'	3
Window	3.0' ÷ 2.0' = 1.5 or	2
Total header drops		7

Step 8— Calculate the *length of header drops* by multiplying the number of drops by the length of each drop:

$$7 \text{ drops} \times 1.75' = 12.25 \text{ or } 13 \text{ LF}$$

Step 9— Calculate the *narrow drops* for the two 6-inch widths next to the closet jambs. You can take them both from one full 24-inch wide drop. So add one full drop for these two narrow wall areas on each side of the closet.

Step 10— Calculate the *short drop* distance under the large window by measuring from the finished floor to the bottom of the window (Figure 21-10). It's 2'8".

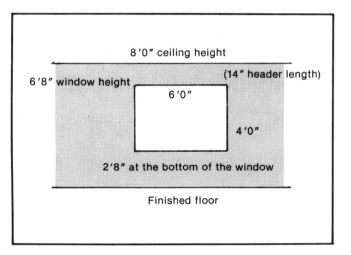

Header drops
Figure 21-10

Step 11— Calculate the drop length required with *pattern repeats* at 18 inches, or 1'6", by adding one pattern repeat length to the 2'8" drop length:

$$2'8" + 1'6" = 4'2" \text{ or } 4.17 \text{ LF}$$

Step 12— Calculate the *number of short drops* required under the large window the same way you figured the header drops in Step 7. There are three drops.

Step 13— Calculate the *total length* of wallcovering required for the drop at the large window:

$$3 \text{ drops x } 4.17' = 12.51 \text{ or } 13 \text{ LF}$$

Step 14— Calculate the *short drop* distance under the small window by measuring from the finished floor to the bottom of the window (Figure 21-11). It's 3'8".

Step 15— Compute the drop length required with pattern repeats at 1'6" by adding one pattern repeat length to the 3'8" drop length:

$$3'8" + 1'6" = 5'2" \text{ or } 5.17 \text{ LF}$$

Step 16— Figure the *number of short drops* under the small window just like the header drops in Step 7. There are two drops.

Step 17— Find the *total length* of wallcovering required for the drops at the small window:

$$2 \text{ drops x } 5.17' = 10.34 \text{ or } 11 \text{ LF}$$

Step 18— Accumulate the total length of header drops and short drops:

Step 8:	Header drops	13 LF
Step 9:	Closet jambs	8 LF
Step 13:	Large window	13 LF
Step 17:	Small window	11 LF
		45 LF

Step 19— Convert the linear feet of header and short drops to rolls:

$$\frac{45 \text{ LF}}{18 \text{ LF/roll}} = 2.5 \text{ single}$$

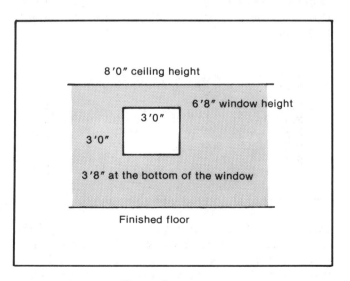

Short drops
Figure 21-11

Step 20— Calculate the total wallcovering by adding the header and short drop rolls to the full drop rolls:

Full drops (Step 16)	8.5 single rolls
Headers and short drops	2.5 single rolls
Total rolls	11.0 single rolls

Step 21— Figure the number of drops needed for the ceiling. First, consider which direction strips should be run to use the least material. That's from the closet to the large window, or the 11'6" length of the room. Since the room is 11'0" wide, and the rolls are 2'0" wide, it'll take six drops to cover the room. Let's see how long those drops will be.

Since you won't cover the closet walls or closet ceiling, four of the drops will be 9'0" long. The other two will be 11'6" long. That's a total of four rolls for the ceiling:

4 drops @ 9'0" =	36'0"
2 drops @ 11'6" =	23'0"
	59'0" ÷ 18'0" =
	3.27 or 4 rolls

Step 22— Now find the total wallcovering needed for the room. The 18-inch pattern repeat increases the amount you need.

Walls	11 rolls
Ceiling	4 rolls
Total	15 rolls

Wallcovering Quantity Charts

Charts are convenient where rooms are a standard size rectangle. If you can't find your room size on the chart, calculate the room perimeter and look up the next larger size.

You'll find charts similar to these in many wallcovering sample books. The roll quantities may differ slightly depending on the estimating methods used. My domestic wallcovering chart (Figure 21-12) and the European wallcovering chart (Figure 21-13) provide a quick way to check your detailed estimates.

When using either of these charts, deduct one roll of wallcovering for each two ordinary doors or windows or for each 50 square feet of opening.

Domestic rolls— The domestic wallcovering chart at Figure 21-12 assumes you're using a standard roll, 8 yards long and 18 inches wide. It also assumes you'll get 30 usable square feet of material from each roll. The other 6 square feet is waste.

European rolls— The European wallcovering chart at Figure 21-13 assumes you're using the standard roll of 20-inch wallcover, containing 28.19 yards per roll. You'll get only 25 usable square feet per roll.

Material Pricing

The price you charge your clients for materials should include:

- Cost of the wallcovering per roll, including tax

- Freight and delivery charges

- Material handling charge to cover cutting errors on expensive material or wallcovering supplied by the owner.

- Tools and supplies, prorated for each job

Wallcovering Tools and Supplies

Since you'll use most wallcovering sundries on more than one job, charge the proportional costs for each job. You can estimate wallcovering sundries like the painting sundries we estimated in Chapter 14. But there's one difference. For painting, we added 10% to the material cost to cover the cost of sundries. Here we'll add the 10% charge to the total *labor cost,* since many wallcovering jobs are contracts for labor only.

Figure 21-14 is a checklist of the sundries you'll need on most wallcovering jobs.

Subcontracts and Commissions

Some painters subcontract either the labor or the entire wallcovering process. If you subcontract any

Room size	Room perimeter	Single rolls on sidewalls Ceiling height			Yards for borders	Rolls for ceiling
		8 ft	9 ft	10 ft		
4 x 8	22	6	7	8	9	2
4 x 10	28	7-8	8	9-10	11	2
6 x 10	32	8	9-10	10	12	2
6 x 12	36	9-10	10	11-12	14	3-4
8 x 12	40	10	11-12	12-13	15	4
8 x 14	44	11-12	12	14	16	4
10 x 14	48	12-13	14	15-16	17-18	5-6
10 x 16	52	13-14	14-15	16	19	6
12 x 16	56	14	16	17-18	20	7
12 x 18	60	15-16	17-18	19-20	21-22	8
14 x 18	64	16	18	20	23	8
14 x 20	68	17	19	21	25	9
16 x 18	68	17	19	21	25	10
16 x 20	72	18	20-21	22	26	10
16 x 22	76	19	21	23	28	11
16 x 24	80	20	22	25	29	12
16 x 26	84	21	23	26	31	13
18 x 22	80	20	22	25	29	12
18 x 25	86	21	24	27	31	14
18 x 28	92	23	26	28	33	16
20 x 26	92	23	26	28	33	17
20 x 28	96	24	27	30	34	18
29 x 34	108	27	30	33	39	21

Domestic wallcover quantity chart
Figure 21-12

Room size	Room perimeter	Single rolls on sidewalls Ceiling height			Rolls for ceiling
		8 ft	9 ft	10 ft	
4 x 8	22	9	11	13	3
4 x 10	28	10	12	14	3
6 x 10	32	11	13	15	4
6 x 12	36	12	14	16	4
8 x 12	40	14	16	18	6
8 x 14	44	16	17	20	7
10 x 14	48	16	19	20	8
10 x 16	52	18	20	22	8
12 x 16	56	20	22	24	9
12 x 18	60	20	24	26	10
14 x 18	64	22	25	28	10
14 x 20	68	24	26	28	12
16 x 18	68	24	26	28	12
16 x 20	72	24	28	30	14
16 x 22	76	24	28	31	15
16 x 24	80	25	29	32	16
16 x 26	84	27	29	33	17
18 x 22	80	25	28	32	16
18 x 25	86	27	30	34	18
18 x 28	92	29	33	35	21
20 x 26	92	29	33	35	22
20 x 28	96	30	34	38	24
29 x 34	108	34	38	42	27

European wallcover quantity chart
Figure 21-13

part of the job, get at least three bids. To do that many, you'll probably have to request bids from five or six subcontractors. See Chapter 15 for more information on hiring subcontractors.

If there's an estimator's bonus or a salesperson's commission, be sure to include it on the estimate.

Contingency, Overhead and Profit

A contingency allowance will protect you against increased costs if the job is delayed or if the scope of work isn't clearly defined.

The final step is to add your company's overhead and profit. We discussed that in detail in Chapter 16.

Sundries Checklist

☐ Broad knife (6″)

☐ Brush for pasting

☐ Brush for smoothing

☐ Bucket

☐ Carpenter's level

☐ Clamp for securing wallcovering to trimming table

☐ Drop cloths

☐ Glue gun for applying finish braid to fabric

☐ Paint roller with 9″ handle for applying adhesive

☐ Paint tray

☐ Plumb bob

☐ Razor blades

☐ Razor knife

☐ Seam roller

☐ Shears or utility scissors

☐ Sponge

☐ Stapler for stapling fabric wallcovering

☐ Stepladder

☐ Straightedge (6′) for measuring and cutting

☐ Water tray

☐ Work table, large and sturdy for trimming

☐ Tape measure

Wallcovering sundries checklist
Figure 21-14

THE GOVERNMENT CONTRACTING PROCESS

Most government projects follow a formal bidding and contract process. If you decide to bid on government projects, expect to deal with a lot more paperwork and red tape than you're used to on private projects.

You'll have to document compliance with these regulations:

- Labor standard provisions

- Bonding

- Requests for change

- Quality control

- Daily log reports

Some painting contractors simply refuse to bid government jobs because of these extra demands — but others learn the ropes and make good money on government work. The government never runs out of work, they tend to make prompt progress payments, and they always have the money to pay you. Getting paid more often and sooner is a big advantage for many painting companies.

That's why bidding government work is usually very competitive. In fact, it's so competitive that some jobs go for far less than the government's own estimate, even though public projects usually require more labor at a higher cost than similar private projects. The bid documents are always complex, with detailed specifications.

Contracting for Government Work

There are two ways you can begin bidding and contracting government work. First, you may be the prime contractor, bidding directly to a public agency for a building that needs repainting. Or you can bid to a general contractor who's bidding on a larger project.

Finding Government Work

Assuming you want to bid government jobs, how do you find the work? Start by considering every

*You can make good money on government work — though there are
few extra demands*

level of government: federal, state, county and city jobs, as well as the military and the GSA (Government Services Agency). You can find announcements of government projects in local construction newspapers and other publications. Government jobs are always published.

Selecting Projects to Bid

Deciding which government jobs to bid is just like qualifying private jobs to bid. Begin by reviewing all the bidding variables. Take time to study the plans and specifications carefully before you decide to bid. Don't waste time estimating a project that's not your cup of tea.

Before you start a take-off, read over all of the bid documents thoroughly at least two or three times. Don't stop until you understand all of the bid requirements. You might review several bid packages before deciding to submit your first bid on a government project.

Here are some specific bidding variables to consider in government projects.

Inspection requirements— Check the requirements for inspections. Public projects usually have at least one inspector to check plans, specifications and construction methods. That inspector is check-

ing for code compliance — and making sure that public funds are being spent properly.

Military projects usually have their own inspectors who make sure construction meets the plans, specifications and military standards.

Substitution of materials— The bid documents will tell you if substitution of materials is allowed. It may not be. Government jobs usually allow very little substitution.

Relief from bid— The bid documents will explain if there's relief (forgiveness) for the following errors:

- Late bids

- Omitting signatures on the certification and representation clauses

- Not listing employment opportunities

- Not acknowledging amendments or addenda

- Not using government bid documents

If there's no relief, any one of these oversights will disqualify your bid.

The Davis-Bacon Act: Wages

On public or government projects, you'll usually have to pay your painters the *prevailing wage* as defined by the Davis-Bacon Act. The law was passed by Congress in 1931 to set minimum wages for U.S. government projects. During the Depression, government projects were about the only work being done. The contractor paying the lowest wages usually got the most government work. The result was starvation wages that gave government jobs a bad reputation. The Davis-Bacon Act was intended to prevent that problem.

Originally, this act was one of the shortest pieces of legislation of all time, only 300 words. But over the years Congress "improved" it, adding an administrative code of labor rules and regulations that fills 27,000 pages. To determine the prevailing wage in hundreds of communities, the Department of Labor conducts 3,000 local wage surveys each year.

The bid documents for each project include the prevailing wages that apply. Anyone can protest that wage, and offer independent surveys as evidence that the Department of Labor figures are wrong. In several areas of the country, the Department of Labor has simply adopted local union rates as the prevailing wages.

Contractors working on prevailing wage projects must prepare a weekly *certified payroll* to verify compliance with the regulations. If your company is an open shop (non-union) contractor, Davis-Bacon wages will probably be higher than you usually pay. And you'll have to pay the required benefits (vacation, education, training, pension and health and welfare) in a separate check each payday if you don't have a benefits trust fund.

There are also rules for the number of apprentices you have to employ on each job, based on the number of journeymen. For example, the bid documents might specify one apprentice for each five journeymen. If you're an open shop with no apprenticeship training program, you have to pay every painter journeyman wages, whether they're skilled journeymen or unskilled apprentices. That's an obvious disadvantage.

Estimating Government Projects

Estimating government work is similar to estimating private work. But remember the prevailing wage requirement. And there are a couple of other areas where you need to pay special attention.

Many architectural drawings for government work are reduced by one-half. There's usually a large note on the cover sheet: "The scale is reduced by 1/2." This means that if the drawings show a scale of 1/4″ equals 1′0″, they'll actually measure at half that, or 1/8″ equals 1′0″. Keep that in mind as you do your take-off.

Visit the site of every government project and examine all bid documents carefully before starting the take-off. You can never tell what you might find on the site of a government project.

Bidding Government Work

Bidding government work is a formal process. The bid and contract documents will explain the bidding procedure. The documents will be complex, but you'll understand them if you take time to review them thoroughly. Follow them to the letter.

Invitation for bids— This is usually a one-page document on the top of the bid package. It summarizes the requirements for the project, including the bid deadline and location. You'll also find bond information, certification requirements, a description of the work, and the estimated cost range.

Bid form— Your bid has to be written on the bid form included in the bid package. It usually asks for the firm name and the name of the contractor's representative. Fill in the bid amount, the start date and length of the job, and an acknowledgment of the addenda, amendments and deletions. The bid form can double as an invitation to bid.

Besides the invitation to bid and bid form, most bid packages contain several other documents. Let's review the bid bond requirements, subcontractor listing, financial statement and specifications.

Bid bond requirements— A bid bond guarantees that the contractor will sign the contract if the bid is accepted. A performance bond guarantees that the work will be done as contracted. Usually, the bonding company that issues your bid bond will also be ready to issue a performance bond. The cost of bid and performance bonds will usually be between 2% and 7% of the bid amount.

Subcontractor listing— A prime contractor who's the apparent low bidder on a project must identify all subcontractors used to obtain the bid. If you used quotes from a sandblasting and wallcovering subcontractor to compile your estimate, you'll have to list them along with your bid for public announcement and publication. That's supposed to eliminate bid shopping.

Financial statement— Occasionally you'll have to submit a financial statement with the bid. That's to verify your company's financial health.

Specific trade information— The painting specification section explains what has to be done.

Submitting the Bid
Public agencies don't accept incomplete bid packages. If your bid isn't submitted according to the rules, it'll usually be rejected on the spot. Bids with unsolicited alternates or exceptions to the plans and specifications are also unacceptable. Bid opening deadlines are inflexible. I recommend hand delivering your bids to make sure they're in the right place at the right time. Contracts are typically awarded within ten days after the bid deadline.

Change Orders
The change order process in government work is tricky. Knowing how to handle change orders can easily make or break a job. There are three types of change orders in government work.

1) Formal change order: This is a written change order issued by the Contracting Officer (C.O.). It includes changes to the original scope of work, issued under the authority of the changes clause in the contract. The contractor will be paid for any additional work done.

2) Constructive change order: This change happens when an authorized official gives either written or oral instructions that require extra work by the contractor. The result is the same as a formal change order. You get paid for the extra work plus a reasonable profit. You also get extra time to complete the work.

3) Differing site conditions: You're entitled to more money when site conditions aren't what the government said they would be or are very different from site conditions on similar jobs. Type I site conditions relate to soil and underground water. Type II includes any other type of unexpected conditions.

For more information, get *Change Order Briefing Papers* from Federal Publications, Inc., 1725 K. St. NW, Washington, DC 20006.

Appendix

A

SAMPLE PLAN

PROJECT NAME: Vista Park

OWNER: Vista Development Corp.

ARCHITECT: Joseph Jones, AIA

GENERAL CONTRACTOR: John Doe Construction, Inc.

PROJECT LOCATION: Your Town (SEE VICINITY MAP)

PROJECT SIZE: Fifteen (15) HOMES

PLAN DATE: 2-1-89

PLAN SET: #7

Sample plan
Sheet 1: Title sheet

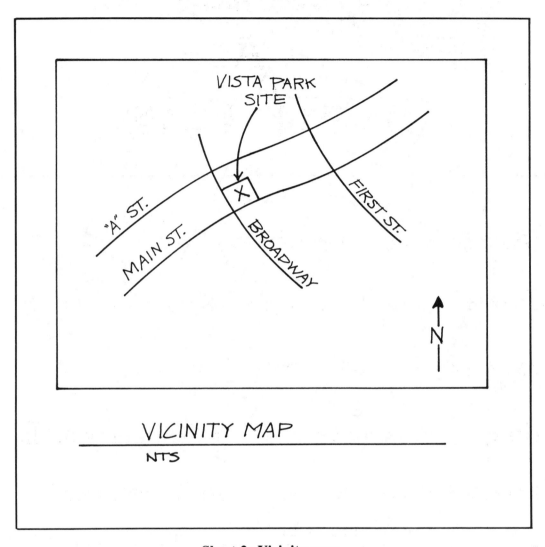

Sheet 2: Vicinity map

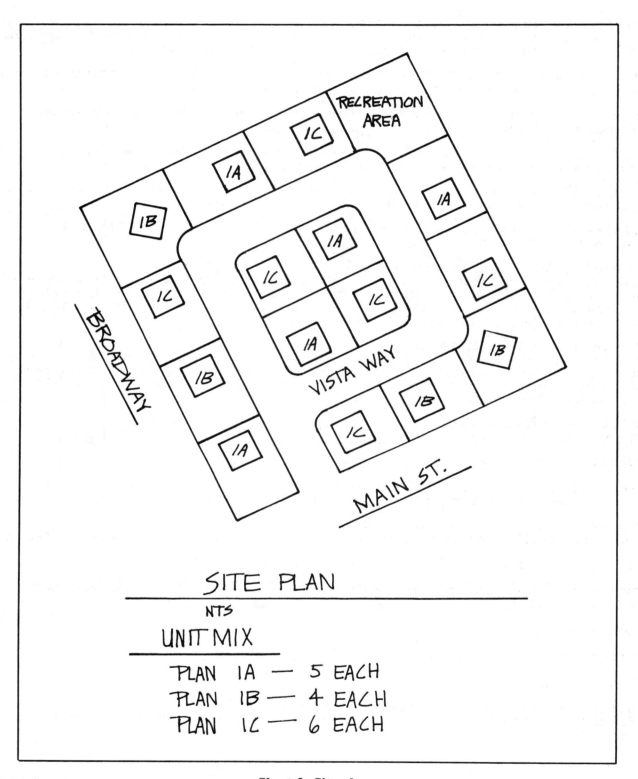

Sheet 3: Site plan

Division 1 - General Requirements

1. General contractor shall conform to the latest adopted edition of the Uniform Building Code (U.B.C.) and all local, state and federal requirements.

2. Trade names and manufacturer's name referred to are for quality standards. "Or Equal" substitutions are to be approved by the Architect or Owner.

3. All notes contained within these drawings are applicable unless otherwise mentioned in the specifications.

4. The Architect is to be held harmless from field operations. Safety, performance and scheduling are not the responsibility of the Architect.

5. General Contractor is to thoroughly review all plans and specifications and is responsible for reporting any errors or omissions at once.

Division 2 through 8, parts of Division and Division 10 through 16 have been omitted for clarity.

Division 09900 - Painting, General

The painting contractor will provide labor, material and equipment to produce a high-quality finished product in a timely manner. All materials to be applied according to manufacturer's specifications. All materials will arrive on the job site in labeled and sealed containers.

Division 09910 - Exterior Painting

The painting contractor will provide labor, material and equipment to produce a high-quality finished product in a timely manner. All materials to be applied according to manufacturer's specifications. All materials will arrive on the job site in labeled and sealed containers.

Division 09910 - Exterior Painting

Wood: One coat heavy-bodied stain

Metal: Preprimed by others, one coat zinc oxide

Stucco: One coat clear hydro sealer from finish grade up to 4'0" all around and 2'0" around all openings

Division 09920 - Interior Painting

Wet area walls and ceilings: One coat sealer and one coat enamel, off-white

Other walls and ceilings: One coat flat paint, off-white

Doors and casings, pullman cabinets: One coat undercoat and one coat enamel, off-white

Beams: One coat heavy-bodied stain

Tongue and groove ceiling: One coat semi-transparent stain

Base: Stain

Division 09930 - Transparent Finishes

Kitchen cabinets: One coat lacquer stain, one coat sealer and two coats lacquer.

Sheet 4: General notes

ELECTRICAL

K	TELEPHONE JACK
⊖	DUPLEX CONVENIENCE OUTLET
⊖---	½ HOT CONVENIENCE OUTLET
⊖ GFI	G.F.I. PROTECTED CONVENIENCE OUTLET
S---	SWITCH
S₃	3-WAY SWITCH
⊨===⊨	FLUORESCENT FIXTURE
O	LIGHT FIXTURE
⊅	WALL-MOUNTED LIGHT FIXTURE
◑	FAN
◑Ⓗ	FAN & HEAT
◑	SMOKE DETECTOR

PLUMBING & HEATING

⊖	GARBAGE DISPOSAL
—⊢FG	GAS LINE
—⊢HB	HOSE BIB
⊢⊖GM	GAS METER
⊢Ⓣ	THERMOSTAT
∿	REGISTER
(W/H)	WATER HEATER

GENERAL SYMBOLS

[W/D]	STACKED WASHER & DRYER SPACE
[R]	REFRIGERATOR SPACE
[ ]MC	MEDICINE CABINET

ABBREVIATIONS

A.B.	ANCHOR BOLT
ALUM	ALUMINUM
BLDG	BUILDING
BM	BEAM
BD	BOARD
₵	CENTERLINE
CLR	CLEAR
d	PENNY
DBL	DOUBLE
DIA	DIAMETER
DF/L	DOUGLAS FIR OR LARCH
DET	DETAIL
EA	EACH
FIN	FINISH
FLR	FLOOR
F.O.S.	FACE OF STUD
F.A.U.	FORCED AIR UNIT
GALV	GALVANIZED
GYP	GYPSUM
HDR	HEADER
H.B.	HOSE BIB
MAX	MAXIMUM
MIN	MINIMUM
MC	MEDICINE CABINET
OC	ON CENTER
φ	DIAMETER
PL	PLATE
℔	PROPERTY LINE
P.T. DF	PRESSURE TREATED DOUGLAS FIR
RWD	REDWOOD
ROS	ROUGHSAWN
T&G	TONGUE & GROOVE
U.B.C.	UNIFORM BUILDING CODE
W/	WITH
WI	WROUGHT IRON
WP	WATERPROOF

ROOM NAMES

Abbr.	Room	Abbr.	Room	Abbr.	Room
BR	BEDROOM	LIV	LIVING ROOM	ENT	ENTRY
BA	BATHROOM	DIN	DINING ROOM	UTIL	UTILITY ROOM
		KIT	KITCHEN		

Sheet 5: Symbols & abbreviations

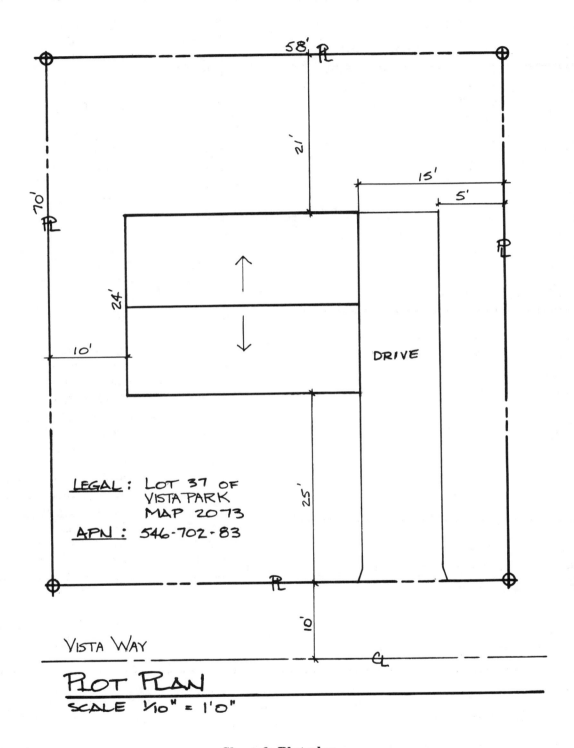

58' PL

21'

15'

5'

70' PL

PL

24'

10'

DRIVE

25'

LEGAL: LOT 37 OF
VISTA PARK
MAP 2073

APN: 546-702-83

PL

10'

VISTA WAY

CL

PLOT PLAN
SCALE 1/10" = 1'0"

Sheet 6: Plot plan

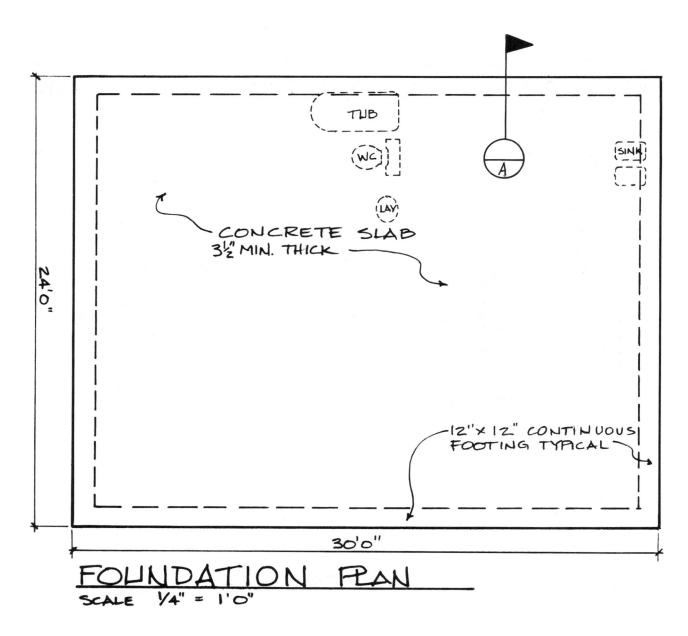

Sheet 7: Foundation plan

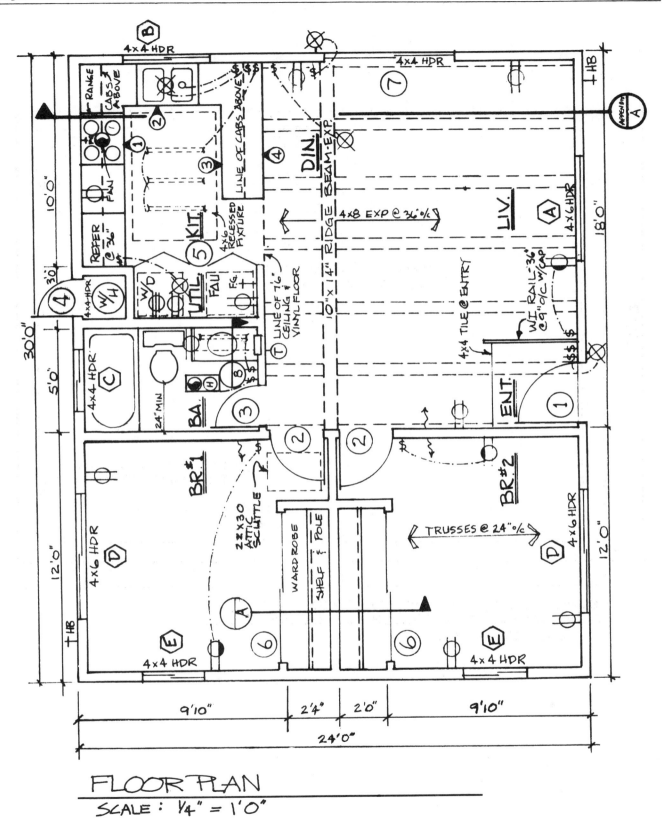

FLOOR PLAN
SCALE: 1/4" = 1'0"

Sheet 8: Floor plan

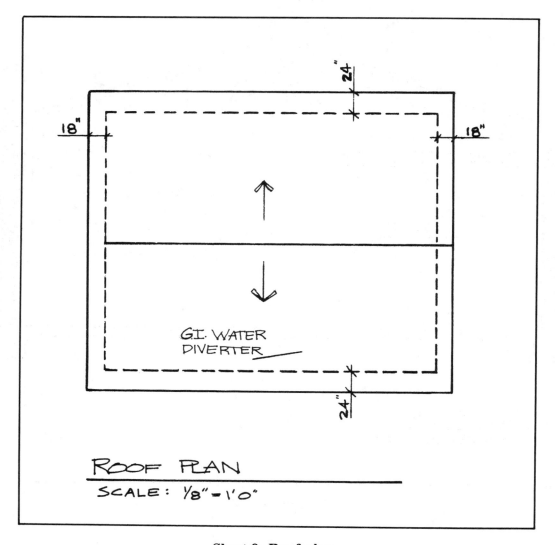

Sheet 9: Roof plan

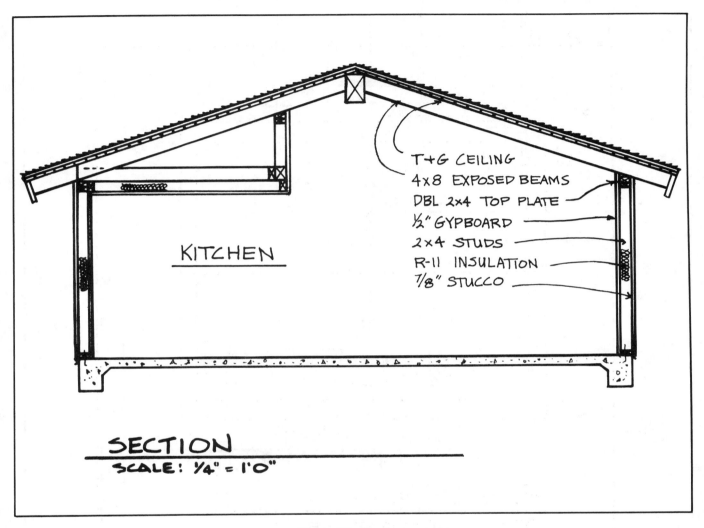

KITCHEN

T+G CEILING
4x8 EXPOSED BEAMS
DBL 2x4 TOP PLATE
½" GYPBOARD
2x4 STUDS
R-11 INSULATION
⅞" STUCCO

SECTION
SCALE: ¼" = 1'0"

Sheet 10: Section

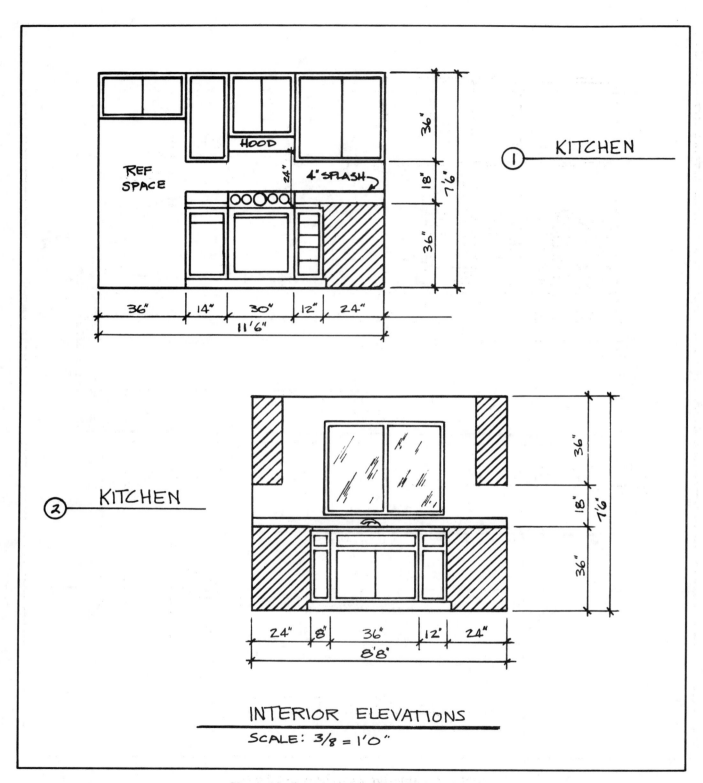

Sheet 11: Interior elevations (kitchen)

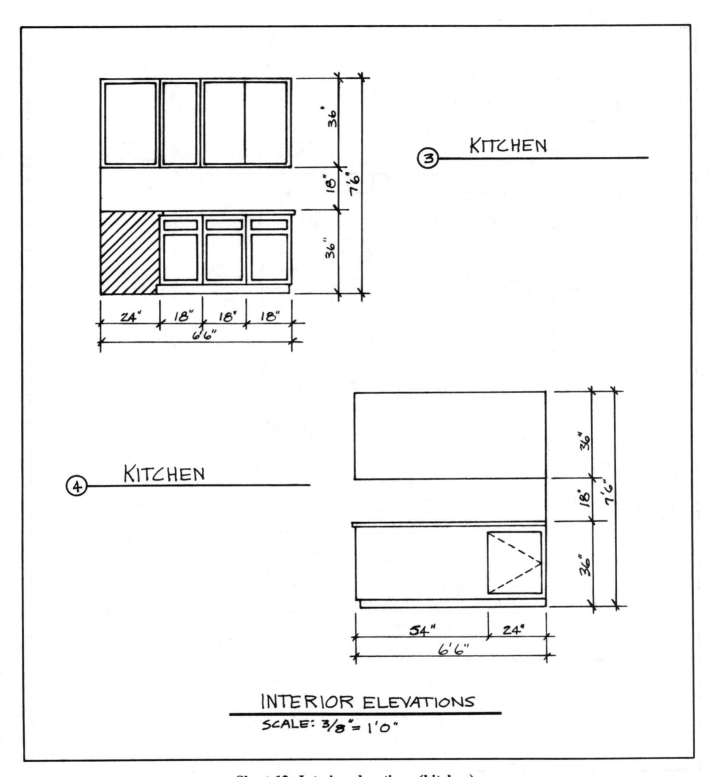

Sheet 12: Interior elevations (kitchen)

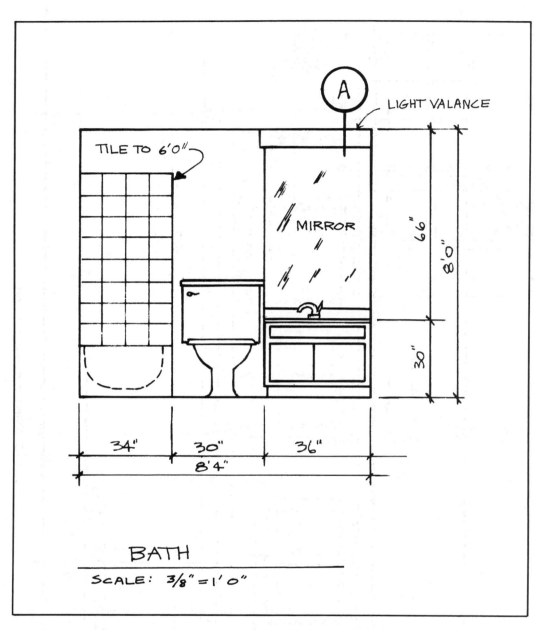

Sheet 13: Interior elevation (bath)

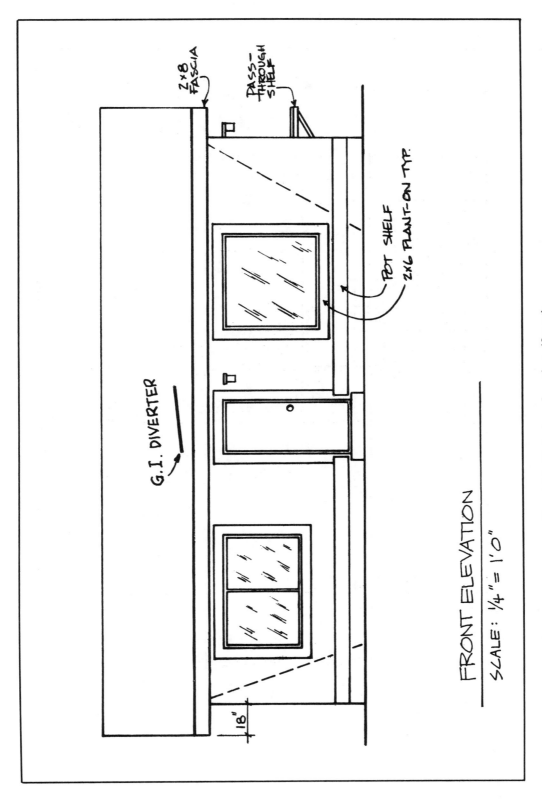

Sheet 14: Exterior elevation (front)

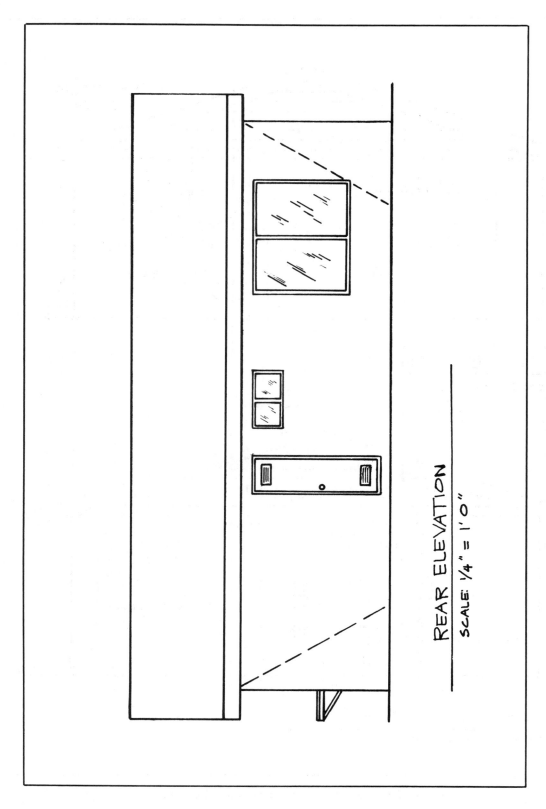

Sheet 15: Exterior elevation (rear)

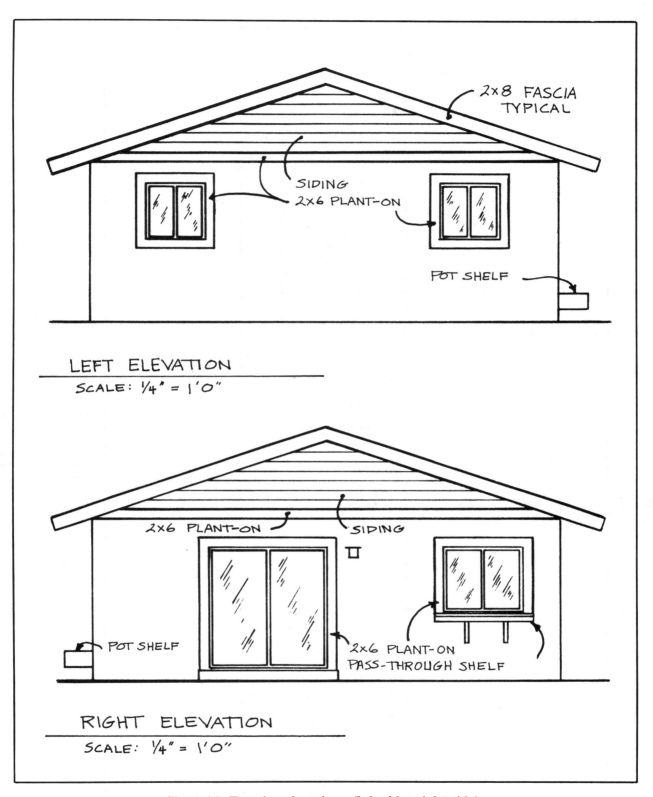

Sheet 16: Exterior elevations (left side, right side)

ROOM FINISH SCHEDULE							
	FLOOR			WALLS		CEILING	
	CARPET	NO WAX VINYL	CERAMIC TILE	½" DRYWALL MEDIUM TEXTURE FLAT PAINT	½" DRYWALL MEDIUM TEXTURE UNDERCOAT & ENAMEL PAINT	¼"×4" TONGUE & GROOVE	½" DRYWALL ACOUSTIC SPRAY	½" DRYWALL MEDIUM TEXTURE UNDERCOAT & ENAMEL PAINT
ENT.			X	X			X	
LIV.	X			X		X		
UTIL.		X			X			X
BA		X			X			X
KIT		X			X			X
BR#1	X			X			X	
BR#2	X			X			X	

Sheet 17: Finish schedule

DOOR SCHEDULE				
SYMBOL	SIZE	TYPE	#	REMARKS
①	3⁰6⁸	SOLID CORE	1	
②	2⁶6⁸	HOLLOW CORE	2	
③	2⁰6⁸	HOLLOW CORE	1	
④	2⁰6⁸	SOLID CORE	1	VENT AS REQ'D
⑤	1⁶8⁰	HOLLOW CORE	4	
⑥	3⁶8⁰	HOLLOW CORE	4	
⑦	6⁰6⁸	AL SL GL DOOR	1	BRONZE FRAME

WINDOW SCHEDULE				
SYMBOL	SIZE	TYPE	#	REMARKS
⟨A⟩	5⁰5⁰	FIXED PANE	1	BRONZE FRAME
⟨B⟩	4⁰3⁶	ALUM. SLIDING	1	" "
⟨C⟩	3⁰1⁶	" "	1	" "
⟨D⟩	6⁰4⁰	" "		" "
⟨E⟩	3⁰3⁰	" "		" "
⟨F⟩	6⁰5⁰	" "		" "

Sheet 18: Door & window schedule

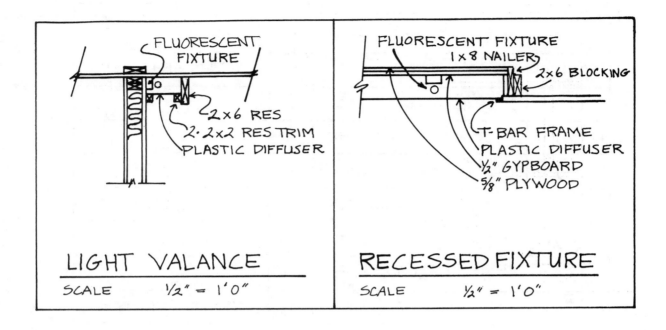

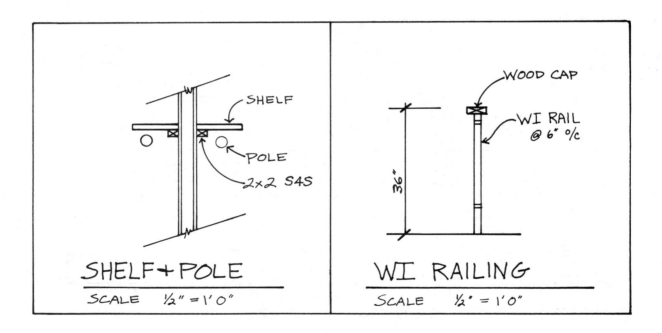

Sheet 19: Details

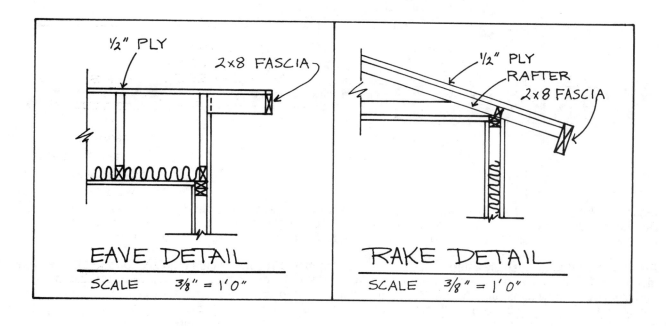

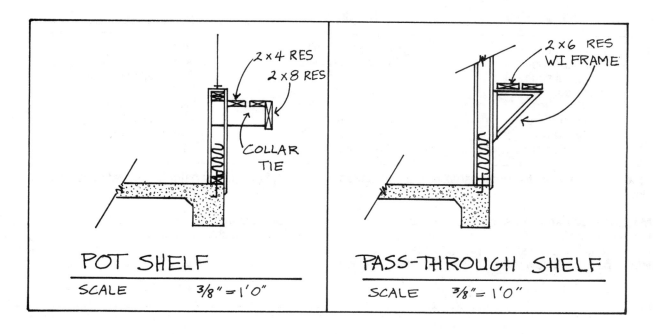

Sheet 20: Details

GENERAL ESTIMATING TABLES

Figure 19-2 has many of the labor and material estimates you'll need to estimate painting new construction. But Figure 19-2 is by no means complete. That's the reason for this appendix. I've tried to include in this Appendix B all the labor and material figures you're likely to need for any type of new construction.

Production rates are usually listed in square feet per manhour. In some cases (such as for doors), rates are given in a decimal fraction of an hour per unit. Estimates include time required for minimum caulking, setup and cleanup on new construction jobs. But no time is included for surface preparation, protecting adjacent surfaces, removing or replacing hardware, preparing samples, mixing paints, placement of equipment or scaffolding, or more than average setup or cleanup. The manhour rates listed here assume journeymen painters working at either a slow, medium or fast pace. Here's a guide that can help you determine whether the pace will be slow, medium or fast on your job.

Slow	Medium	Fast
Good quality	Average quality	Minimum quality
No supervision	Some supervision	Good supervision
High difficulty	Average difficulty	Low difficulty
Poor conditions	Average conditions	Good conditions
Small job	Medium size jobs	Large projects
Low production	Average production	High production
Single units	Two to four units	Over four units
Unskilled crew	Semiskilled crew	Skilled crew

Production rates for flat paint usually range from medium to fast. For enamel paint, the usual range is from slow to medium.

Material coverage rates are usually listed in square feet (SF) per gallon and assume paint that's been thinned according to the manufacturer's recommendations. In some cases (such as for doors), rates are given in units painted per gallon of paint. Rates are listed in this chapter by coverage classification, either heavy or light. The table below will help you decide if coverage will be heavy or light on your job.

Heavy	Light
Heavy application	Light application
Heavy usage	Light usage
High absorption	Low absorption
High waste	Low waste
Standard paint	Production paint
Unskilled painters	Skilled painters

Repainting a surface usually requires about 35% more time than new construction because more time is needed to protect adjacent surfaces. But each gallon of coating will cover 10% to 15% more surface because previously painted surfaces absorb less coating.

Baseboard

	LF per hour			LF per gallon	
	Slow	Med	Fast	Heavy	Light
Flat latex, paint grade, 1 coat					
Roll with walls, brush touchup	2500	2750	3000	1000	1500
Water or oil based enamel, paint grade					
Brush, 1 coat	100	120	140	650	700
Lacquer stained in a boneyard, stain grade					
Spray, 1 coat	--	4000	5000	1200	1350

Figures are based on baseboard up to 2'' wide.

Beams

	LF per hour			LF per gallon	
	Slow	Med	Fast	Heavy	Light
To 13' high	35	40	45	40	50
13' to 17' high	24	27	30	40	50
18' + high	16	18	20	40	50

These figures assume 4" by 6" to 8" by 14" beams are painted with a roller and brush using oil or water-base stain.

Bookcases and shelves
Paint grade

	SF per hour			SF per gallon	
	Slow	Med	Fast	Heavy	Light
Brush					
1st coat	25	30	35	260	300
2nd coat	35	40	45	295	340
3rd coat	40	45	50	305	350
Split coat	40	45	50	305	350
Spray					
1st coat	150	165	175	120	145
2nd coat	225	250	275	145	170
3rd coat	245	270	295	170	195

These estimates are based on overall (length times width) dimensions to 6 feet high and include painting all exposed interior and exterior surfaces (including stiles, interior shelves and backs).

Bookcases and shelves

Stain grade	SF per hour			SF per gallon	
	Slow	Med	Fast	Heavy	Light
Stain, seal & lacquer (7 step process)					
Step 1: Sand & putty	100	125	150	--	--
Steps 2 & 3: Stain					
Brush & wipe, 1 coat	75	85	95	450	500
Spray & wipe, 1 coat	300	400	500	100	175
Step 4: Sanding sealer					
Brush, 1 coat	130	140	150	500	550
Spray, 1 coat	375	475	575	100	175
Step 5: Sand lightly	175	225	275	--	--
Steps 6 and 7: Lacquer, 2 coats					
Brush					
1st coat	140	185	245	350	400
2nd coat	155	210	260	400	425
Spray					
1st coat	340	450	575	100	175
2nd coat	430	530	630	125	200
Complete 7 step stain, seal and 2 coat lacquer process					
Brush, all coats	30	35	40	140	160
Spray, all coats	65	83	100	35	60
Shellac, varnish or wax					
Shellac, brush, each coat	205	230	255	520	570
Varnish					
Gloss or flat, brush each coat	175	200	225	425	450
Penetrating stain wax & polish					
1st coat	150	175	200	520	595
2nd or additional coats	175	200	225	550	600

These estimates are based on overall (length times width) dimensions to 8 feet high and include coating all exposed interior and exterior surfaces (including stiles, interior shelves and backs).

Cabinets

Paint grade	SF per hour			SF per gallon	
	Slow	Med	Fast	Heavy	Light
Roll & brush, undercoat or enamel					
1st coat	75	93	110	240	260
2nd coat	85	103	120	275	300
3rd coat or split coat	95	113	130	285	310
Spray					
1st coat - undercoat	125	140	155	100	125
2nd coat - enamel	185	210	235	125	150
3rd coat or split coat	200	225	250	150	175

These figures include painting the cabinet face, back of doors, stiles and rails. Use these figures to estimate paint grade kitchen cabinets. Estimates are based on overall (length times width) dimensions as described in Chapter 19. Use the opening count method to estimate paint grade pullmans, vanities, bars or linen cabinets.

Cabinets	SF per hour			SF per gallon	
Stain grade	Slow	Med	Fast	Heavy	Light
Stain, seal & lacquer (7 step process)					
Step 1: Sand & putty	125	150	175	--	--
Steps 2 & 3: Stain					
Brush & wipe, 1 coat	65	75	85	350	450
Spray & wipe, 1 coat	250	350	450	100	175
Step 4: Sanding sealer					
Brush, 1 coat	110	120	130	400	450
Spray, 1 coat	330	430	530	100	175
Step 5: Sand lightly	200	250	300	--	--
Steps 6 and 7: Lacquer, 2 coats					
Brush					
1st coat	120	165	215	325	375
2nd coat	130	175	225	375	400
Spray					
1st coat	275	388	500	75	150
2nd coat	350	475	600	125	200
Complete 7 step stain, seal and 2 coat lacquer process					
Brush, all coats	20	25	30	100	125
Spray, all coats	40	50	60	21	40
Stain, seal and lacquer cabinet faces only (7 step process)					
Brush, all coats	30	40	50	165	190
Spray, all coats	85	110	135	35	67
Shellac, varnish or wax					
Shellac, brush, each coat	175	200	225	500	525
Varnish, brush, gloss or flat, each coat	155	180	205	450	475
Penetrating stain wax & polish					
1st coat	125	150	175	500	575
2nd or additional coats	150	175	200	550	600

Use these figures to estimate staining kitchen, bar, linen, pullman or vanity cabinets. For the stain and lacquer process, the figures include finishing both sides of cabinet doors, stiles and rails with a fog coat or stain on shelves and the wall behind the cabinet. Estimates are based on overall dimensions (length times width) as described in Chapter 19.

Cabinet backs	SF per hour			SF per gallon	
	Slow	Med	Fast	Heavy	Light
Brush, 1 coat, flat	150	175	200	250	300
Brush, 1 coat, enamel	125	150	175	225	275

Use these figures to estimate the cost of painting the wall behind stain grade cabinets. Measurements are based on the square foot of cabinet face.

Ceiling panels, suspended
Fiber panels in T-bar frame

	SF per hour			SF per gallon	
	Slow	Med	Fast	Heavy	Light
Brush					
Prime coat	80	110	140	200	260
Added coats	130	150	170	250	300
Roll					
Prime coat	150	200	280	200	270
Added coats	225	275	350	240	280
Spray					
Prime coat	300	345	390	225	250
Added coats	500	545	590	275	325

Use these figures to estimate the cost of painting fibrous suspended ceiling panels with water base latex. All manhour rates assume a 9-foot ceiling height. For heights over 8 feet, use *High time difficulty factors.*

Ceiling pans, metal

	SF per hour			Water base		Oil base	
				-------------- SF per gallon --------------			
	Slow	Med	Fast	Heavy	Light	Heavy	Light
Brush, each coat	80	100	125	325	450	275	400
Roll, each coat	175	200	225	300	425	250	375
Spray, each coat	550	600	650	260	380	210	330

For heights over 8 feet, use *High time difficulty factors*.

Ceilings, acoustic on drywall
Acoustic spray-on texture

	SF per hour			SF per gallon	
	Slow	Med	Fast	Heavy	Light
Spray, primer	250	300	350	80	100
2nd coat	400	450	500	160	180
Added coats	500	550	600	175	200

				SF per pound	
Stipple finish texture paint (Dripowder mixed)					
Each coat	225	250	275	5	10

Drywall is also called gypsum wallboard or sheetrock. For heights over 8 feet, use *High time difficulty factors.*

Ceilings, drywall Smooth finish	SF per hour Slow-Med-Fast	Water base	Oil base	Epoxy coating
		------------------- SF per gallon -------------------		
		Heavy-Light	Heavy-Light	Heavy-Light
Brush				
1st coat	175- 200- 225	300-325	325-350	--
2nd coat	200- 225- 250	350-400	375-400	375-425
3rd coat	225- 250- 275	375-425	400-425	400-450
Stipple	200- 225- 250	--	--	--
Roll				
1st coat	325- 375- 425	300-350	275-300	--
2nd coat	375- 413- 450	350-375	325-350	350-400
3rd coat	425- 450- 475	375-400	350-375	375-425
Spray				
1st coat	750- 850- 950	250-300	275-300	--
2nd coat	850- 950-1050	300-350	325-350	--
3rd coat	900-1000-1100	325-350	350-375	--

For heights over 8 feet, use *High time difficulty factors*.

Ceilings, drywall Orange peel	SF per hour Slow-Med-Fast	Water base	Oil base	Epoxy coating
		------------------- SF per gallon -------------------		
		Heavy-Light	Heavy-Light	Heavy-Light
Brush				
1st coat	150-175- 200	275-300	250-275	--
2nd coat	175-200- 250	325-350	300-325	300-350
3rd coat	200-225- 250	350-400	350-400	325-375
Roll				
1st coat	325-350- 375	250-300	250-275	--
2nd coat	350-375- 400	300-325	275-300	275-300
3rd coat	400-425- 450	325-350	300-325	300-375
Spray				
1st coat	650-750- 850	175-225	175-200	--
2nd coat	775-875- 975	200-250	200-225	--
3rd coat	825-925-1025	225-275	225-250	--

For heights over 8 feet, use *High time difficulty factors*.

Ceilings, drywall Sand finish texture	SF per hour Slow-Med-Fast	Water base Heavy-Light	Oil base --- SF per gallon --- Heavy-Light	Epoxy coating Heavy-Light
Brush				
1st coat	175-200-225	300-325	275-300	--
2nd coat	200-238-275	350-400	325-375	325-375
3rd coat	225-263-300	375-425	350-400	350-400
Roll				
1st coat	300-350-400	275-325	250-300	--
2nd coat	350-388-425	325-350	300-325	300-350
3rd coat	425-450-475	325-350	325-350	325-375
Spray				
1st coat	700-800- 900	225-275	225-240	--
2nd coat	800-900-1000	275-325	275-300	--
3rd coat	850-950-1050	300-325	300-325	--

Use these figures to estimate the cost of painting gypboard ceilings with an orange peel or knockdown texture. For heights over 8 feet, use *High time difficulty factors.*

Ceilings, drywall Casein or resin emulsion paint	SF per hour Slow	Med	Fast	SF per gallon Heavy	Light
Roll & brush					
1st coat	175	240	300	300	375
2nd coat	200	250	325	375	425

For heights over 8 feet, use *High time difficulty factors.*

Ceilings, drywall Anti-graffiti stain eliminator	SF per hour Slow	Med	Fast	Latex primer and sealer Heavy	Light	Pigmented primer and sealer Heavy	Light
Roll & brush, each coat	350	375	400	400	450	375	400

For heights over 8 feet, use *High time difficulty factors.*

Ceilings, tongue & groove
Paint grade

	SF per hour			Water base		Oil base	
				SF per gallon			
	Slow	Med	Fast	Heavy	Light	Heavy	Light
Brush							
1st coat	55	65	75	275	300	325	350
2nd coat	65	75	85	325	350	350	375
3rd coat	80	90	100	350	375	400	425
Roll							
1st coat	90	110	130	250	275	300	350
2nd coat	140	155	170	300	325	350	375
3rd coat	190	200	210	325	350	375	400
Spray							
1st coat	300	360	420	125	180	180	200
2nd coat	420	470	520	200	250	230	270
3rd coat	520	570	620	300	350	300	325

For heights over 8 feet, use *High time difficulty factors.*

Ceilings, tongue & groove
Stain grade

	SF per hour			SF per gallon	
	Slow	Med	Fast	Heavy	Light
Semi-transparent stain					
Roll & brush, 1 coat	200	240	280	250	300
Spray, 1 coat	300	350	400	180	220
Stain, seal & 2 coat lacquer system					
Stain & wipe					
Roll, brush and wipe, 1 coat	75	100	125	250	300
Spray & wipe, 1 coat	275	300	325	100	150
Sanding sealer					
Brush, 1 coat	125	150	175	275	325
Spray, 1 coat	350	400	450	100	150
Lacquer, brush					
1st coat	150	200	275	325	350
2nd coat	200	250	325	350	400
Lacquer, spray					
1st coat	425	525	625	250	350
2nd coat	475	588	650	325	425
Complete stain, seal & 2 coat lacquer system					
Brush, all coats	30	35	40	145	165
Spray, all coats	60	70	80	40	60

For heights over 8 feet, use *High time difficulty factors.*

Closet pole
Stain grade, penetrating stain

	LF per hour			LF per gallon	
	Slow	Med	Fast	Heavy	Light
Brush & wipe, 1 coat	40	50	60	200	225

For staining poles in new construction, apply stain before installation. On repaints, remove the pole before applying stain. When estimating by the opening count method, count one opening for each 10 linear feet.

| **Closets** | LF per hour | | | LF per gallon | |
Paint grade, undercoat or enamel	Slow	Med	Fast	Heavy	Light
Molding at closet perimeter, brush, 1 coat	70	85	100	200	225
Shelves, brush, 1 coat	25	33	40	80	100
Shelf and pole, brush, 1 coat	15	20	30	60	80

Measurements are based on lineal footage.

| **Corbels, wood trim** | LF per hour | | | LF per gallon | |
Average size 4" x 8"	Slow	Med	Fast	Heavy	Light
Brush, each coat	15	20	25	45	50

Deck overhangs (wood)   Multiply the horizontal surface area by 1.5 to allow for painting floor joists and use the overhang table for manhour and material calculations.

Deck surfaces, steps, stair treads & porches (wood)   Measure the surface area and apply the formulas for smooth siding.

| **Door frames and trim only** | LF per hour | | | LF per gallon | |
Per linear foot	Slow	Med	Fast	Heavy	Light
Brush, each coat	200	250	290	425	510

These estimates include painting interior frames and trim on two sides. Usually there will be about 17 linear feet of frame at each opening.

| **Door frames and trim only** | Frames per hour | | | Frames per gallon | |
Per opening	Slow	Med	Fast	Heavy	Light
Brush, each coat	12	15	17	25	30

These estimates include painting interior frames and trim on two sides. Usually there will be about 17 linear feet of frame at each opening.

Doors, exterior   The tables that follow include both time and material needed to apply two coats of a high quality finish to all six sides of the door, jamb and trim, and to lay off each door smoothly. This is in addition to the time allowed for painting interior surfaces from *Doors, interior openings*.

Stain grade exterior doors get a coat of stain, sealer and then either a marine spar varnish or polyurethane finish. Paint grade doors get two coats of exterior enamel. For example, a French door will take stain, sealer and two coats of polyurethane or marine spar varnish.

| **Doors, exterior, flush** | Hours per door | | | Doors per gallon | |
Per set of two coats	Slow	Med	Fast	Heavy	Light
Paint grade, roll & brush	.5	.4	.3	5	7
Polyurethane, brush	.7	.6	.5	4	5
Marine spar varnish, brush	.5	.4	.3	4	6

Minimum preparation time for varnishing: Steel wool buff, 150 SF per hour or 5 doors per hour. Wax application, 150 SF per hour or 5 doors per hour.

Doors, exterior, French	Hours per door			Doors per gallon	
	Slow	Med	Fast	Heavy	Light
Paint grade, roll & brush, 2 coats	1.0	.8	.6	8	12
Polyurethane finish, brush 2 coats	1.5	1.3	1.0	7	8
Marine spar varnish finish, brush, 2 coats	1.0	.8	.6	8	12

These figures are based on French doors with from 10 to 15 lites. Minimum preparation for varnishing: Steel wool buff,150 SF per hour or 7 doors per hour. Wax application, 150 SF per hour or 7 doors per hour.

Doors, exterior, louvered	Hours per door			Doors per gallon	
	Slow	Med	Fast	Heavy	Light
Paint grade, roll & brush, 2 coats	1.4	1.0	.7	5	7
Polyurethane finish, brush 2 coats	1.7	1.5	1.2	4	5
Marine spar varnish finish, brush 2 coats	1.4	1.0	.7	5	7

Minimum preparation for varnishing: Steel wool buff, 100 SF per hour or 5 doors per hour. Wax application, 100 SF per hour or 5 doors per hour.

Doors, exterior, panel (entry)	Hours per door			Doors per gallon	
	Slow	Med	Fast	Heavy	Light
Paint grade, roll & brush, 2 coats	1.4	1.1	.7	2	4
Polyurethane finish, brush, 2 coats	1.7	1.5	1.2	2	4
Marine spar varnish finish, brush, 2 coats	1.4	1.1	.8	2	4

Panel exterior doors are also known as entry doors. Minimum preparation for varnishing: Steel wool buff, 150 SF per hour or 5 doors per hour. Wax application, 150 SF per hour or 5 doors per hour.

Doors, interior openings Based on opening count	Manhours per opening per coat			Undercoat gallons per opening		Enamel gallons per opening	
	Slow	Med	Fast	Heavy	Light	Heavy	Light
Roll and brush, each coat							
1 opening	0.4	0.3	0.2	.09	.08	0.10	.08
2 openings	0.7	0.5	0.3	.18	.16	0.20	.17
3 openings	1.0	0.8	0.5	.27	.23	0.30	.25
4 openings	1.3	1.0	0.7	.36	.31	0.40	.33
5 openings	1.6	1.3	0.9	.45	.38	0.50	.42
6 openings	1.9	1.5	1.0	.54	.46	0.60	.50
7 openings	2.2	1.8	1.2	.64	.54	0.70	.58
8 openings	2.5	2.0	1.4	.73	.62	0.80	.67
9 openings	2.8	2.2	1.5	.81	.69	0.90	.75
10 openings	3.1	2.4	1.7	.90	.77	1.00	.83

Many painting contractors estimate paint grade doors, jambs, frames, wood windows, pullmans, linens, bookcases, wine racks and other interior surfaces that take an undercoat and enamel finish by the "opening." Each opening is considered to take the same time regardless of whether it's a door, window, pullman, etc. These figures are based on the number of openings finished per 8-hour day and the material required per opening. The opening count method of estimating is explained in Chapters 18 and 19. If you decide to estimate by counting openings, use Figure 18-9 or 19-6 to find opening allowances. Then use this table to find the time and material required. Undercoat is based on 11 to 13 openings per gallon. Enamel is based on 10 to 12 openings per gallon.

Doors, interior, flush

Per door coated	Doors per hour	Hours per door Slow	Med	Fast	Doors per gallon Heavy	Light
Paint grade doors						
Roll & brush each coat						
Undercoat	2.5 - 5	.40	.30	.20	10	13
1st finish	3 - 6	.33	.25	.17	11	14
Additional finish	4 - 7	.25	.20	15	12	15
Spray						
Undercoat	10 - 12	.10	.09	.08	15	17
1st finish	13 - 15	.08	.08	.07	16	18
Additional finish	15 - 17	.07	.07	.06	17	19
Stain grade doors, spray finish both sides, stain, seal and						
2 coat lacquer system	1.1 - 1.4	.90	.80	.70	4	6

These estimates include coating all six sides of each door, and the frame and jamb on both sides. For doors which are not exposed to weather on the exterior.

Doors, interior, French

Per door coated	Doors per hour	Hours per door Slow	Med	Fast	Doors per gallon Heavy	Light
Paint grade doors						
Roll & brush each coat						
Undercoat	2 - 3	.45	.38	.30	12	14
1st finish	2.5 - 3	.43	.35	.28	13	15
Additional finish	2.5 - 4	.40	.33	.25	14	16
Stain grade doors, spray finish both sides, stain, seal and						
2 coat lacquer system	.8 - 1.0	1.50	1.30	1.00	10	12

These estimates include coating all six sides of each door, and the frame and jamb on both sides. For doors which are not exposed to weather on the exterior.

Doors, interior, louvered

Per door coated	Doors per hour	Hours per door Slow	Med	Fast	Doors per gallon Heavy	Light
Paint grade doors						
Roll & brush each coat						
Undercoat	1.5 - 2.5	.67	.54	.40	6	8
1st finish	2 - 3	.50	.42	.33	7	9
Additional finish	2.5 - 4	.40	.30	.20	8	10
Spray						
Undercoat	6 - 8	.13	.11	.10	10	12
1st finish	8 - 11	.09	.09	.08	11	13
Additional finish	10 - 13	.08	.08	.07	12	14
Stain grade doors, spray finish both sides, stain, seal and						
2 coat lacquer system	.6 - .8	1.70	1.50	1.20	3	5

These estimates include coating all six sides of each door, and the frame and jamb on both sides. For doors which are not exposed to weather on the exterior.

Doors, interior, panel
Per door coated

	Doors per hour	Hours per door			Doors per gallon	
		Slow	Med	Fast	Heavy	Light
Paint grade doors						
Roll & brush each coat						
Undercoat	2 - 4	.50	.40	.30	8	10
1st finish	2.5 - 5	.45	.35	.25	9	11
Additional finish	3 - 6	.40	.30	.20	10	12
Spray						
Undercoat	8 - 10	.13	.12	.10	13	15
1st finish	11 - 13	.09	.09	.08	14	16
Additional finish	13 - 15	.08	.08	.07	15	17
Stain grade doors, spray finish both sides, stain, seal and						
2 coat lacquer system	.6 - .8	1.70	1.50	1.30	3	5

These estimates include coating all six sides of each door, and the frame and jamb on both sides. For doors which are not exposed to weather on the exterior.

Fascia
One coat "to cover" with solid body stain

	LF per hour			LF per gallon	
	Slow	Med	Fast	Heavy	Light
2" x 4"					
Brush	80	100	130	150	170
Roll	180	205	230	120	140
Spray	275	325	375	90	110
2" x 6" to 2" x 10"					
Brush	70	90	110	120	140
Roll	150	175	200	100	120
Spray	225	300	350	70	90
2" x 12"					
Brush	60	80	100	80	100
Roll	110	130	150	60	90
Spray	200	275	325	40	60

These figures include one full coat and any touchup required to meet the "to cover" specifications.

Fence, chain link or metal wire mesh
Oil or water base material

	SF per hour			SF per gallon	
	Slow	Med	Fast	Heavy	Light
Brush					
1st coat	90	110	125	500	600
2nd coat	130	145	160	550	650
Roll					
1st coat	260	275	290	475	575
2nd coat	280	300	320	525	625

To calculate the area, measure overall dimensions on one side. Then multiply by a difficulty factor of 3 and use the table above.

Fence, wood For *solid plank fence*, measure the surface area of one side and multiply by 2 to find the area for both sides. Then use the manhour rates for siding. For *good neighbor fence* (planks on alternate sides of the rail), measure the surface area of one side and multiply by 2 to find the area for both sides. Then multiply by a difficulty factor of 1.5 and use the manhour rates for siding.

Fence, picket	SF per hour Slow Med Fast			Water base		Oil base	
				Heavy	Light	Heavy	Light
Brush							
1st coat	75	113	150	375	400	425	450
2nd or additional coats	120	145	170	425	450	475	500
Roll							
1st coat	120	145	170	325	360	375	400
2nd or additional coats	200	225	250	375	400	425	450
Spray							
1st coat	400	500	600	250	300	300	350
2nd or additional coats	500	600	700	300	350	375	425

For picket fence, measure the overall area of one side and multiply by 4 for painting both sides. Then apply these manhour rates.

Fireplace masonry Oil or water base masonry paint	SF per hour Slow Med Fast			SF per gallon Heavy Light	
Brush, 1 coat	70	75	80	120	140
Roll, 1 coat	140	150	160	100	120
Spray, 1 coat	400	450	500	90	110

Fireplace trim Oil or water base stain	LF per hour Slow Med Fast			LF per gallon Heavy Light	
Mantle, rough sawn 4" x 12"					
Roll & brush, each coat	15	18	20	40	50
Plant-on trim, interior					
Roll & brush, each coat	75	80	85	125	135
Siding, interior, tongue & groove					
Roll & brush, each coat	50	75	100	90	100

Firewood boxes Oil or water base stain	Hours each Slow Med Fast			Gallons each Heavy Light	
Brush, 1 coat	.40	.35	.30	.25	.20

Based on rough sawn wood boxes to 3'0" x 3'0" x 3'0" deep.

Floors, concrete, interior or exterior

| | SF per hour | | | Water base | | Oil base | |
	Slow	Med	Fast	Heavy	Light	Heavy	Light
Brush							
1st coat	90	140	200	225	250	275	300
2nd coat	125	200	275	275	325	375	400
3rd coat	150	225	300	285	335	500	550
Roll							
1st coat	135	218	300	250	275	320	370
2nd coat	195	268	340	300	350	450	500
3rd coat	210	300	390	325	375	500	550
Spray							
1st coat	800	900	1000	150	175	175	200
2nd coat	900	1000	1100	250	275	275	300
3rd coat	1000	1100	1200	300	325	325	350
Roll on penetrating stain							
1st coat	225	250	275	--	--	400	450
2nd coat	325	340	365	--	--	450	500
3rd coat	365	380	400	--	--	475	525

Also use these formulas for concrete steps, stair treads, porches and patios.

Floors, wood, interior
Paint grade

| | SF per hour | | | Water base | | Oil base | |
	Slow	Med	Fast	Heavy	Light	Heavy	Light
Brush							
Prime	275	300	325	400	450	450	500
2nd coat	300	325	350	425	475	500	550
Roll							
Prime	400	438	475	375	425	425	475
2nd coat	425	463	500	425	475	475	525

Floors, wood, interior

Stain grade	SF per hour			SF per gallon	
	Slow	Med	Fast	Heavy	Light
Stain, wipe & fill, brush					
1st coat	225	250	275	450	500
2nd coat	400	425	450	475	525
3rd coat	425	450	475	500	525
Sealer					
Maple or pine, brush each coat					
1st coat	375	400	425	425	475
2nd coat	425	450	475	500	550
Oak, brush					
1st coat	400	425	450	475	525
2nd coat	500	525	550	575	625
Shellac or varnish					
Shellac, brush each coat					
1st coat	275	300	325	425	475
Added coats	400	425	450	450	500
Varnish, brush each coat					
1st coat	275	300	325	425	475
2nd coat	350	375	400	550	600
Penetrating stain wax & wipe					
1st coat	200	250	300	500	550
2nd coat	250	300	350	550	600
Wax & polish, 1 coat, by hand	175	200	225	900	1000
Buffing with machine	400	450	500	--	--

Garage door backs, seal coat

Spray one coat	Hours per garage			Gallons per garage	
	Slow	Med	Fast	Heavy	Light
1 car garage door - 8' x 7'	.30	.25	.20	.6	.4
2 car garage door - 16' x 7'	.40	.35	.30	1.0	.8
3 car garage door - 16' x 7' and 8' x 7'	.60	.55	.50	1.2	1.0

Use the figures for siding when estimating the cost of painting garage door fronts. These figures assume a one-car garage door measures 7' x 8' and a two-car garage door measures 7' x 16'. A three-car garage has one single and one double door. Government funded projects (FHA, VA, HUD) usually require sealing the garage door back on new construction projects. They're usually sprayed along with the cabinet sealer coat or stained along with the exterior trim.

Gutters and downspouts

Zinc oxide paint	LF per hour			LF per gallon	
	Slow	Med	Fast	Heavy	Light
Gutters, brush					
1st coat	80	90	100	350	400
2nd coat	100	110	120	375	425
3rd coat	120	130	140	400	450
Downspouts, brush					
1st coat	30	35	40	200	250
2nd coat	50	60	70	225	275
3rd coat	70	80	90	250	300

These figures assume that all exposed surfaces of 5" gutters and 4" downspouts are painted. For ornamental gutters and downspouts, multiply the lineal footage by 1.5 before using these figures.

High time difficulty factors

Painting takes longer and may require more material when heights above the floor exceed 8 feet. *For ceilings above 8 feet high,* multiply the factor listed below by the area to be painted when figuring manhours only. *For walls above 8 feet,* multiply the factor listed below by the area to be painted only when figuring manhours. This allows additional time for reaching, applying an extension to the roller pole, attaching a wand to a spray gun or going up and down a ladder or scaffolding. Little or no additional coating material will be required for walls.

Over 8'0" to 13'0"	Add 30% (multiply the area by 1.3)
Over 13'0" to 17'0"	Add 60% (multiply the area by 1.6)
Over 17'0" to 19'0"	Add 90% (multiply the area by 1.9)
Over 19'0" to 21'0"	Add 120% (multiply the area by 2.2)

Mailbox structures, apartment type
Measure the length of each board to be painted and use the manhours and materials given for *Trellis* or *Plant-on trim.*

Masonry: brick, new	SF per hour			Water base		Oil base	
				SF per gallon			
Smooth surface	Slow	Med	Fast	Heavy	Light	Heavy	Light
Brush							
1st coat	200	225	250	250	300	300	350
2nd or additional coats	250	275	300	275	325	325	400
Roll							
1st coat	325	350	375	175	250	250	325
2nd or additional coats	375	400	425	225	275	275	350
Spray							
1st coat	650	750	850	200	250	225	275
2nd or additional coats	750	825	900	250	275	275	300
Waterproofing, clear hydro sealer							
Roll							
1st coat	200	225	250	--	--	125	175
2nd or additional coats	225	250	275	--	--	180	200
Spray							
1st coat	700	800	900	--	--	80	120
2nd or additional coats	800	900	1000	--	--	125	150

Use these figures for new smooth surface brick with joints struck to average depth.

Masonry: brick, used	SF per hour			Water base SF per gallon		Oil base	
Rough surface	Slow	Med	Fast	Heavy	Light	Heavy	Light
Brush							
1st coat	150	175	200	250	300	275	325
2nd or additional coats	200	225	250	325	375	350	400
Roll							
1st coat	300	325	350	200	250	225	275
2nd or additional coats	350	375	400	275	325	300	350
Spray							
1st coat	600	700	800	150	200	175	225
2nd or additional coats	700	800	900	200	225	225	250
Waterproofing, clear hydro sealer							
Roll							
1st coat	150	175	200	--	--	100	125
2nd or additional coats	175	200	225	--	--	125	150
Spray							
1st coat	600	700	800	--	--	70	80
2nd or additional coats	800	900	1000	--	--	80	100

Use these figures for rough surface, dry pressed used brick, clay brick tile, or adobe block with joints struck to average depth.

Masonry: concrete masonry units (CMU), filled block, slump stone, precision block	SF per hour	Water base	Oil base	Epoxy coating
Smooth surface	Slow-Med-Fast	SF per gallon Heavy-Light	Heavy-Light	Heavy-Light
Brush				
1st coat	140-190-230	240-310	290-350	265-325
2nd or additional coats	170-250-325	340-410	390-450	365-425
Roll				
1st coat	300-350-390	215-240	260-285	240-265
2nd or additional coats	350-400-450	300-325	340-375	325-355
Spray				
Primer	725-788-850	190-240	230-280	220-255
2nd or additional coats	800-950-1100	270-320	310-345	290-325

The more porous the surface, the rougher the texture, the more time and material will be required.

Masonry: concrete masonry units (CMU), filled block, slump stone, precision block
Smooth surface

	SF per hour			SF per gallon	
	Slow	Med	Fast	Heavy	Light
Waterproofing, clear hydro sealer					
Brush					
1st coat	150	175	200	75	100
2nd or additional coats	230	275	295	100	140
Roll					
1st coat	170	200	245	80	110
2nd or additional coats	275	300	325	100	150
Spray					
1st coat	500	750	900	50	75
2nd or additional coats	600	800	1000	75	100
Industrial waterproofing					
Brush					
1st coat	90	100	110	90	100
2nd or additional coats	150	173	195	175	200
Roll					
1st coat	100	113	125	100	125
2nd or additional coats	180	195	215	175	200
Industrial bonding & penetrating oil paint, brush					
1st coat	325	350	375	220	240
2nd or additional coats	340	370	400	250	300

The more porous the surface, the rougher the texture, the more time and material will be required.

Masonry: concrete masonry units (CMU), porous
Rough surface

	SF per hour	Water base	Oil base	Epoxy coating
	Slow-Med-Fast	Heavy-Light	Heavy-Light	Heavy-Light
Brush				
1st coat	110-130 150	75-100	110-130	85-110
Added coats	185-210-230	155-180	160-200	175-200
Roll				
1st coat	245-300-350	65- 90	85-110	75-100
Added coats	275-325-420	125-160	155-185	145-175
Spray				
Primer	600-700-800	55-100	65-100	50- 85
Added coats	700-800-900	110-155	125-160	115-145

The more porous the surface, the rougher the texture, the more time and material will be required.

Masonry: concrete masonry units (CMU), porous
Rough surface

	SF per hour			SF per gallon	
	Slow	Med	Fast	Heavy	Light
Waterproofing, clear hydro sealer					
Brush					
1st coat	125	150	175	70	90
2nd or additional coats	230	275	295	90	130
Roll					
1st coat	170	200	245	85	110
2nd or additional coats	275	300	325	115	175
Spray					
1st coat	500	700	900	40	60
2nd or additional coats	600	800	1000	60	90
Industrial waterproofing					
Brush					
1st coat	85	110	135	45	65
2nd or additional coats	145	170	195	145	180
Roll					
1st coat	100	110	125	90	125
2nd or additional coats	180	195	215	125	175
Industrial bonding & penetrating oil paint, brush					
1st coat	225	250	275	175	200
2nd or additional coats	230	260	290	225	275

Use these figures for CMU where the block surfaces are rough, porous or unfilled, with joints struck to average depth. The more porous the surface, the rougher the texture, the more time and material will be required.

Masonry: block filler

	SF per hour			SF per gallon	
	Slow	Med	Fast	Heavy	Light
Brush, 1 coat	95	125	155	55	75
Roll, 1 coat	190	215	240	50	70
Spray, 1 coat	425	525	625	45	65

Masonry: stone, marble or granite
Waterproofing, clear hydro sealer, sprayed

	SF per hour			SF per gallon	
	Slow	Med	Fast	Heavy	Light
1st coat	600	700	800	180	220
2nd or additional coats	700	800	900	200	225

Molding, interior
Stain grade, smooth surface

	LF per hour			LF per gallon	
	Slow	Med	Fast	Heavy	Light
Stain, seal & 2 coat lacquer system					
Sand & putty	150	175	200	--	--
Stain					
Brush & wipe, 1 coat	150	175	200	500	550
Spray & wipe, 1 coat	400	425	450	200	250
Sanding sealer - light sand					
Brush 1 coat & sand	260	280	300	550	575
Spray 1 coat & sand	450	475	500	200	250
Lacquer					
Brush					
1st coat	200	275	350	275	300
2nd coat	225	300	375	325	375
Spray					
1st coat	250	350	450	175	200
2nd coat	300	375	475	200	250
Complete stain, seal and 2 coat lacquer system					
Brush, all coats	50	75	100	40	60
Spray all coats	100	150	200	20	40

These figures are based on linear foot measurements for all molding up to 12" wide. The spray figures are based on finishing large quantities of molding in a boneyard before it's installed. Use the brush figures for small quantities. Use the fast brush rate for molding that's finished before it's installed. If the molding is attached and has to be masked off, use the slow brush figures. The time spent masking is not included. See Chapter 17 for masking rates. Trim stained the same color as the surface behind it will take no more time than staining the wall itself.

Molding, interior or exterior
Stain grade, smooth surface

	LF per hour			LF per gallon	
	Slow	Med	Fast	Heavy	Light
Stain, fill and shellac or varnish, brush					
Stain & fill	80	130	180	500	550
Shellac	180	230	280	500	550
Gloss varnish	115	150	210	500	550
Flat varnish	125	173	220	500	550
Steel wool buff	100	110	125	--	--
Wax & polish	100	110	125	--	--
Penetrating stain wax					
Brush, each coat	225	275	325	400	500
Polish, added coats of wax	150	175	200	--	--

These figures are based on linear foot measurement for all molding up to 14" wide. The spray figures are based on finishing large quantities of molding in a boneyard before it's installed. Use the brush figures for small quantities. Use the fast brush rate for molding that's finished before it's installed. If the molding is attached and has to be masked off, use the slow brush figures. The time spent masking is not included. See Chapter 17 for masking rates. Trim stained the same color as the surface behind it will take no more time than staining the wall itself.

Molding, paint grade	LF per hour			LF per gallon	
	Slow	Med	Fast	Heavy	Light
Brush					
1st coat	135	205	275	500	700
2nd coat	125	163	200	600	750
3rd coat	115	145	175	600	750
Split coat	125	135	145	600	750
Stipple finish	80	90	100	--	--
Glazing or mottling over enamel					
Glaze & wipe, brush, 1 coat	55	65	75	850	950

Consider all trim to be at least 1 foot wide (even if it's much less than 1 foot wide) when calculating the area to be painted. Trim painted the same color as the wall or ceiling behind it may take no more time than painting the wall or ceiling itself. Use the slow rate when cutting in is required to paint molding that's a different color than the surface behind the molding.

Overhang difficulty factors (Eaves, cornice)	Boxed eaves		Exposed rafters	
	One color	Two color	One color	Two color
One story, repaint				
Standard	1.5	2.0	2.0	2.5
Ornamental	--	--	2.5	3.0
One story, new construction	--	1.5	1.5	2.0
Two story, with scaffolding, repaint				
Standard	1.5	2.0	2.0	2.5
Ornamental	--	--	2.5	3.0
Two story, without scaffold, repaint				
Standard	3.0	3.5	3.5	4.0
Ornamental	--	--	4.0	4.5
Two story, new construction				
With scaffolding	--	1.5	1.5	2.0
No scaffold	2.0	2.5	2.5	3.0

Before using the figures in the tables for overhangs, apply these difficulty factors to the surface area to be painted. Multiply the factor in this table by the overall (width times length) surface area of the overhang. This allows for slower work on high eaves and the extra time needed to paint rafter tails. This table adjusts for the kind of eaves, the eave height, the number of colors used, and whether scaffolding is available. Boxed eaves have plywood covering the rafter tails.

Overhang, carport
Large quantities
Oil or water base paint, sprayed

	SF per hour			SF per gallon	
	Slow	Med	Fast	Heavy	Light
1st coat	550	600	650	85	95
2nd coat	600	650	700	150	175
Added coats	650	700	750	200	225

Use this table after multiplying the overall area (width times length) by the factor listed under **Overhang, difficulty factors.**

Overhang, eaves or rake
Widths up to 2 feet
Oil or water base paint, sprayed

	SF per hour			SF per gallon	
	Slow	Med	Fast	Heavy	Light
1st coat	350	375	400	85	95
2nd coat	490	515	540	150	175
Added coats	550	575	600	200	225

Use this table after multiplying the overall area (width times length) by the factor listed under *Overhang, difficulty factors.*

Overhang, eaves or rake
Widths greater than 2 feet
Oil or water base paint, sprayed

	SF per hour			SF per gallon	
	Slow	Med	Fast	Heavy	Light
1st coat	475	500	520	85	95
2nd coat	590	615	640	150	175
Added coats	650	675	700	200	225

Use this table after multiplying the overall area (width times length) by the factor listed under *Overhang, difficulty factors.* These figures are used for deck, overhang or entry overhang areas.

Pass-through shelves
Wrought iron support,
wood top, oil base material

	SF per hour			LF per gallon	
	Slow	Med	Fast	Heavy	Light
Brush, each coat	30	35	40	100	125

Most jobs will average 0.2 hours plus $1.00 for materials per shelf.

Plant-on trim, exterior
Rough sawn or resawn
Roll and brush

	LF per hour Slow-Med-Fast	Water base LF per gallon Heavy-Light	Oil base LF per gallon Heavy-Light	Varnish LF per gallon Heavy-Light
2" x 2" to 2" x 4"				
1st coat	80-100-120	240-310	330-400	240-270
2nd coat	90-120-150	300-350	400-475	300-330
3rd or additional coats	100-140-180	325-375	425-500	320-350
2" x 6" to 2" x 8"				
1st coat	70- 85-100	140-210	230-300	140-170
2nd coat	80-110-140	200-250	300-375	200-240
3rd or additional coats	90-130-170	225-275	325-400	220-260
2" x 10" to 2" x 12"				
1st coat	60- 75- 90	80-150	220-290	80-120
2nd coat	70-100-130	140-190	240-315	140-190
3rd or additional coats	80-120-160	165-215	265-340	150-200

1) Don't add additional time for plant-on trim if it's painted with the same coating as the adjacent siding.
2) Use *High time difficulty factors* for heights over 8 feet.
3) Use slow rates when cutting in or masking adjacent surfaces.
4) Use fast rates when plant-on trim is finished before it's installed.

Plaster or stucco, interior or exterior

Medium texture	SF per hour			SF per gallon	
	Slow	Med	Fast	Heavy	Light
Water base latex					
Brush					
1st coat	100	120	140	100	150
2nd coat	150	165	175	200	250
3rd or additional coats	160	173	185	220	270
Roll					
1st coat	245	273	300	150	225
2nd coat	300	320	340	210	275
3rd or additional coats	320	340	360	235	300
Spray					
1st coat	600	675	750	90	200
2nd coat	700	800	900	125	225
3rd or additional coats	750	850	950	135	235
Oil base paint					
Brush					
1st coat	80	100	120	235	265
2nd coat	145	165	185	250	300
3rd coat	155	175	195	300	350
Roll					
1st coat	250	275	300	200	250
2nd coat	225	275	325	225	275
3rd coat	235	285	335	300	350
Spray					
1st coat	550	650	750	90	225
2nd coat	650	775	900	125	350
3rd coat	700	825	950	135	375
Waterproofing, clear hydro sealer					
Brush					
1st coat	125	150	175	75	100
2nd coat	175	200	225	100	135
Roll					
1st coat	325	363	400	125	150
2nd coat	400	425	450	180	200
Spray					
1st coat	650	725	800	100	225
2nd coat	800	900	1000	150	250

For heights above 8 feet, use *High time difficulty factors.* For oil base paint and hydro sealer, I recommend spraying. For painting interior plaster, see *Walls, plaster.*

Pot shelves

Oil base or water base, 12" to 18" wide	SF per hour			SF per gallon	
	Slow	Med	Fast	Heavy	Light
Roll and brush, each coat	50	68	75	40	50

Railing, exterior: decorative wood

Varnish finish applied by brush	LF per hour			LF per gallon	
	Slow	Med	Fast	Heavy	Light
1st coat	22	24	26	80	100
Added coats	30	32	34	100	120

Use these figures to estimate the cost of finishing railing that's from 36" to 42" high and with spindles spaced at 6" on center. These figures include the rail cap, baluster, newels and spindles. These figures include a steel wool buff at 100 LF per hour and wax application at 100 LF per hour.

Railing, exterior:
rough sawn or resawn wood
Oil or water base stain

	LF per hour			LF per gallon	
	Slow	Med	Fast	Heavy	Light
Brush, roll and brush, each coat	16	18	20	15	20

Use these figures to estimate the cost of finishing railing that's 36" to 42" high and with 2" x 2" verticals spaced 6" on center. These figures include painting the rail cap, baluster, newels and spindles.

Railing, interior: handrail

	LF per hour			LF per gallon	
	Slow	Med	Fast	Heavy	Light
Paint grade, undercoat or enamel					
Brush each coat	30	35	40	100	120
Stain grade, 7 step stain, seal and 2 coat lacquer system					
Spray application	55	60	65	75	100

Railing, interior: wood
Paint grade

	LF per hour			LF per gallon	
	Slow	Med	Fast	Heavy	Light
Brush					
1st coat	11	14	17	40	50
2nd coat	13	16	18	50	60
3rd or additional coats	15	18	21	60	70
Split coat	15	18	21	60	70
Spray					
1st coat	50	60	70	30	40
2nd coat	55	65	75	35	45
3rd or additional coats	65	75	85	40	50

Use these figures to estimate the cost of applying undercoat or enamel to railing in a living unit. Railing is assumed to be 36" to 42" high and with spindles at 6" on center. These figures include painting the rail cap, baluster, newels and spindles. For wrought iron railing or rough sawn wood railing with 2" by 2" spindles spaced each 6" on center, see the tables for exterior wood railing.

Railing, interior: wood

Stain grade	LF per hour			LF per gallon	
	Slow	Med	Fast	Heavy	Light
Stain seal and lacquer process					
Sand & putty	50	60	70	--	--
Stain, brush 1 coat & wipe	25	30	35	50	60
Spray 1 coat & wipe	75	85	95	25	35
Sealer, brush 1 coat & sand	45	50	55	55	65
Spray 1 coat & sand	125	138	150	25	35
Lacquer					
Brush					
1st coat	40	50	60	55	65
2nd coat	45	55	65	60	70
Spray					
1st coat	75	85	95	45	55
2nd coat	85	95	105	50	60
Complete stain, seal & 2 coat lacquer system					
Brush all coats	8	10	12	20	30
Spray all coats	16	20	24	10	20

Use these figures to estimate the cost of finishing railing that's from 36" to 42" high and with spindles spaced 6" on center. These figures include staining the rail cap, baluster, newels and spindles. The usual process is a coat of stain, one coat of sanding sealer, sand, putty, and two coats of lacquer.

Railing: wrought iron

	LF per hour			LF per gallon	
	Slow	Med	Fast	Heavy	Light
Brush each coat					
42" high with @ 6" to 9" o/c and wrought iron cap					
Prime - rust inhibitor	20	25	30	100	110
2nd coat - synthetic enamel	25	30	35	110	120
3rd or additional coats	35	40	45	125	135
42" high with bars @ 6" to 9" o/c and wood cap					
Prime - rust inhibitor	15	18	20	80	90
2nd coat - synthetic enamel	20	23	26	90	110
3rd or additional coats	30	35	40	115	125
60" to 72" high with bars @ 6" to 9" o/c					
Prime - rust inhibitor	10	15	20	80	90
2nd coat - synthetic enamel	15	20	25	110	120
3rd or additional coats	25	30	35	125	135

Use these figures to estimate the cost of painting preprimed, prefabricated wrought iron railing with ½" square verticals, supports each 6 feet to 10 feet and ½" by 1½" rails.

Registers, HVAC

	SF of floor area per hour			SF of floor per bomb	
	Slow	Med	Fast	Heavy	Light
Repaint jobs, 1 coat	900	950	1000	600	700
New construction, 1 coat	2500	2750	3000	700	800

These figures assume HVAC registers are painted with spray cans to match the adjacent walls. Estimates are based on square feet of floor area. These rates include time to remove, paint and replace the HVAC registers. Use the square feet of floor area divided by these rates to find the manhours and the number of spray bombs needed to paint all the heat registers in a building. **Rule of thumb:** 2 minutes per 100 square feet of floor area for new construction.

Roof jacks	Hours per 1500 SF of roof area			Gallons per 1500 SF	
	Slow	Med	Fast	Heavy	Light
1 story building	.60	.55	.50	.6	.5
2 story building	.80	.85	.70	.8	.7

Production rates and coverage figures are minimum values based on 1 or 2 story buildings of up to 1500 square feet of roof area. For example, to paint roof jacks on a 3000 SF one-story building at a medium rate, estimate twice .6 hours or 1.2 hours. See the paragraphs "Roof pitch difficulty factors" and "Roof area conversion factors" to adjust for roof slope and type.

Roof pitch difficulty factors   It's harder to paint on a sloped surface than a flat surface. The steeper the slope, the more difficult the work. Roof slope is usually measured in inches of rise per inch of horizontal run. For example, a *3 in 12 pitch* means the roof rises 3 inches in each 12 inches measured horizontally. Use the difficulty factors that follow when estimating the time needed to paint on a sloping roof. On a flat roof or roof with a pitch of less than 3 in 12, calculate the roof area without modification. If the pitch is 3 in 12, multiply the surface area by 1.1. If the pitch is 4 in 12, multiply the surface area by 1.2. If the pitch is 6 in 12, multiply the surface area by 1.3.

Roof area conversion factors   For an arched roof, multiply the building length by the building width. Then multiply by 1.50. For a gambrel roof, multiply the building length by the building width. Then multiply by 1.33.

Roofing: asbestos shingle Water base paint	LF per hour			Water base latex LF per gallon		Oil base paint LF per gallon	
	Slow	Med	Fast	Heavy	Light	Heavy	Light
Brush							
1st coat	45	60	80	180	220	230	270
2nd coat	65	80	100	290	330	330	360
3rd coat	85	100	120	365	405	385	425
Roll							
1st coat	150	170	200	170	190	190	220
2nd coat	250	305	360	280	300	310	330
3rd coat	360	385	420	365	385	385	405
Spray							
1st coat	325	350	375	160	200	180	230
2nd coat	425	450	475	270	290	290	310
3rd coat	500	538	575	345	365	360	380

See the paragraphs "Roof pitch difficulty factors" and "Roof area conversion factors" to adjust for roof slope and type.

Roofing: asbestos shingle Waterproof sealer	SF per hour			SF per gallon	
	Slow	Med	Fast	Heavy	Light
Roll, 1st coat	100	200	300	250	300
2nd or additional coats	150	250	350	300	350
Spray					
1st coat	550	600	650	75	100
2nd coat	600	650	700	100	150

See the paragraphs "Roof pitch difficulty factors" and "Roof area conversion factors" to adjust for roof slope and type.

Roofing: shingle or shake	SF per hour Slow-Med-Fast	Water base Heavy-Light	Oil base SF per gallon Heavy-Light	Penetrating stain Heavy-Light
Brush				
1st coat	100-155 210	215-240	140-160	140-160
2nd coat	150-195-240	265-290	240-260	185-205
Roll				
1st coat	210-258-305	225-250	130-150	180-200
2nd coat	250-300-350	250-275	225-245	275-295
Spray				
1st coat	600-700-800	200-230	130-170	140-200
2nd coat	700-800-900	220-250	200-230	240-300

Coverage figures are based on shingles or shakes with average moisture content. See the paragraphs "Roof pitch difficulty factors" and "Roof area conversion factors" to adjust for roof slope and type.

Roofing, shingle or shake Waterproof sealer, spray applied	SF per hour Slow	Med	Fast	SF per gallon Heavy	Light
1st coat	450	475	500	50	75
2nd coat	500	525	550	125	150

Coverage figures are based on shingles or shakes with average moisture content. See the paragraphs "Roof pitch difficulty factors" and "Roof area conversion factors" to adjust for roof slope and type.

Sheet metal cap or flashing Oil or water base material	LF per hour Slow	Med	Fast	LF per gallon Heavy	Light
3" to 8" wide, brush each coat					
1st coat	215	228	240	475	525
2nd or additional coats	275	288	300	500	550
8" to 12" wide					
1st coat	200	215	230	450	500
2nd coat	250	265	280	475	525

Sheet metal diverters and gravel stop

Oil or water base material	LF per hour			LF per gallon	
	Slow	Med	Fast	Heavy	Light
3" wide, brush each coat					
1st coat	230	240	250	500	600
2nd or additional coats	300	313	325	550	650

Sheet metal vents and flashing

Brush application, per coat	Hours per home			Hours per home	
	Slow	Med	Fast	Heavy	Light
1 story detached home	.7	.6	.5	.5	.4
2 story detached home	.9	.8	.7	.6	.5
Attached units (per unit)	.6	.5	.4	.5	.4

Use this table for oil base paint. This table shows the time needed to paint sheet metal vents on an average home or attached dwelling unit. Use it to estimate residential units without having to take off each vent or piece of flashing.

Shutters or blinds

Per coat	Shutters per hour			Shutters per gallon	
	Slow	Med	Fast	Heavy	Light
Brush					
Undercoat	2.5	3.0	3.5	10	12
Split coat	3.0	3.5	4.0	13	15
Enamel coat	2.0	2.5	3.0	13	15
Spray					
Undercoat	8.0	9.0	10.0	8	10
Enamel coat	7.0	8.0	9.0	10	12
Split coat	8.0	10.0	12.0	10	12

Use these figures to estimate the time and material needed to paint all four sides of solid face, paint grade interior or exterior shutters or blinds. Estimates are based on the number of single-panel 2' x 4' false shutters or blinds that can be painted in an hour. For real louvered shutters, multiply the quantity of shutters by a difficulty factor of 1.5.

Siding, aluminum

Brush application	SF per hour			Water base SF per gallon		Oil base SF per gallon	
	Slow	Med	Fast	Heavy	Light	Heavy	Light
1st coat	215	235	255	300	330	400	440
2nd coat	265	285	305	350	380	450	480

Don't deduct for openings under 100 square feet. For heights over 8 feet, use *High time difficulty factors.*

Siding, asbestos shingle	SF per hour			Water base SF per gallon		Oil base	
	Slow	Med	Fast	Heavy	Light	Heavy	Light
Brush							
1st coat	65	85	105	200	240	250	290
2nd coat	90	110	130	320	350	360	390
3rd or additional coats	110	130	150	385	425	405	445
Roll							
1st coat	140	160	180	200	230	220	260
2nd coat	190	220	230	300	330	330	360
3rd or additional coats	250	275	300	375	395	395	420
Spray							
1st coat	325	350	375	140	160	170	190
2nd coat	350	375	400	215	240	245	270
3rd or additional coats	425	450	425	275	300	295	320
Waterproofing, clear hydro sealer							
Roll							
1st coat	75	150	225	--	--	225	275
2nd coat	125	200	275	--	--	275	300
Spray							
1st coat	475	525	575	--	--	75	100
2nd coat	500	550	600	--	--	100	150

Don't deduct for openings under 100 square feet. For heights over 8 feet, use **High time difficulty factors.**

Siding, rough wood	SF per hour Slow-Med-Fast	Water base SF per gallon Heavy-Light	Oil base Heavy-Light	Penetrating stain Heavy-Light
Brush				
1st coat	100-135 170	225-250	225-275	190-230
2nd coat	135-168-200	275-300	300-350	235-275
3rd coat	150-183-215	350-375	375-425	310-350
Roll				
1st coat	150-225-275	210-235	200-250	100-150
2nd coat	200-275-350	260-285	280-330	200-280
3rd coat	260-335-410	325-350	365-415	295-365
Spray				
1st coat	400-500-600	240-280	130-170	160-200
2nd coat	450-550-650	290-330	215-255	200-290
3rd coat	550-650-750	390-430	315-355	330-390
Spray, waterproof sealer				
1st coat	400-500-600	--	75-150	--
2nd coat	650-675-700	--	125-175	--
3rd or additional coats	700-725-750	--	150-200	--

Use this table to estimate the cost of painting shingle, shake, resawn or rough sawn wood or plywood siding with an average moisture content. Don't deduct for openings under 100 square feet. For heights over 8 feet, use the *High time difficulty factors.* For wood or composition drop siding with exposed beveled edges, multiply the surface area by 1.12 to allow for the extra time and material needed to paint the underside of each board.

Siding, smooth wood

Siding, smooth wood	SF per hour Slow-Med-Fast	Water base Heavy-Light	Oil base SF per gallon Heavy-Light	Penetrating stain Heavy-Light
Brush				
1st coat	100-125- 150	250-275	325-400	290-315
2nd coat	135-168- 200	300-350	375-450	330-355
3rd coat	150-188- 215	375-425	450-525	405-430
Roll				
1st coat	100-125- 150	250-275	300-350	100-200
2nd coat	175-250- 325	300-350	350-400	150-250
3rd coat	260-335- 410	375-400	400-425	200-300
Spray				
1st coat	400-500- 600	100-150	130-170	75-150
2nd coat	550-725- 900	200-250	245-300	150-225
3rd coat	650-825-1000	300-350	345-400	200-250
Spray, waterproof sealer				
1st coat	550-675-800	--	150-250	--
2nd coat	625-750-875	--	200-300	--
3rd coat	675-800-925	--	225-325	--

Use this table for butt or tongue and groove siding, joint lap, drop, beveled or board and batten, in redwood, plywood, fir, hemlock or pine. Don't deduct for openings under 100 square feet. For heights over 8 feet, use *High time difficulty factors.* For wood or composition drop siding with exposed beveled edges, multiply the surface area by 1.12 when figuring both material and labor to allow for painting the underside of each board.

Stair steps, interior or exterior, wood

Stair steps, interior or exterior, wood To estimate the time and material needed to paint or stain stairs, find the surface area. Then use the tables for wood siding. To find the surface area of each tread and riser, multiply the length by the width. To find the tread length, add the run, the rise, and the tread nosing. For example, for a tread with a 12" run, an 8" rise and a 1" nosing, total measurement is 23". For estimating purposes, figure any length from 14" to 24" as 2'0". Use the actual width of the tread if the stringers are calculated separately. If the tread in our example is 3'0" wide and we use 2'0" for the length, the surface area is 6'0". If there are 15 treads, the total top surface area is 90 square feet. See Chapter 19 for stair sections.

If you're calculating the area for painting the stair treads and stringers in one operation, add 2'0" to the actual tread width to include the stringer. That would make the effective width of the tread in our example 5'0" (3'0" + 2'0"). Then multiply 5'0" by 2'0" to find the area of each tread, 10'. For 15 treads, the total surface area is 150 square feet.

Stair stringers, exterior, metal

Stair stringers, exterior, metal	LF per hour Slow	Med	Fast	LF per gallon Heavy	Light
Metal shape, up to 14" wide Roll & brush, each coat	50	55	60	110	120

Use these figures for finish coats of paint on installed stringers pre-primed by others. Measurements are based on the linear footage of each stringer.

Stair stringers, exterior, wood

Stair stringers, exterior, wood Oil or water base material	LF per hour Slow	Med	Fast	LF per gallon Heavy	Light
Rough sawn wood up to 4" x 12" Each coat, roll & brush	40	45	50	60	70

Measurements are based on linear footage of each stringer.

Stair stringers, interior, metal

	LF per hour			LF per gallon	
	Slow	Med	Fast	Heavy	Light
Roll & brush, each coat	45	50	55	120	130

Use these figures for finish coats of paint on installed stringers, pre-primed by others. Measurements are based on the linear footage of each stringer.

Stair stringers, interior, wood
Oil or water base stain

	LF per hour			LF per gallon	
	Slow	Med	Fast	Heavy	Light
Roll & brush, each coat	35	40	45	45	60

Measurements are based on linear footage of each stringer.

Touchup

	% of manhours			% of material	
	Slow	Med	Fast	Heavy	Light
Brush, as required	20%	18%	15%	2%	1%

Touchup will be required on all jobs. The skill of your paint crews and the type of job will determine the time needed. The time and materials shown here are average allowances. Figure the touchup time and material needed and then add the appropriate percentage to your estimate. Figures are based on a percentage of the interior labor and material needed to touch up all interior and exterior work. If you're painting only the interior or the exterior, use half of these figures.

Trellis or lattice
Oil or water base stain

	LF per hour			LF per gallon	
	Slow	Med	Fast	Heavy	Light
To estimate by the linear foot (roll, each coat):					
2" x 2" to 2" x 6"	120	125	130	110	130
2" x 8" to 4" x 12"	100	110	120	80	100
To estimate by the square foot (spray, each coat):					
2" x 2" at 3" o/c		SF surface area			SF surface area	
with 2" x 8" supports	50	55	60	50	60

These figures are based on staining all four sides of each member.

Valances for light fixtures
Oil or water base stain

	LF per hour			LF per gallon	
	Slow	Med	Fast	Heavy	Light
Roll & brush, each coat	30	35	40	90	100

These figures are based on applying stain to rough sawn or resawn 2" by 6" to 2" by 8" valances.

Walls, gypsum drywall
Per SF of *wall* coated

Smooth finish drywall	SF per hour Slow-Med-Fast	Water base Heavy-Light	Oil base Heavy-Light	Epoxy coating Heavy-Light
		------- SF per gallon -------		
Brush				
1st coat	175-200-225	300-325	325-350	--
2nd coat	225-250-275	350-400	375-400	375-425
3rd or additional coats	250-275-300	375-425	400-425	400-450
Stipple	225-250-275	--	--	--
Roll				
1st coat	300-513-725	300-350	275-300	--
2nd coat	375-563-750	350-375	325-350	350-400
3rd or additional coats	450-625-800	375-400	350-375	375-425
Spray				
1st coat	750- 850- 950	250-300	275-300	--
2nd coat	850- 950-1050	300-350	325-350	--
3rd or additional coats	950-1050-1150	325-350	350-375	--

Per square foot of wall coated. These figures assume flat wall paint is being applied over a smooth finish. For heights over 8 feet, use *High time difficulty factors.*

Walls, gypsum drywall
Per SF of *wall* coated

Sand finish drywall	SF per hour Slow-Med-Fast	Water base Heavy-Light	Oil base Heavy-Light	Epoxy coating Heavy-Light
		------- SF per gallon -------		
Brush				
1st coat	175-200-225	300-325	325-350	250-275
2nd coat	200-225-275	350-400	350-400	325-375
3rd or additional coats	225-250-275	375-425	375-425	350-400
Roll				
1st coat	275-500-700	275-325	250-300	--
2nd coat	350-550-725	325-350	300-325	300-350
3rd or additional coats	425-600-775	325-350	325-350	325-375
Spray				
1st coat	700-800- 900	225-275	250-275	--
2nd coat	800-900-1000	275-325	300-350	--
3rd or additional coats	850-950-1050	300-325	325-350	--

Per square foot of wall coated. These figures assume flat wall paint is being applied over a sand finish. For heights over 8 feet, use *High time difficulty factors.*

Walls, gypsum drywall
Per SF of *wall* coated

Orange peel texture	SF per hour Slow-Med-Fast	Water base (SF per gallon) Heavy-Light	Oil base (SF per gallon) Heavy-Light	Epoxy coating (SF per gallon) Heavy-Light
Brush				
1st coat	150-175-200	275-300	225-250	--
2nd coat	175-200-225	325-350	325-375	300-350
3rd or additional coats	200-225-250	350-400	350-400	325-375
Roll				
1st coat	400-538-675	250-300	250-275	--
2nd coat	500-600-700	300-325	275-300	275-300
3rd or additional coats	550-650-750	325-350	300-325	300-325
Spray				
1st coat	700-800- 900	200-250	225-250	--
2nd coat	800-900-1000	250-300	250-275	--
3rd or additional coats	850-950-1050	275-325	275-300	--

Per square foot of wall coated. These figures assume flat wall paint is being applied over an orange peel finish. For heights over 8 feet, use *High time difficulty factors.*

Walls, gypsum drywall
Per SF of *wall* coated

Sealer or enamel coating Orange peel texture	SF per hour Slow	SF per hour Med	SF per hour Fast	SF per gallon Heavy	SF per gallon Light
Water base sealer on orange peel or knockdown texture					
Roll					
1st coat	325	500	675	250	300
2nd coat	350	525	700	300	350
Enamel on orange peel or knockdown texture					
Roll					
1st coat	300	450	600	240	285
2nd coat	325	475	625	275	350

Per square foot of wall coated. These figures assume sealer or enamel is being applied over an orange peel finish. For heights over 8 feet, use ***High time difficulty factors.***

Walls, gypsum drywall
Per SF of *floor area*
Water based latex
Orange peel texture

Walls only, roll	SF per hour			SF per gallon	
	Slow	Med	Fast	Heavy	Light
1st coat	250	325	400	140	175
2nd coat	300	400	500	175	200

Per square foot of floor area. These figures assume flat wall paint is being applied on walls only over an orange peel finish. For heights over 8 feet, use **High time difficulty factors.**

Walls, gypsum drywall
Per SF of *floor area*
Water base sealer
Orange peel texture

Walls and ceiling, roll	SF per hour			SF per gallon	
	Slow	Med	Fast	Heavy	Light
1st coat	100	175	240	75	100
2nd coat	200	275	300	150	200

Per square foot of room area. These figures assume water base sealer is being applied on walls and ceilings over an orange peel finish. For heights over 8 feet, use **High time difficulty factors.**

Walls and ceiling, gypsum drywall
Per SF of *floor area*
Enamel
Orange peel texture

Walls and ceilings, roll	SF per hour			SF per gallon	
	Slow	Med	Fast	Heavy	Light
1st coat	70	100	135	80	100
2nd coat	125	175	225	100	150

Per square foot of room floor area. These figures assume enamel paint is being applied on walls and ceilings over an orange peel finish. For heights over 8 feet, use **High time difficulty factors.**

Walls, plaster, exterior   See *Plaster and stucco*.

Walls, plaster, interior
Smooth finish

Smooth finish	SF per hour Slow-Med-Fast	Water base Heavy-Light	Oil base Heavy-Light	Epoxy coating Heavy-Light
Brush				
1st coat	150-175-200	300-350	350-400	--
2nd coat	175-200-225	325-375	375-425	375-400
3rd or additional coats	200-225-250	350-400	400-450	400-425
Stipple finish	130-150-170	--	--	--
Roll				
1st coat	260-430-640	300-350	325-375	--
2nd coat	300-488-675	325-375	350-400	325-375
3rd or additional coats	325-513-700	350-400	375-425	375-425
Spray				
1st coat	500-600-750	300-375	350-425	--
2nd coat	550-700-850	325-400	375-450	275-325
3rd or additional coats	600-775-950	350-425	400-475	325-375

Per square foot of wall coated. These figures assume paint is being applied over a smooth finish plaster. For heights over 8 feet, use *High time difficulty factors*.

Walls, plaster, interior
Smooth finish

Smooth finish	Slow	Med	Fast	Heavy	Light
Glazing & mottling, brush					
Each coat	75	95	120	800	900
Stipple	100	120	135	--	--

Per square foot of wall coated. These figures assume paint is being applied over a smooth finish plaster. For heights over 8 feet, use *High time difficulty factors*.

Walls, plaster, interior
Medium texture

Medium texture	SF per hour Slow-Med-Fast	Water base Heavy-Light	Oil base Heavy-Light	Epoxy coating Heavy-Light
Brush				
1st coat	125-150-175	275-300	300-325	--
2nd coat	150-168-185	300-325	350-400	375-400
3rd or additional coats	160-185-210	325-350	375-425	400-425
Stipple finish	125-143-160	--	--	--
Roll				
1st coat	225-450-650	225-250	250-275	--
2nd coat	250-475-675	275-300	300-350	320-350
3rd or additional coats	275-500-725	300-325	325-375	350-400
Spray				
1st coat	475-575-725	275-350	325-400	--
2nd coat	525-675-825	300-400	350-425	275-325
3rd or additional coats	575-750-925	325-450	375-450	300-350

Per square foot of wall coated. These figures assume paint is being applied over a medium finish plaster. For heights over 8 feet, use *High time difficulty factors*.

Walls, plaster, interior
Medium texture

	SF per hour			SF per gallon	
	Slow	Med	Fast	Heavy	Light
Glazing and mottling					
Brush, each coat	50	60	80	700	900
Stipple	100	·110	125	--	--

Per square foot of wall coated. These figures assume paint is being applied over a medium finish plaster. For heights over 8 feet, use *High time difficulty factors.*

Walls, plaster, interior
Rough texture

	SF per hour Slow-Med-Fast	Water base ------------------------ Heavy-Light	Oil base SF per gallon Heavy-Light	Epoxy coating ------------------------ Heavy-Light
Brush				
1st coat	115-140-165	250-300	275-300	--
2nd coat	125-153-180	275-325	325-375	350-375
3rd or additional coats	135-168-200	300-350	350-400	375-400
Stipple finish	115-130-150	--	--	--
Roll				
1st coat	200-450-625	225-250	275-300	--
2nd coat	225-475-650	275-300	300-350	300-350
3rd or additional coats	250-500-675	300-325	325-375	350-400
Spray				
1st coat	500-600-700	250-325	275-325	--
2nd coat	600-700-800	300-400	325-400	300-325
3rd or additional coats	700-800-900	325-425	350-425	350-375

Per square foot of wall coated. These figures assume paint is being applied over a sand finish plaster. For heights over 8 feet, use **High time difficulty factors.**

Walls, plaster, interior
Rough texture

	SF per hour			SF per gallon	
	Slow	Med	Fast	Heavy	Light
Casein or resin emulsion paint					
Roll & brush, each coat	135	350	550	300	350
Glazing and mottling					
Brush					
Each coat	40	50	60	800	875
Stipple	90	100	115	--	--

Per square foot of wall coated. These figures assume paint is being applied over a rough finish plaster. For heights over 8 feet, use High time difficulty factors.

Walls, paneled, interior

Paint grade	SF per hour			Water base SF per gallon		Oil base SF per gallon	
	Slow	Med	Fast	Heavy	Light	Heavy	Light
Brush							
1st coat	65	75	85	275	300	350	375
2nd coat	80	95	110	325	350	375	400
3rd or additional coats	100	110	120	350	375	400	425
Roll							
1st coat	200	300	400	250	275	300	350
2nd coat	250	375	500	300	325	350	375
3rd or additional coats	300	425	550	325	350	375	400
Spray							
1st coat	350	425	500	125	175	175	200
2nd coat	500	550	600	200	250	250	300
3rd or additional coats	600	650	700	300	350	350	400

These figures are based on applying undercoat and enamel to interior T&G, wood veneer or plain wainscot paneling. For heights over 8 feet, use **High time difficulty factors.**

Walls, paneled, interior

Stain grade	SF per hour			SF per gallon	
	Slow	Med	Fast	Heavy	Light
Stain, seal & lacquer process					
Sand & putty	175	200	225	--	--
Stain					
Brush & wipe, 1 coat	100	125	150	350	400
Spray & wipe, 1 coat	350	425	500	125	175
Sanding sealer					
Brush & sand, 1 coat	200	220	240	400	450
Spray & sand, 1 coat	400	500	600	125	175
Lacquer					
Brush					
1st coat	175	225	300	325	375
2nd coat	225	288	350	375	400
Spray					
1st coat	450	550	650	100	150
2nd coat	500	575	675	100	150
Complete stain, seal and 2 coat lacquer system					
Brush all coats	40	45	50	125	150
Spray all coats	70	80	90	30	50
Penetrating stain wax or casein or synthetic resin emulsion paint					
Brush, each coat	300	350	400	450	500

These figures are based on staining interior T&G, wood veneer or plain wainscot paneling. For heights over 8 feet, use *High time difficulty factors.*

Window screen frames

Paint grade, brushed on	Frames per hour			Frames per gallon	
	Slow	Med	Fast	Heavy	Light
Undercoat	5	6	7	40	50
Split coat	8	9	10	55	60
Enamel coat	6	7	8	50	55

These figures will apply when painting all sides of wood window screens up to 15 SF (width times length).

Window seats, wood
Per SF coated

	SF per hour			SF per gallon	
	Slow	Med	Fast	Heavy	Light
Paint grade, brush					
Prime coat	20	25	30	40	45
Split coat	30	35	40	55	60
Finish coat	25	30	35	50	55

Window sills, wood
Per LF coated

	LF per hour			LF per gallon	
	Slow	Med	Fast	Heavy	Light
Paint grade, brush					
Prime coat	40	50	60	120	140
Split coat	60	70	80	160	180
Finish coat	50	60	70	150	175

Window storm sash
Per 15 SF painted, brush

	Sash per hour			Sash per gallon	
	Slow	Med	Fast	Heavy	Light
Undercoat	3	4	5	22	25
Split coat	5	6	7	30	35
Enamel coat	4	5	6	25	30

These figures will apply when painting all sides of two-lite wood storm sash measuring up to 15 SF (width times length).

Windows, exterior The estimates that follow include the time and material needed to paint the sash (mullions or muntins), trim, frames, jambs, sill and apron on the exterior side only. Manhour and material rates are the same for painting either the exterior or interior of windows. These estimates are per window painted and are based on a window size of 15 square feet overall (width times length). Add preparation time and for protecting windows. For larger windows estimate time and material proportionately.

Windows, exterior
1, 2 or 3 lite

	Windows per day (Medium)	Hours per window			Windows per gallon	
		Slow	Med	Fast	Heavy	Light
Paint grade, brush						
Undercoat	40	.25	.20	.15	14	15
Split coat	32	.30	.25	.20	16	17
Enamel coat	27	.35	.30	.25	15	16
Stain, seal & 1 coat varnish	12	.70	.65	.60	9	11
Added coats of varnish	36	.25	.23	.20	18	22

Windows, exterior 4 to 6 lite	Windows per day (Medium)	Hours per window			Windows per gallon	
		Slow	Med	Fast	Heavy	Light
Paint grade, brush						
Undercoat	27	.35	.30	.25	13	14
Split coat	22	.40	.35	.30	15	16
Enamel coat	18	.45	.40	.35	14	15
Stain, seal & 1 coat varnish	11	.80	.75	.60	8	10
Added coats of varnish	30	.30	.25	.20	17	21

Windows, exterior 7 to 8 lite	Windows per day (Medium)	Hours per window			Windows per gallon	
		Slow	Med	Fast	Heavy	Light
Paint grade, brush						
Undercoat	20	.45	.40	.35	12	13
Split coat	16	.55	.50	.45	14	15
Enamel coat	13	.65	.60	.55	13	14
Stain, seal & 1 coat varnish	10	.90	.80	.70	7	9
Added coats of varnish	24	.35	.30	.25	16	20

Windows, exterior 9 to 11 lite	Windows per day (Medium)	Hours per window			Windows per gallon	
		Slow	Med	Fast	Heavy	Light
Paint grade, brush						
Undercoat	16	.55	.50	.45	11	12
Split coat	13	.65	.60	.55	13	14
Enamel coat	11	.75	.70	.65	12	13
Stain, seal & 1 coat varnish	9	1.0	.90	.80	5	7
Added coats of varnish	20	.40	.35	.30	15	19

Windows, exterior 12 lite	Windows per day (Medium)	Hours per window			Windows per gallon	
		Slow	Med	Fast	Heavy	Light
Paint grade, brush						
Undercoat	13	.65	.60	.55	10	11
Split coat	12	.70	.65	.60	12	13
Enamel coat	10	.80	.75	.70	11	12
Stain, seal & 1 coat varnish	8	1.1	1.0	.90	4	6
Added coats of varnish	18	.45	.40	.35	14	18

Staining usually includes one coat of stain, sanding sealer, sand, putty, and one coat of varnish. Minimum preparation for varnishing usually includes a steel wool buff at 110 SF per hour and wax at 110 SF per hour.

Windows, exterior Square foot basis	SF per hour			SF per gallon	
	Slow	Med	Fast	Heavy	Light
Brush					
Undercoat	150	165	180	440	460
Split coat	120	135	150	480	520
Enamel coat	100	113	125	460	500

Use this table when estimating the labor and material needed to paint windows larger than 15 square feet (width times length). When calculating the window area, add 1 foot to each dimension before multiplying width by the height. For example, a window measuring 4'0" by 4'0" overall would have a calculated surface of 36 square feet: Width of 4' + 1'0" + 1'0" is 6'0". Total area is 6' times 6' or 36 square feet per side. Add an extra 2 square feet to the calculated area for each window lite. This allows for the extra time needed to finish muntins, mullions and sash. For similar windows that are stained, sealed and varnished, use the previous tables based on window lites.

Windows, interior The estimates that follow include the time and material needed to paint the sash (mullions or muntins), trim, frames, jambs, sill and apron on the interior side only. Manhour and material rates are the same for painting either the exterior or interior of windows. These estimates are per window painted and are based on a window size of 15 square feet overall (width times length). Add preparation time and for protecting windows. For larger windows, estimate time and material proportionately.

Windows, interior 1, 2 or 3 lite	Windows per day (Medium)	Hours per window			Windows per gallon	
		Slow	Med	Fast	Heavy	Light
Paint grade, brush						
Undercoat	40	.25	.20	.15	14	15
Split coat	32	.30	.25	.20	16	17
Enamel coat	27	.35	.30	.25	15	16
Stain grade, stain, seal & lacquer	13	.70	.65	.60	9	11

Windows, interior 4 to 6 lite	Windows per day (Medium)	Hours per window			Windows per gallon	
		Slow	Med	Fast	Heavy	Light
Paint grade, brush						
Undercoat	27	.35	.30	.25	13	14
Split coat	22	.40	.35	.30	15	16
Enamel coat	18	.45	.40	.35	14	15
Stain grade, stain, seal & lacquer	11	.80	.75	.70	8	10

Windows, interior 7 or 8 lite	Windows per day (Medium)	Hours per window			Windows per gallon	
		Slow	Med	Fast	Heavy	Light
Paint grade, brush						
Undercoat	20	.45	.40	.35	12	13
Split coat	16	.55	.50	.45	14	15
Enamel coat	13	.65	.60	.55	13	14
Stain grade, stain, seal & lacquer	10	.90	.80	.70	7	9

Windows, interior 9 to 11 lite	Windows per day (Medium)	Hours per window			Windows per gallon	
		Slow	Med	Fast	Heavy	Light
Paint grade, brush						
Undercoat	16	.55	.50	.45	11	12
Split coat	13	.65	.60	.55	13	14
Enamel coat	11	.75	.70	.65	12	13
Stain grade, stain, seal & lacquer	09	1.0	.90	.80	6	08

Windows, interior 12 lite	Windows per day (Medium)	Hours per window			Windows per gallon	
		Slow	Med	Fast	Heavy	Light
Paint grade, brush						
Undercoat	13	.65	.60	.55	10	11
Split coat	12	.70	.65	.60	12	13
Enamel coat	10	.80	.75	.70	11	12
Stain grade, stain, seal & lacquer	8	1.10	1.00	.90	5	7

Windows, interior Square foot basis	SF per hour			SF per gallon	
	Slow	Med	Fast	Heavy	Light
Undercoat	140	165	190	440	460
Enamel coat	95	110	125	460	500
Split coat	120	135	150	480	520

Use these figures to estimate the time and material needed to paint wood windows with a brush. For stain grade work, use the per window estimates in the previous tables. This table will apply when estimating windows larger than 15 square feet (width times length). When calculating the window area, add 1 foot to each dimension before multiplying width by the height. For example, a window measuring 4'0" by 4'0" overall would have a calculated surface of 36 square feet: Width of 4' + 1'0" + 1'0" is 6'0". Height of 4' + 1'0" + 1'0" is 6'0". Total area is 6' times 6' or 36 square feet per side. Add an extra 2 square feet to the calculated area for each window lite. This allows for the extra time needed to finish muntins, mullions and sash. For smaller windows that are stained, sealed and varnished, use the previous tables based on window lites.

Window conversion factors   The table below gives you a faster way to figure the manhours and material needed to paint windows. First, calculate the square feet of window area. For example, assume you're undercoating a 3'0" x 5'0" window with four lites. Multiply length times width to find square feet: 3'0" x 5'0" = 15 square feet. Then multiply the area by the manhour conversion factor for a four-lite window, 3.0 in this case. 15 SF times 3.0 is 45 square feet. Then divide 45 SF by the medium manhour rate from the previous table, 165 square feet per hour. 45 SF divided by 165 per hour is .27 hours. It should take .27 manhours to paint the window.

To find the material needed to paint the same window, multiply the 15 square feet by the factor in the right column below for a 4 lite window, 2.2. 15 SF times 2.2 is 33 square feet. Now divide that figure by the light coverage rate, 460 square feet per gallon. It will take .072 gallons to undercoat that window. Divide 1 gallon by .072 to find that you can undercoat 13.9 windows with 1 gallon of undercoater.

The following factors are for each coat when painting one side only.

Lites	Manhours per SF conversion factor	Material per SF conversion factor
2 to 3 lites	L x W x 2.0	L x W x 2.0
4 to 6 lites	L x W x 3.0	L x W x 2.2
7 to 8 lites	L x W x 4.0	L x W x 2.4
9 to 11 lites	L x W x 5.0	L x W x 2.6
12 lites	L x W x 6.0	L x W x 2.9

Wine racks

Per SF of face, spray all coats	SF per hour			SF per gallon	
	Slow	Med	Fast	Heavy	Light
Paint grade, spray undercoat or enamel					
1st coat	50	65	80	75	100
2nd coat	65	88	100	100	125
3rd coat	75	100	125	125	150
Stain grade, stain, seal & lacquer process					
Sand & putty	50	75	100	--	--
Stain, spray & wipe, 1 coat	100	175	225	75	150
Sanding sealer, spray, 1 coat	130	208	275	75	150
Sand lightly	75	100	125	--	--
Lacquer, spray					
1st coat	100	200	300	50	100
2nd coat	175	313	450	50	100
Complete stain & lacquer process including 2 coats of lacquer					
Spray, all coats	20	28	35	15	25

These figures include coating all exterior and interior surfaces and are based on overall dimensions (length times width) of the wine rack face.

Appendix C

FORMS FOR PAINT CONTRACTORS

This section contains blank copies of most of the forms used in the book. They are yours to copy and use. An instant print shop can print copies and bind them into a pad for a very reasonable cost. Add your company logo and make any changes that make the forms more applicable to your company.

List of forms:

- Contract Information Log (Figure 9-5)

- Contract Follow-up Log (Figure 9-8)

- Progress Report (Figure 11-8)

- Historical Cost Log — Single Family Homes (Figure 12-1)

- Historical Cost Log — Apartments and Commercial Projects (Figure 12-2)

- Sundry Inventory Checklist (Figure 14-1)

- Repaint Take-off Sheet (Figure 18-4)

- Repaint Recap (Figure 18-16)

- New Construction Take-off Sheet (Figure 19-4)

- New Construction Recap Sheet (Figure 19-16)

Contract Information

Project name: _____

Address: _____

Cross streets: _____

Project number: _____

Model number: _____

Owner: _____

_____

Builder: _____

_____

Lender: _____

_____

Contract amount: _____

Authorized signature: _____

Start date:_____

Projected completion date:_____

Building type: _____

# of buildings: _____

# of models: _____

# of actual manhours: _____

_____Contract signed — President	_____Field manhours 1052 — Estimator
_____Plans in house — Estimator	_____Contract prices correct
_____Specifications — Estimator	_____Billing set up — Accounting
_____Sequence list — Estimator	_____Release forms — Accounting
_____Plot plan (site location)	_____Preliminary notices sent (all three)
_____Color schedule — Estimator (with cabinets and beams)	_____Union registration sent
	_____Master file set up (six tab)
_____Certificate of insurance	_____Office map labeled — Estimator

Contract Information Log

Field manhours	union reg.	Billing info. releases ect.	Map site loc. in-house	Proj. map to field	Color sched.	Seq. list	Plan	Spec	Contract Rec'd Sent	Cert. ins.	Prelim. notice	Contract price	Job name & address	Job & Builder

Contract Follow-up Log

Progress Report

Job foreman _____

Job name _____

Week ending _____

		Estimated hours per operation	Units completed	Total hours
EXTERIOR PRIME	Fascia			
	Overhang			
	Siding & Garage door			
	Plant-ons			
	Exterior doors			
	Entry doors			
	Clear seal			
EXTERIOR FINISH	Fascia			
	Overhang			
	Siding & Garage door			
	Plant-ons			
	Exterior doors			
	Entry doors			
	Vents & flashing			
	Roof jacks			
	Garage door, inside			
	Stucco			
	Seal K & B			
	Undercoat			
	Split coat			
	Caulking			
	Woodwork			
	Blot out			
INTERIOR FINISH	Stain cabinets			
	Walls			
	K & B enamel			
	Enamel trim			
	Beams			
	Railing			
	Interior wood			
	Base			
	Touch-up			
	Customer service			
	Extras			
	Supervision			
	Total hours per unit			

	This week	To date
Estimated hours		
Actual hours		
Over or under		

Progress Report

Specifications

Interior: _____

Exterior: _____

Date	Contractor	Plan #	Square footage	Hours per unit	# of stories	# of openings	High ceilings	Hours for siding	Excessive Exterior painting	$ unit	$ /SF	Profit (loss)

Historical Cost Log — Single Family Homes

Specifications:

Interior:

Ceilings (height and finish) _____

Flat walls (number of coats) _____

Wet area walls (number of coats)_____

Trim (number of coats) _____

Windows (aluminum or wood) _____

Cabinets (prefinished, enamel or stain & laquer)_____

Base (painted or stained) _____

Wallcover _____

Exterior:

Wood trim (number of coats)_____

Stucco (paint, seal or no finish) _____

Metal trim (number of coats) _____

Location	Contract date	Number of floors	Total units	Gross SF	Avg unit SF	$ unit	$ SF	% profit (loss)

Historical Cost Log — Apartments & Commercial Projects

Sundry Inventory Checklist

Suppliers: _____
                _____
                _____
                _____
                _____

Supplier	Product number	Product	Inventory quantity	Unit	Cost
	#	Bender paint pads		Each	$
	#	Brush - 3" nylon		Each	$
	#	Brush - 4" nylon		Each	$
	#	Brush - 5" nylon		Each	$
	#	Brush - 3" bristle		Each	$
	#	Caulking bags		Each	$
	#	Caulking -DAP		Each	$
	#	Caulking gun (Newborn)		Each	$
	#	Hydraulic fluid		Qt	$
	#	Lemon oil		Pint	$
	#	Masking paper 18" wide		Roll	$
	#	Masking tape 1½"		Roll	$
	#	Lacquer		5's	$
	#	Sanding sealer		5's	$
	#	Resin sealer		5's	$
	#	PVA sealer		5's	$
	#	Particle masks		Box	$
	#	Putty (Crawfords)		Qt	$
	#	Respirators		Each	$
	#	Respirator cartridges		Box	$
	#	Respirator filters		Box	$
	#	Rags		Lb	$
	#	Roller covers 9" x ¾"		Each	$
	#	Roller covers 9" x ⅜"		Each	$
	#	Roller covers 7" x ¾"		Each	$
	#	Roller covers 7" x ⅜"		Each	$
	#	Roller covers mini		Each	$
	#	Roller frames 9"		Each	$

Supplier	Product number	Product	Inventory quantity	Unit	Cost
	#	Roller frames 7"		Each	$
	#	Roller frames mini		Each	$
	#	Roller poles 4' wood tip		Each	$
	#	Roller poles 6' wood tip		Each	$
	#	Roller pole tips metal		Each	$
	#	Sandpaper (120C production)		Slve	$
	#	Sandpaper (220A trimite)		Slve	$
	#	Sandpaper (220A garnet)		Slve	$
	#	Spackle (Synkloid)		Qt	$
	#	Spray bombs (black/white)		Each	$
	#	Spray gun tips #3 or #4		Each	$
	#	Spray gun couplers		Each	$
	#	Spray socks		Box	$
	#	Stip fill		Gal	$
	#	Strainer bags		Each	$
	#	Staples - $\frac{5}{16}$"		Box	$
	#	Thinner, lacquer		Drum	$
	#	Thinner, paint		Drum	$
	#	Thinner, shellac (alcohol)		Gal	$
	#	Work pots (2 gal, plastic)		Each	$
	#				$
	#				$
	#				$
	#				$
	#				$

Order date

Ordered by: (initials)

Purchase order no.

Form #_____

Sundry Inventory Checklist (continued)

Interior room _____   Size _____   Job name: _____

Exterior _____   SF _____   Estimate number: _____

Manhours

Operation	Dimension	LF/ SF	Method	Coats	Judgment hours	Formula Feet/hr	hour	Final hours
1. _____	_____	_____	_____	_____	_____	_____	_____	_____
2. _____	_____	_____	_____	_____	_____	_____	_____	_____
3. _____	_____	_____	_____	_____	_____	_____	_____	_____
4. _____	_____	_____	_____	_____	_____	_____	_____	_____
5. _____	_____	_____	_____	_____	_____	_____	_____	_____
6. _____	_____	_____	_____	_____	_____	_____	_____	_____
7. _____	_____	_____	_____	_____	_____	_____	_____	_____
8. _____	_____	_____	_____	_____	_____	_____	_____	_____
9. _____	_____	_____	_____	_____	_____	_____	_____	_____
10. _____	_____	_____	_____	_____	_____	_____	_____	_____
11. _____	_____	_____	_____	_____	_____	_____	_____	_____
12. _____	_____	_____	_____	_____	_____	_____	_____	_____
13. _____	_____	_____	_____	_____	_____	_____	_____	_____
14. _____	_____	_____	_____	_____	_____	_____	_____	_____

Crosscheck: Manhour totals _____   vs.   _____ = _____

Manhour bid total _____

Material

Operation	LF/ SF	Color	Coats and type	Judgment gallons	Formula Ft/gal	gallons	Price per gallon	Final cost
1. _____	_____	_____	_____	_____	_____	_____	$ _____	$ _____
2. _____	_____	_____	_____	_____	_____	_____	$ _____	$ _____
3. _____	_____	_____	_____	_____	_____	_____	$ _____	$ _____
4. _____	_____	_____	_____	_____	_____	_____	$ _____	$ _____
5. _____	_____	_____	_____	_____	_____	_____	$ _____	$ _____
6. _____	_____	_____	_____	_____	_____	_____	$ _____	$ _____
7. _____	_____	_____	_____	_____	_____	_____	$ _____	$ _____
8. _____	_____	_____	_____	_____	_____	_____	$ _____	$ _____
9. _____	_____	_____	_____	_____	_____	_____	$ _____	$ _____
10. _____	_____	_____	_____	_____	_____	_____	$ _____	$ _____
11. _____	_____	_____	_____	_____	_____	_____	$ _____	$ _____
12. _____	_____	_____	_____	_____	_____	_____	$ _____	$ _____
13. _____	_____	_____	_____	_____	_____	_____	$ _____	$ _____
14. _____	_____	_____	_____	_____	_____	_____	$ _____	$ _____

Crosscheck: Gallons_____   vs.   _____

Total material cost $_____

SURRPTUCU

Operation	Description	Labor hours	Labor cost (at _____)	Material cost	Totals
Setup _____	_____	_____	_____	+ _____	= $ _____
_____	_____	_____	_____	+ _____	= $ _____
Remove/replace ____	_____	_____	_____	+ _____	= $ _____
_____	_____	_____	_____	+ _____	= $ _____
Protection _____	_____	_____	_____	+ _____	= $ _____
_____	_____	_____	_____	+ _____	= $ _____
Touchup _____	_____	_____	_____	+ _____	= $ _____
Cleanup _____	_____	_____	_____	+ _____	= $ _____
_____	_____	_____	_____	+ _____	= $ _____

SURRPTUCU total $_____

Repaint Take-off Sheet

Date _____   Due date _____
Customer _____   Job name _____
Address _____   Job site _____
City/State/Zip _____   Estimate # _____
Phone _____   Total square footage _____
Estimated by _____   Checked by _____

Sketch

Specifications
_____
_____
_____
_____
_____
_____

Notes and comments
_____
_____
_____
_____
_____
_____

(Sketch on back of form if necessary)

Recap

Equipment description	Rental days	Daily cost	Total cost
_____	_____ $	_____ $	_____
_____	_____	_____	_____
_____	_____	_____	_____
_____	_____	_____	_____
_____	_____	_____	_____
Equipment total		_____	

Exterior or room	Final hours	Material costs	SURRPTUCU costs
Exterior	_____ $	_____ $	_____
_____	_____	_____	_____
_____	_____	_____	_____
_____	_____	_____	_____
_____	_____	_____	_____
_____	_____	_____	_____
Totals _____	Hours $	Material _____ $	SURRPTUCU _____

Extensions

Rate $ _____/hour
Hours _____ x rate = $ _____
Supervision _____ Hrs _____
Subtotal _____

Burden _____ % _____
Material _____
Equipment _____
SURRPTUCU _____
Subcontract _____ % _____

Commissions _____ % _____
Contingency _____ % _____
Subtotal _____

Overhead _____ % _____
Direct cost _____

Profit _____ % _____
Base bid total _____
Adjustment _____ % + / − _____
Final bid total _____
Price/SF _____
Price/room _____

Crosscheck to historical costs:
    This project $/SF $ _____
    Historical costs ($/SF) range from $ _____ to $ _____

    This project $/room $ _____
    Historical costs ($/room) range from $ _____ to $ _____

Repaint Recap

Company _____   Project _____
Plan # _____   # units _____
Sq. Ft. _____ Stories _____   Plan date _____
Prepared by: _____   Checked by: _____

Interior

High ceiling _____

Kitchen _____ Util. ⟶
Bath _____
Walls _____ −
Clip _____ x

Seal	(	) _____	+ _____
U/C	(	) _____	+ _____
Cabs	(	) _____	+ _____
Walls	(	) _____	+ _____
K & B	(	) _____	+ _____
Trim	(	) _____	+ _____
Beams		_____	+ _____
T & G ceiling	(	) _____	+ _____
Rail	(	) _____	+ _____
Stringers	(	) _____	+ _____
Valance	(	) _____	+ _____
Fireplace	(	) _____	+ _____
Base P E S		_____	+ _____

_____
_____
_____

Subtotal _____ + _____
T/U _____ + _____
Tax _____
Totals _____ + _____

Notes - Options - Alternatives - Exclusions

Exterior

Elevation A

Fascia	(	)	_____	+ _____
O/H	(	) x 1.5 =	_____	+ _____
Side	(	) ST HB	_____	+ _____
P/O	(	)	_____	+ _____
Doors F L E X			_____	+ _____
V & F			_____	+ _____
RJ & BGD			_____	+ _____

_____
_____
_____

Subtotals _____ + _____

Tax _____

Totals _____ + _____

Elevation B

Fascia	(	)	_____	+ _____
O/H	(	) x 1.5 =	_____	+ _____
Side	(	) ST HB	_____	+ _____
P/O	(	)	_____	+ _____
Doors F L E X			_____	+ _____
V & F			_____	+ _____
RJ & BGD			_____	+ _____

_____
_____
_____

Subtotals _____ + _____

Tax _____

Totals _____ + _____

Elevation C

Fascia	(	)	_____	+ _____
O/H	(	) x 1.5 =	_____	+ _____
Side	(	) ST HB	_____	+ _____
P/O	(	)	_____	+ _____
Doors F L E X			_____	+ _____
V & F			_____	+ _____
RJ & BGD			_____	+ _____

_____
_____
_____

Subtotals _____ + _____

Tax _____

Totals _____ + _____

Recap	Manhours	+	Material cost
Elevation A	_____	+	_____
Elevation B	_____	+	_____
Elevation C	_____	+	_____
Option #	_____	+	_____
Option #	_____	+	_____

New Construction Take-off Sheet

Project _____ **Builder** _____ **Date** _____
Prepared by _____ **Checked by** _____

Rate $ _____/hour

Hours _____ × Rate =	$_____	_____ $ _____	_____ $ _____	_____ $ _____
Supervision _____ Hrs			
Subtotal			
Burden _____%			
Material			
Subtotal			
Overhead _____%			
Direct cost			
Profit _____%			
Base bid total			
Price/SF			
Adjustment _____% + −			
Final bid total			
Final price/SF			

Rate $ _____/hour

Hours _____ × Rate =	$_____	_____ $ _____	_____ $ _____	_____ $ _____
Supervision _____ Hrs			
Subtotal			
Burden _____%			
Material			
Subtotal			
Overhead _____%			
Direct cost			
Profit _____%			
Base bid total			
Price/SF			
Adjustment _____% + −			
Final bid total			
Final price/SF			

Rate $ _____/hour

Hours _____ × Rate =	$_____	_____ $ _____	_____ $ _____	_____ $ _____
Supervision _____ Hrs			
Subtotal			
Burden _____%			
Material			
Subtotal			
Overhead _____%			
Direct cost			
Profit _____%			
Base bid total			
Price/SF			
Adjustment _____% + −			
Final bid total			
Final price/SF			

New Construction Recap Sheet

Glossary

A

Abrasive A substance used for grinding, polishing or wearing away a surface, such as emery or sand in sandblasting or sandpaper.

Acetone A colorless, flammable, volatile liquid solvent used for removing paint, certain oils and other organic compounds.

Acoustic paint A ceiling coating which absorbs sound.

Acrylic A plastic-like resin used to bind pigment, water and other components in latex paint.

Adhesion The act of sticking or the state of being stuck together or attached.

Adhesive bond The relationship between two materials in contact with each other which causes them to be attached. The bond strength between a surface and a coating.

Air entrapment Minute air bubbles trapped in paint or coating products.

Air spray Spraying paint by using hydraulic pressure instead of air to atomize the liquid by forcing it through an orifice.

Alcohol A colorless, volatile, pungent liquid. Ethyl or methyl alcohol are commonly used in the painting trade.

Alkali A soluble salt in masonry or concrete that will leach or bleed through painted surfaces.

Alkyd An oil-based paint made with synthetic resins. All interior oil-based paints today are alkyds.

Alligatoring (1) Cracks in the surface layer of materials which widen from contraction caused by a sudden change in temperature, lack of binder, insufficient drying time between coats, poor penetration, or applying a hard film over a soft undercoat. (2) Extensive breaking of paint film when the second coat is applied over a primer not thoroughly dried. Sometimes referred to as *crocodiling*.

Aluminum paint A paint which contains particles of aluminum. It can prevent discoloration where mildew is present, resist corrosion when applied to steel, serve as a heat and flame retardant, and coat asbestos-cement siding.

Amalgamate To join together into one, to unite or combine. To restore old paint or lacquer products by using chemicals.

Ambient temperature The temperature around a given area.

Aniline dye Any dye produced synthetically from coal tar products. Commonly a blue, poisonous dye.

Apprentice painter A person who works under a skilled journeyman painter while learning the trade.

Arching Spray painting in a semi-circular arc and not vertically or horizontally to the ground.

Asbestine A white talc extender used in paint.

Asphalt A petroleum by-product used as a waterproofing protective coating.

Atomize To reduce to a fine spray or mist, as in airless spray painting.

B

Back prime To coat the back side of a surface with paint. Exterior siding is often "back primed" to prevent moisture from penetrating into the wood and causing swelling and warpage.

Ball mill A horizontal, cylindrical milling machine which rotates to mix paint pigments and carrier vehicles.

Baluster (1) A short vase-shaped supporting column or member. (2) A support for a railing, especially one of the upright columns of a balustrade.

Balustrade A railing or parapet consisting of a handrail on a base member and sometimes interrupted by piers.

Barite (baryte) A white mineral composed mainly of barium sulfate. It is the chief source of barium used in making paint.

Benzene A clear, flammable, poisonous, aromatic liquid. It is used in making lacquers, varnishes and many dyes.

Binder That part of a paint medium which holds the pigment in a coherent film and is not volatile. It may be oil, size or resin. The higher the binder content, the greater the durability of the paint.

Bitumen Asphalt found in a natural mineral or pitch state.

Bleaching Restoring discolored or stained wood to its natural color, or to a lighter color.

Bleeding Subsurface coloring (dyes or stains) acids, rust or undercoats working their way through to discolor the surface coat.

Blistering Bubbles formed in a painted surface caused by subsurface moisture resulting from poor surface preparation techniques.

Bloom A thin film that reduces the gloss on painted or varnished surfaces, caused by the presence of humidity while a surface is being finished.

Blue lead A bluish rust preventer which contains lead sulfide and carbon.

Blushing A bloom or gray cloudy film appearing on a newly-finished surface on humid days. This effect is usually caused by the condensation of moisture or by the too rapid evaporation of the solvents.

Body The consistency of liquid paint, or solidity of the dried paint film.

Boiled linseed oil Linseed oil is boiled to temperatures from 400 to 600 degrees F, then a small quantity of a drier (lead monoxide or manganese dioxide) is added to promote quick drying of a newly painted surface.

Bolt Wallcover material can be purchased by the bolt. A bolt is usually two or three roll lengths of wallcover, but may be more. Sometimes referred to as yardage goods.

Boneyard An area where building parts are painted prior to installation.

Boxing Pouring paint from container to container to insure proper mixing of all components.

Bridging The covering or filling of a gap, pore, crack or void in a surface by a film.

Bright Unstained.

Brightness The degree of lightness of any surface emitting or reflecting light.

Bronzing Applying a liquid paint vehicle which contains a metallic powder.

Brush hand Slang term for an expert brush painter.

Brushability The ability of a liquid to be applied to a surface with a brush. Brushable paints are not thick and gooey and join easily to the previously-applied paint coating.

Brushing Applying paint with a brush.

Brushing lacquer A slow-drying lacquer which doesn't show brush marks.

Bubbling Blisters caused by air below a painted surface

Build up A thick surface created by successive layers of coatings.

Burning off Removing old paint by heating with a torch and scraping it off while hot.

Burnt sienna A yellow pigment which turns reddish brown when burnt.

Burnt umber A dark yellow pigment which turns medium brown when burnt.

Butt joint work Wallcovering work where the wallcover is placed edge to edge without overlapping.

C

Caking The settling or hardening of paint into a mass.

Calcimine A water-based white or tinted paint made of whiting, glue, coloring matter and water, used as a wash for interior plaster. Any calcimine coat must be covered by a prime coat prior to application of a finish coat of paint.

Calcium carbonate Commonly called chalk, it's used in lime and portland cement, and as a paint extender and colorant.

Casein paint Paint in which a casein solution takes the place of the drying oils of common paints. For outdoor use, lime and cement supply the hiding property; for inside work, it's lime, powdered chalk or kaolin. The paint is sold as a powder, to be mixed with water for use.

Cat eye A flaw or skip in the finish coat, also called a *holiday, cat face, skipper* or *fish eye.*

Catalytic coating Any coating which hardens due to a chemical reaction instead of drying.

Caulking The process of filling cracks and crevices where materials meet, especially at door jambs and windows. Caulking compounds are applied with a putty knife or caulking gun.

Caulking compound A semidrying or slow-drying plastic mastic material used to seal joints or fill cracks and crevices.

Caulking gun An injecting tool for sealing joints with caulk.

Ceiling paint A thick, flat coating, sometimes tinted to reduced glare.

Cellulose acetate Any of several compounds produced by the action of acetic acid or acetic anhydride upon cellulose in the presence of concentrated sulfuric acid. Used as a paint binder and in the making of varnish.

Cellulose nitrate Any ester of nitric acid and cellulose. It is highly flammable, soluble in ether and alcohol or organic solvents and used as a base in making many paints and lacquers. Also called *nitrocellulose.*

Chair rail A wooden or plaster molding which protects a wall from damage from the backs of chairs.

Chalking Disintegration of oils in paint coatings caused by weathering, which leaves a chalk-like powder on the surface of the paint.

Cheapener A slang term for a paint extender.

Checking Fissures or cracks in paint coatings that follow the wood grain, caused by age.

Chime The indentation in the rim of a paint can in which the lid seats.

Clip A drywall slang term for additional wall area above the 8'0" ceiling line at a vaulted, cathedral, or high ceiling.

Close-grain wood Hardwood lumber which has narrow, inconspicuous annual rings and tight pores.

Clouding Loss of luster, shine or gloss caused by a porous undercoat.

Cloudy A painted surface which has not been uniformly coated.

Coal tar enamel A bituminous black coal liquid used to coat vessels.

Coat A film or layer of paint or other liquid material applied in a single operation.

Coating Material applied by brushing, rolling, spraying, dipping, mopping or troweling to protect, decorate, seal or smooth the subsurface.

Coating in Applying a uniform coat of paint.

Cohesion The mutual attraction of particles which causes them to stick together or to bond.

Cold checking Checking caused by cold weather.

Cold cracking Cracking caused by cold weather.

Cold water paint A paint where the binder or vehicle is composed of glue, latex, casein and other components dissolved in water.

Collusion A secret agreement for fraudulent or illegal purposes. A conspiracy.

Color-coding Identification of electrical wires or piping.

Color-fast Material which will retain or keep its original color without fading or running. Same as *color retention.*

Color person An expert at blending and matching colors.

Coloring pigment A pigment or stain which is added to a paint when the final color desired is different from the original color.

Condensation The act or process of changing a substance from a vapor to a liquid state due to cooling.

Construction Specification Institute (CSI) The organization that has established a format for construction specifications. The format includes 16 Divisions under four headings: Bidding Requirements, Contract Forms, General Conditions, and Specifications.

Corbel A short piece of wood, stone or brick projecting from the face of a wall to form a support for a timber.

Cornice Projection at the top of a wall; the construction under the eaves or where the roof and side walls meet; the top course, or courses, of a wall when treated as a crowning member.

Corrosion Disintegration, deterioration, or away of a material by rusting and oxidation.

Corrosion inhibitor An additive such as zinc chromate, zinc dust, fish oil or red lead which is mixed with primer or paint to help prevent rust and oxidation.

Corrosion inhibitor Any material which resists the formation of rust and oxidation by insulating against water and other oxidizing agents in the atmosphere.

Cracking In paint, the breakdown of the paint film with cracks through at least one coat. Some of the types of cracking are alligatoring, hair cracking, crawling, and crazing.

Crawling A defect in a painted surface where the film breaks, separates or rises, because the paint was applied over a slick or glossy surface.

Crazing A minute cracking of a finish coat of paint due to uneven shrinking of paint.

Creeping A condition where the paint forms into small droplets caused by improper cleaning of wax, grease or dirt from the applied surface.

Crocodiling (See *Alligatoring*)

Cross spraying Spray painting in two directions which cross each other.

Curing The process that results in the setting and hardening of a coating.

Curtain A scallop effect which occurs when paint sags or runs down a vertical surface.

Cut in In painting, to carefully paint a clean edge, usually a straight line which is parallel to an adjacent surface.

D

Dead flat Without gloss or luster.

Decimal equivalent The value of a fraction expressed as a decimal, for example 1/2 = 0.5.

Deck paint Enamel paint which is very resistant to mechanical wear, used on such surfaces as porch floors.

Deglossing Any means of abrading a surface about to be painted.

Delamination The separation of a piece of material, layer by layer, due to failure of the adhesive.

Density The ratio of the mass or weight of an object to its volume.

Dew point The temperature at which moisture in the air condenses to liquid.

Dipping tank A vessel filled with paint or a coating material used for submerging articles which must be coated on all sides.

Door schedule A list included in a plan set which gives symbols (numbers or letters) for each type of door used in the building.

Door trim The casing around an interior door opening used to conceal the break between the interior wall finish and the door frame or jamb.

Drag Resistance to the brush or roller by paint or other coatings while they are being applied.

Drier A varnish-like material that's added to paints and other coatings to accelerate drying.

Drop (1) In wallcovering, a drop is a length of wallcover from the ceiling to the floor. The total number of drops per room is the total width of the walls to be covered divided by the width of each roll. (2) One vertical descent of a scaffold.

Drop cloth A canvas tarp or plastic covering used to protect surfaces adjacent to the painting work.

Dry colors Powdered colors which are mixed with water, mineral spirits or alcohol to form paint and other coatings.

Dry to handle A painted surface in the final drying stage when the paint film can be touched or handled without being damaged.

Dry to recoat A painted surface in the last stage in the drying when the paint film can be painted over or recoated without damage to the previous layer.

Dry to touch A painted surface in the drying process when the paint film can be painted or touched without being damaged.

Drying oil An organic oil used in paints and varnishes to allow a thin layer of application to dry to form a hard but solid elastic surface film.

Drying time The time necessary for a painted surface to dry to the last stage in the drying process where it is ready to recoat.

Dull finish Without luster, shine or gloss, but not flat.

Dumping Using a spray application to apply excessive amounts of paint material.

Dust free A painted surface that is dry enough so dust won't stick to the finish.

E

Earth pigments A class of pigments which are produced and processed directly from materials mined from the earth. Commonly referred to as natural or mineral pigments of color.

Eaves That portion of a roof which projects over the side wall.

Edging To scribe or remove excess paint or to apply paint by cutting-in at corners or edges of surface intersections; the ceiling and wall, for example.

Edging stick A custom-shaped wood stick used for touching up the unfinished edges of cabinets and other wood trim.

Efflorescence A deposit of soluble salts, usually white, that appears on the surface of concrete or masonry construction where paint will not adhere.

Eggshell A matt or dull finish of paint resembling the sheen of an eggshell.

Elasticity The property of a material that tends to spring back to its original size and shape without damage after being deformed.

Elevation An architectural drawing of a horizontal view of a surface. Exterior elevations show all sides of a building. Interior elevations show the front view of an interior structure such as cabinets or bookshelves.

Emulsifier A substance which modifies the surface tension of a solid, liquid or gas, causing it to stay suspended.

Emulsion A mixture of liquids which are insoluble in one another.

Emulsion paint Paint with a pigment powder suspended in the liquid portion of the paint.

Enamel A type of paint that dries to a hard, smooth semi-glossy or glossy finish.

Epoxy A plastic-like paint which uses a catalyst to form a very hard, strong, durable and chemical-resistant coating.

Epoxy resins Catalytic chemical bonding systems used in the preparation of special coatings or adhesives.

Escalator clause A provision in a contract stipulating an increase or decrease, as in wages, benefits, or prices, under certain conditions, such as changes in the cost of living or in the cost of materials.

Estimating Forecasting the costs at a future time by calculating the approximate value of labor, material, equipment, overhead, profit and other costs required to produce a finished product or phase of a product.

Etching The process of cutting or engraving lines into a surface with a cutting tool or by the use of a strong acid. Etched surfaces allow greater paint adhesion.

Extender A finely-divided inert mineral added to provide economical bulk in paints.

Extensions Applying an arithmetic process (addition, subtraction, multiplication or division) to a set of estimated values which result in an intermediate or final cost value.

Exterior trim Wood or metal moldings on the exterior of a structure.

Extra work Construction operations which are in addition to the scope of work on the original contract agreement.

F

Fadding Applying shellac with a pad called a fad.

Fanning Moving the arm back and forth, like a oscillating fan, while spray painting.

Fascia The flat, vertical member or band on the outside edge of a cornice or eaves. A decorative trim or panel projecting from the face of a wall.

Fast to light Colors which are not affected by light.

Fat edge A ridge of paint which forms at the bottom edge of a painted surface when too much free-flowing paint has been applied.

Fattening An increase in the thickness or viscosity of paint after storage which can make it unsuitable for use without an additive.

Feathering To blend the edge of a new material smoothly into the old surface.

Feeding The process that changes a paint or varnish, while in the container, into a rubbery jelly so it cannot be used. Also called livering.

Feel The working qualities of paint. The paint can be mixed and thinned until it has the right "feel" for each individual painter.

Felting down Deglossing a dry varnish or painted surface with a felt pad loaded with abrasive powder and lubricated with water.

Ferrous metal A metal containing or derived from iron and subject to rust.

Ferrous sulfate A green, crystalline salt compound used in the making of inks, dyes and paint.

Field painting Painting at the site of the work -- in the field, not in the shop.

Filler (1) A finely-divided inert compound which is added to portland cement paint to reduce shrinkage, improve workability or act as an extender. (2) A compound used for stopping up holes, cracks, checks, pores and blemishes in wood before applying a finish such as stain, varnish or paint.

Filler coat The first coat of paint applied to fill the cracks, pores and holes in wood to make a smooth surface for the finish coat. Also called prime coat or priming.

Film One or several coats of dried paint or varnish.

Film build The repetitive application of layers of paint or varnish to a surface.

Film integrity The existing quality of the layers of paint or varnish on a surface.

Film thickness The mil thickness of the various coats of paint or varnish applied to a surface.

Filter A screen or cloth used to remove solid material from a liquid. Paint is filtered before spray painting.

Fingering The improper application of paint that causes lines (fingers) in the finished surface. In spraying, when more paint is applied to one part of the pattern than another. In brushing, when bristles stick together. Also called tails.

Fire resistance rating The measured time in hours that an assembly will withstand fire or give protection from it.

Fire-resisting finishes Paints which contain silicones, polyvinyl chloride, chlorinated waxes, urea formaldehyde resins, casein, borax or other noncombustible substances which reduce the spread of fire on combustible materials.

Fire retardant chemical A chemical compound used to reduce the spread of flame or to reduce flammability.

Fire retardant rating A standard test rating of fire-resistive or protective qualities in building materials or assemblies.

Fish eyes A skip in the finished surface. Also called cat eyes, cat face or holidays.

Fish oil A component of many primer paints which prevents or inhibits rust.

Flaking The peeling or breaking off of paint.

Flammability A material's ability to burn.

Flash A patchy variation in the color of paint due to inconsistencies in the painted surface.

Flashing Sheet metal used for waterproofing between open joints on exterior surfaces.

Flash point The lowest temperature at which the vapor of a volatile liquid or oil will ignite with a flash.

Flat A finish paint without a gloss.

Flat coat The first coat of paint applied, usually a primer coat.

Flat spots Spots on a finished surface which lack gloss or luster.

Flat wall paint A term used to describe the flat finish paint which is usually applied to walls.

Flatting A finish applied to painted surfaces which leaves no gloss or luster.

Flatting agent A paint or varnish additive which reduces the gloss of a finished surface.

Flatting down Using an abrasive such as cuttlefish, powdered pumice and felt or glass paper to sand a painted surface.

Flatting varnish A varnish undercoat which contains hard resin.

Flocking Forming a textile-appearing surface by blowing textile material such as silk or cotton on a freshly painted tacky surface.

Floor plan An architectural drawing of the top view of a building showing the location of each of the rooms.

Floor varnish Varnish which contains a non-slip, non-skid abrasive.

Flying scaffolding Scaffolding hung from an outrigger beam.

Foots Paint solids which settle to the bottom of the paint container.

Forced drying Drying paint at temperatures below 150 degrees F.

Framing plan An architectural plan which locates and identifies all the wood framing members necessary to build a structure.

French door An architectural term used to describe a door with glazed panels extending its full height and width.

Fresco Painting wet plastered walls or ceilings.

Frosting A translucent, finely-wrinkled finish formed during drying.

Full gloss The highest grade of gloss paint.

G

Gable The end of a building; the triangular end of an exterior wall below the eaves; the end of a ridged roof which, at its extremity, is not returned on itself but is cut off in a vertical plane which is triangular in shape due to the slope of the roof.

Galvanizing A coating of factory-applied zinc which prevents rust when applied to iron or steel.

Ghosting A shadowed effect caused by an inconsistent sheen.

Glaze (1) In painting, the process of applying a nearly transparent coat over an existing finish to enhance the color. (2) A thin mixture of oil and mineral spirits, usually tinted, used to achieve special painting effects.

Gloss A paint or enamel that contains a low proportion of pigment and dries to a sheen or luster. The terms *high, enamel* or *mirror* are trade terms for the highest gloss or luster. *Semi-gloss, eggshell* or *flat* are trade terms used to indicate decreasing degrees of gloss.

Grain The direction, size and arrangement of the fibers in wood.

Grain raising The extending of the fibers in wood due to exposure to water or sanding sealer.

Grass cloth A paper-backed wallcovering material made from arrowroot bark.

Grit blasting Sandblasting with grit.

Grit number A number assigned to the coarseness of sandpaper.

Ground coat The first coat of paint applied, usually a primer coat.

Guide coat A thin coat of paint applied before rubbing down a surface, used as a guide for showing high spots.

Gypsum A naturally-occurring mineral consisting of calcium sulfate combined with two molecules of water, in crystalline form.

Gypsum wallboard A prefabricated sheet used in drywall construction as a substitute for plaster. It's made of gypsum or anhydrite plaster, usually enclosed between two sheets of heavy paper, which can be painted, textured or wallpapered.

H

Hair cracks Minute cracks in a painted or plastered surface.

Hardener A curing agent catalyst used to give a hard film to paint or varnish.

Hardwood Wood from broadleaf trees such as oak, maple, ash or walnut.

Hazing Applying a lusterless fog-like finish.

Header The area above a door or window.

Hiding power The ability of paint to cover the subsurface colors. Also called *opacity.*

Holiday A skip in the paint coverage. The painter was "taking a holiday."

Hot spray Paint which has been thinned by heat for finer atomization during spray application.

Hot wall A plastered wall with an excess of free lime which burns out oil-based paints.

House paint Exterior paint formulated to withstand the elements.

Humidity The amount of moisture in the air.

I

Interior trim Wood or metal moldings, such as baseboards, door and window casings, chair rail or crown molding.

Internal mix Air and paint mixed inside the gun in conventional spray methods.

Iron phosphate coating A primer for industrial equipment which helps the new finish adhere to the existing finish.

Isocyanate resin A paint binder which is a salt of isomeric cyanic acid. It has good heat and electrical insulation properties.

J

Journeyman painter A painter who has served a four-year apprenticeship or any painter who has learned his or her trade.

K

Ketone An organic chemical compound, such as acetone, used as a solvent.

L

Lacquer A material based on cellulose compounds that has a glossy finish and dries rapidly by evaporation.

Laitance A chalky white compound composed of salt and lime which rises to the surface of poorly finished concrete as moisture evaporates. This substance prevents paint adhesion.

Lampblack A pigment used in paint and ink derived from a fine soot produced by the incomplete combustion of oils and other forms of carbon.

Latex A milky white liquid containing resins and proteins, present in rubber trees, milkweed and poppies. It's the basis of rubber and an ingredient in some adhesives and paints.

Latex emulsions Rubber or any synthetic resin dispersed in water. The best known is poly vinyl acetate (PVA).

Latex paints Water-base paints, sometimes called *vinyl* or *acrylic* paints, which can be cleaned up and thinned with soap and water.

Lead carbonate A white lead pigment used in metal primer.

Lead drier Lead compounds which accelerate the hardening of drying oils in paint.

Lead oxide A pigment used as a rust inhibitor, composed of red lead and *lead monoxide.*

Lead paint Any paint in which white lead is used as a base.

Leaded zinc oxide White pigments which are mixtures of zinc oxide and basic lead sulfate, used as a primer.

Leveling The smoothing out or flow of the paint liquid being applied.

Linoleum varnish A highly flexible and elastic varnish.

Linseed oil A yellowish drying oil extracted from flaxseed, used as a vehicle in many oil-based paints, printer's ink and linoleum.

Liquid driers Soluble driers.

Liquid wood filler A thin varnish used to coat and fill the tight-grained hardwoods.

Litharge A pale yellow or brown pigment and drier used in vitreous enamels. Also called lead monoxide.

Lithopone Zinc sulfide and barium sulfate used as a white paint pigment.

Livering The process of paint thickening to the consistency of liver.

Long oil A high ratio of oil to resin in a varnish.

Long-oil alkyd An alkyd resin containing more than 60% oil as a modifying agent.

Long oil varnish An oleoresinous varnish, other than an alkyd, containing at least 2-1/2 parts of oil to one part of resin. It dries slower than short oil varnish and results in a tough but flexible finish.

Lump sum contract A contract that sets forth a specific amount as the total payment for performance of the contract. Also called a *stipulated sum agreement.*

M

Maintenance painting The upkeep, repair and repainting of painted surfaces on a regular schedule.

Maintenance period The period of time after the completion of a contract when the work is guaranteed and any defects must be repaired by the subcontractor. It is typically one year on new construction. Also called *warranty time.*

Marine varnish A waterproof varnish formulated to withstand submerging in salt or fresh water.

Marking paint The material used to mark the laying lines on saturated felt and roofing.

Masking Protecting or shielding the edges of a painted surface, usually with tape, paper or with a metal guide.

Masking tape An adhesive tape used for covering and protecting edges, margins and borders of a painted or stained surface.

Mil thickness The thickness of a dry paint film measured in millimeters.

Mildew A mold which can stain, discolor or mar wood finishes. This parasitic fungus flourishes in high moisture areas.

Mineral spirits Petroleum-based paint thinner.

Miscible Mixable without separation at any ratio.

Misses (See *Holiday*)

Mist-coat A thinly-applied spray coat.

Mobility The ability of the paint to flow with ease.

Mottler A thick brush used for graining and marbling.

Mottling Uniform, rounded speckled marks. Mottling is a defect in sprayed coats.

Mud-cracking Paint or plaster which cracks like dried mud when applied too thick.

Mullion The thin members which divide multiple glass lites in a window frame, screen or French door. Often confused with muntin.

Muntin The small vertical bars that divide the glass in a casement window frame or vertical separators between panels in a door.

Muriatic acid Diluted form of hydrochloric acid which can be used to clean alkali deposits on masonry surfaces.

N

Naphtha A strong-smelling thinner distilled from petroleum at high temperatures.

Neoprene A synthetic rubber paint modifier which is highly resistant to oil, heat, light and oxidation.

Newel An upright post supporting the handrail at the top and bottom of a stairway or at the turn on a landing. Also the main post about which a circular staircase winds or a stone column carrying the inner ends of the treads of a spiral stone staircase. Also called *newel post.*

Newel cap A top or cap for the newel post.

Newel drop A downward decorative projection on a newel post through a soffit.

Newel joint A joint between the newel and the handrail.

Nitrocellulose (See *Cellulose nitrate*)

Non-union shop A firm whose employees are not covered by a collective bargaining agreement; an open shop.

O

Oil-based paints Paints with resins and other ingredients made of various oils which are soluble in solvent.

Oil bloom An iridescent appearance that occurs after a surface is rubbed or polished and free oil floats to the top.

Oil gloss paint An interior paint made with boiled oil and raw linseed oil.

Oil paint A paint that contains a drying oil or oil varnish as the basic vehicle.

Oil varnish A varnish used in wood finishing which contains a drying oil such as linseed, china wood, cotton seed, poppy seed, soya bean, castor oil or tung oil. It hardens slowly through oxidation.

Oleoresin A pine gum obtained by distilling dead wood or by bleeding living trees.

Oleoresinous varnish A varnish containing vegetable drying oil and natural or hardening synthetic resin.

Opacity The hiding property of paint. The opposite of transparency.

Open-grain wood Wide-ringed or coarse-timbered lumber with visible pores. Mahogany, oak and walnut are open-grain.

Open shop A firm whose employees are not covered by collective bargaining agreements; a non-union shop.

Orange peel (1) The pinholing or pocketing effect on poorly-applied paint. (2) A drywall texture which is spray applied.

Orange shellac Unbleached, amber-colored shellac.

Orifice The hole or opening in the tip of a spray gun.

Overcoat The final or finish coat.

Overlap The area on a painted wall where the new coat crosses over or covers the previous coating.

Overspray Paint which is sprayed beyond the intended surface area.

Oxidize To unite with oxygen, as in burning material, rusting metals or chalking paint.

P

Padding pad A paint application tool made from a soft textile, such as cotton, used for furniture or to apply paint in tight areas such as under doors.

Paint A colored pigment in a liquid vehicle which dries to form an opaque solid film when thinly spread on a surface.

Paint base Zinc, white lead or any similar material used as a base for paint.

Paint drier Commonly a compound of lead and manganese which helps paint dry quickly. This compound can be harmful if used in excess.

Paint remover A liquid solvent which softens a paint or varnish film, so that it can be scraped, sanded or brushed off.

Paint system A succession of coats designed to protect a surface and give a decorative finish.

Paint thinner Turpentine or petroleum spirits used to thin heavy-bodied paint for easy application. Petroleum spirits cost less and are more commonly used than turpentine.

Painter One who is knowledgeable and has skill in the painting trade.

Painter's putty A plastic substance made of whiting and linseed oil, sometimes including white lead. It's used as a filler for fixing panes of glass in window frames or to fill nail holes and defects in wood in preparation for painting.

Pass To move forward through in a single motion, from top to bottom or from one side to another, when applying paint, plaster or gunite.

Paste filler (See *Wood filler*)

Patchal stick A soft stick of putty colored to match stains, used as a wood filler on cabinetry and furniture.

Pattern length The distance of one pass with a spray gun. Usually arm's length.

Pattern width The width of a sprayed paint coating laid down in one pass.

Peeling The process where paint stripes off or flakes away due to improper cleaning or scuffing of the subsurface.

Penetrating finish A paint or stain material which is absorbed into the surface.

Phenolic resin A class of synthetic oil-soluble resins, or plastics, made from phenol and formaldehyde.

Piano-like finish The highest quality, hand-rubbed finish.

Pick up sags Brushing upward to level off a heavy coating of paint that has run down or sagged.

Pickling Cleaning metals by dipping them into an acid or solvent solution.

Pigment The insoluble fine powder which gives paint its opacity and color.

Pitting Small holes or cavities in a paint film caused by moisture in the air while drying, improper surface preparation or mixing incompatible materials. Also called *pinholing*.

Plastic finish The finished appearance after polyurethane, varnish, lacquers, acrylics or vinyls are applied.

Pockmarks Small craters or cavities in the paint film.

Pole gun An attachment which extends the reach of a spray gun.

Polishing (1) Rubbing a surface. (2) Shiny spots on painted surfaces resulting from rubbing, washing, wiping or vigorous scrubbing.

Polymerization The bonding reaction of two or more molecules of the same substance. This process forms plastics and plastic paints.

Polystyrene resin Synthetic resins used in concrete paints and varying in color from white to yellow.

Polyurethane A clear plastic coating made from resin which forms a tough, durable, abrasion-resistant finish when applied to floors, trim and doors.

Polyvinyl acetate (PVA) A colorless thermoplastic resin used as a drywall primer and in concrete paints. It's flexible, stable in light, transparent to ultraviolet rays, strong, tough, hard and abrasion resistant.

Porous surface A surface which has a high rate of liquid absorption.

Pot life The length of time a two-part paint product will remain usable.

Powdering The crumbling of varnish into a fine dust-like powder.

Prefinished Material such as doors, moldings, cabinets or paneling which has been painted, stained, varnished or otherwise finished in the shop prior to arriving at a job site for installation.

Prehung doors Doors that are delivered to the site already hung in a frame.

Prime coat The first coat in most painting processes. It fills wood pores or protects metal surfaces and provides a hard opaque base for the application of following coats. Also called *undercoat, sealer* or *ground coat*.

Primer The first coat of paint when two or more coats are applied, acting as a bond for the remaining coats.

Print free Paint dried to the stage where the impression of a hand or brush will not show.

Protective life The length of time a paint or stain coating continues to protect a surface.

Pullman A bathroom vanity.

Pumice A highly porous, fine lava used as a rubbing compound for varnish or enamel.

Punchlist A list, made near the completion of work, which indicates items of work which must be completed by a contractor or subcontractor before the job is complete as specified in the contract documents.

Putty A stiff, dough-like material consisting of a pigment and a vehicle used to fill imperfections in wood or metal surfaces.

Putty coat The final smooth coat of plaster.

Pyroxylin (See *Cellulose nitrate*)

Q

Quick drying A paint material which dries in a short time because of added drying agents and modifiers.

R

Rake The angle, incline or slope of a roof rafter.

Raw linseed oil The crude product extracted from flaxseed which needs no further treatment.

Recapitulate To repeat as a summary in concise review or form.

Recoat time The drying time needed between coatings.

Red label Identification for flammable liquids with a flash point under 80 degrees Fahrenheit.

Red lead Lead oxide, used as a drying agent and as a pigment in the linseed oil of primers for protection against rust.

Refined shellac Processed white or orange shellac with the wax removed.

Remove and replace Removing door and window hardware, cabinet hardware, electrical switch plates and outlet covers before painting and replacing them when finished.

Repeat The patterns on a roll or bolt of wallcover which are typically repeated every 18 inches.

Resin A natural or synthetic, solid or semi-solid organic material which serves as the prime binding agent in most modern paints.

Respirator A protective device worn over the nose and mouth, like a mask, to minimize inhalation of harmful fumes.

Ride the brush To press down too hard on a paint brush causing a streaked finish and damaged brush.

Ripple finish A uniformly wrinkled finish which is intentionally obtained by *stoving*.

Rise and run A term used to describe the degree of incline of a staircase. The rise is the vertical measurement and the run is the horizontal measurement.

Riser (1) A vertical board under the tread of a stair step. (2) The member of an open staircase which supports the stair treads and runs at an angle from the bottom to the top of the staircase. This is commonly called the *stringer*.

Roll goods Wallcovering sold in rolls. A single roll is 36 square feet no matter what the width. A double roll is always 72 square feet.

Ropey Paint material which dries with slight ridges and does not flow out when applied.

Rosin Sap resin from a pine tree.

Rottenstone A siliceous limestone which is decomposed to a fine powder, used for polishing metals.

Rubbed finish Using oil and fine abrasive to produce a gloss finish on lacquers, varnishes or enamels.

Run (1) A narrow ridge of paint which has flowed down to a teardrop caused by applying too much paint. (2) The horizontal measurement of a staircase.

Rust Any coating or film formed on ferrous metals, iron or steel, caused by oxidation when exposed to air and moisture.

Rustic siding Drop siding.

S

Sag (See *Run*)

Sand down To use sandpaper or other abrasive to smooth a new surface or to remove the gloss of an old finish.

Sand dry surface A surface on which sand will not stick.

Sand finish A sand-like finish applied to an interior or exterior wall.

Sanding sealer A first coat of paint which seals or fills wood but does not hide the grain.

Sap-streak Streaks showing through a finished wood surface which contains sapwood.

Sash The framework which holds the glass in a window or door.

Sash bar A strip which separates the panes of glass in a window sash. Also called *muntin*.

Scaffold height The height of the wall which requires another raising of the scaffold to continue the building process.

Scaffolding Any temporary elevated platform and its supporting structure used for supporting workers and materials.

Scale (1) A measuring device used in proportional drafting. (2) Rust which has formed into thin layers.

Scuff sand A light surface sanding.

Scuppers Water overflow outlets in parapet, deck or courtyard walls.

Sealer Liquid coating, usually clear, used to close or fill the pores of wood and other building materials before applying the finish coats.

Section drawing An illustration of an object cut lengthwise to show its structure and components.

Seedy A painted surface with small grains of dirt and old paint particles left by the dirty heel of a brush. Also called *sandy*.

Semi-gloss finish A finish with a low luster.

Semi-gloss paint A paint or enamel with a reduced quantity of non-volatile vehicle. Its dry coating is lacking in luster and not very glossy.

Set A condition of paint or varnish that has stopped flowing but is not in the final hardening stage.

Setup (1) The hardened state of a paint coating film. (2) Ready to begin preparation and painting operations.

Settling The sinking of paint pigment and other particles as they separate from the paint vehicle and accumulate on the bottom of the paint can.

Shade The degree of darkness or gradation of a color.

Shadowing Subsurface coatings showing through the finish coat. Also called *show-through*.

Sheen The gloss seen at a glancing angle on an otherwise flat paint finish.

Shelf life The maximum time a material may be stored and remain usable.

Shellac A thin type of varnish consisting of lac dissolved in denatured alcohol used as a wood coating and sealer.

Shiner A spot which has more gloss than the rest of the same surface.

Shingle stain A form of oil paint very thin in consistency, intended for coloring wood surfaces, such as shingles, without forming a coating of significant thickness or gloss.

Shop primed Prime coated in the manufacturing facility.

Short paint Paint with poor qualities.

Shorts Wallcovering term for those areas which are not a full drop or a header. Shorts occur at cut-up areas and under windows.

Silica Silicon dioxide used as an extender, derived from ground quartz or sand.

Silicone When combined with paint it is highly resistant to dirt, fungus, high temperatures, water and graffiti.

Sizing A seal coat, usually clear, used for filling porous surfaces in preparation for the application of finish coats of paint or wallcovering.

Skin (1) The outer layer of a dried paint film. (2) Roller cover.

Skipper A spot on a painted surface which has been skipped. Also see Cat eye and *Holiday*.

Skippy Paint which causes the brush to skip leaving uncoated spots and other areas which dry too quickly.

Skips Areas left unpainted by mistake.

Slip under the brush A description of coating materials which are easy to apply.

Slow-dry A coating which takes more than 24 hours to dry before the next operation.

Softwood Lumber cut from needle-bearing trees of the conifer type without reference to the actual hardness of the wood.

Solids The film of paint, varnish or lacquer film which dries on the surface after the vehicle has evaporated.

Solvent A liquid which is capable of dissolving another substance. Solvents are used to increase the flow of various paints and to clean paint from application tools.

Spackling compound A dry powder that mixes with water to form a paste used for patching and filling holes and cracks in plaster, gypsum wallboard and sometimes wood.

Spackling paste A pliable clay or putty-like material used for patching and filling holes and cracks in plaster, gypsum wallboard, and sometimes wood.

Spalling Surface cracking, chipping or particles flaking from a surface.

Spar varnish Varnish that is primarily used on exterior surfaces. It forms a hard, durable, weather-resistant protective finish.

Specifications Written instructions for a project that describe the nature of the materials, finishes and quality of workmanship.

Spindle (1) A small axle, as the spindle of a vane on which doorknobs are fixed. (2) A short turned member, as that on a baluster.

Spirit stain A dye used for darkening wood which is dissolved in alcohol and shellac or other resin used as a binder.

Spirit varnish A varnish produced by dissolving a resin or gum in alcohol.

Split coat A mixture of half enamel and half undercoater which is applied between the undercoat and the enamel coat. It is an upgrade from the usual undercoat and enamel process.

Split face A rough face formed by guillotining cast or natural stone units (masonry block).

Splitting A later stage of alligatoring that occurs when paints or varnishes are applied over subsurface coatings which were not completely dry or hardened.

Spray A fine jet of liquid particles or mist from an atomizer, aerosol or spray gun.

Spray can A can in which gas under pressure is used to disperse the contents in the form of a spray.

Spray gun A device that shoots out a spray of liquid by air pressure from a compressor.

Spray painting Applying paint, lacquer or other coating with a spray unit.

Spray texture Mechanically-applied material that produces various decorative finishes, common in the drywall trade.

Spread rate The square feet of surface area covered by one gallon of mixed paint.

Stain Color in a dissolving vehicle. When spread on an absorbant surface, it penetrates and gives its color to the wood or other material.

Stain grade A description of high-quality material, usually wood, that will have a pleasing appearance when stained.

Stain, shingle A form of oil paint, very thin in consistency, intended for coloring wood with rough surfaces, such as shingles, without forming a coating of significant thickness or gloss.

Stand oil Oil which is thickened by heat.

Steeple A tower and spire, usually on a church.

Steeplejack A worker who repairs and paints steeples or other tall structures.

Stipple Dabbing a coat of paint with a stippler brush to remove regular brush marks immediately after coating, to break up the color coat with spots of a different color, or to break up its texture with a bristle or rubber stippler.

Stippler A paint brush with many tufts of soft bristles set in a flat stock with the bristle tufts all ending in the same plane, used to even up the coat of paint, remove brush marks and leave the wet surface with a uniform, slightly granulated finish. A rubber stippler is used for breaking up texture.

Stippling Using the brush point, a sponge or other texturer to create a texture different from brush strokes or spraying.

Stipulated sum agreement (See *Lump sum contract*)

Storm sash An extra window usually placed on the outside of an existing window as additional protection against cold weather.

Stoving Using heat to dry painted surfaces.

Stringer The inclined member which supports the treads and risers of a staircase.

Stretch The width of the area that a painter can reach to apply a coating without changing location.

Strip Complete removal of old finish coating with paint removers or other mechanical means.

Striping Applying pavement markings.

Stroke One single movement or pass of a brush, roller or spray application.

Stucco Any of various plasters used as covering for walls that are put on wet but become hard and durable when dry.

Subcontractor A contractor who has contracted to construct a portion of a building or structure.

Substrate A British term for the surface area to be painted.

Subsurface Lying below the finished surface.

Suction The absorption rate of a plastered surface.

Surface drying A paint that drys faster on the surface than below the surface in the body of the film.

SURRPTUCU An acronym for Setup (SU), Remove and Replace (RR), Protection (P), Touchup (TU) and Cleanup (CU).

Synthetic paint A vague term sometimes meaning paints containing synthetic resin.

Synthetic resin Urea-, melamine- or phenol-formaldehyde glues and casting resins and other synthetic resins which are immune from attack by molds and bacteria and are highly water resistant.

T

Tack rag Cheesecloth or other cotton fabric used to remove dust from surfaces prior to painting. The cloth is usually dampened with slow-drying varnish.

Tacky Very sticky condition of paint when the film is not dry but dust will not stick.

Tails (See *Fingering*)

Take off The process of measuring and listing the quantities of materials to be used from a set of plans and specifications. These materials are listed by type or by operation in an organized manner.

Talc A white magnesium silicate paint extender which is greasy or soapy to the touch.

Taupe A dark, brownish grey color, the color of moleskin.

Tempera A pigment in water or in a vehicle soluble in water.

Thinner Volatile liquid used to regulate the consistency of paint and other finish materials as well as to clean up oil-base paints.

Through dry A condition of paint being completely dry.

Tie coat A coating applied between two coats which will not bond.

Tint A color made by mixing white pigment with a small amount of colored pigment.

Tinting Final adjustments in the coloring of paint.

Tipping off The final smoothing brush coat, usually on enamel trim such as a door and casing. Also called *laying off*.

Titanium dioxide A white pigment.

Tongue and groove In carpentry, a joint made by joining two pieces of timber, one having a tongue cut in the edge and the other having a groove to receive the corresponding tongue.

Tooth A characteristic of good wall primer, it's a slight roughness which allows a better distribution of the finish coat.

Top coat The last or final finish coat of paint or varnish.

Touch up To improve, repair or finish by minor changes or additions.

Toxic Poisonous.

Traceability The ability of a material to be traced back to its point of origin.

Trade union A combination of tradesmen organized for the purpose of promoting their common interests in regard to wages, hours of work, safety measures, unemployment compensation and other benefits.

Trisodium phosphate (TSP) A heavy-duty cleaning agent in powder form. Mixed with water, it acts as a degreaser and deglosser.

Tung oil A fast-drying oil from the seeds of tung trees grown in China and Japan. It is used in place of linseed oil in paints and varnishes for a more water-resistant coating.

Turpentine The distilled sap of the long-leaf pine used as a paint thinner.

U

Umber (See *Burnt umber*)

Undercoat The first coat or a coating applied prior to finish coats or top coats of paint. Also called *prime coat*.

Undertone The color obtained when pigment is reduced with a large amount of white pigment and a faint subdued color can be seen through other colors.

Union shop A firm whose employees are covered by collective bargaining agreements.

U.S. gallon Contains 8.336 pounds of distilled water at 62 degrees Fahrenheit. Equals 3.17 kilograms, eight U.S. pints or four U.S. quarts.

Useful life The life span of a paint coating.

V

Value Relative lightness or darkness of a color.

Varnish An oil-based paint containing a solvent and an oxidizing or an evaporating binder, used to coat a natural wood surface with a hard, glossy, thin transparent finish.

Varnish stain Varnish combined with stain.

Vegetable oils Any of various liquid fats derived from the fruits or seeds of plants, used as drying agents in paint products.

Vehicle The liquid carrier of the color pigment.

Vinyl A class of resins. For example, vinyl acetate is used in latex paints and polyvinyl chloride is used in some solvent-thinned coatings.

Viscosity The internal friction of a liquid which makes it resist a tendency to flow.

Volatile A description of liquids which evaporate or vaporize quickly and boil at ordinary temperatures or at temperatures below the boiling point of water (100 degrees Celsius).

Volatile thinner A liquid that evaporates readily, used to thin or reduce the consistency of finishes without altering the relative volumes of pigments and nonvolatile vehicle.

W

Water-based paints (See *Latex paints*)

Water blaster A machine that uses pressurized water to remove old paint. Also called *power washer*.

Water paint Paint containing water or water emulsion as the vehicle.

Water spotting Light colored spots on a film of paint caused by drops of water on the surface.

Water stain A stain or dye which is soluble in water.

Water-thinned paint A paint with water as the vehicle.

Wet edge Paint on a surface wet enough to be brushed back into the next stretch and not lap.

Wet film thickness The mil thickness of paint while still wet.

White lead A white pigment, hydrated carbonate of lead, which is used in the making of paint.

Whiting A chalk pigment used in paint and putty.

Wire brushing Removing old paint and debris by hand with a wire brush.

Wood filler A soft, moist smooth-textured substance used to fill the pores and grain in wood.

Wrinkle The prune-like appearance of paint film which has been applied too heavily.

Z

Zinc chromate Bright yellow pigments used in metal primers.

Zinc dust A powdered zinc in paint primer used on galvanized iron.

Zinc oxide A white pigment.

Zinc sulfide A yellowish-white pigment.

Zinc white A white pigment.

Zinc yellow (See *Zinc chromate*)

Index

Other Practical References

Basic Plumbing with Illustrations

The journeyman's and apprentice's guide to installing plumbing, piping and fixtures in residential and light commercial buildings: how to select the right materials, lay out the job and do professional quality plumbing work. Explains the use of essential tools and materials, how to make repairs, maintain plumbing systems, install fixtures and add to existing systems. **320 pages, 8½ x 11, $22.00**

Drywall Contracting

How to do professional quality drywall work, how to plan and estimate each job, and how to start and keep your drywall business thriving. Covers the eight essential steps in making any drywall estimate, how to achieve the six most commonly-used surface treatments, how to work with metal studs, and how to solve and prevent most common drywall problems. **288 pages, 5½ x 8½, $18.25**

Spec Builder's Guide

Explains how to plan and build a home, control your construction costs, and then sell the house at a price that earns a decent return on the time and money you've invested. Includes professional tips on the time and money you've invested. Includes professional tips to ensure success as a spec builder: how to plan and build a decent to judge the housing market, cutting costs at every opportunity without sacrificing quality, and taking advantage of construction cycles. Every chapter includes checklists, diagrams, charts, figures, and estimating tables. **448 pages, 8½ x 11, $27.00**

Painting Cost Guide

A complete guide for estimating painting costs for just about any type of residential, commercial, or industrial painting, whether by brush, spray, or roller. Provides typical costs and bid prices for fast, medium and slow work, including: material costs per gallon, square feet covered per gallon, square feet covered per manhour, labor cost per 100 square feet, material cost per 100 square feet, overhead and taxes per 100 square feet, and how much to add for profit. **448 pages, 8½ x 11, $27.50. Revised annually**

Paint Contractor's Manual

How to start and run a profitable paint contracting company: getting set up and organized to handle volume work, avoiding the mistakes most painters make, getting top production from your crews and the most value from your advertising dollar. Shows how to estimate all prep and painting. Loaded with manhour estimates, sample forms, contracts, charts, tables and examples you can use. **224 pages, 8½ x 11, $19.25**

Painter's Handbook

Loaded with "how-to" information you'll use every day to get professional results on any job: the best way to prepare a surface for painting or repainting; selecting and using the right materials and tools (including airless spray); tips for repainting kitchens, bathrooms, cabinets, eaves and porches; how to match and blend colors; why coatings fail and what to do about it. Thirty profitable specialties that could be your gravy train in the painting business. Every professional painter needs this practical handbook. **320 pages, 8½ x 11, $21.25**

Video: Paint Contractor's 1

How to run a paint contracting business, set up jobs for good production and prepare surfaces for painting. Topics include planning, scheduling, using job work orders, setting production targets, advising on color selection, patching, textures, and the most common reasons for paint failure. **40 minutes, VHS, $24.75**

Video: Paint Contractor's 2

How to select the right tools for the best results, get the most from spray paint equipment, lay down a glass-like finish in enamel, quick ways to paint doors, jambs, windows, and cabinets, and much more. **40 minutes, VHS, $24.75**

Contractor's Survival Manual

How to survive hard times in construction and take full advantage of the profitable cycles. Shows what to do when the bills can't be paid, finding money and buying time, transferring debt, and all the alternatives to bankruptcy. Explains how to build profits, avoid problems in zoning and permits, taxes, time-keeping, and payroll. Unconventional advice includes how to invest in inflation, get high appraisals, trade and postpone income, and how to stay hip-deep in profitable work. **160 pages, 8½ x 11, $16.75**

Manual of Professional Remodeling

This is the practical manual of professional remodeling written by an experienced and successful remodeling contractor. Shows how to evaluate a job to avoid 30-minute jobs that take all day, what to fix and what to leave alone, and what to watch for in dealing with subcontractors. Includes chapters on calculating space requirements, repairing structural defects, remodeling kitchens, baths, walls and ceilings, doors and windows, floors, roofs, installing fireplaces and chimneys (including built-ins), skylights, and exterior siding. Includes blank forms, checklists, sample contracts, and proposals you can copy and use. **400 pages, 8½ x 11, $19.75**

Remodeling Contractor's Handbook

Everything you need to know to make a remodeling business grow: Identifying a market for your business, inexpensive sales and advertising techniques that work, and how to prepare accurate estimates. Also explains building a positive company image, training effective sales people, placing loans for customers, and bringing in profitable work to keep your company growing. **304 pages, 8½ x 11, $18.25**

Remodeling Kitchens & Baths

This book is your guide to succeeding in a very lucrative area of the remodeling market: how to repair and replace damaged floors; how to redo walls, ceilings, and plumbing; and how to modernize the home wiring system to accommodate today's heavy electrical demands. Show how to install new sinks and countertops, ceramic tile, sunken tubs, whirlpool baths, luminous ceilings, skylights, and even special lighting effects. Completely illustrated, with manhour tables for figuring your labor costs. **384 pages, 8½ x 11, $26.25**

Remodeler's Handbook

The complete manual of home improvement contracting: Planning the job, estimating costs, doing the work, running your company and making profits. Pages of sample forms, contracts, documents, clear illustrations and examples. Chapters on evaluating the work, rehabilitation, kitchens, bathrooms, adding living area, re-flooring, re-siding, re-roofing, replacing windows and doors, installing new wall and ceiling cover, repainting, upgrading insulation, combating moisture damage, estimating, selling your services, and bookkeeping for remodelers. **416 pages, 8½ x 11, $23.00**

Profits in Buying & Renovating Homes

Step-by-step instructions for selecting, repairing, improving, and selling highly profitable "fixer-uppers." Shows which price ranges offer the highest profit-to-investment ratios, which neighborhoods offer the best return, practical directions for repairs, and tips on dealing with buyers, sellers, and real estate agents. Shows you how to determine your profit before you buy, what bargains to avoid, and simple, inexpensive upgrades that will charm your buyers and ensure your profits. **304 pages, 8½ x 11, $19.75**

Running Your Remodeling Business

Everything you need to know about operating a remodeling business, from making your first sale to insuring your profits: how to advertise, write up a contract, estimate, schedule your jobs, arrange financing (for both you and your customers), and when and how to expand your business. Explains what you need to know about insurance, bonds, and liens, and how to collect the moeny you've earned. Includes sample business forms for your use. **272 pages, 8½ x 11, $21.00**

10 Day Money Back Guarantee

Craftsman Book Co
6058 Corte del Cedro
Carlsbad, CA 92009

☎

In a hurry?
We accept phone orders charged to your
MasterCard, Visa or American Express
Call 1-800-829-8123
FAX (619) 438-0398

Name _____

Company _____

Address _____

City/State/Zip _____

Total enclosed _____ (In Calif. add 6% tax)

☐ Visa ☐ MasterCard or ☐ AmEx

Card # _____

Exp. date _____

☐ 95.00 Audio: Const. Field Super.
☐ 65.00 Audio: Estimating Electrical
☐ 65.00 Audio: Estimating Remodel
☐ 19.95 Audio: Plumbers Examination
☐ 22.00 Basic Plumbing with Illust.
☐ 30.00 Berger Building Cost File
☐ 11.25 Bluprt Read for Bldg Trades
☐ 19.75 Bookkeeping for Builders
☐ 24.95 Blder's Comp. Dictionary
☐ 20.00 Blder's Guide to Account Rev.
☐ 15.25 Blder's Guide to Const. Fin.
☐ 15.50 Blder's Office Manual Revised
☐ 14.00 Building Cost Manual
☐ 11.75 Building Layout
☐ 22.00 Cabinetmaking: Design-Finish
☐ 25.50 Carpentry Estimating
☐ 19.75 Carpentry for Resid. Const.
☐ 19.00 Carpentry in Com. Const.
☐ 16.25 Carpentry Layout
☐ 17.75 Computers: Blder's New Tool
☐ 14.50 Concrete and Formwork
☐ 20.50 Concrete Const. & Estimating
☐ 26.00 Const. Estimating Refer. Data
☐ 22.00 Construction Superintending
☐ 19.25 Const. Surveying & Layout
☐ 19.00 Cont. Growth & Profit Guide
☐ 24.25 Cont Guide to Bldg Code Rev

☐ 16.75 Contractor's Survival Manual
☐ 16.50 Cont. Year-Rd Tax Guide
☐ 15.75 Cost Records for Const. Est.
☐ 9.50 Dial-A-Length Rafterule
☐ 18.25 Drywall Contracting
☐ 13.75 Electrical Blueprint Reading
☐ 25.00 Electrical Const. Estimator
☐ 19.00 Estimating Electrical Const.
☐ 17.00 Estimat. Home Blding Costs
☐ 28.00 Estimating Painting Costs
☐ 17.25 Estimating Plumbing Costs
☐ 21.50 Est. Tables for Home Building
☐ 22.75 Excav. & Grading Hndbk Rev.
☐ 9.25 E-Z Square
☐ 23.25 Fences & Retaining Walls
☐ 15.25 Finish Carpentry
☐ 24.75 Hdbk of Const. Contr. Vol. 1
☐ 24.75 Hdbk of Const. Contr. Vol. 2
☐ 15.00 Home Wiring: Improv. Ext. Repair
☐ 17.50 How to Sell Remodeling
☐ 19.50 How to Succ'd w/Own Const Bus.
☐ 24.50 HVAC Contracting
☐ 24.00 Illustrated Guide to NE Code
☐ 20.25 Manual of Electrical Contr.
☐ 19.75 Manual of Prof. Remodeling
☐ 17.25 Masonry & Concrete Const.
☐ 26.50 Masonry Estimating

☐ 22.50 National Const. Estimator w/ free Estimate Writer on 5¼" (1.2Mb) disk *Add $10 for Estimate Writer on either* ☐ 5¼" (360K) disk or ☐ 3½" (720K) disk.
☐ 26.50 Nat. Repar& Remodel Est.
☐ 19.25 Paint Contractor's Manual
☐ 21.25 Painter's Handbook
☐ 27.50 Painting Cost Guide
☐ 13.00 Plan & Design Plumb System
☐ 19.25 Planning Drain, Waste & Vent
☐ 21.00 Plumber's Exam Prep. Guide
☐ 18.00 Plumber's Handbook Rev.
☐ 19.75 Profits Buy & Renov Homes
☐ 14.25 Rafter Length Manual
☐ 23.00 Remodeler's Handbook
☐ 18.25 Remodeling Contr. Handbook
☐ 26.25 Remodeling Kitchens & Baths
☐ 11.50 Residential Electrical Design
☐ 16.75 Residential Electr. Hndbk.
☐ 18.25 Residential Wiring
☐ 22.00 Roof Framing
☐ 14.00 Roofers Handbook
☐ 17.00 Rough Carpentry
☐ 21.00 Run. Your Remodeling Bus.
☐ 27.00 Spec Builder's Guide
☐ 15.50 Stair Builder's Handbook
☐ 14.25 Wood-Frame House Const.

10 Day Money Back Guarantee

Craftsman Book Co
6058 Corte del Cedro
Carlsbad, CA 92009

☎

In a hurry?
We accept phone orders charged to your
MasterCard, Visa or American Express
Call 1-800-829-8123
FAX (619) 438-0398

Name _____

Company _____

Address _____

City/State/Zip _____

Total enclosed _____ (In Calif. add 6% tax)

☐ Visa ☐ MasterCard or ☐ AmEx

Card # _____

Exp. date _____

☐ 95.00 Audio: Const. Field Super.
☐ 65.00 Audio: Estimating Electrical
☐ 65.00 Audio: Estimating Remodel
☐ 19.95 Audio: Plumbers Examination
☐ 22.00 Basic Plumbing with Illust.
☐ 30.00 Berger Building Cost File
☐ 11.25 Bluprt Read for Bldg Trades
☐ 19.75 Bookkeeping for Builders
☐ 24.95 Blder's Comp. Dictionary
☐ 20.00 Blder's Guide to Account Rev.
☐ 15.25 Blder's Guide to Const. Fin.
☐ 15.50 Blder's Office Manual Revised
☐ 14.00 Building Cost Manual
☐ 11.75 Building Layout
☐ 22.00 Cabinetmaking: Design-Finish
☐ 25.50 Carpentry Estimating
☐ 19.75 Carpentry for Resid. Const.
☐ 19.00 Carpentry in Com. Const.
☐ 16.25 Carpentry Layout
☐ 17.75 Computers: Blder's New Tool
☐ 14.50 Concrete and Formwork
☐ 20.50 Concrete Const. & Estimating
☐ 26.00 Const. Estimating Refer. Data
☐ 22.00 Construction Superintending
☐ 19.25 Const. Surveying & Layout
☐ 19.00 Cont. Growth & Profit Guide
☐ 24.25 Cont Guide to Bldg Code Rev

☐ 16.75 Contractor's Survival Manual
☐ 16.50 Cont. Year-Rd Tax Guide
☐ 15.75 Cost Records for Const. Est.
☐ 9.50 Dial-A-Length Rafterule
☐ 18.25 Drywall Contracting
☐ 13.75 Electrical Blueprint Reading
☐ 25.00 Electrical Const. Estimator
☐ 19.00 Estimating Electrical Const.
☐ 17.00 Estimat. Home Blding Costs
☐ 28.00 Estimating Painting Costs
☐ 17.25 Estimating Plumbing Costs
☐ 21.50 Est. Tables for Home Building
☐ 22.75 Excav. & Grading Hndbk Rev.
☐ 9.25 E-Z Square
☐ 23.25 Fences & Retaining Walls
☐ 15.25 Finish Carpentry
☐ 24.75 Hdbk of Const. Contr. Vol. 1
☐ 24.75 Hdbk of Const. Contr. Vol. 2
☐ 15.00 Home Wiring: Improv. Ext. Repair
☐ 17.50 How to Sell Remodeling
☐ 19.50 How to Succ'd w/Own Const Bus.
☐ 24.50 HVAC Contracting
☐ 24.00 Illustrated Guide to NE Code
☐ 20.25 Manual of Electrical Contr.
☐ 19.75 Manual of Prof. Remodeling
☐ 17.25 Masonry & Concrete Const.
☐ 26.50 Masonry Estimating

☐ 22.50 National Const. Estimator w/ free Estimate Writer on 5¼" (1.2Mb) disk *Add $10 for Estimate Writer on either* ☐ 5¼" (360K) disk or ☐ 3½" (720K) disk.
☐ 26.50 Nat. Repar& Remodel Est.
☐ 19.25 Paint Contractor's Manual
☐ 21.25 Painter's Handbook
☐ 27.50 Painting Cost Guide
☐ 13.00 Plan & Design Plumb System
☐ 19.25 Planning Drain, Waste & Vent
☐ 21.00 Plumber's Exam Prep. Guide
☐ 18.00 Plumber's Handbook Rev.
☐ 19.75 Profits Buy & Renov Homes
☐ 14.25 Rafter Length Manual
☐ 23.00 Remodeler's Handbook
☐ 18.25 Remodeling Contr. Handbook
☐ 26.25 Remodeling Kitchens & Baths
☐ 11.50 Residential Electrical Design
☐ 16.75 Residential Electr. Hndbk.
☐ 18.25 Residential Wiring
☐ 22.00 Roof Framing
☐ 14.00 Roofers Handbook
☐ 17.00 Rough Carpentry
☐ 21.00 Run. Your Remodeling Bus.
☐ 27.00 Spec Builder's Guide
☐ 15.50 Stair Builder's Handbook
☐ 14.25 Wood-Frame House Const.

**NO POSTAGE
NECESSARY
IF MAILED
IN THE
UNITED STATES**

BUSINESS REPLY MAIL
FIRST CLASS PERMIT NO. 271 CARLSBAD, CA

POSTAGE WILL BE PAID BY ADDRESSEE

Craftsman Book Company
6058 Corte Del Cedro
Box 6500
Carlsbad, CA 92008-0992

**NO POSTAGE
NECESSARY
IF MAILED
IN THE
UNITED STATES**

BUSINESS REPLY MAIL
FIRST CLASS PERMIT NO. 271 CARLSBAD, CA

POSTAGE WILL BE PAID BY ADDRESSEE

Craftsman Book Company
6058 Corte Del Cedro
Box 6500
Carlsbad, CA 92008-0992

**NO POSTAGE
NECESSARY
IF MAILED
IN THE
UNITED STATES**

BUSINESS REPLY MAIL
FIRST CLASS PERMIT NO. 271 CARLSBAD, CA

POSTAGE WILL BE PAID BY ADDRESSEE

Craftsman Book Company
6058 Corte Del Cedro
Box 6500
Carlsbad, CA 92008-0992